PUBLISHED ON THE FOUNDATION ESTABLISHED
IN MEMORY OF PHILIP HAMILTON McMILLAN
OF THE CLASS OF 1894 YALE COLLEGE

O. C. Marsh

O. C. MARSH

PIONEER IN PALEONTOLOGY

BY

CHARLES SCHUCHERT

PROFESSOR OF PALEONTOLOGY, EMERITUS,
IN YALE UNIVERSITY

AND

CLARA MAE LeVENE

RESEARCH ASSISTANT
IN THE PEABODY MUSEUM OF NATURAL HISTORY
YALE UNIVERSITY

NEW HAVEN
YALE UNIVERSITY PRESS
LONDON   HUMPHREY MILFORD   OXFORD UNIVERSITY PRESS

1940

CONTENTS

Oct 45

ILLUSTRATIONS

PLATES

FIGURES

PREFACE

THE sequence of events that was to lead to the writing of this life of Professor Marsh had its inception fifty years ago, when I first met Charles Emerson Beecher, who was to become one of my most intimate friends. I was then personal assistant in Paleontology to State Geologist James Hall, at Albany, New York, and Beecher, who had held a similar position on the State Survey, was a member of Professor Marsh's staff at Yale. He returned to Albany from time to time, however, on official business, and it was on one of these occasions that we met, in 1889. At his invitation, I went to New Haven for the winter holidays that year, and we spent Christmas Eve at the home of another of Marsh's assistants, George Baur. During this visit Professor Marsh was absent, but I heard much of him from both Beecher and Baur. I did not have the pleasure of meeting him personally until April, 1892, when I was sent to the Peabody Museum by the United States Geological Survey to spend a year cleaning certain Lower Carboniferous crinoids which were a part of the Marsh Collections, and which were wanted for use in the Government exhibit at the Chicago Exposition. In the course of this year I not only saw Professor Marsh almost every day, but often talked with Beecher about him, and especially about his difficulties with his staff and his quarrel with Professor Cope. Indeed, Marsh so dominated the Museum scene, as he did any other of which he was a part, that he furnished conversational matter for the entire staff. Beecher had by this time become his most trusted assistant, and, being a cool and keen observer, he probably understood his chief's enigmatic nature better than any other person.

My personal relations with Professor Marsh were always very pleasant. I realized early that it would be an advantage to please him, because I needed friends in my chosen career, and I evidently succeeded, because he more than once helped me with advice. On one occasion, when he was having trouble with

Hatcher, his best field man, and learned that the latter had been confiding in me, he asked me point-blank what Hatcher had said. I told him truthfully, but to my surprise he did not resent this in the least. After I went back to Washington, Marsh called on me many times at the United States National Museum, and one day he asked me to walk back with him to his hotel, a flattering request from the president of the National Academy of Sciences to a comparative newcomer like myself!

In 1904, when I came to Yale to fill the chair of Paleontology —Marsh's chair—again left vacant by the all-too-early death of Beecher, I found in my department in the Peabody Museum an enormous mass of memorabilia relating to Marsh and his paleontological collections—endless letters, newspaper clippings, and notes, all preserved in the original envelopes and tied up in bundles by years. As it is instinctive with me to arrange, catalogue, and classify, I asked Mr. Thomas A. Bostwick of the Museum staff to take the letters and clippings and receipts out of their envelopes and unfold them, but to retain the chronological arrangement. All the notes that had to do with the Marsh Collections, on the other hand, I assembled and arranged and then turned over to my associate, Professor Richard S. Lull, who had come to Yale to take charge of the fossil vertebrates; I knew that a paleontologist can never have enough detail as to the source of his fossils and as to their field relations—both geographic and stratigraphic—and it was well known that Marsh rarely gave such details in his published descriptions of species.

In 1909, when the junior author was appointed librarian in the Peabody Museum, one of her early tasks was to arrange the Marsh letters under authors chronologically. In the course of this rearrangement she read a good deal of the correspondence, so that by the time it was bound into twenty-six fat volumes, averaging four hundred letters apiece, she had acquired considerable knowledge of the Museum Collections and of conditions under which they had been made.

It is hard to remember, now, when the idea of writing a life of Professor Marsh first began to take shape in our minds.

At intervals, however, we talked over the many bits of history that lay buried in the mass of Marshiana, and lamented that no one seemed likely to use them. With my retirement in 1923, and the greater amount of time available for research, a biography of Professor Marsh, to be written "some day," began to seem more of a possibility; but what had been merely a pious hope was crystallized into determination in April, 1931, when I purchased Professor Henry Fairfield Osborn's *Cope: Master Naturalist. The Life and Letters of Edward Drinker Cope.* As I read this book from cover to cover, conviction grew ever stronger within me that an account of Professor Marsh must also be written, to give future generations of geologists and other scientists a true picture of this great paleontologist, with no attempt to minimize the unfortunate aspects of his career, but with strong emphasis on his far-reaching achievements in Vertebrate Paleontology. He was, indeed, among the greatest scientists whom America has produced, and it would be most unjust if he should be remembered chiefly as one of the parties to an outrageous quarrel of almost twenty-five years' duration.

Only a few months previous to the publication of the present book, an interesting autobiography came to hand which has considerable to say of Vertebrate Paleontology in America in Marsh's lifetime. This is *Some Memories of a Paleontologist*, by Professor William Berryman Scott of Princeton University. It was of value to us for its different viewpoint, and the reader will find in it many a commentary on the curious network of human relationships.

Once the decision to write a life of Professor Marsh was arrived at, the task of sifting and coördinating material was begun, the major part of this falling to the lot of the junior author. The division of work agreed upon gave me the chapters on Marsh's scientific work, which I wrote during two winters' sojourn in Florida, and those dealing with Marsh's place in Washington affairs, leaving for my co-author the story of his early life and his western explorations, together with his last decade. All the chapters, of course, have undergone criticism and emendation by us both. The work was carried on in intervals between other tasks until early in 1937, when I was asked by the National Academy of Sciences to prepare a memoir on Professor Marsh for its biographical series. From that time on, most of the junior author's time was spent on the book, and, in 1938, the major part of mine as well. It has been an interesting labor of love, and if, at the end of it, Marsh takes the place in the history of American science that is rightfully his, the many weeks of patient search and careful checking will be amply repaid.

The quest for Marsh material led farther afield than either of us had dreamed, as the letters revealed the part he played in certain phases of the history of Yale University, of the United States Geological Survey, and of the National Academy of Sciences. In his day, he was one of the well-known public figures, as is apparent from the widespread press comment at his death, and it is our feeling that he should not be submerged by time until "Marsh" becomes merely a proper name following a word or two of classical derivation used to differentiate one fossil vertebrate from another. So striking a personality as his deserves a better fate!

The *Yale Daily News*, writing at the time of Marsh's death, said: "This place, Yale, he loved." No truer word was spoken of him, and no story of his career would be complete without emphasis on this point. Entering Yale in 1856, although most of his family went to Harvard, graduating from Yale College in 1860 and from the Sheffield Scientific School in 1862, appointed professor of Paleontology in 1866, he remained a vital part of Yale until his death in 1899. Yale gave him most of his education and his unsalaried professorship. He brought to Yale through his uncle, George Peabody, a great museum of natural history, and through his own efforts and with his own money he amassed for her one of the greatest collections of vertebrate fossils ever brought together by a single individual. In addition, he enlarged her prestige by thirty years of productive research of a high order, and he served her in many other ways. Yale has been fortunate in her sons, but few of them gave her more single-minded devotion than Othniel Charles Marsh.

In the nature of things, a biography is bound to be a mosaic of ideas and opinions, and hence the giving of credit where credit is due is even more difficult than with other types of books. This is still harder when a book has been growing over a long period of years. However, we have certain special indebtednesses which should be gratefully acknowledged.

To Professor Russell H. Chittenden our thanks are due for constant encouragement and advice, particularly in the last stages of the book's progress. As historian of the Sheffield Scientific School, of which he was long director, Professor Chittenden was in a position to appreciate fully the upwelling of natural science that bore Marsh along with it. Moreover, he of course knew Marsh personally and recognized his mastery of his special branch of science.

To Professor Richard S. Lull, one of Marsh's successors in the professorship of Paleontology at Yale, we are indebted for much assistance along various lines where our own knowledge was less secure. Although he never met Professor Marsh, the latter's collections in Vertebrate Paleontology were for many years in his charge, and his work upon them gave him ample opportunity to evaluate both the material and the man who collected it. To Professor Carl O. Dunbar, also of the Peabody Museum, we owe thanks for reading certain of the earlier chapters, and for encouragement as to their value.

The task of unraveling Professor Marsh's tangled relations with his assistants in the Museum was much lessened by long talks with two of those helpers, Hugh Gibb and Dr. Richard W. Westbrook, both of whom died while the book was in progress. The frankness and discernment with which these two men pictured the Marsh laboratory in its heyday during the 'eighties were of inestimable value.

In the matter of Marsh's family, light came from an unexpected quarter one day when Professor Lull brought into our office one of his former students at Massachusetts State College, Mr. Jasper Marsh of Danvers, Massachusetts. Mr.

Marsh, of the tenth generation of the American family, is a grandson of the Honorable James Marsh, who was an older brother of Professor Marsh's father; and his wife was a Peabody —a fortunate combination for us. In July, 1934, we spent a delightful day with Mr. and Mrs. Marsh at their charming home, and under their guidance journeyed to the two Marsh homesteads and to the house where George Peabody was born, thus acquiring a knowledge of the surroundings of Professor Marsh's parents that could have been come by in no other way. With them we also visited the Peabody Institute at Peabody (formerly South Danvers), to see the magnificent miniature of Queen Victoria presented by her to Mr. Peabody in recognition of his generosity toward the laboring people of London. Mr. and Mrs. Marsh supplied certain details for the first chapter of the book, and were kind enough to read and comment on it in manuscript.

Further points in regard to the family have been contributed by Mrs. Raymond Marsh Walker of Batavia, New York, daughter-in-law of Martha Marsh Walker, Professor Marsh's half sister; and by Mrs. Ethel Williamson Ely of Old Lyme, Connecticut, daughter of Mary Marsh Williamson, another half sister. Their ready coöperation calls for our best thanks.

In July, 1934, we spent another very pleasant day in the library of Phillips Andover Academy, legatee of the extensive correspondence of George Peabody, which was placed at our disposal by the authorities of the Academy, notably by Mr. Scott H. Paradise. Mr. Paradise was good enough, also, to add a number of interesting details regarding Marsh's studies at Andover and his classmates in that venerable institution.

Two men who knew Professor Marsh, although in quite different capacities, kindly set down for us their recollections of him. One of these was Sir Arthur Smith Woodward, sometime keeper of Geology in the British Museum and himself a vertebrate paleontologist; the other was the late Professor Henry W. Farnam of Yale, who was a member of the Yale Expedition of 1873, and whose brother, Mr. W. W. Farnam, was one of Marsh's neighbors and friends, and a co-trustee of his estate.

It is a great pleasure to acknowledge our particular indebtedness to Mrs. Ernest Howe of Litchfield, Connecticut, and her daughter, Miss Margaret Howe. Among the papers left by Dr. Howe's stepfather, Arnold Hague, whose family were among Professor Marsh's few intimates, were five chapters written by Marsh himself, describing some of his western experiences. In view of the almost total lack of manuscript left by Professor Marsh, these chapters would be of high value under any circumstances, but they are so vividly written that they bring a feeling of intense regret that he did not finish the book of which they were intended to be a part—a book, incidentally, which he had been urged to write by many of his associates, among them Thomas H. Huxley and Sir Archibald Geikie. When this manuscript came into Dr. Howe's hands, he conceived the idea of adding to it enough of his own knowledge of Marsh and of the background of the chapters to make a small volume for publication. He had made considerable progress in this direction when his untimely death in 1932 put an end to the project as such. It had been the hope of the present authors that the task might be carried to completion by Mrs. Howe and her daughter, so that the material, once published, would be available for this book. This eventually seemed not to be possible, and with great generosity they turned over to us not only the Marsh chapters but the many notes that Dr. Howe had gathered. It was not possible to keep all this material together, but it appears here and there in our book. The Marsh chapters themselves are inserted in the section on Yale student expeditions, and it is with much gratitude that we acknowledge the friendly gesture that enabled us to put them there.

Thanks are due to Professor L. C. Glenn of Vanderbilt University, who had copies made for us of newspaper reports about the Nashville meeting of the American Association for the Advancement of Science in 1877, at which Marsh delivered his first remarkable address, and who put us on the track of the Winchell episode—the first outbreak of the Evolution conflict in Tennessee—which helped give it such timely significance.

Fortunate indeed are the biographers who have access to

a great library! Without the varied and rich collections of the
Sterling Memorial Library at Yale University, this book
could never have been written. Here, in the Rare Book Room,
are letters of Benjamin Silliman and James D. Dana, which
we were permitted to peruse through the courtesy of Miss Maria
Trumbull Dana, granddaughter and daughter of these two
great scientists. The Yale Memorabilia Room has a great and
growing store of information regarding the sons of Yale, which
was often sought out for us by its custodian, Miss Jane W. Hill;
its finest yield proved to be a large bound volume of newspaper
clippings about Professor Marsh, presented by Mr. William
W. Farnam. Yale's collection of newspapers is one of the best
in the country, and the files of the New York *Tribune* in the
'seventies and 'eighties have been of very great value indeed.

Two previous biographical sketches—one by George Bird
Grinnell and one by Professor Beecher—have furnished us a
foundation on which to build. These two men were associated
with Marsh at the beginning and end of his career, respectively,
and in all probability they knew him as well as anyone ever
did. Beecher's tribute appeared in the *American Journal of
Science* a few months after Marsh's death; Grinnell's came
eleven years later, as a chapter in *Leading American Men of
Science*, under the editorship of David Starr Jordan.

When all is said and done, however, our greatest indebtedness
is to Professor Marsh himself. The task of preserving the
memory of what he was and what he did would never have been
undertaken save for the wealth of material that his collector's
instinct had led him to keep, and that ranges all the way from
a lock of his mother's hair to a wooden box filled with his
financial records! The Peabody Museum possesses hundreds
of his family letters, Marsh and Peabody alike, including many
that fill us with regret because they cannot be printed here for
lack of space. With the publication of this book, these personal
letters will be turned over to the Sterling Memorial Library.
In addition, there are volumes of correspondence, already
mentioned, which are retained in the Museum because of their
store of information about the Marsh Collections.

With all this material, there is one great lack—Marsh's own letters, of which we have for the most part only infrequent pencil copies. Because of this, we were more than once faced with the necessity of reconstructing an event from a one-sided correspondence. Marsh once quoted in print the lawyers' adage, "Give me three letters from a man and I will hang him!" We are ready to believe that he held this thought before him most of his days! This lack of Marsh letters makes our thanks particularly due to Mrs. Louis V. Pirsson, who allowed us to reproduce letters written by him to her father, Professor George J. Brush; and to the British Museum (Natural History) for copies of letters that he wrote to Sir Richard Owen, transmitted to us by its librarian, Mr. A. C. Townsend.

In the matter of illustrations, we also have thanks to say. The Essex Institute at Salem, Massachusetts, sent us the print of Judith Peabody Russell Daniels which is found in these pages, and its companion institution, the Peabody Museum, gave us permission to reproduce the charming lithograph of George Peabody in its possession. Mr. Robert Bruce of New York City, from his collection of historical material relating to frontier days in the West, furnished us with photographs of Marsh's Army friend, Col. T. H. Stanton, and of Col. William F. Cody and Maj. Frank North, famous Indian scouts who accompanied one of the early student expeditions. Mr. Bruce also was patient under a barrage of questions about this early period. The picture of Judge William A. Carter on Plate XIII came from his son, Mr. W. A. Carter of La Jolla, California, who says he recalls distinctly Marsh's visits to Ft. Bridger in the 'seventies. Mr. Harold Lakes of Nelson, British Columbia, son of one of Marsh's successful collectors of dinosaurs, Arthur Lakes, sent us a picture of his father, as well as of several of the restorations of fossil animals that the latter painted in water color. The Yale Memorabilia Room furnished a photograph of George Bird Grinnell, Yale '70, from his classbook; and Miss Hill assisted in the fascinating task of identifying certain of the student members of Marsh's expeditions by comparison with their class pictures. We regret that, even by this method, not all the men in the groups can be named. Pictures of Hugh Gibb were furnished by Mr. F. W. Darby and Mr. C. B. Allderige of the Peabody Museum.

Copies of the photograph showing the officers of the American Association for the Advancement of Science at the Nashville meeting in 1877 traveled a good many miles in the hope that all the men could be identified. Several of the identifications were made by Mr. Sam Woodley, executive assistant in the Washington office of the Association, but two of the men still remain nameless. It is rather a pity that we can not reproduce the whole of another group picture, showing the International Congress of Zoology assembled for a picnic during its meeting in England in the summer of 1898. The identifications in the small group immediately surrounding Marsh, which is all that it seemed feasible to publish, were made for us by Sir Arthur Smith Woodward.

For the interesting picture we call "The Four Directors," we are indebted to Professor H. F. Reid of Johns Hopkins University, who took it in 1896 at Harpers Ferry during a geological excursion arranged in honor of Sir Archibald Geikie, director of the Geological Survey of Great Britain, then lecturing at Baltimore.

Thanks are due also to Mr. Childs Frick and to the American Museum of Natural History for permission to use the drawing of the skull of the curious mammal, *Prosynthetoceras,* and the chart of reptilian evolution prepared by Dr. C. C. Mook, and to Mr. C. W. Gilmore and the United States National Museum for the photograph of the skeleton of the dinosaur *Triceratops* mounted in that institution.

Much of our account of the Yale Expedition of 1870 is taken from a contemporary article that appeared in *Harper's Magazine,* from which we have quoted freely and from which we have reproduced the route maps and two delightful woodcuts. The proprietors of *Punch* kindly gave permission for the use of the cartoon of "Ringmaster Marsh," which was printed in 1890; and a similar courtesy was extended by the Nebraska State Historical Society with reference to a map of the route of the

1873 Expedition, which was published in *Nebraska History Magazine*, July-September, 1929.

Publishers and authors have been generous with permissions to quote, and we are grateful for their courtesy. Such permission was received from the following: D. Appleton-Century Company, *The Atlantic Monthly*, Dodd, Mead & Company, Mrs. George Bird Grinnell, Harper & Brothers, Harvard University Press, Houghton Mifflin Company, Little, Brown & Company, Mr. E. A. McCornack, Macmillan & Co., Ltd., Princeton University Press, G. P. Putnam's Sons, Mr. Charles H. Sternberg, and Yale University Press.

It is a special pleasure to record our satisfaction that this book is published by the Yale University Press, and our gratitude to the Press for making its publication possible on the Philip Hamilton McMillan Foundation. Our thanks are due also to the officers and staff of the Press, especially to Mr. George Parmly Day, its director, Mr. Eugene A. Davidson, its editor, Mr. Norman V. Donaldson, its secretary, and Mrs. Ruth Bernier, head of its manufacturing department, for their courtesy and coöperation while the book was in process of publication.

CHARLES SCHUCHERT.

Peabody Museum of Natural History,
  Yale University, October, 1939.

O. C. MARSH: PIONEER IN PALEONTOLOGY

FOREWORD

ACHIEVEMENTS IN BRIEF

OTHNIEL CHARLES MARSH had all the physical, mental, and monetary equipment for a successful career. Devoted to natural science from boyhood, he came to Yale for training, and through his uncle, George Peabody, he brought to the University a large natural history museum, and this at a time when there were few such institutions in America. For this museum he accumulated the largest and most valuable collection of fossil vertebrates made in his day. He was the first professor of Paleontology in the Americas, and he did more than any other person to introduce Vertebrate Paleontology into the curriculum of American universities.

Above all, he was preëminent as a collector, and the collections which he made for the United States Government and for Yale University form his greatest and most enduring monument. His material was of importance both quantitatively and qualitatively, many of the individual skeletons being almost complete; he was the first to insist upon having every bone of a given skeleton that his collectors could be made to find, and time and again he sent them back to rework their diggings in search of some missing part. He was, moreover, the inventor or promoter of most of the innovations in collecting technique that were developed during his time, and he trained most of the country's leading vertebrate paleontologists and the most skilful preparators of fossil bones. Because of the completeness of his fossil skeletons, he became the leader in the art of making lifelike skeletal restorations of extinct dinosaurs, birds, and mammals, of which he presented 22 (12 of dinosaurs, 1 of pterodactyls, 3 of birds, and 6 of mammals).

One of America's earliest and most ardent exponents of the Darwinian theory of natural selection, his startling discovery of birds possessing teeth and other reptilian characteristics bridged a gap in the evolutionary series, fulfilling a prophecy made by Huxley; and his carefully collected series of fossil horses demonstrated not only that the development of the horse had taken place mainly in this country, and not in Europe, as was formerly held, but that the line of descent so traced was an unanswerable argument in favor of the Darwinian hypothesis. These contributions of his were acknowledged by Darwin to be the best support that the evolution theory had received since the publication of *The Origin of Species* in 1859.

His research on fossil vertebrates is embodied in about 270 publications, including 3 outstanding monographs. In addition, he prepared more than 200 plates for monographs, the text of which he never found the time to write. In these publications he described as new 496 species, 225 genera, 64 families, 8 suborders, 19 orders, and 1 subclass.

The 'seventies and 'eighties of the last century were his most striking years for bringing to light the extinct vertebrates buried in the richest of all "boneyards," those of the high plains of the Rocky Mountain country. His attention was directed first to the mammal life in such notable fossil fields as the Bridger, Uinta, Green River, and John Day basins of Wyoming, Utah, Colorado, and Oregon, and the White River badlands of Nebraska and the Dakotas. Among these he found almost the earliest primates known, prophetic of living man, and previously supposed to have been confined to other continents. Here, also, he found many kinds of fossil horses, ranging from the tiny four-toed *Eohippus* to the Pleistocene *Equus* of modern size. Two other groups of mammals received his especial attention, both early Cenozoic in age and both now wholly extinct: the horned Dinocerata and the elephantine brontotheres. These groups he made known from a wonderfully complete collection. He devoted to mammals 85 of his publications, describing 264 new species and 127 new genera.

In the early 'seventies, also, he made three of his most striking discoveries, in the Cretaceous tablelands of western Kansas: birds with teeth, hitherto wholly unknown; "sea serpents" or mosasaurs, in astonishing preservation; and toothless pterodactyls or flying dragons of a size such as it was never dreamed that these winged reptiles could attain.

He was swerved from his original intention of devoting his

main interest to the mammals by the finding of bones of gigantic reptiles belonging to a much older time, the Mesozoic or medieval era, which were first reported to him by amateur collectors in Colorado and Wyoming. As a result of these finds, he set to work to build up a great collection of these reptiles, and within a few months he was describing the largest and most curious monsters of all time, the dinosaurs. Some of these, called sauropods, included creatures that were 70 feet in length, weighed 40 tons in the flesh, and yet had a brain less than one half the weight of that of a human baby. Other species were no larger than a domestic cat. Some were without armor; some wore huge bony plates along the back and heavy spikes on the tail; still others had huge horned and frilled heads, the largest known in any land animal, fossil or living. All in all, Marsh described 80 new forms of dinosaurs and 34 new genera. They were the most astonishing creatures unearthed in his time and he knew them better than any other paleontologist, inaugurating a sweeping reform in their classification. In doing so, however, he spent the greater part of his fortune and so much of his time that he had to leave a vast amount of work uncompleted.

Associated with the dinosaurs, Marsh's collectors, under his constant urging, found tiny jaws and teeth of mammals which had lived in late Jurassic and late Cretaceous times, and which he was the first to reveal to science in this country, with the exception of one Cretaceous mammal tooth discovered earlier. Although these Mesozoic mammal remains are very fragmentary, they outrank in importance any of his other mammal discoveries, because of their extreme rarity and because they represent the earliest genetic divergences in the class Mammalia.

In his collecting of fossil vertebrates, Marsh not only strove for quantity and completeness, but also had a positive gift for picking out the most important, the largest, or the most bizarre types, his "choicest plums," and, by giving these spectacular finds full publicity, he became known the country over, to the general public as well as to the scientist. Moreover, he went to Europe many times and visited all the important museums there, so that his influence on Vertebrate Paleontology extended far beyond the United States.

From the beginning of his descriptive work on fossil vertebrates, he was interested in brain development, and as early as 1876 he was able to show, not only that all Cenozoic mammals had had small brains, but that there had been a gradual increase in size with the passage of geologic time, and especially in the upper portion of the brain; "in the long struggle for existence in Tertiary time," he said, "the big brains won, then as now." He showed, further, that there had been a growth in mentality among the vertebrates beginning at least in the reptiles of the late Paleozoic and continuing through the various stocks up to man himself.

In the scientific world, Marsh stood among the leaders, not only in this country but in Europe as well. He attained this eminence early in his career and held it undiminished for nearly forty years. He served as president of the National Academy of Sciences, the highest scientific body in the country, for two terms of six years each, a longer time than any president before or since. He was the first Vertebrate Paleontologist of the United States Geological Survey, holding that position for ten years, and to his success in collecting, the Government owes much of the wonderful fossil vertebrate material that is now deposited in the United States National Museum.

Professor Richard S. Lull, who, as professor of Vertebrate Paleontology at Yale from 1911 to 1936, had abundant opportunity to judge of the lasting value of Marsh's scientific work, had the following comment to make of it at the time of Marsh's centenary:

His anatomical knowledge was marvelous, and his paper restorations, though in but one plane of space and therefore open to possible error, became classic. To those of us who are privileged to carry on his work, the storehouse seems inexhaustible, and we are struck with the almost uncanny accuracy with which he seized upon the essentials of a new and but partially complete or developed specimen upon which to base his terse but significant description of a new species. While these descriptions, in the light of further revelation, can often be amplified, they can rarely be improved.

Then, too, as we are privileged to mount one after another of his paper-restored creatures, we are so impressed with his accuracy that if we would differ from the findings of the master, we must indeed show cause.

That Marsh did not accomplish more in the way of monographic work on his great collections was in part the result of his becoming overwhelmed by the very wealth of his material and by the numerous staff whose activities he had to direct. A too comprehensive ambition, an autocratic tendency that led him into difficulties with his staff and with his colleagues, and a growing habit of procrastination were additional factors. The description of the magnificent collections which he assembled, and which have been studied continuously ever since, is still far from complete, forty years after his death, and he left an impress upon his chosen science of Vertebrate Paleontology that will last as long as the bones he gathered and the pages he printed endure.

CHAPTER I
ANCESTRY AND BOYHOOD

"Every man is a quotation from all his ancestors."
EMERSON.

INSOFAR as a man's ancestors determine what he shall be, Othniel Charles Marsh was the product of the New England strains that were blended in 1827 by the marriage of his parents, Caleb Marsh and Mary Gaines Peabody.

John Marsh, the first of his name known to have emigrated from England to America, is believed to have reached these shores in the year 1634. He settled in Salem, where his name (spelled Marshe, as was then customary) appears in the town records on January 2, 1637, when he received twenty acres of land, to which half as many more were added two years later. This relatively small tract, on which he built a "substantial dwelling house" in 1638, lay in the north portion of the town, then called Northfield, some two miles from the present Peabody Square; it later became a part of the town of Danvers, was separated from the latter in 1855 under the name of South Danvers, and since 1868 has been known as Peabody. A cordwainer by trade, John Marsh had little need of land. However, as the Marsh genealogy remarks: "Had he then thought of having a family of 11 children he no doubt could have had 100 or more acres of land granted him." [1]

If foresight was lacking to John Marsh in the matter of acquiring land for his children, the same can not be said concerning his choice of their mother. Susanna Skelton, whom he took to wife in 1635-6, consummating an agreement entered into in England some years before, was the eldest daughter of the Reverend Samuel Skelton, a graduate of Cambridge and the close friend and spiritual adviser of Governor Endicott. She thus brought to her husband an assured social standing.

1. *The Genealogy of John Marsh of Salem and His Descendants, 1633–1888*. Collected and published by Col. Lucius B. Marsh of Boston, Mass. Revised and edited by the Rev. Dwight W. Marsh of Amherst, Mass. Amherst, 1888.

Their oldest child, Zachary, the first Marsh to be born in America, probably saw daylight in the log house once occupied by his pastor grandfather. Ten other children followed Zachary, but it is his line that has most interest in the present connection, since his descendant of the sixth generation, John Marsh, remaining in Salem as the head of the younger branch of the family, and marrying Mary Brown in 1798, became the father of Caleb Marsh.

On the distaff side, Professor Marsh's ancestry can be traced back much further. The name Peabody, indeed, is said to have originated at the beginning of the Christian era, when one of Queen Boadicea's kinsmen called Boadie rendered her great service in her losing struggle with the Romans. After the queen's death, he escaped with a remnant of his followers to the mountains of Wales, where he came to be known as Peabodie, the two words signifying "hill" or "mountain" and "man" or "great man," respectively.

Lieutenant Francis Peabody, first of the American family, came to New England from Hertfordshire in 1635 in the ship, *Planter*—a "husbandman," twenty-one years of age.[2] He lived first in Ipswich but three years later became one of the original settlers of Hampton. When the state lines were run, this town was found to be in New Hampshire, and, "being minded to live nearer Boston," he moved to Topsfield in 1650. Like John Marsh, he picked a helpmeet from a distinguished family, his wife being the daughter of Reginald Foster (or Forster), whose kin were honorably mentioned by Scott in *The Lay of the Last Minstrel* and *Marmion*. David Peabody of Andover and Haverhill, fourth-generation descendant from Lieutenant Francis, married Mary Gaines of Ipswich, and the sixth of their ten children, Thomas, married Judith Dodge of Rowley. This last union also produced ten children, one of whom, George Peabody, became a banker and philanthropist of international renown, and another, Mary Gaines Peabody, was the mother of Professor Marsh.

The high quality of the Peabody strain, with its many notable figures, is well known; but also to be considered in this

2. *A Genealogy of the Peabody Family, as Compiled by the late C. M. Endicott of Salem.* Revised and corrected by William S. Peabody of Boston. Boston, 1867.

matter of family inheritance is the fact that Judith Dodge was
a member of the Spofford family which, although less well
known, has a length of authenticated European ancestry surpassed by few American families.[3] Her grandfather, Col.
Daniel Spofford, was in command of the Seventh Regiment of
Militia in Essex County, Massachusetts, a town representative, and a member of the State Constitutional Convention; in
addition, he was an architect, building several churches. His

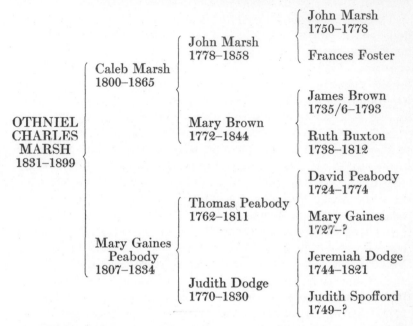

taste for architecture and engineering was handed down to his
son Moody, who built the bridge across the Connecticut River
at Windsor, Vermont, and those across the Merrimac at Andover, Haverhill, and Rocks Village, as well as churches in
Andover and elsewhere. Another son, Amos, was the first physician in Georgetown, and one of the original members of the
Massachusetts Medical Society. It is interesting to note that
the name Judith was handed down to Professor Marsh's grand-
mother through at least six generations, with only one break:

3. See *A Genealogical Record . . . of . . . Descendants of John Spofford
and Elizabeth Scott . . .*, by Jeremiah Spofford of Groveland, Mass. Memorial
edition by his daughter, Aphia T. Spofford. Boston, 1888.

Judith Dodge, Judith Spofford, Judith Follansbee, Judith Moody, Judith Hall, Sarah Somerby, Judith Greenleaf.

The purity of racial stock that lay behind Professor Marsh is rather exceptional. The families represented by his great-grandparents can be traced back to colonial times, and several of them are known for many generations in England; and in none of the marriages so far recorded in this country does there appear any name indicative of other than English or Scottish blood.

The beginning of the nineteenth century found the two households with which we are immediately concerned living as neighbors in that part of the village of Danvers which is now known as Peabody. John and Mary Marsh shared the so-called "new homestead" with their seven children, of whom Caleb was the second. It was a comfortable home, kept from ready money by the father's tendency to acquire still more land, but with definite educational traditions that sent the sons to near-by academies and at least two of them to college. The mother, so far as our records go, was a rather shadowy figure, the management of the household devolving upon the unmarried daughter, the Aunt Mary Marsh of the family letters.

Ezekiel, the fourth son in the family, early felt the call to the ministry and was ordained to it after study at Bowdoin, at Andover, and at Yale. He fell a victim to "consumption" at the age of thirty-six, however, and his only influence upon the subject of the present biography was through his marriage to Eliza, sister of Senator Dixon of Connecticut.

The eldest son of the house, on the other hand, had a remarkable career which has recently been rescued from obscurity by George D. Lyman in a lively book called *John Marsh, Pioneer* (Scribner's, 1930). Aside from its intrinsic historical value, John Marsh's story is of interest here as illustrative of some of the traits that were to reappear in his nephew, Othniel. John hated farm work, and sought education as a means of escape from it. After graduation from Harvard, in 1823, he went out to Fort St. Anthony (later Fort Snelling) as tutor in the family of the commandant, and shortly thereafter he opened the first school in Minnesota. He became very influential among the Indians there and at Prairie du Chien, but a few years later he was again on the move, first to Independence,

Missouri, then to Santa Fe, and finally to California, which he reached in 1836. There, becoming wealthy in the days of the gold rush, practicing medicine and buying stock and land, he played a considerable part in the settling and organization of the state, and in its admission into the Union. According to his biographer, "he wanted action, not peace. . . . Wherever John Marsh went, there was romance and adventure."

It is a curious twist of heredity that Othniel Marsh, who had so many of the traits of "Dr. John," should have been the son of his younger brother, who seems to have had none of these characteristics. Of Caleb Marsh as a boy we know very little. In 1815 he accompanied his older brother to Franklin Academy, and two years later he was at Bradford Academy, apparently boarding with the Peabody family. Some time previous to 1824 he taught school. In 1821, a letter written to him by George Peabody indicates that Caleb had asked about possible employment. The following year he repeated his request in January and again in November, but still received no encouragement. He first comes alive to us as a personality in a letter to Mary Peabody dated December 10, 1825, which shows that the Peabodys had moved to West Bradford, where he was planning to visit them on December 23, especially (we may surmise) to see that member of the household whom he addresses as "My lovely friend."

Of the Peabody home we know but little up to 1811, when the father, as the result of a fatal accident, left his widow to find food and shelter for her five younger children, the smallest a babe of two years. The oldest son, David, had arrived at his majority the year of his father's death and seemed well established in the drapery business in Newburyport, where the third son, George, then aged sixteen, was working for him as clerk. Appointed administrator of his father's estate, David found it so involved that it was declared insolvent, the chief asset being the heavily mortgaged twelve-acre farm on the old Boston–Salem road (now Washington Street, Peabody), on which the family lived. With the usual repetitiousness of ill fortune, two weeks after the death of the elder Peabody Newburyport was visited by a great fire which destroyed 250 stores and houses. David Peabody's store was not among these, but his business was ruined, as was that of his uncle, Col. John Peabody, one of the leading citizens of the town. However, this seeming second calamity was to prove a blessing in disguise for the Peabody family, because it led Colonel Peabody to seek new fields for enterprise in Georgetown, D.C., taking his nephew George with him. So successful was the latter in the new place of business that by 1819 he had taken over the family homestead and the complete support of his mother and his younger brothers and sisters, shipping them supplies of flour and sugar and clothing from his growing establishment, not to mention such occasional extras as "an elegant gold watch, a chain for the neck, and a hook . . . small, with pearls set around the face and back," for each of his three sisters.[4]

By the time the two younger girls were ready for schooling, George was providing the family with a comfortable living, and it was at his request that Mary and Sophronia went to Bradford Academy. And it is at Bradford Academy that we get our first picture of Mary Peabody, in the yellowed pages of a letter written to Caleb by a fellow student of hers, who said:

That handsome . . . young creature. I have often wondered how so beautiful an object could live in a neighborhood like yours so long and pass unnoticed, whenever she enters the Academy or Church, she attracts the attention of every individual present. . . . I have often thought that "Grace was in her steps."

Caleb's visit to the Peabody home at the Christmas season of 1825 seems to have settled matters between himself and Mary, for his letter to her on February 18 says he has had a consultation with his father "on the subject of our friendship . . . he has not the least objection to yourself but under my present existing circumstances he does not wish to see me connected with anyone, because I have not at present the means of maintaining a family in the manner he could wish." At Caleb's request, Mary wrote her brother George about the engagement and asked if he would not help Caleb find work so that they might marry. The banker's reply was that there was no opening in his business for an inexperienced person like Caleb; however, approving of the young man and his family, he proposed that he and Caleb's father, by joint arrangement, should make such financial provision as would justify the marriage.

4. The story of George Peabody's life is told in more detail in Chapter IV.

This settlement was made during his visit home that summer, the only hitch in the proceedings arising over Mr. Peabody's insistence that, in the event of his sister's death, the money he gave her should be turned over to her children; or, if she died without issue, that it should revert to him. This condition met with strong objection from Caleb, as shown by his letter of August 9, 1826. Nevertheless, Mr. Peabody held fast to these terms, and his gift was settled upon his sister and her children—a fact that had several important consequences.

In view of the discouraging outlook in business pointed out in George Peabody's letters, Caleb seems to have decided to turn to farming, and it was the feeling of the family that his opportunities therefor would be better in the newer western territory. With this idea in mind, he made two trips to Detroit —the first in company with his brother John, returning West after a visit home—and he even bought land there; but his final choice fell upon western New York, where he purchased a farm that he described to Mr. Peabody on December 15, 1826, as

situated 3 miles from [east of] the village of Lockport and about 1 from the Canal [on the north side of the Old Post Road to Albany], 60 miles from Rochester, 25 from Niagara Falls and 31 from Buffalo. The farm contains about 120 acres of land about 70 under improvement, well watered and I should think very healthy. There are two orchards on place beginning to bear, and in addition to the farm buildings which are a good two story log house and a good framed barn a new framed house with 4 rooms on the floor and a large stable which with about 15 acres of land is now rented for 150 dolls. per annum which is $7\frac{1}{2}$ per cent on the price of the whole farm, so that I can have the farm to live on and at the same time have the interest on the purchase money, and I am very certain that real estate in that vicinity increases very fast in value. The price . . . is 2000 dolls., 850 of which I paid down and took a deed and the balance is to be paid the 10 of May next, or before. If I take possession. It is my intention to spend the winter here [South Danvers], to fulfil my matrimonial engagement with your Sister about the last of March and as soon as the Canal opens which will be about the 10 of April to remove and take possession of my farm.

PLATE I

CALEB MARSH 1800–1865

MARY GAINES PEABODY
1807–1834

PLATE II

MARSH'S BIRTHPLACE
ON CHESTNUT RIDGE NEAR LOCKPORT, NEW YORK
THE HOUSE HAS BEEN CHANGED BY THE ADDITION OF
PORCHES AND BY A REAR EXTENSION

WILSON COLLEGIATE INSTITUTE, WILSON, NEW YORK
WHICH MARSH ATTENDED IN 1847–1849

With the matter of a home settled, and Caleb indicating to George Peabody on March 27 that he was ready to give his bond "to any amount if you wish it, that what you think proper to give shall be made use of agreeably to your wishes," Caleb Marsh and Mary Peabody were married in South Danvers on April 12, 1827, and fifteen days later set out for Lockport, with George Peabody's draft for $1,500 in their hands. Mary's natural reluctance to leave home and her shrinking from the fatigue of travel disappeared once she was actually embarked on her great adventure. Her delight with her new home and surroundings shines through all her letters to her brother and to her girl friends in Massachusetts. The new country is the "garden of America," she is finding herself unexpectedly equal to her new duties, and she has a "kind, indulgent husband," who anticipates her every need. She does not mourn unduly the immediate loss of her first-born the year after her marriage, but accepts it with Christian resignation, and finds consolation in the coming of a daughter Mary, in August, 1829, and of a son, Othniel Charles,[5] on October 29, 1831. There were temporary reverses of fortune such as are wont to fall to a farmer's lot, but no major catastrophes. They found their first home "not convenient to the farm," and built another one; they bought an additional one hundred acres or so of land; and they reported that the village of Lockport had become incorporated, and had acquired a bank, factories, and stores. On August 18, 1834, Mary gave birth to a second son, named for her generous brother, to whom Caleb at once wrote the glad news. She was apparently making a normal recovery, but on the twenty-seventh she was suddenly stricken with "cholera," and died within fourteen hours, in spite of the efforts of two physicians to save her.

In view of the fact that influences which are lacking have as much to do with the shaping of characters and events as those which are present, it may be well to consider for a moment

5. Othniel, a scriptural name meaning "powerful man of God," appears in the book of Joshua as belonging to the son of Caleb's younger brother, who was also the husband of Caleb's daughter Achsah; one of the Marsh family remarked later that she "wished Caleb had chosen some other saint!" The name was seldom used by Marsh after his youth, and is omitted entirely on his European passports, the combination of consonants probably proving difficult for foreign tongues. The reason for the name Charles is less clear, as it does not appear in either immediate family.

what her children lost in the early death of Mary Peabody. That she was fair of face and graceful of carriage we already know. Her silhouette, the only likeness left to us, has a peculiarly soft and feminine appeal, but her beauty was even deeper than appeared on the surface. It is apparent from the family letters that she was the favorite, particularly of her older sister Judith and of her brother George, and the latter gave expression to this when he wrote her, shortly before her marriage:

Port Tobacco, Md., Feb. 12, 1827.

I must do you the justice to say that your conduct has never given me a moment's uneasiness but on the contrary every trait in your character that has ever come to my knowledge has met my entire approbation and greatly added to my happiness. Such a course of conduct is the best evidence of gratitude for the services which I have rendered, and I do not doubt that in all situations in which you may be placed the natural aimiability of your disposition will always cause you to act as you have acted, and feel as you now feel, and assured of this my feeling towards you will remain unchanged and you may with confidence apply to me for any favor that you would ask of a Father, Brother, or Friend. If I know my own heart, it has possessed towards my sister the combined feelings of those three characters.

That Mary Peabody was not forgotten by her husband, even long after her death and his remarriage, we know from a certain envelope upon which is written, "From the grave of my beloved Mary, 1858," and which contains rose leaves, now almost crumbled to dust, gathered from that last resting place which Mary herself chose one day when they were walking about the farm—surely a strange thing to come to lie in the vault of a scientific museum!

The sudden loss of his lovely helpmate left Caleb in consternation. His letter to his parents is a heartrending appeal for advice and help, whose poignancy belies the crumbling pages on which it was penned a century ago. His panic led him to take a step which seems to have been the beginning of all his later troubles—the hasty sale of his property in Lockport and a return to Danvers, leaving the infant George in care of a nurse (where he died the following January).

At the time Caleb returned to Massachusetts, he was worth $5,000, exclusive of the children's property, and he was entirely out of debt. He was never again to reach this economic level. Shortly after his return East, he entered into a partnership in the shoe-manufacturing business in Haverhill, leaving his small son and daughter at the homestead in Danvers, in charge of their Aunt Mary Marsh. That he was contemplating remarriage as early as the beginning of 1836 is apparent from a letter of January 14 to Judge W. Latten (sometimes spelled Latting) of Lockport, which, after dealing with sundry matters of business, adds:

The subject which is perhaps most interesting to both Father and Daughter as well as your humble servant, I intend to make the subject of another communication, merely observing that the Society which I ever intend to move in, will require a larger sum to supply the necessary materials, than it would in your country.

In April, he was suggesting to Judge Latten that it would be advantageous for his daughter to come East to complete her education at, say, Charlestown Academy. He comments, also, that he and his partner are employing nearly one hundred persons, "men, women, and children," and that they "expect to manufacture the present season 40–50 thousand dollars worth of shoes besides selling 20 to 25 thousand dollars worth of goods." He went to Lockport in June, evidently for the purpose of ratifying his engagement to Mary Latten, and in August, in the midst of a letter to his betrothed, his old preoccupation with the matter of wifely dowries crops out: "Give my respects to your father and tell him I shall expect on his part a fulfillment of the arrangement we made respecting the dowry of his daughter." Apparently Judge Latten lived up to Caleb's financial specifications, because the marriage took place shortly before Thanksgiving, 1836, and the young couple settled down in Bradford (or West Bradford), rents in Haverhill being too high. Mary and Othniel came to live with them, and in November, 1837, they acquired a half sister, Martha, the first of a considerable succession of half brothers and half sisters.

Despite Caleb's hopes for his shoe business, this year of 1837 proved his undoing, as it was that of countless other businessmen, the "revulsion of trade" and the Federal bankrupt law causing a loss of nearly half his property. He was burdened with debt and in legal difficulties with his partner. Finally, it seemed best for him to leave Massachusetts, and by 1839 he was back in Lockport. Mary and Othniel, however, stayed behind in Danvers, and, so far as is apparent from the letters, Mary spent most of her time thereafter in the East.

After his return to Lockport, Caleb at first had a store, and did well. In 1844, he conveyed to his brother James, in Danvers, to be held in trust for his two oldest children until they should come of age, two pieces of land that represented the settlement made upon their mother by George Peabody. The property thus set aside for Othniel was "a small farm of 20 acres, well improved, with small new house on it situated 3 miles from the town of Lockport and near where the family formerly lived . . . rents for ca. $75 a year." The next year, however, Judge Latten died suddenly and Caleb had great trouble in settling his estate; Mary Latten wrote to Mary Marsh in November, from the small new farm that they had purchased, that they were "constantly harassed by debts," because Caleb had always been considered well off and "public sentiment cannot be turned to the contrary." Along with these financial troubles, the number of small mouths to feed had increased to six by 1852, so that the family's later years were somewhat of a struggle against adversity. The young Othniel's early days, therefore, were considerably different than they would have been had his own mother lived, with a generous brother constantly in the background.

As he grew into a strong boyhood, the oldest son in a rapidly increasing household, he was expected to be his father's mainstay in the farm work, and his reluctance to do so was a source of friction between them. He preferred, instead, to roam the fields and woods, hunting the small game then still abundant in the Lockport region. He himself, in later life, cited as among the more noteworthy events of his early youth

still remembered to his credit by his contemporaries, who did not approve all his boyish conduct, . . . the saving of a schoolmate from drowning in the Erie Canal . . . and about the same time rescuing a young girl from burning to death. The latter and her friends have since shown their gratitude by various acknowledgments, but the schoolboy proved especially ungrateful!

His outdoor life gave him two precious assets, the abundant health he always enjoyed, and habits of observation that were to stand him in great stead when he turned to science as a vocation. It was during these years, also, that he came into contact with the man who was probably responsible for turning his mind definitely toward the collecting of scientific objects, Col. Ezekiel Jewett (1791–1897). The Marsh farm, it will be remembered, was only about a mile from the Erie Canal, the dream-come-true of the thrice elected governor of New York, DeWitt Clinton, whose opponents called it "Clinton's Ditch." As this canal was being cut through the richly fossiliferous rocks of western New York, the heaps of debris along its banks became happy hunting grounds for many a mineralogist and paleontologist, professional and amateur. When the canal first reached Lockport, in 1823, and twenty years later when it was being widened at this point to make the series of locks more effective, it was blasted through a stratum known as the Lockport dolomite, which has in abundance a special type of rocks (geodes) whose hollow spaces reveal many mineral crystals. Below this Lockport dolomite lies an older formation, the Rochester shale, which is full of fossils, and fossils such as readily strike the eye—plain and highly ornate trilobites, flowerlike crinoids and cystids, brachiopods and bryozoans. It is highly improbable that these fascinating objects were unknown to any small boy in the neighborhood, least of all to so active and observant a one as Othniel. Indeed, we have testimony to the fact that the Marsh family had fine trilobites in its possession, for John M. Clarke says, in his biography of State Geologist James Hall, that Caleb Marsh was among the local collectors approached by a little stock company that had been formed to mine the canal banks at Lockport. However, Caleb would not part with his trilobites![6]

6. John M. Clarke, *James Hall of Albany, Geologist and Paleontologist, 1811–1898*, p. 87. Albany, 1923. The Yale Museum has a fair collection of Rochester shale fossils that Marsh presented to it in 1877; it includes several large and excellent specimens of trilobites, quite possibly the very ones that Caleb would not sell to James Hall.

A year or so before this incident, the abundance of fossils at Lockport had attracted the attention of Colonel Jewett, and he came to live there at a time when he is said to have been unsurpassed in America as a field paleontologist. A retired soldier who had fought with Scott in Mexico, he had come to James Hall's notice during the preparation of the second volume of the great series called *Paleontology of New York*. Clarke describes him as "intelligent, quick of apprehension and understanding, exquisitely and effectively profane . . . as noted a figure among the amateur geologists of his time as he was successful collector." [7] He held a summer school in Geology at Lockport for four years, and he was visited there by many a noted geologist, both from this country and from abroad. Such a combination of vivid personality and collecting skill, we may assume, drew young Othniel like a magnet. Moreover, Jewett was as skilful with a rifle as he was with a collecting hammer, and Marsh told Ray Stannard Baker many years later that his first great ambition had been to shoot as well as the colonel. "I was not satisfied," he said, "until I could bring down a squirrel from the top crotch of a big hickory where I could see only the tip of a red nose and one eye." It is known that the boy came under Colonel Jewett's influence some time about 1845, and learned from him where and how to collect fossils and minerals; and from that time on he seems to have had even less taste for farming.

Of Othniel's early schooling we know little, except that it was mainly in the winter terms. However, by 1847 he had advanced far enough to enter the Collegiate Institute in the nearby town of Wilson, where he remained at least two years, making satisfactory progress, as reported to his father by the preceptor, Benjamin Wilcox, Jr. In 1850, at the age of nineteen, he was a pupil in the newly erected Lockport Union School, and during this period he was characterized by Caleb in a letter as "a boy of good natural abilities and some mechanical ingenuity —much inclined to a roving disposition." In fact, he had a touch of gold fever that year, and Caleb wrote his brother John in California that the two of them might come out there, saying that, if Othniel should choose to remain, his property, worth $1,200 to $1,500, might be pledged as security for his passage

7. *Ibid.,* p. 242.

out. Caleb even went so far as to make plans for the organization of a company that he should lead to the gold fields; and young James Marsh, son of Caleb's brother in Danvers, did make the long journey. The idea doubtless appealed greatly to Othniel also, but for some reason it was abandoned. He tried the much less exciting job of schoolteaching (at $16 a month, in Millport), but gave it up because of headaches, due possibly to the eye trouble that was to bother him later on in life. However, he stayed at it long enough to earn the money that permitted him to follow out a long-cherished wish—to go back East.

At this point in Marsh's life, fortunately for his biographers, he undertook to keep a diary, which he prefaced with the following statement:

Danvers, June 1st, '51.

Believing that a diary, with regular additions, will be highly advantageous in improving my style of writing, and penmanship, and also a valuable assistant to my memory, I shall now commence to note down the most important events of each day, in as plain and concise a manner as possible.

[Signed] O. C. MARSH.

The pages of the diary show him doing odd jobs for his relatives, hunting, walking out with the girls, going to church twice each Sunday, reading voluminously—Dickens, a life of Napoleon, *Dinks on Dogs* (by Frank Forrester), Combe's *Phrenology*,[8] *Mysterys* [*sic*] *of Paris*, and *The Seaman's Friend*. Apparent also from the daily record is a marked tendency to "visit around" among his relatives, especially at the home of his sister Mary, then married to a sea captain, Robert H. Waters, and living in Salem. On June 17 he went to Bunker Hill to attend the celebration of the anniversary of the battle, but found "not so much excitement as I expected." He did, however, note as of interest the Foucault pendulum swung in the monument to explain the rotation of the earth. A significant entry is that of September 12, when he was "trying to write a letter to Uncle George," but there is no indication as to its subject matter. He was still undecided what to do in life, lean-

8. His copy is still in the Peabody Museum Library.

ing somewhat to the carpenter's trade (more specifically, the making of window blinds and sashes), or thinking possibly that he might become a surveyor.

His diary, it must be admitted, shows considerable immaturity for a young man of twenty, and this judgment is confirmed by Captain Waters, who wrote Caleb that Othniel's character at this time was "hardly formed and developed." And yet this year of 1851–52 was the turning point in his life. Coming of age, he received a settlement, in part at least, of the property that had been held for him since his mother's death—a mortgage of $1,200—and with it he decided to follow the example of other Marsh and Peabody sons and go to Phillips Academy at Andover.

CHAPTER II

ANDOVER AND YALE COLLEGE

JUST what decided young Marsh to go to Andover we do not know from direct evidence. It was about this time, however, that the Peabody influence began to loom large in his life. His mother's older sister, Judith, now married to Jeremiah Russell and living in Georgetown, Massachusetts (formerly New Rowley—renamed in honor of George Peabody), was a strong character, possessing some of the determination and ability of her famous brother, and serving as his steward in his beneficences to his many nephews and nieces. Othniel's sister Mary had spent much time with Mrs. Russell, who had but one son of her own and who had had an unusually deep affection for the lovely sister who had died so young. (Incidentally, she never liked Caleb.) Whether or not it was upon Judith Russell's advice that Othniel went to Andover, it seems probable that he had not been there long when she laid his case before George Peabody and persuaded the latter to extend a helping hand. This had no special significance at first, because similar help was being given to another nephew, Robert Singleton Peabody, who was in Andover at the same time, and to several other nephews and nieces. In fact, education, general or particular, was one of the things for which George Peabody liked best to give money. As he said in a letter to one of his nephews on May 18, 1831:

Deprived, as I was, of the opportunity of obtaining anything more than the most *common education* I am *well qualified* to estimate its value by the *disadvantages* I labour under in the society [in] which my business and situation in life frequently throws me, and willingly would I now give *twenty times* the expence attending a good education could I possess it, but it is now too late for *me* to learn and I can only do to those that come under my care, as I could have wished circumstances had permitted others to have done by me.

Although Marsh entered the Academy before the turn of the year, he was still without any strong leanings toward a scholastic career, if we may judge from a letter written by his sister to their father in February, 1852, which says:

I have not seen O. since before Christmas when he left me to go to school at Andover. I have heard from him only once not long since, he was then well and pleased with his school. I think he intends to remain there through the spring and then work at some mechanical trade. He thinks with a little practical knowledge of most kinds of mechanical work he would be able to earn his living in that way without attempting to serve an apprenticeship at any. I do not know but what he may have changed his mind but that *was* his intention when he left.

Phillips Academy at Andover was at this time under the principalship of Dr. Samuel H. Taylor, who was assisted by five instructors. There were two buildings, and the student body totaled 267, about half of whom were enrolled in the English Department, wherein regular courses of lectures were given in "Chemistry and Natural Philosophy; besides occasional lectures of Astronomy, Geology and various other subjects, as the wants of particular classes require." Marsh elected to enter the English Department, and that first year he studied Mineralogy, Geology, and other sciences under James S. Eaton and his assistant, Lucius Barrows, apparently making little impression as a student.

During the summer of 1852, he made use of his growing knowledge of minerals by arranging the specimens in the Essex Institute at Salem; the rest of the vacation he spent collecting minerals in Massachusetts and New York. More important, it was at some time in the course of this summer that he made his final decision to get down to study in earnest. Confessing, later, that he had spent half his time at Andover the first year playing backgammon, he adds: "I changed my mind during an afternoon spent on Dracut Heights [Lowell]. I resolved that I would return to Andover, take hold, and really study." In proof of this he took four studies instead of the usual three. Asked why he was working so hard, he replied: "To make up for lost time; I have spent enough time shooting ducks to fit myself for college." [1]

1. George Bird Grinnell, in *Leading American Men of Science* (1910), p. 286. Henry Holt & Company.

PLATE III

COL. EZEKIEL JEWETT
1791–1877

FROM A MEDALLION POR-
TRAIT THOUGHT TO HAVE
BEEN MADE AT ALBANY
ABOUT 1863 BY THE SCULP-
TOR ERASTUS PALMER

TRILOBITES (*DALMANITES LIMULURUS*)
FROM THE ROCHESTER SHALE AT LOCKPORT, PRE-
SENTED TO THE PEABODY MUSEUM BY PROFESSOR
MARSH AND UNDOUBTEDLY COLLECTED BY HIM OR
HIS FATHER

PLATE IV

JUDITH PEABODY RUSSELL DANIELS 1799–1879
Reproduced by courtesy of the Essex Institute, Salem, Massachusetts

With his return to Andover in the fall of 1852, Marsh was squared away on the long academic voyage that was to bring him to so many notable harbors. Discovering that he could master studies when he put his mind to them, he decided to go on from academy to college, and accordingly, in the spring of 1853, he shifted his course from the English to the Classical Department, where his most notable instructor (in Latin!) was Charles A. Young, later to become Princeton's "grand old master" of Astronomy. For a variety of reasons, his next three years deserve more consideration than need be given to such a period in the lives of most men. To begin with, he was older than most of his classmates, being almost two years past his majority when he began to prepare for college; in background and in worldly experience, however, he was still behind many of them. He was, if we may judge from his diary of 1851, a real country boy, with not much consecutive schooling, with a wide knowledge of natural history, a love of sport (especially hunting), a considerable mineral collection—and not much else! One asset he discovered himself to have—determination; and feeling at Andover, perhaps for the first time, the stimulus of competition, he indeed started to make up for lost time, with the result that at the end of his course he was graduated valedictorian, having, as one of his classmates put it, "made a clean sweep of all the honors of Phillips Academy."

That he was growing in other ways than scholastically has been pointed out by this same classmate, W. E. Park, one of his most intimate friends. Of these Andover days Park says:

In Phillips Academy there were then two paths of glory; one was high standing in the class, the other was the Philomathean Society, a boys' debating club.

After Marsh really began to study, he stood first in class every term without exception. He studied intensely, but tried to make the impression that he achieved his success without any work at all. In the debating club, he also took hold strongly, although he was at this time a slow and halting speaker, and never in his life was anything of a rhetorician. His superiority in managing practical affairs soon impressed all, and he became manager of the society and held the whole thing in his hands. . . .

I remember an instance of his foresight and shrewd management—shrewd with a touch of cunning in it. The President of the society for the third term had been taken from the senior class for years, but one year the candidate was unpopular, a revolution started, and the middlers resolved to run a candidate of their own. Marsh, then a junior, threw himself into the movement with might and main. He said to me: "We can elect the middler and next year I will be candidate; the precedent for the election of a middler will be established." He worked with much energy and skill and caused the election of the middler, now Dr. Alexander McKenzie of Cambridge. The next year this President left school, and his place was supplied by the Vice-President, now Dr. Franklin Carter, ex-president of Williams College. Carter was the best candidate the seniors had for the third term presidency, and would have been a hard man for Marsh to beat. But Marsh, with some assistance from myself, persuaded the Vice-President to remain in his place and perform the President's duties during the remainder of the term. Then all the school politicians said that Carter had practically been the President for a term, and of course could not run again. This took him out of the way; the time for nomination approached; the seniors put up a weak fellow, but fought for him like tigers, not wanting their class to be defeated. Marsh organized the middlers with great skill, held the class firmly together, picked up the loose votes lying around the school, and defeated the senior candidate by a majority of one. The excitement in the school was tremendous, and Marsh became a great hero. The foresight shown in pushing in a middle-class candidate a year before, and getting McKenzie and Carter on the shelf by previous elections so as to provide a weak opponent for himself was quite exceptional in one so young.[2]

Marsh began another diary at Andover on September 1, 1854, and continued it until the fall of his sophomore year at Yale. Although of course more mature than that of 1851, it has much the same objective quality—a record of events, rather than of the writer's reaction to such. As in Danvers, he continued to be a frequent caller in the homes of his friends and acquaintances. His first honor at Andover, he states, was to be chosen foreman of the Academy Fire Engine Company. An entry on December 31, 1854, might be taken as prophetic of his whole career: "I am so busy I have not had time to moralize

2. In Grinnell, *op. cit.*, pp. 286–287.

on the departure of the Old Year," and to a psychologist, the most interesting thing about the diary might well be the recurrence of the word "success."

Marsh's first taste of what it meant publicly to be a nephew of George Peabody came in October, 1854, when, by invitation, he and his cousin, George Peabody Russell, attended the dedication of the Peabody Institute at Danvers and heard their uncle eulogized by Rufus Choate in "a splendid address exceeding an hour in length."

To help him in his own public speaking, Marsh in this same year began a "Common Place Book," the only notebook of many, incidentally, that he ever filled from cover to cover. Its contents consist largely of quotations, one from the senior Silliman proffering the excellent advice: "Never part with a good mineral until you have a better, and never let a fine one go in the expectation of getting (at some future time) something for it." The book also has a note showing that he knew of the much discussed book on evolution, *Vestiges of the Natural History of Creation,* said to have been written by R. Chambers; but, as appears later, it apparently did not change his orthodox views.

In the summer of 1854, he decided to widen the scope of his collecting by going to Nova Scotia, then becoming renowned for its variety of minerals. An incident that occurred on the return trip illustrates his resourcefulness. Leaving the schooner on which he was a passenger fogbound in the harbor at Machiasport, he set out at midnight and walked fifteen to twenty miles through the forest to catch a small steamer that sailed at four in the morning. He lost his way because of poor directions, and when daylight came he saw the boat already under way down the river. Making a hasty run to a point about a mile ahead, he hailed her as she passed; she stopped for a few moments and the captain pointed to a skiff tied to a tree, which Marsh confiscated and rowed to the steamer. She brought him to Rockland in time to catch the night boat for Boston, "a week ahead of my schooner and just in time to get to Andover the day the term began, thus saving my record of never missing a recitation during my whole Academy course."

The following summer he was again in Nova Scotia, this time in company with Park, and about this vacation we know a good deal from his diary and from letters that he sent to a Lockport (?) newspaper. The immediate destination of the two young men was Parrsboro, a scenic place also of considerable geologic interest, but in the course of their stay there they made an excursion to the Cumberland coal mines on Chignecto Bay—a part of the famous Joggins geologic section (so called because the shoreline jogs in and out). Here they collected fossil plants of Upper Carboniferous age, occurring in great abundance. In some places whole fossil trees were imbedded in the cliffs, "their bark and limbs being perfectly distinguishable." Marsh notes further that "Mr. Lyell [a well-known British geologist] and also Prof. Silliman have visited this locality and call it one of the most interesting in the country." There is no mention, however, either in the diary or in the newspaper letters, of the discovery at this locality of the fossils that were to play so important a part in Marsh's career—*Eosaurus acadianus*, the first vertebrate bones that he ever found.

Marsh's minerals, and his passion for adding to them, were well known to his classmates at Andover, and many of the sentiments written in his autograph album mention either his collection or his love of Nature. His address at the thirtieth anniversary of the Philomathean Society was on "The study of Nature." This address, of which a copy is preserved, along with earlier compositions dating from his days at Wilson Collegiate Institute, is of high quality, a prototype of the kind of writing to which he resorted in his masterly Nashville Address of 1877, but which he seldom had occasion to use in his descriptive work. It puts beyond a doubt his natural flair for science, although at this time it was largely interwoven with his love for the out-of-doors. That science fascinated him even at a much earlier date can be seen from an essay on Astronomy that he wrote in 1849. "The study of Astronomy," he begins, "possesses charms which to myself at least are not equaled by those of any other study I have ever perused."

Writing, indeed, does not seem to have been the hard task for Marsh that it often is for young people. From the first evidence that we have—an essay on "Early rising," written at the end of 1847—his pen showed facility of expression, and the stilted phrases of the day flowed from it with an ease that should have delighted his instructors. Confronted one morning with the task of presenting a composition at eight o'clock, a duty he had neglected the day before, he promptly wrote one on "Procrastination."

While in Andover, and, in fact, during the year previous at Danvers, he wrote contributions for the Wilson school paper, *Isis*, and at Andover he was editor of another such paper, *The Mirror*. Whether he continued this practice while in college is not known; however, when he went to Europe he made arrangements with one of his friends, who was an editor of the New York *Times*, to send letters from abroad, and thus began a connection with the metropolitan press that was to stand him in good stead in later years.

Marsh's graduation from Andover took place on July 29, 1856, and was attended by his Aunt Mary and three cousins from Danvers, by his Aunt Judith and his cousin George, and by the "Misses W." from Salem. At one-thirty, his diary says,

our procession was formed and we marched to the "Old Brick" with our band and at 2 the Exhibition commenced. Everything went off as well as we could ever wish. . . . I saw many of my old friends in the audience who wished me success as I went on the stage, and who congratulated me afterwards on my success. . . . In the evening our supper came off, and we had a rousing time till 2 A.M.

It may be of interest—historical as well as personal—to set down here a record of expenses at Andover in those days, such as we find in one of Mrs. Russell's reports to George Peabody. The account, dated December 31, 1855, and probably for that year, shows that Othniel's expenditures were as follows:

Tuition	$21.00
Books and stationery	32.30
Board	97.00
Washing	9.47
Fuel	15.93
Light	8.50
Room rent	30.75
Furniture	5.25
Clothing	58.00
Travel	23.28

Postage	2.70
Newspaper	2.00
Present to teacher	3.00
Pocket money	8.82
Mem. of A. Lawrence, $1.25. Frame $1.25	2.50
Cash on hand	7.00
Total	$327.50

Singleton Peabody's expenses for the same period were $246.

It is apparent, from Marsh's diary, that he had for some time been planning to go to Yale after his graduation from Andover. His choice of that institution rather than of Harvard, to which several members of his family had gone, and for which Singleton Peabody was headed, was influenced, as we may assume, by the increasing attention that scientific studies were being given at New Haven. He may well have found confirmation of his judgment in an address delivered to the Yale alumni in August, 1856, by Professor James D. Dana, which made a strong plea for science in the curricula of higher institutes of learning, saying in part:

We have reason for gratulation, that our country is beginning to appreciate the importance of scientific culture. A general movement in its favor, is in progress over the land. . . . The Yale School of Science . . . is without endowment. Still, there is here an organization, embracing nearly all that is required in theoretical science, with a part of the practical; and though incomplete, it has had a good measure of success. . .

The department of philosophy and the arts, here instituted to embrace these various subjects, stands on the same independent basis with that of theology, law or medicine. While each is alike independent of the College proper, or academic department, one mantle covers all. . . .

The plan . . . bears its own evidence that in the will of her men and the breadth of her aims, Yale is determined to be up to the times. The desire is manifest that the College, as it now stands, shall not longer mark the limit of American training in literature or science, but that higher paths be laid out, and broader fields surveyed and occupied. . . . Why not have here, THE AMERICAN

UNIVERSITY—where nature's laws shall be taught in all their full-ness, and intellectual culture reach its highest limit![3]

With the beginning of Spring in his senior year at Andover, Marsh went down to New Haven to visit friends who were al-ready there in college, particularly William Abernethy and Addison VanName. With the latter he inspected Linonian Hall, and with the former he heard Professor Dana lecture "on the Ocean," and then visited the "Cabinet," laboratory, etc. In July he had a letter from another Yale friend, Franklin D. Carter,[4] "exhorting me to join the Brothers Society. . . . As I prefer the Linonian it had but little influence on me."

It was probably at his Aunt Judith's suggestion that Marsh approached his uncle with regard to going to Yale. His letter on the subject, sent to her for approval, elicited the response that it was "perfectly proper in style of sentiment," but that it contained two words that were misspelled and one that was wrongly divided! It read as follows:

Andover, May 12, 1856.

My dear Uncle:

As my Academic course of study is nearly completed, I should deem myself most ungrateful to you, if I did not again express to you my sincere thanks for the invaluable advantages, which through your generosity I have so long enjoyed.

I should have renewed to you my expressions of gratitude much sooner than this, had I not judged that you would much prefer to have me show, by my conduct, that I appreciated and rightly improved the opportunities afforded by your bounty, than to testify it by words.

For the last three years I have been preparing for College at Phillips Academy in this place, which is under the charge of Dr. Taylor and which is called the first institution of the kind in this country. Aside from my regular studies I have devoted a large

3. J. D. Dana, "Science and Scientific Schools," pp. 19, 25–26, 28. An address before the alumni of Yale College at the Commencement Anniversary, August, 1856. Published at request of the alumni. S. H. Babcock, New Haven, 1856.

4. The Carter mentioned earlier in connection with the historic Philomathean election at Andover. He entered Yale with the class of 1859, but was forced to leave in his sophomore year because of ill-health. After recovery, he finished his college course at Williams, and later became its president. He served Yale as professor of Modern Languages from 1872 to 1881.

share of my leisure hours and also of my vacations to the Natural Sciences, especially Mineralogy and Geology, for which I have a great fondness, and which will I think be of much service to me.

My Andover course has been by far the happiest period of my life, and I also trust, has been spent in such a manner as to meet with your approbation. Such at least has been, not only my desire, but also my most earnest endeavor.

In July next I shall graduate from this Academy and then if it is in accordance with your wishes I should like to enter Yale College and reap the advantages which its more extensive course of study affords, inasmuch as I have always had an eager desire for a Collegiate education, and especially in such an institution.

In conclusion I must again thank you for your continued liberality to me, and also assure you that, so far as it may be in my power to prevent it, you shall never have occasion to regret the kindness you have shown to me for my dear mother's sake.

I remain your most affectionate nephew,

[Signed] O. C. MARSH.

To this request, George Peabody's reply was evidently favorable, for on August 3, together with nine of his classmates, Othniel went to New Haven for examination. He did not miss a single question, he reported in his diary, and next morning "started for Boston with my cirtificate in my pocket, a hapy youth." He returned to New Haven on September 11, with the promise of an allowance from his uncle to cover his expenses and with $100 a year pocket money; and before college opened he had settled himself in a room at 28 Elm Street, opposite the present site of Durfee Hall. With him in the class of 1860 were at least fifteen other men from Andover.[5]

The day before class assignments were made, Marsh settled one of the major questions then confronting a freshman by joining the Linonian Society, as he had previously indicated

5. The list, kindly compiled for the authors by Mr. Scott H. Paradise of the Academy, includes Alonzo B. Ball, Edward Boltwood, Richard B. Brown, Thaddeus H. Brown, Henry Champion, Frederick C. Colton, Joseph L. Daniels, Robert S. Davis, Charles C. Dodge, Edward B. Furbish, Josiah E. Kittredge, Edward deC. McKay, James H. Schneider, William T. Smith, and Morris Woodruff. The class of 1859 had ten Andover men: Edward S. Beard, Henry L. Breed, Robert J. Carpenter, Franklin D. Carter, Thomas B. Dwight, Charles Easton, Edward T. Fairbanks, Gilbert O. Fay, Thomas B. Raynolds, and Eugene Smith.

he would do. The two debating societies, of which this was the older (founded in 1756 as against 1768 for Brothers in Unity), conducted a campaign for new members at the opening of the fall term in which the competition was "fierce and unwearied . . . when the new-comers began to make their appearance in New Haven, 'not even liberty and the pursuit of happiness was allowed them until they had decided the momentous question.' " [6] The campaign culminated a week or ten days after college opened, with the "Statements of Facts," when rival orators set forth alternately "the incomparable history, the superior prize lists, the immense advantages," of one society or the other. Marsh, however, having already joined Linonia the week before, says about this occasion only that "the class of '59 endeavored to stop our class from entering the hall, unless with hats off. We formed a body and tried to force an entrance. The result was a free fight. I succeeded in getting [in] morning and noon with uncovered head." Both on the occasion of his joining the society and at the "Statements of Facts" he was called on for a speech.

Of the freshman Greek-letter societies, Marsh chose Kappa Sigma Epsilon. He later became a member of Psi Upsilon, but refused election to the senior society of Scroll and Key.

On the scholastic side, Marsh continued at first with the classical studies that he had been pursuing at Andover, there being at that time no scientific course as such open to undergraduates. He had three recitations a day, and reports on September 29 that "although I have not yet got accustomed to go to prayers at 6 in the morning I feel quite at home." His diary is sparse in comments about courses and instructors, and what follows is generalized from his notebooks, which are rather fragmentary, and from the College catalogues of the day.

The first two years were given up entirely to Greek, Latin, Mathematics, Rhetoric, and History. The fall and winter terms of junior year continued the first four of these subjects but substituted Natural Philosophy (Physics) for History. With the spring term of this third year, the curriculum began to diversify, requiring Greek, Natural Philosophy, Astronomy, and Logic, but offering, as an elective, Greek, Latin, Hebrew,

6. E. B. Coe, in W. L. Kingsley, *Yale College* (1879), I, 320.

a modern language, or practical surveying. In senior year, the student was fed "Philosophy" in large doses: Mental Philosophy, Moral Philosophy, Political Philosophy, and History of Philosophy. In addition, he was given a generous sprinkling of science in the form of Astronomy, Chemistry, Geology, Mineralogy, Meteorology, and Anatomy. Another course in History and two terms of Theology rounded out a schedule which, it must be admitted, struck a fair balance between humanities and science, when we consider that the time was prior to 1860.

An analysis of the faculty of the time bears out this last conclusion, and is a further indication of the reason for Marsh's choice of Yale. The humanities were represented in this teaching body by six active professors, medicine by six, theology by five, law by two, and science by eight. This seeming preponderance of science was due, of course, to the growing strength of the Yale Scientific School, then listed as Section I of the Department of Philosophy and the Arts; i.e., the Graduate School. But Marsh did not have to wait until his postgraduate years to come into contact with the group of scientific professors, because his course in Yale College gave him Geology with Dana, Chemistry with the younger Silliman, Mathematics with Hubert A. Newton, Astronomy and Natural Philosophy with Denison Olmsted, and Anatomy with Jonathan Knight. Those were the days when the student was coming more and more into direct contact with the great leaders of thought in the colleges, and less with tutors and instructors, as was the earlier custom. Aside from the scientific group, Marsh sat under such a galaxy of savants as President Theodore Dwight Woolsey in Political Philosophy and the History of Philosophy; Noah Porter (an uncompromising opponent of certain of the sciences with their "dangerous" tendencies) in Mental and Moral Philosophy; Thomas A. Thacher, of long and beloved memory, in Latin; James Hadley, of whom it has been said: "The best course in science in Yale College was Professor Hadley's course in Greek," and: "His spirit of research could never be satisfied until it had reached the farthest limits of possibility"; and the great philologist, William Dwight Whitney, in German, although this last subject may have been deferred to his postgraduate years.

Professor Dana's course in Geology, as given to students in

Yale College and the Sheffield Scientific School, is fortunately preserved in outline at least, in the form of a printed Synopsis. The thirty lectures were divided into the following sections:

Introduction: Geology, a history; its aim. Relations of the Earth to the system of the Universe.

Part I. Physiognomic Geology; or the Earth's exterior features.

Part II. Lithological Geology; or the structure and constitution of rocks and rock strata.

Part III. Historical Geology; or the stratigraphical arrangement and historical relations of the rocks as records of events.

Part IV. Palaeontological Geology; Progress of Life on the Globe.

Part V. Dynamical Geology; or Causes of the Earth's changes and progress.

The greater part of the course was taken up with Part III, which first discussed the Azoic Age, then paused for a "Review of the Vegetable and Animal Kingdoms" before proceeding with the rest of the geologic column. Next above the Azoic came the "Silurian Age, or Age of Molluscs," divided into Lower Silurian, embracing Potsdam to Hudson time, and Upper Silurian, embracing Niagara to Lower Helderberg time. The Devonian Age, or Age of Fishes, took in the Oriskany, the Upper Helderberg, the Hamilton, Chemung, and Catskill, and was followed by a "Carboniferous Age, or Age of Acrogens" that included Subcarboniferous, Carboniferous, and Permian. The Mesozoic and Cenozoic eras were delimited about as they are today, with the exception of the later-defined Oligocene epoch.

As might have been expected from Dana's own work on corals and coral reefs, these received special attention in one of the later lectures in the course.

The section on Paleontological Geology, subtitled "Review of the progress of life on the globe," was evidently intended to lay before the students the philosophical conclusions to which Dana's study of Geology led him. These of course constituted his *credo* with regard to evolution, although, at the time Marsh took the course, Darwin's *Origin of Species* had not yet appeared.

We have also a synopsis for another of the courses that

the class of 1860 absorbed in its progress toward a B.A. degree. This consisted of eleven lectures on Natural Philosophy delivered by Professor Denison Olmsted, who held the chair of Natural Philosophy and Astronomy from 1836 to 1859. Lecture I dealt with the "Progress of the arts and sciences in the United States, during the last fifty years"; Lecture II was a promulgation of "General views," one of which set forth the "Tendency of science to produce social equality." The third lecture discussed the "Great mechanical powers of Nature," and the remaining ones were concerned with motion, resistances, hydrostatics, hydraulics, and pneumatics.

George Peabody made his first visit to America for many years in the fall of his nephew's freshman year at Yale, and Othniel met him at his Aunt Judith's home in Georgetown. Next day he attended the great celebration arranged by Danvers to welcome its returning native son. Quite characteristically, on his way back to New Haven he fell to talking with his seatmate on the train, and found her to be "Mrs. George Bancroft, the historian's lady. She was very well acquainted with Uncle George in London and had many questions to ask about the reception. She gave me an invitation to call and see her in New York, which I shall not fail to do." Mr. Peabody, with his niece Julia, paid the Yale freshman a visit in July, inspected the college, and professed himself much pleased with it.

In August, Marsh and his cousin, George Peabody Russell, went to Newport to attend the "fête champêtre" given for Mr. Peabody by Mr. William Shepard Wetmore, and the diary speaks of this event as "probably the greatest affair of the kind ever given in this country. Over ten thousand guests were said to have been present"—an estimate slightly in excess of the one given by the statistically minded reporter for the New York *Times* on August 12, who placed the number present at 2,500, although he said that invitations had been sent to 3,000. This garden party de luxe was held on the grounds of "Chateau sur Mer," one of the most magnificent houses in Newport, on the ocean side of Bellevue Avenue. Music, the *Times* tells us, was furnished by the Germania Musical Society, whose conductor, Mr. William Schultze, produced a special "Fête Champêtre March" for the occasion. There was a pavilion for dancing 100 feet square, and for this and other temporary pavilions 32,000 feet of lumber was used, as well as $2,000 worth of canvas. "Wreaths and bouquets of choice flowers were flung about in the wildest profusion. . . . Ladies wore morning costume with bonnet, and the gentlemen kept their hats in hand." Present to make the day complete for the fair sex were two young members of the British peerage (unmarried), the British and Russian ministers (marital state not noted), and visitors from the 40 yachts then lying in Newport harbor. Refreshments, in charge of "that accomplished colored *Chef* Downing, who seemed to regard the whole affair as his apotheosis," were truly ample and varied; in fact, no abridgment of the menu could possibly do it justice, so we quote it *in toto*, as given in the *Times:*

CARD OF REFRESHMENTS

Fresh Salmon, à la Montpellier
Woodcocks
Chicken Partridges
Pickled Oysters
Gelatine of Turkey
Gelatine of Ham
Gelatine of Tongue
Boned Partridges, in jelly
Crisp Potatoes, à la Downing
Lobster Salad
Celery Salad

Golden Plover
Snipes
Fried Oysters
Soft Crabs
Pâte de Fois Gras
Pâte de Truffles
Escolloped Oysters
Coquettes [sic] of Chicken
Chicken Salad
Italian Salad

Ice Creams

Vanilla
Almond
Pistachio
Strawberry
Lemon
Mille Fruits Ice
Mille Fruits Crême
Variety of Sherberts
Fancy Ices
Statuettes of Washington and
   Lafayette

Vases of Fancy Cream
Messerole Pudding
Plum Pudding, glacé
Meruenge Basquets a la Crême
Jelly Russe
Variety of Fancy Cakes
Bonbons, in large variety
Charlotte Russe
Marasquine Jelly
Rum Jelly
Wine Jelly

Peaches, Apricots, Pears, Nectarines, and 250 pounds Black Hamburg Grapes (from Mr. Wetmore's own hot-house), 24 baskets of Champagne Frappé, Amontillado Sherry, six bowls of Lemonade, Sangarees, Madeira, Cognac, etc.

Shortly after the Newport affair, Marsh and several of his classmates made a trip to Nova Scotia, his third, and the entry about this trip is the last one in his diary. For the rest of his college course we have to rely on outside information entirely, and meager enough at first it seemed to be. His maturity, in comparison to the other men in the class, gave him the nickname of "Daddy," but another, more common sobriquet was "Captain," as in the following excerpt from a description of a trip to the Thimble Islands, east of New Haven, written by Charles H. Owen of the class of 1860:

Captain's portly form looks odd enough in his well-worn shooting jacket; which tells, however, many a tale of swift destruction to innocent snipe and plover, in its ooze-drabbled edges, and the evident traces of Charm's muddy paws. His moustache, too, takes a still fiercer curl as he carefully sifts the powder into his flask. One cannot look at him without thinking of Kingsley's ideal naturalist. "He must be strong in body, able to haul a dredge, climb a rock, turn a boulder, walk all day uncertain where he shall eat or rest; ready to face sun and rain, wind and frost, and to eat or drink thankfully anything, however coarse or meagre; he should know how to swim for his life, to pull an oar, to sail a boat, and ride the first horse which comes to hand; and, finally, he should be a thoroughly good shot and a skillful fisherman; and, if he go far abroad, be able on occasion to fight for his life." [7]

During his freshman year, Marsh became a member of the crew of the shell "Wenona"; the "Wenona," however, was not destined to play any very glorious rôle in the annals of Yale rowing!

A cross section of the sentiments inscribed by Marsh's classmates in his 1860 album shows that his college hours had not been devoted to any one pursuit, but rather presented the medley of interests advisable for a well-rounded personality. His aquarium and his mineral cabinet were subjects of frequent

7. *Yale Lit. Mag.,* XXV (1859–60), 218.

mention, as the latter was in his Andover days. Aside from this leaning toward science, the traits most stressed were all embodied by W. H. Hurlbut, who wrote:

I shall always remember you for your generous and frank disposition, for your love of fun, and your scholarly attainments. As the hero of the *all but* bloody affair in Wooster Place, as the undisputed champion at the Strawberry Festival with the *blue dress* upon your arm; as the most celebrated sportsman in our class; as the owner of the dog "Charm" whose deeds are inscribed in verse . . . and as the inventor of the distinguished patent invisible double back-actioned cramming platform. . . .

None of these statements, however, gives as intimate a picture of Marsh in his student days at Yale as the one that came to the authors as the result of an unexpected call from a visitor to the Peabody Museum. This was Mrs. Guy C. Menefee of Rochester, Minnesota, whose mother, Mrs. E. L. Curial, née Libby Treat, was a little girl in the house at 28 Elm Street where Marsh lived while he was in college. The house belonged to Mrs. Curial's father, Atwater Treat, a builder and architect who was a member of the construction firm that later built the Museum and Marsh's home on Prospect Street—and, incidentally, the present Museum. The house, now destroyed, was a three-story one of brick, and it was the four large rooms on the third floor, reached by a separate stairway, that Marsh had for his quarters. As his collections grew, they overflowed into the attic and the weight of them became so great that Mr. Treat had to reinforce the floor. Her brothers, Mrs. Curial said, felt strongly that he should be asked to move, but her father and mother and she were much too fond of him to agree.

When mother was small [Mrs. Menefee writes on July 12, 1937] he would carry her upstairs on his shoulders and set her down on one of the huge packing boxes containing minerals. Then he would tell her, "Libby, if you'll promise not to touch anything I'll show you some wonderful things." Arthur Hadley [later president of Yale] often played with mother and she said she once asked Professor Marsh if he wouldn't let Arthur come up and see the things too, but he said "No, he couldn't trust him [!]" . . . He showed her specimens of "fool's gold" and real gold and explained the difference to her. He gave her many specimens of minerals and fossils and made notes for her about them. . . . When he returned from his field trips he would work long hours writing and studying his specimens in his rooms. Mother says he was always very odd and for most people it was "like running against a pitchfork to get acquainted with him."

Turning from this personal account to the colder record of figures, a fair idea of college expenses during the period of Marsh's studentship may be gleaned from bills kept in his archives. Tuition was $15 a term, or $45 a year. Rent at 28 Elm Street was $15 a term, heat an additional $11 to $12, and board (at various places, including the "Tiger Club") from $3 to $3.75 a week. A clothing bill for 1857–58 has the following items:

1 figured vest	$10.00
1 umbrella	2.50
1 dressing gown	4.50
1 pr. gloves	1.00
1 pr. black pants	10.00
Repairing overcoat	1.00
1 pr. gloves	1.25
1 pr. checked pants	7.50
1 mixed f. coat	17.00
1 pr. gloves	1.00
1 " "	1.00
1 muffler	1.25
	$58.00

Marsh's summary of his expenses for the four years 1857 to 1860, preserved on odd slips of paper—a habit that was to grow on him—shows the following totals:

	1857	1858	1859	1860
Clothing	$157.11	$109.85	$137.50	$142.20
Board	135.40	161.28	181.00	183.74
Lights	9.94			
Washing	22.03	29.70	33.25	41.62
Room and heat	88.79	75.42	82.38	94.65
Books and stationery	57.55	68.14	104.23	124.32

College bills	86.28	83.21	75.40	109.50
Postage	7.51			
Society taxes	18.18	28.00	27.62	23.00
Traveling expenses	31.80	45.35	33.52	45.00
Dentist	12.25			
Pocket money	100.00	100.00	100.00	100.00
Class pictures				56.00
	$726.84	$700.95	$774.90	$920.03

That these expenditures were somewhat above those of the average student seems to be indicated by the Yale catalogue of 1857, which cites the necessary expenses about as follows:

College bills	$69	$ 69
Board	90	140
Fuel and light	10	20
Books and stationery	5	15
Furniture, etc.	5	20
Washing	12	24
Society taxes	9	12
	$200	$300

It is to be hoped that these "optimum" figures, and especially the items for books and stationery, did not come under the eye of Mrs. Russell, who was paying Othniel his allowance. That bookkeeping was never one of Marsh's major accomplishments she had found out while he was at Andover, where, she complained to her brother, he spent twice as much as her own son, and one third more than his cousin Singleton. He is, she said drily, "exceeding economical of his own fund . . . a good scholar, a smart, energetic man, but in pecuniary matters he is decidedly Marshey." When he went to Yale, he had to render no account of the $100 a year allowed him for pocket money, but of the allowance for expenses Mrs. Russell struggled in vain to make him keep a detailed record. Quite probably it was the relatively high amounts for books and for traveling expenses that caused her to write him thus sharply in 1857:

I consider an irregular and careless way of keeping accounts dishonesty. . . . I think I have never received an account from you yet that would stand Law. . . . If I were to send the whole matter

to your uncle, together with your receipts, I should not wonder
if it relieved you from further hard study.

Again, in 1861, during his graduate work, she remarked
that his account the previous year had run over $900 and that
if it exceeded $1,000 the allowance would probably be stopped.
George Peabody, she writes,

is eagle-eyed and if he thought you were laying up, at his expense,
anything for your future benefit, and not expressly needed in your
present studies, it would be greatly to your pecuniary disadvantage. Minerals, and books on that subject, are to you, just what a
Law Library is to George and Singleton—and I am certain it
would not do for them to get them. They are tools to work with—
after the business is learned.

This matter of Marsh's inability to keep within his allowance is reflected also in several appeals made to his father for
small loans while he was in college. "I can of course write for
the money elsewhere," he says, "but might lose ten times the
amount eventually by so doing." Again, "You know that I
have no means at present at my command, although it is possible I may have as much as I want at some future time." It
should be stated here, however, as the other side of the picture,
that he at times loaned his father money, that in 1857 he offered
to take over Caleb's Lockport property to protect it from
creditors, that when his half brother Caleb was to go to Danvers for a year or so, a "respectable outfit" was provided for
the boy at his expense, and that in later years he paid for expensive schooling for his youngest half sister Mary.

The Yale class of 1860 had the usual quota of men destined
to prominence, among them Francis Delafield, professor of
Pathology at Columbia University and president of the American Association of Physicians; Capt. Clarence E. Dutton,
Army geologist and National Academician; Marcus P.
Knowles, chief justice of the Superior Court of Massachusetts; William W. Phelps, minister plenipotentiary to Austria
and to Germany; Eugene L. Richards, Yale professor of
Mathematics; and William Thayer Smith, professor of Physiology and dean of the Medical School at Dartmouth. Nevertheless, the class record for the twenty-fifth reunion says: "Marsh

is *primus inter pares*, if not *facile princeps*, among the eminent men of our class." At class dinners, the odd nature of his work and his bachelor state, which continued to the end of his life, were frequent topics.

As might have been expected in one so much older than his classmates, Marsh found some of his closest friendships in classes ahead of his own. Noteworthy among these was the bond between him and Addison VanName of the class of 1858, which dated from their Andover days and lasted until broken by Marsh's death. VanName, a junior, was living at 28 Elm Street when Marsh came there as a freshman. Appointed tutor at Yale in 1862 and instructor in Hebrew in 1863, he was made university librarian in 1865 and held that post for forty years, becoming one of the best-known and best-beloved university figures.

Marsh was graduated in 1860, eighth in a class of 109, receiving a "High Orations" stand, his other honors including a Latin prize and election to Phi Beta Kappa. More important for his future, he received a Berkeley Scholarship, awarded to the senior who passes the best examination in the Greek Testament (Pauline epistles), the first book of Thucydides, and the first six books of Homer's *Iliad*, Cicero's *Tusculan Questions*, *Tacitus* (except the Annals), and Horace; and carrying with it the proviso that the winner must spend one to three years at Yale in graduate study.

CHAPTER III

SHEFFIELD SCIENTIFIC SCHOOL AND EUROPE

"Every man is said to have his peculiar ambition."
LINCOLN.

IF IT was Marsh's love of science that brought him to Yale in the first place, certainly his four years in the College only intensified his enthusiasm. Moreover, they developed in his mind a clear picture of a career that would enable him to continue scientific work amid the academic surroundings which he found so much to his liking—that of a professorship in Natural Science. About the time of his graduation, he wrote his uncle concerning his ambitions for a professorial career, and received the following reply:

Dalguise [by Dunkeld] Sept. 28th, 1860.

My dear Nephew,

I duly received your letter dated 13th July, stating your wishes to fit yourself for a "Professorship of Natural Science in Yale or some other College." It has always been my intention to consult the wishes and act liberally towards all those who are in a pecuniary point of view, comparatively dependent upon me, and who show by their character and exertions that they are worthy of my confidence. From my own observation and from the report of others I place you on that list.

The rank you have obtained at Yale I trust will stimulate you to still greater efforts to become prominent in the Profession on which you have fixed your mind, and with that understanding, and my conviction that you will do so I heartily accede to what you propose, requesting, however, that you will at all times treat your Aunt Russell with the utmost confidence with regard to your expences as she will, as usual, pay them as authorized by me, and consequently feel the responsibility attending them. . . .

I have not been in London more than two weeks for 4 months having long since determined to make business subservient to health. I have been here in the Highlands of Scotland for the past two months passing 8 or 10 hours in the open air daily and have entirely escaped gout and my health is very good for an old man nearly 66.

Very Truly Yours,
[Signed] GEORGE PEABODY.

Mr. O. Marsh.

Certainly it was quite in keeping with the great banker's own career to foster high ambition when he saw it! The amount of money that he was called upon to supply for his nephew's two postgraduate years at Yale was $2,200.

Courses in science, to which Marsh turned his whole attention when his undergraduate work was behind him, had been recognized as important at Yale since the fortunate appointment of Benjamin Silliman to a professorship of Chemistry and Mineralogy in 1802. By 1845, we learn from Professor Russell H. Chittenden, historian of the Sheffield Scientific School, "Yale College, though generally considered as perhaps the most conservative of the larger colleges of the country, was not much if any behind her sister institutions . . . in the recognition of science." [1] The ensuing year, 1846–47, saw the first steps made at both Harvard and Yale toward the establishment of definite schools of science, in the former by the gift of Abbott Lawrence, and at Yale by the appointment of two new professors, John Pitkin Norton in Agricultural Chemistry and Animal and Vegetable Physiology, and Benjamin Silliman, Jr., in Practical Chemistry. To these two professorships, whose incumbents forged ahead under heavy odds, the College lending them little but moral support, others were gradually added, until in 1854–55 the chemical and engineering schools were grouped together as the Yale Scientific School.

In 1850, Silliman the elder had been succeeded as professor of Mineralogy and Geology in Yale College by James D. Dana, who also became instructor in these subjects in the Scientific Department. Likewise of great significance was the appointment of George Jarvis Brush, one of the earliest students of the school, to a newly created professorship of Metallurgy.

1. Russell H. Chittenden, *History of the Sheffield Scientific School* (1928), I, 22.

This growing staff, and the increasing number of students, made some sort of definite financial foundation imperative, and it was in this connection that Professor Dana made the appeal to the alumni mentioned in the previous chapter. The school finally found its good angel in the person of Mr. Joseph Earl Sheffield, who not only made it a gift of $10,000, but turned over to it in 1858 a building on Grove Street which should house its activities, and added a permanent fund for the maintenance of professorships.

This upwelling of science was going on while Marsh was a student in Yale College, and as if in answer to his particular needs came the announcement that the Yale Corporation, at its meeting on July 24, 1860, had provided for the establishment of advanced courses in the Scientific School. Thus, when he entered the school in the fall of 1860, it was as one of its first class of graduate students. By 1869, according to Harvard's historian, "Yale already had a graduate school, and better scientific instruction than Harvard." [2]

The students in the Scientific School in 1860 constituted the bulk of the Department of Philosophy and the Arts (i.e., the Graduate School), numbering forty out of a total of forty-four, divided as follows among the courses: Chemical, sixteen; General Course, twelve; Engineering, twelve. Marsh chose the Chemical Course—really Chemistry and Natural Science. The studies pursued in the first year were General, Agricultural and Organic Chemistry, Chemical Analysis, Metallurgy, Mineralogy, Botany, and French or German. Those of the second year were Physical Geography, Physics, History of the Inductive Sciences, Geology, and Logic. Some modification from the above schedule was, however, permitted, to allow for more intensive specialization if the student wished.

Here, again, Marsh's instructors were a notable group, and one whose youthful enthusiasm for science furnished exactly the sort of "culture" in which a student of his type would grow rapidly. Included in it, besides Olmsted, Dana, and the younger Silliman, were John Addison Porter, who succeeded John Pitkin Norton in the professorship of Agricultural Chemistry in 1852;

2. S. E. Morison, *Three Centuries of Harvard* (1936), p. 323. Harvard University Press. Reprinted by permission of the President and Fellows of Harvard College.

PLATE V

BENJAMIN SILLIMAN   JAMES DWIGHT DANA

GEORGE J. BRUSH   BENJAMIN SILLIMAN, JR.

THE GROUP OF YALE PROFESSORS WHO GUIDED
MARSH'S STUDIES IN THE SHEFFIELD SCIEN-
TIFIC SCHOOL

PORTRAITS OF THE ELDER SILLIMAN AND DANA FROM
PAINTINGS BY DAVID HUNTINGTON

PLATE VI

E. G. EHRENBERG

W. K. H. PETERS

MARSH IN 1862

H. R. GOEPPERT

FERDINAND ROEMER

MARSH IN 1862 AND THE GERMAN SAVANTS WHO GAVE
HIM MOST OF HIS PROFESSIONAL TRAINING

Samuel W. Johnson, then professor of Analytical Chemistry, but later to become one of the most potent factors in welding agriculture to science; and, most important of all, George Jarvis Brush, in the fifth year of his professorship of Metallurgy.

Marsh's first scientific paper appeared while he was a student in the Sheffield Scientific School in November, 1861. During the previous summer, on his last trip to Nova Scotia, he had explored the newly discovered gold fields, and on his return he described what he had there seen, his being apparently the first observations about them to be published. The paper therefore attracted considerable attention, "being copied," he writes his father, "into over thirty papers and scientific journals in this country and Europe." Moreover, he was asked by the Geological Society of London to send the article to be read at one of its meetings and to be published in its *Transactions*. Flattering as the reception of this article must have been to the young student, the paper that followed in 1862, describing certain vertebrate remains that he had found several years earlier in Nova Scotia, was to create still wider ripples of interest in the scientific world. Moreover, these two isolated vertebrae were quite probably the means of turning Marsh toward Vertebrate Paleontology.

In order to see what gave these Nova Scotian fossils their significance, we must translate ourselves into the knowledge of some eighty years ago. We are told by Park, Marsh's companion on the trip, that when Marsh found the bones in the Coal Measures (Upper Carboniferous) along Chignecto Bay, he had no idea of their value, remarking only: "That is the backbone of a halibut." He was always hoping to find further remains, and so published no description of the vertebrae for nearly seven years. After a further reëxamination of the locality, and probably at Dana's suggestion, he showed the bones in 1861 to Louis Agassiz, who at once became greatly interested, so much so, in fact, that he wrote a letter to Silliman about them, which the latter printed in the *American Journal of Science* for January, 1862. In this letter, Agassiz—then the world's authority on fossil fishes—said that the bones excited his interest "in the highest degree. . . . We have here undoubtedly a nearer approximation *to a synthesis between Fish and Reptile* than has yet been seen." The publication of this letter created some little upset at New Haven, and Marsh, unwilling to have any more of the cream skimmed off his discovery by others, published a preliminary description of the vertebrae in the *Journal* for March, in the form of a letter to Professor Silliman, naming them *Eosaurus acadianus*, and stating that they showed "Enaliosaurian characters." This was followed in July by a more extended description.

Before the appearance of the Agassiz letter, Marsh had thought the vertebrae belonged to the marine reptile called *Ichthyosaurus*, but Agassiz, noting an "angular notch" in the margin of one of them, with a corresponding elevation on the anterior surface, expressed the opinion that these were "organic, rather than accidental; and as such were indicative of an inferiority of structure, which would place the genus of reptiles to which the remains belong somewhat lower than the *Ichthyosauri*." However, on further development out of the matrix, this notch and elevation were seen to be lacking on the other vertebra. Professor Jeffries Wyman of Harvard, to whom Marsh submitted the vertebrae, therefore considered these features "purely accidental" and was of the opinion that, in any case, they were not "sufficiently important . . . to affect at all the Enaliosaurian character of the remains." Hence the vertebrae were left by Marsh in the same order as the Ichthyosauri, though belonging to another genus. Subsequent study has shown that they represent a primitive, probably land-living amphibian of the order Stegocephalia. Some years after Marsh made his discovery, tiny bones of small amphibians (Microsauria) were found at the same place in tree stumps, and described by J. W. Dawson with the help of Sir Richard Owen.

From the vertebrae, Marsh deduced that *Eosaurus*, when restored on the basis of *Ichthyosaurus*, would have been twelve to fifteen feet in length, that it was an air-breathing, cold-blooded, carnivorous, aquatic type, capable of rapid progress through the water after its prey, which doubtless consisted of fishes.

Aside from the part that this discovery may have played in turning Marsh toward the vertebrate side of Paleontology, the paper describing the vertebrae is of interest for several other reasons. In the first place, it shows that writing was never to be any difficulty for him. Second, certain passages in it seem to indicate that he was already thinking along genetic lines. Again, the deductions given at the end of the previous paragraph foreshadow his tendency to re-create, from fossil bones, the living animal in its environment, a tendency which later led to the restorations that did so much to spread his fame. And finally, it may be that here was an early illustration of his readiness to capitalize on striking discoveries that would bring him into the center of the scientific stage.

Aside from this paper, we know little of Marsh's life during these two years in the Sheffield Scientific School, other than that he was working mainly with Professors Dana, Brush, and Silliman, Jr., and that his attention was centered about equally on Chemical Geology and Mineralogy, and possibly a shade less on Geology–Paleontology. At the outbreak of the Civil War he was offered a major's commission in a Connecticut regiment, but was obliged to decline it on account of defective eyesight. "I am drilling every day with the Graduate Guards. . . . I shall go to the war if necessary," he wrote his father on June 12, 1861; and on August 13, 1862, he wrote that he was even then undecided whether to go abroad or to go into the Army.

The statement has been made that, upon his graduation from the Sheffield Scientific School in 1862 with the degree of Master of Arts, Marsh was offered a professorship at Yale, but declined it. This is probably true, as the statement occurs also in an outline of his life prepared by Marsh himself, but there is naturally no record of it otherwise. A portion of a letter from him to his father in August, 1862, may or may not throw light on this point:

New Haven, 13 August, 1862.

I have just rec'd your kind letter and also a copy of the *Lockport Journal and Courier*, containing a notice of myself . . . . very sorry that some one had no more discretion than to preface the notice with some statements which are calculated to do me much more injury than a thousand such notices could do good. The published statement that I am *expecting* a Professorship at Yale would do not a little towards preventing my getting it. So also that my expenses at College were paid by Uncle George and that he intended to make me his heir, were certainly very injudicious remarks, and entirely uncalled for.

This notice was reprinted from a Danvers paper, but with a "preface" added.

The idea of study abroad had been in the mind of Marsh for some time, for he wrote his uncle on June 9, 1862: "If the plan of completing my studies in Germany, which you once so kindly approved, still meets with your approbation, I should like to go in September next." Mr. Peabody readily assented and arranged to give him a letter of credit for £200.

Marsh started for Europe in November, 1862, going first to England, where he visited the International Exhibition and spent some time in the various museums. On December 2, according to the *Quarterly Journal* of the Geological Society of London, the communications read before that honorable body included a "Description of the remains of a new Enaliosaurian (*Eosaurus acadianus*) from the Coal formation of Nova Scotia. By O. C. Marsh, Esq., M.A. Communicated by Sir Charles Lyell, V.P.G.S." That Marsh was not present at this meeting is likely, because he was already in Berlin on November 26, whence he wrote to Benjamin Silliman, Jr. His paper on *Eosaurus* was published by the Geological Society in abridged form only, he wrote, "because, owing to an unfortunate misunderstanding, it was not received until after it had been published in the 'American Journal of Science and Arts' for July 1862." Commenting on this further to Silliman on May 10, 1863, Marsh said: "As I sent my paper on the *Eosaurus* to the Geological Society of London in pamphlet form and not in MSS (which the regulations required) it was not published in full in the Transactions, as I had supposed it would be. As a consolation, I suppose, the Society elected me a member."

Letters of introduction given to Marsh by Professor Dana indicate that he was intending to study Analytical Chemistry and Mineralogy, and for these subjects he went first to the University of Berlin, to place himself under Professors H. and G. Rose. It was his plan, also, to spend most of the winter in perfecting his knowledge of German. A letter to Silliman junior in February, 1863, shows that he liked Berlin very much; in response to the latter's offer of further letters of introduction, he says: "I shall not need them, as those I brought from London have given me a very pleasant circle of friends, who show me every attention"—doubtless in part an indication of the fashion

in which his path was to be smoothed by the magic of George
Peabody's name, and by the note from the latter on the margin
of his letter of credit. In the spring of 1863, he moved on to
Heidelberg, to work under Bunsen, Blum, and Kirchhoff. With
Bunsen's work he was, of course, familiar from his studies in
New Haven, but he was attracted to him particularly because
of his analyses of zeolites, a group of minerals in which Marsh
himself had long been interested.

In May of this year, Marsh was summoned to Homburg to
meet his uncle and to continue a discussion of the latter's future
donations to American institutions, about which they had had
a long talk earlier in England. The important results of that
conference, insofar as Yale was concerned, are related in the
chapter that deals with George Peabody and his gift to that
institution of funds for a natural history museum. In the same
envelope with the letter to the junior Silliman announcing this
gift, although bearing a date of some days previous to the
meeting with Mr. Peabody, was the following letter:[3]

Heidelberg, May 10, 1863.

My Dear Professor:

I fear you will think me a troublesome correspondent, but I wish
to consult you in regard to a question which I must soon decide,
and on which you can advise me better than anyone else. I refer to
my course of scientific study; and as I remember that you once
spoke to me on the subject, I shall venture to ask your opinion
on one or two points in regard to it. I intended to have done this
before I left New Haven, but I was undecided whether to go into
the army, or abroad until a few days before I sailed, and as you
were then out of town most of the time I had no good opportunity
of doing so.

Hitherto, as you know, I have devoted a good deal of time to
Natural Science; but my studies have been much more general
than I intend them to be in future. I am now sufficiently familiar
with the German language and with scientific matters in Germany
to pursue with advantage some particular branch of study, and
I wish to commence upon it as soon as possible, and to concentrate
all my efforts upon it. I am, however, nearly equally interested in

3. For this and other letters in the Silliman–Marsh–Dana correspondence,
the Peabody Museum is indebted to Miss Maria T. Dana, who kindly added
them to the Marsh archives.

Chemical Geology, Mineralogy, and Palaeontology: and my choice of one of these will depend on the prospect of making the result of my studies available on my return to America. Chemical Geology or Mineralogy I should certainly prefer, as my previous studies have been much more in that direction, and my cabinet and library, on which I have spent and am spending a good deal of time and money, relate more especially to these departments.

Supposing, for example, that during my stay in Europe, I should study Chemical Geology, including some of its practical branches, and should enlarge my cabinet and library in that direction, would there probably be an opportunity of making such attainments useful on my return? Would it be more advisable for me to devote myself to *Palaeontology*,—making an especial study of some one of its branches; e.g., the *Vertebrates?*

From your familiarity with science in America you can easily advise me what branch it would be most advantageous for me to pursue, and I shall be greatly obliged for your opinion. From this point of view it is very difficult to judge, especially as the war is changing affairs in America so rapidly.

Prof. Dana's Geology[4] is spoken of in the highest terms by the geologists here who have seen it. At a meeting of the Geological Soc. of Germany, which I attended in Berlin, Prof. Ehrenberg showed a copy he had just received and said it was the best book of the kind ever published. I heard Prof. Geinitz say the same, while showing his copy to the Nat. History Soc. of Dresden, and he added that the Author was the "Humboldt of America." . . .

Mr. Peabody has been spending the winter in Nice for his health, but will soon come to Wiesbaden, where I shall hope to see him often, and to discuss with him one or two important *scientific questions*. . . .

Desiring a kind remembrance to Mrs. Silliman and the young ladies, I remain

Very truly yours,
[Signed] O. C. Marsh.

Prof. B. Silliman, Jr.

Of equal importance are the replies to this letter from Professors Silliman and Dana, abstracted below:

4. The first edition of Dana's *Manual of Geology,* which was published in 1862, not 1863 as is stated in some bibliographies.

New Haven, June 15, 1863.

My dear Marsh,

. . . .

Yours of May 10th was written before you had enjoyed the pleasure of visiting your uncle at Wiesbaden, but I am glad it came in the same envelope which brought us such good news. Besides, the task of answering the important questions which you propound is much simplified by what has happened. It now seems clear that you have to fit yourself by suitable studies for duty *here* in connection with the science of Geology and *Palaeontology*. It is Prof. Dana's view that you should devote yourself with zeal and your well known perseverance to the subject of Palaeontology, and especially to the palaeontology of the older rocks. Palaeozoic rocks abound in the U.S. and demand by far more study than they have received. It requires you to amass as soon as you can a good collection of fossils in this department of European geology for comparison. Our collections are weak in European Palaeozoic except in the Permian of which Dr. Geinitz has sent Prof. D. a good series. In obtaining this special knowledge you will of course study General Geology, so as to be prepared to give instruction, if required, on this subject in the post-graduate courses. Things now tend strongly toward placing these studies in what may be called the university studies, Mineralogy being now studied almost solely in that way. There is now every reason why I should write you with entire frankness on matters which so deeply interest us both and which are especially interesting to you personally. I may say then that you have only to show your fitness for such a chair as I have indicated, involving perhaps the curatorship of the museums, and you will receive the appointment. The fund contemplated in your uncle's codicil would be insufficient for such an endowment in view of all else we must do with it. But I can not doubt if he has this view of the subject before his mind that he will authorize you to go on and fit yourself and to use any available means to amass the collections needed to give a first class effect to your department. This done I do not question he will see the desireableness of having the museums in process of construction so that he may enjoy the pleasure of seeing you installed in his lifetime in a manner so honorable to both. The *most* desirable thing, of course, would be that he should authorize this—endow your professorship and have the fund named in his will unimpaired to sustain all the departments contemplated in our plan, there being no other means to sustain them and nothing more useless than costly establishments without foundations. I am well aware how very much this plan exceeds the limits named. But I have faith to believe that your noble relative will rise to the level of the occasion, if the subject is properly presented to his consideration, as I am sure you know how to present it. . . .

Believe me yours very faithfully,
[Signed] B. Silliman, Jr.

New Haven, June 16 [*1863*].

My dear Mr. Marsh.—

. . . .

Prof. S. has spoken of my advice to you. I would say that there is no department that affords an opening now, excepting Paleontology; and if you could prepare yourself for Paleozoic Pal. (as this is specially needed in America), I think there would be no difficulty as to your appointment to the place. I w^d recommend your studying abroad for a couple of years. Prof. Roemer of Germany w^d be a good teacher, I think, and at the same time to attend to general Zoology and especially to Invertebrates (Mollusks, etc.) and then, besides this, to purchase and collect specimens of European species largely, for in no other way exc^t by handling specimens and their labels can you familiarize yourself with characters and names of genera or species . . . .

Sincerely your friend,
[Signed] James D. Dana.

Also of interest here are portions of a letter from Marsh to Silliman, of two letters from Marsh to his uncle, and of a reply by the latter.

August 20 [*1863?*].[5]

[To Benjamin Silliman, Jr.]
My dear Sir:

. . . .

The 2d part of your letter relating more particularly to myself, was certainly a very agreeable surprise, although what you and

5. Most of the letters from Marsh, here quoted, are taken from pencil copies preserved with his correspondence, and may, therefore, differ slightly from the letters actually sent, which have not been seen by the authors.

also Prof. Dana once said to me had inspired a hope that I might at some time be connected with Yale. There is certainly no institution in America that I should prefer, and the present position will be to me a very pleasant one on many accounts, provided of course I can fit myself for its duties. I only regret that I had not devoted to Pal. the time I have spent on Mineralogy, although in the Curatorship of the Museum of which you speak, all such knowledge will be far from lost.

I am sure my proposed connection with Yale will please Mr. P. as he has of late manifested no little interest in my future scientific prospects, and several times expressed a wish that I might obtain a position at Yale or Harvard. Knowing however the many applications he is constantly receiving, and in view of what I said above, I could not, at present, think of proposing to him to endow the professorship aside from the large donation he has just given. There are, moreover, I think some particular reasons, why such an endowment should come from another source, even if the present donation should be increased, as I certainly hope it may be. . . .

[O. C. MARSH.]

Heidelberg, July 12, 1863.

My Dear Uncle:

One immediate result of your munificent donation to Yale has been to more than realize my highest hopes of obtaining an honorable position when my studies here are completed. Although there is at present no vacancy at Yale the Faculty propose to create a new Professorship of Geology and Palaeontology (the science of fossil remains) and give me the position as soon as I can fit myself for its duties. They tell me there is no branch of science in America which offers so fine a field for research as Palaeontology, and that this position will give me excellent opportunities for pursuing it.

This Professorship is certainly a much higher [better?] position than I had any just reason to expect. There is no other in America which I shall prefer. It corresponds to that held by the great Agassiz at Harvard, and in point of rank is the same as that of Prof. Silliman Senior, or Prof. Dana. Prof. S. Jr. is only a Professor in the Medical Department at Yale and before obtaining even this, he served an apprenticeship of 6 years in a western college as have several other Yale Profs. Aside from these considerations the position itself will on many accounts be a very agreeable one to me. I shall have entire control of the cabinets of the *Peabody Museums* in which as *Trustee* I shall feel a special interest, and my other duties will allow me time for study, and for publishing any original results I may be able to obtain.

This unexpected offer may to some extent change my previous plans of study, as these will now in a measure be directed by the scientific faculty who having nearly all studied here understand exactly what is necessary.

By this appointment I shall at once be placed on a level with men all of much greater age and experience than myself. They are also men eminent in the scientific world while for such eminence I can only hope in the future. The first thing, then, I must consider is how best to fill the position with honor to the University and myself, and I am well aware that I have no easy task before me.

I shall do everything in my power to prove myself worthy of the confidence reposed in me, but it seems also necessary to give me an equal chance with the other Profs and to make my labors effective that I should have a library and cabinet in a measure equal to those possessed by my colleagues. A library and cabinet is to a Prof. of Science exactly what capital is to a man in business; with the advantage that in the former case that no risk of loss is incurred. Such a library and cabinet as the position requires can only be obtained in Europe and while I am here I shall have opportunities for collecting them such as I may never again possess.

The amount necessary for this object would be 3 or 4 thousand dollars. There is not, I think, a Prof. in Yale who has not an equal amount thus invested while Profs. S. and D. and several others have each private libraries and cabinets of much greater value. If I do not have similar means of study and advancement at my command, as the other Profs. possess, the disadvantages which at first I must necessarily labor under, on account of my inexperience, will be much increased.

I have felt some hesitation in asking you for this assistance in view of all you have already done for me, but I have thought it much the best way to state the whole case frankly and leave the matter with you. If you should think best to grant me this aid I should first consult Prof. S. and D. as to what my position would particularly require, and then endeavor to apply the amount strictly and judiciously to the object proposed.

[O. C. Marsh.]

Inbergarry, Fort Augustus, N. B., Aug. 22, 1863.

My dear Nephew:

. . . .

With regard to your request that, in the event of your obtaining the prominent position in the College you name, I would allow you 3,000 to 4,000$ to enable you to supply yourself with the necessary Library, I beg to state that if such a Professorship is promised, with a liberal salary, I will give you the sum of five hundred pounds (now equal to $3,500) for that purpose, you can therefore get all the information that may be required before my return to London in November, when I will arrange to place you in a situation to meet your views. . . .

Very truly yours,

[Signed] GEORGE PEABODY.

To Mr. Othniel C. Marsh.

Berlin, Dorotheen Str., 63, Oct. 12, 1863.

My dear Uncle:

For your kind offer to furnish me with the means of procuring the library and cabinet necessary to the position offered me at Yale I can now only thank you most heartily but I shall endeavor when in the position to show my gratitude in a way which I am sure you will prefer to mere words. There can be no doubt of my obtaining the Professorship as soon as I can fit myself for its duties as I have the assurance to that effect from both Prof. Dana and Prof. Silliman with whom the appointment rests, and my present preparatory studies are selected and directed by their advice, wholly with that position in view.

The salaries of the Profs. at Yale, and I believe of those at Harvard also, are small, the honor of the position, being considered such an equivalent, that the applicants for every vacancy are always numerous, and are frequently willing to make considerable pecuniary sacrifices. A Prof. now in the law department, an ex-governor, had formerly, I have heard, a law practice worth $6- or $8,000 per annum, but preferred a Professorship with a salary of $1,600. This is about the average of the salaries at Yale, the difference between them depending I believe on the amount of the original endowment or its subsequent investment. Although such remuneration is small there is no position in the world that I should prefer to a Professorship at Yale, as it is for life, and besides the honor it confers, it will afford me unsurpassed opportunities for carrying out my scientific plans, which in a smaller college I should have to relinquish. . . .

Your affectionate nephew,

[O. C. MARSH.]

By the summer of 1863, Marsh had begun to feel that his position at Yale was a certainty, and he so wrote his father, in confidence, on August 18. After the summer lectures at Heidelberg were over, he spent two weeks in Switzerland, walking nearly three hundred miles (thirty-three miles in one day, down the Rhône Valley), and making a special study of glaciers. In the fall he went back to Berlin to take up in earnest the study of Paleontology, in accord with Professor Dana's suggestion, his instructors being the eminent paleontologist, Heinrich Ernst Beyrich (1815–96), the zoologist W. K. H. Peters (1815–83), and C. G. Ehrenberg (1795–1876) whose field was microgeology. His notebooks on their lectures, preserved in the Peabody Museum, testify to the thoroughness of his training.

Beyrich's course of 83 lectures was devoted in part to Geognosy but mainly to Invertebrate Paleontology. It was a disappointment to his American student, because he devoted 64 lectures to the mollusks and but 45 minutes to all the reptiles of the Mesozoic and Cenozoic! Peters' 105 lectures in Zoology, on the other hand, lasting from the end of October to the middle of March, undoubtedly gave Marsh the solid training in systematics that was to stand him in such good stead when he began his work in Paleontology. Beginning with 11 lectures on general morphology, Peters proceeded to a detailed discussion of group after group, from Mammalia to Protozoa, extending even in many instances to species. Mammals occupied 29 lectures, birds 13, amphibians (which then included reptiles) 13, fishes 14, mollusks 10, articulates or annulates 11, worms 2, radiates 2, and protozoans 1. About this course Marsh remarked to Professor Dana in a letter written January 12, 1864:

I cannot tell you how much I have become interested in Zoology through the lectures of Prof. Peters, and the treasures of the great museum here under his charge. It often seems to me a more interesting study than Palaeontology of which it certainly is the only sure foundation.

Ehrenberg's "Lectures and Conversations" on Microgeology, given (or continued) in the summer of 1864, had a strong paleontological trend; Marsh records in his notebook that this professor had "more microscopic preparations from the rocks of America than from Europe." Ehrenberg was, moreover, a most interesting lecturer, and a decided iconoclast with respect to certain of the cherished theories of the time. Among the ideas which he delighted to disprove was that life was something apart from matter, that it could be produced in the laboratory, that infusoria can be transformed into other types, that they can be made out in granite, that single infusoria placed in rows make confervae, and that if these rows are put together seaweeds result! He found a world of micro-organisms everywhere, in the living and fossil realm, in the air, water, mud, and rocks.

During the spring and Whitsuntide vacations of 1864, Marsh made excursions to South Germany and to the Harz Mountains, not neglecting to make the acquaintance of distinguished geologists as well as of new scenes. Likewise he had the good fortune to discover a couple of interesting fossils (Jurassic annelids), which he duly described in the *American Journal of Science* and in the *Zeitschrift* of the Deutsche Geologische Gesellschaft, of which he had been elected a member. Shortly before he left for further geological excursions in Switzerland and the Tyrol, he wrote a long and gossipy letter to Professor Brush—one of the few holograph letters of his left to us—which is quoted here through the courtesy of Professor Brush's daughter, Mrs. Louis V. Pirsson:

Berlin, Dorotheen Str. 63, May 5th, 1864.

Dear Prof. Brush,

For the last year and a half, I have been intending to write and tell you something of my European experiences, and since the receipt of your letter, my conscience has reproached me daily for my neglect; but the fact is writing a letter is to me a very serious undertaking, and hence it results that I am such a bad correspondent.

The increasing prosperity and prospects of Yale are a source of great pleasure to me, and I sincerely hope the great University of which you speak will soon be an accomplished fact. The Government grant of land which your exertions have so successfully secured,[6] is a most important step towards such a desirable result. I greatly feared from what I had heard of the Ct. Legislature, that the Agricultural College of that state would be destined to struggle through a wretched existence, the pride of some country village perhaps but a disgrace to science; and hence I appreciate your efforts all the more, and heartily congratulate you on your success.

In regard to the other late donations, I am very glad to see that the friends of Yale are improving the present golden opportunity. The depreciation of the currency has made money very abundant, and the wealthy men of New York will look with much more favor on a donation to a college or an investment in a gold mine now than a year or two hence when "Greenbacks" and specie have equal values. All of this, however, is nothing new to you. . . .

I spent a day in Göttingen in April, and Sartorius v. Walterhausen showed me his collection of zeolites from Iceland, but I was quite disappointed in them. He has recently rediscovered the locality of Haidingerite, and obtained a large quantity of fine specimens. Charley Sheppard [7] is at Heidelberg, and doing well.

During my late excursion I also visited Tübingen, Munich, and Vienna. I spent an hour or two very pleasantly with Haidinger, who showed me cartes de visites of Prof. Dana and yourself. . . . I think you must have been very fortunate in making friends when in Europe, for I met them wherever I go. . . .

You remember perhaps that I brought quite a number of minerals here with me—most of them from N[ova] S[cotia]. The gypsum crystals containing sand, Löchtung [?] says are the most interesting instances of "Einschlüsse" he has seen, and he was as much puzzled to account for the peculiar arrangement of the sand as others who had seen them. Rose was also pleased with them, and invited me to write an account of the crystals and locality for the Geologische Gesellschaft, but at present I have not the time to spare.

When will the new edition of the Mineralogy be published? I have made quite a number of analyses of zeolites, and as I have not now the time to make such a paper of them as I could wish, I will send the results for the Mineralogy if you think best.

Prof. Blum tells me I have quite a number of new Pseudomorphs

6. Under the Morrill Act. See further, Chapter IV.
7. Charles Upham Shepard, later the noted mineralogist at Amherst College.

from U. S. which I ought at once to describe, but I think of a remark Prof. Johnson made to me just before I came away, viz.—"Do nothing in Europe that you can do just as well when you return," and I try to follow his advice.

The so called Ledererite from N. S. I analyzed at Heidelberg. It contains no PO_5, and is . . . but a variety somewhat different from that found at other localities.

Last, but not least, present appearances indicate that I have a new zeolite from N. S., which would be nothing very wonderful, considering how many summer vacations I spent in looking for it. I fancy I hear you saying "There are quite enough zeolites now, and wo be to the man, who attempts to add another!" Your instructions, however, in years past have inspired me with such a wholesome awe of proposing a new species, that I certainly shall be in no haste to announce one, so long as it can claim the benefit of a doubt. I am quite sure you are still on guard at the portals of the science, and that no contraband species will be allowed to enter, especially if it be labeled "Brushite" (which name my mineral will bear, if it prove worthy of a name), for in that case, I am sure your natural antipathy to a new species (or rather to a new name), would be considerably increased.

So much for mineralogy, which with me is now a reminiscence of the past, and yet I think it not unlikely that a tender feeling for my "first love" will always remain.

I have become greatly interested in my present studies, and am trying to make the most of my opportunities, although time seems to go very fast, even in such a slow country as Germany. During my late excursion I added greatly to my collections, especially from Solenhofen, where by good luck (and a week's hard work) I found a new fossil (Articulate) which has interested the paleontologists who have seen it very much. At another locality I found what is here said to be a new species of starfish. . . .

Please give my kind regards to Prof. Silliman's family; and also to Prof. Johnson, and tell him not to be too severe on the trout streams during my absence.

> Most sincerely yours,
> [Signed] O. C. MARSH.

Marsh had expected to take up his position at Yale in June of 1864, but was advised that the appointment could not be made for another year. He voiced his disappointment to Silliman, but put a cheerful face on the matter to his uncle, thus:

Berlin, June 13th, 1864.

My Dear Uncle:

. . . .

I was intending to write you on the subject of my return home, as soon as I received a letter I am expecting from the faculty of Yale—who, as you know, have directed my studies during the last year—but, as you request an early answer I will reply at once.

I have recently learned that it is the wish of the Yale faculty that I should pursue one special branch of my studies in Europe a few months longer than the time I mentioned to you before the present high position was offered to me; and although I should on many accounts much prefer to commence my professional duties as soon as possible, I should be glad to have this additional preparation, especially as I have reason to believe that my New Haven friends will expect a great deal from me on my return, and as I have thus far been able always to exceed their expectations, I should be very much mortified to fall below them at last, and I wish to make sure of not doing so. I may add that one reason for this proposal of the Faculty is that the present arrangement of the lectures at New Haven is such, that my active services would not be required during this year. Hence, if I return this autumn, I should have to continue my studies either at Cambridge or New Haven until that time, and the expense of so doing would be fully equal to that of remaining here, while the advantages for study would be far inferior. . . . The course of lectures I am now attending will end about the 10th of Aug. and after that time, or before if you prefer, it will afford me great pleasure to join you in Scotland. . . .

The next course of lectures commences in Oct. and ends in May and it is during this period only that the Faculty of Yale wish me to continue my studies abroad. I may add that with my present knowledge of the language and acquaintance among German geologists such a period of study would be far more valuable than twice the amount a year or so ago.

If the long cherished object of my ambition were still distant and uncertain as it was when I came to Europe, I should not think of asking for an extension of your already unexampled generosity

to me, but as so high a position is now perfectly certain and so
soon to be attained, I have thought it but right to tell you just
how the case stands, and I shall most cheerfully comply with any
decision you may think best to give. . . .

Mr. Peabody's reply to this letter apparently was favorable,
because October of 1864 found Marsh at the University of
Breslau, to work under Adolph E. Grube, Heinrich R. Goeppert (1800–84), and Ferdinand Roemer (1818–91), the last
of whom was especially recommended by Professor Dana because he had spent several years in America studying its geology.[8]

Grube's course was devoted almost entirely to living echino-
derms, and ran to 33 lectures; Goeppert's, on fossil plants, was
interrupted by illness at the end of the eighteenth lecture. The
latter's treatment was evolutionary in viewpoint; his estimate
of the number of fossil plants then known was about 3,750
(Cenozoic 2,000, Mesozoic 400, Paleozoic 1,350).

Roemer's 80 lectures seem to have paralleled those of Beyrich
at Berlin in general subject matter, but they evidently had
much more influence upon Marsh, if we may judge from his
notes which, filling three notebooks, are much more copious
than those for any of his other courses in Germany. Also in
support of this idea are various "axioms" scattered through
the notes, to wit:

No branch of knowledge requires so great a number of other
sciences to assist it as Geology, and hence the Geologist is in no
danger of becoming one-sided.

Dana's Manual. No book of similar comprehension and accuracy,
in any language.

The most inviting field for Palaeontology in North America is
in the unsettled regions of the West. It is not worth while to spend
time on the thickly inhabited regions.

It is not worth while to spend time on fossils that are indistinct,

8. Professor Roemer visited Texas in 1842 in the interests of a large party
of immigrant Germans settling in the Fredericksburg region. For their benefit, he published in that year a general account of the region; and the Cretaceous fossils that he gathered were described in his *Kreidebildung von Texas*
(1852), a work of great paleontological value. He also studied the Silurian
glades and the Helderbergian outcrops of western Tennessee and described
their fine fossils in *Die Silurische Fauna des Westlichen Tennessee* (1860).

or in fragments that do not admit of full determination. There is
enough to do with the good ones.

Do not describe and figure bad or imperfect fossils simply
because they are new, because better specimens will surely turn
up in time.

The figures of a palaeontological work are the main thing and
should always be good, and they may thus remain of value long
after the text has become antiquated. This will be true of Bar-
rande's figures which are very fine, while those of Hall are generally
the reverse.

No geological survey should be undertaken until a good topo-
graphical map of the country has been made. Without such a base
a geological map is a mere *sketch*. It is greatly to be regretted that
such a map had not been made of N. Y. long ago, as then the
different points in the formations would have been accurately fixed.

In addition to the regular notes on the course, the notebooks
contain seventeen pages of notes on European papers discussing American fossils, and twenty-five pages of "Notes on
Geology and Paleontology." Included in the latter are suggestions for future publications on American paleontology. Roemer's interest in American political affairs is apparent when
Marsh's notes state that he opened his sixth lecture on November 8, 1864, with "Three cheers for Lincoln," the latter having
been reelected to the presidency.

Roemer's five-months' course ended on March 17, 1865, when
Marsh's notes indicate that the professor found himself in a
situation not unknown to some of his present-day successors.
The last lecture was on the Permian flora. Following this is the
heading "Fauna" and under it the laconic addition: "No time
left for this."

Marsh was the first American to study at Breslau, he says,
and for this reason was granted special privileges and shown
much attention. He was naturally highly pleased with his treatment there, but nevertheless he returned in the spring of 1865 to
Berlin, which he regarded as his "European home." "I have
now a circle of friends there," he writes his uncle, "that will, I
am confident, prove of the greatest service to me through life,
as among them are men eminent in science. . . . The formation of such friendships is to me quite an unexpected advantage

of my residence in Europe." During the vacation he renewed his acquaintance with Sir Charles Lyell, then in Berlin on a visit to his wife's sister, Madame Pertz, who was, according to Marsh, "one of my best friends in Europe."

After completing his studies in Germany, Marsh went to Paris, where he made further valuable acquaintances, dining with De Verneuil, "the greatest of the French geologists and one of the nobility, who showed me much attention." Going next to London, he found tickets to opera and theater and flower show left for him by Mr. Peabody, but, instead of using them, he spent most of his time working in the British Museum, "fearing that I might not know enough to be Professor at Yale." One of his fellow guests at the Buckingham Palace Hotel was Cyrus W. Field, then busy with his Atlantic Cable project, and the two of them often breakfasted together at the early hour of seven, to the surprise of the other guests. Marsh attended a meeting of the Geological Society and of the Geographical Society, and was a dinner guest of the president of the latter, Sir Roderick Murchison. It was during this visit also that he met Henry Woodward, Keeper of Geology in the British Museum, who was to become one of his warmest friends and admirers; among the things over which they conferred with special interest was the great collection from the lithographic slates of Eichstätt, Bavaria, which the Museum had recently secured, and which contained the famous "headless" specimen of the Jurassic bird, *Archæopteryx*. All these things, reported to George Peabody, doubtless confirmed his judgment that he was making no mistake in investing money in this particular nephew.

Marsh's next visit was to his uncle's castle in Scotland, after which he sailed for home the latter part of July, 1865, having as fellow passengers such eminent Bostonians as John L. Gardner, patron of art, and Abbott Lawrence, former minister to Great Britain and founder of the Lawrence Scientific School at Harvard. Before college opened, he made a trip to Ohio to study the burial mounds so common there—a subject suggested to him by Lyell—and he also visited his uncle, Jeremiah Peabody, in Zanesville, reporting at some length about that branch of the family in a letter of January 24, 1866, which showed that the banker was beginning to look to him for advice about family matters in the States. Julia, daughter of the oldest Peabody brother, David, the young lady who had been at New Haven with her Uncle George in 1857, had, he reported, married a Mr. C. W. Chandler; she later lived in Germantown, Pennsylvania, and saw Marsh fairly often. Jeremiah's son Singleton, who had been with Marsh at Andover, had married into "one of the best families in Zanesville," and his wife "is generally regarded as a superior woman"; these were the parents of Charles Peabody, the Harvard archeologist. Marsh, it is evident, was well aware of the interest Mr. Peabody took in the marriages of his nephews and nieces, and of his decided views as to the qualifications necessary for their helpmates.

A second subject dealt with in this same letter was the state of the writer's finances, about which he says:

The morning I left I did not have time to explain to you so fully as I intended how I came to need so large a sum as 70£ for my expenses while in England, and I wish to do so now, as I feel confident you will approve of what I did. My last letter of credit for 100£ lasted me seven months, the last of which I spent in Paris. As it was then exhausted I borrowed 5£ from a friend, and this I returned on reaching London. As my wardrobe greatly needed replenishing I spent about 21£ for this purpose. I had as you know intended to visit some of the most interesting geological localities in England and Scotland, and collect fossils for my cabinet, but my experience on the South Coast taught me that I should save both time and money by purchasing of the dealers in London the specimens I needed, and I invested about £19 in this way. My hotel bill, traveling expenses, etc., amounted to about 19£ and the balance of the 70£ I brought back with me in gold and exchanged for greenbacks when I arrived in Boston.

In this same long letter, Marsh tells his uncle that, although his appointment at Yale has received the unanimous vote of the faculty—"a very unusual thing"—he has not yet been formally instated, "owing to a delay in securing a permanent endowment for the new Professorship, which I wish to have made before entering on my regular duties." This report was somewhat disturbing to Mr. Peabody, and evidently he suggested that some part of his prospective gift to Yale be diverted to the professorship. Marsh refused to have this done, however, a decision that drew the following comment from Professor Dana:

Your uncle is one of the noblest of men living. And you are remarkably generous too that you should have withstood his offer. It would be most gratifying to have your chair rest on a moneyed foundation. But we need, besides the $100,000 for the building, a fund for its increase and another for its care.

In spite of the disappointment over the nonmaterialization of his professorship, Marsh remained at Yale the rest of the academic year, taking over some of the classes that Professor Dana was unable to carry because of illness. His formal appointment to his long-sought goal, a professorship at Yale, was made by the Yale Corporation at its meeting of July 24, 1866, by the following vote:

A memorial was presented from the Governing Board of the Sheffield School, requesting the establishment of a distinct chair of Palaeontology in the University, and recommending Mr. Othniel Charles Marsh as a suitable incumbent.

Voted, in accordance with said memorial, to establish the Chair of Palaeontology, and Mr. Othniel Chas. Marsh was duly chosen by ballot, Professor of Palaeontology, but without salary from existing funds.[9]

The lack of a salary attached to his professorship probably was no real hardship to Marsh, as it is likely that he was already receiving an ample allowance from his uncle. True, he remarked to Professor Dana that, in view of the expense incurred in acquiring material abroad, a salary would be very acceptable "for a few years anyway." However, Grinnell says that, although he did give instruction for the first few years, "he did not wish to make his professorship a teaching one, and preferred to serve Yale without salary in order that his time might be devoted to research and exploration."[10] It may be stated here that he continued to serve the university without salary for twenty-six years, and was only placed on its payroll in 1896, when a finan-

9. R. H. Chittenden, *op. cit.,* p. 107.
10. G. B. Grinnell, In *Leading American Men of Science* (1910), p. 291.

cial crisis arose in his own affairs, occasioned by difficulties connected with the closing up of the George Peabody estate.

The statement has commonly been made that Marsh's professorship in Paleontology was the first established in that science in the world. However, this is not correct, as has been called to the writers' attention by Professor Gilbert D. Harris of Cornell University, who says that Alcide d'Orbigny's chair of Paleontology at Paris was created thirteen years earlier. Marsh's was, of course, the first such appointment in America.

Although of no direct connection with Marsh, it may be interesting to digress a moment to set forth the circumstances surrounding this appointment of D'Orbigny's, since they seem not to be familiar in this country. As presented by P. Fischer in a eulogy of D'Orbigny, delivered before the Geological Society of France twenty-one years after the death of the French paleontologist, the story is as follows:[11]

D'Orbigny insisted that the most important thing about a fossil was its age, and working on this principle, he divided the sedimentary rocks into twenty-seven named stages, each with its own fauna. After the publication of his *Paléontologie française* (8 vols., 1840–55), his *Prodrome* (3 vols., 1850–52) and his *Cours élémentaire* (3 vols., 1849–52), the science that he was thus establishing on a firm basis took on real importance in France, becoming the indispensable auxiliary of Stratigraphy. However, the geologists objected to its invasion with keen displeasure.

Absorbed in his collecting and his writing, D'Orbigny for some time paid little attention to the real needs of life, possibly thinking, naïvely, that one had only to deserve a position to obtain it. Finally, however, irritated by the negligence, if not the hostility, of the official savants, he demanded a place as professor. His request was badly received; the zoologists did not appreciate his original work on the distribution of animals, any more than his efforts to arrive at a classification of the foraminifers, bryozoans, and cephalopods, and they attached no significance to his taxonomic work, so carefully done; the geologists were exasperated by his novel ideas; his period-terminology provoked a concert of recriminations or ridicule; finally, zoologists and geologists agreed marvelously well that Paleon-

11. *Bull. Soc. Géol. France,* VI (1878), 434–453.

tology was not a science, but solely the zoology or botany of extinct organisms. Nevertheless, a decree of the head of the State triumphed over this resistance, and in 1853 a chair of Paleontology was established at the Museum of Natural History, and D'Orbigny named to it.

Returning to the subject of Paleontology at Yale, one other important result of Marsh's stay in Europe should be mentioned. As apparent from letters already quoted, he and his uncle, Professor Dana concurring, had agreed that it would be advantageous for him during these years to buy extensively such books and collections as would be needed for the new professorship at Yale. Through Mr. Peabody, arrangements were made with Sowerby, the London bookseller, to act as purchasing agent. In 1864, Mr. Peabody writes: "You can go to 400£ *altogether* for your library which is now nearly $5,000 [i.e., gold converted]." That the money was all expended seems apparent when Marsh writes his cousin Julia's husband in 1866: "My library and collections have also recently arrived from Europe and it is no small task to get 2½ tons of fossils and books safely through the New York Custom House." These same books form the basis of the Peabody Museum's large library in Geology and Paleontology, which is especially strong in European publications of the first half of the nineteenth century.

CHAPTER IV

GEORGE PEABODY, BENEFACTOR OF AMERICAN SCIENCE

"Great men exist that there may be greater men."

EMERSON.

IT IS already evident, from the foregoing chapters, that the financial background provided by his uncle, George Peabody, was an important factor in the career of Professor Marsh. If Marsh's mental equipment and his determined will were the two major elements on which his success was built, a third was certainly the money placed in his hands by the Peabody fortune. However, it must not be forgotten that the diversion of another part of this fortune to the needs of science was also brought about through Marsh's influence, and the interaction of all these matters deserves to be related.

It is somewhat strange, in these days when life histories are widely read, that no biographer has chosen as a subject so notable a figure in early international finance as George Peabody, especially since his life follows the favorite American pattern of rise to great heights from small beginnings. Our best modern sketch, *George Peabody, Esq., an Interpretation*, by Philip Whitwell Wilson, was written in connection with the fiftieth anniversary of the George Peabody College for Teachers in Nashville, in 1925; and it is supplemented by an address delivered by William Dismore Chapple at the Peabody Museum in Salem, in February, 1933.[1] In these sketches, however, as in the ones of years ago, the man himself and the history of his financial growth are somewhat submerged under the tale of his benefactions. The library at Phillips Academy, Andover, lega-

1. The Nashville book (94 pages) was published privately in 1926, with an introduction by President Bruce R. Payne, through whose courtesy it came into the authors' hands. The address by Mr. Chapple (43 pages) was published by the Peabody Museum in 1933. Probably the best of the older biographies is *The Life of George Peabody*, by Phebe Hanaford. B. B. Russell, Boston, 1870, 308 pp.

tee of his large correspondence, has a rich mine of information waiting for the complete chronicler.

George Peabody, third son of Thomas and Judith (Dodge) Peabody, and older brother of Mary Gaines Peabody, mother of Professor Marsh, was born February 18, 1795, in South Danvers. That he was a smart, hard-working youngster there can be no question. With but four years' schooling, followed by an equally long apprenticeship to Capt. Sylvester Proctor in his general store (net yield: board, $5, and a new suit of clothes), by a year on his Grandfather Dodge's farm in Thetford, Vermont, and by a year in his older brother's store in Newburyport, he had established the reputation for hard work, for efficiency in business methods, and for fair dealing that gave him his next opening. This opportunity stemmed straight out of seeming calamity; as Wilson says: "If anything in Peabody's luck was exceptional, it was his ill luck." Early in 1811 his father died, and two weeks later his brother's business was swept to ruin in the aftermath of a disastrous fire that visited Newburyport. Also a financial victim of the fire was the boys' uncle, Col. John Peabody, one of the prominent merchants of the town. In the effort to mend his fortunes, Colonel Peabody decided to migrate to the vicinity of Washington, the new capital on the estuary of the Potomac. Because of his insolvency, it was advisable for him to have an associate in whose name the new business could be carried on, and his choice fell on George, then sixteen years of age. The wisdom of his selection was justified almost at once, when a Boston merchant, to whom George was sent to make arrangements for the purchase of stock, was so favorably impressed by the lad that he extended him more credit than he had asked for. With the stock thus purchased, the new firm started business in Georgetown on May 15, 1812. A month later war was declared against Great Britain, and normal activity around Washington was suspended. The youthful merchant, remembering his father's service in the Revolution, enlisted in a battery of artillery commanded by Col. John Peters, a nephew by marriage of George Washington. Numbered among its gunners was a young lawyer by the name of Francis Scott Key, but of more moment to young Peabody was another dry goods merchant, Elisha Riggs, with whom he became well acquainted during his year's service with the battery.

When affairs were again normal, George's chief burden in his uncle's business became a very real one—no less than a pack on his back, with which he walked many miles through the surrounding country, doubtless bringing to bear on the house-wives the knowledge of salesmanship that he had learned in Proctor's store. Confidence in the seller must have played a large part in the door-to-door sales of these "hawkers and walk-ers," as Richardson Wright calls them; and it is likely that the personality that had already impressed his uncle and the Boston wholesaler stood him in good stead here also. It was not long, however, before he found himself dissatisfied with a business that was yielding him insufficient return for the use of his name and for his hard work, and, looking for new associations, he turned to Elisha Riggs. The two young merchants, one twenty-nine years old and the other but nineteen, formed the partner-ship of Riggs and Peabody, to engage in the wholesale dry goods business, Riggs putting in $5,000 and Peabody $1,-650.40. This partnership lasted until 1829, when Riggs re-tired, Peabody became the senior partner, and the firm changed its name to Peabody, Riggs, and Company. For the first few years George continued to be the outside representative of the firm, traveling through New York, Pennsylvania, Maryland, and Virginia, no longer on foot as before, but with a horse, and dealing no longer with housewives at their doors, but with retail stores. Before long the partners saw that the barter system could be applied to other countries as well as our own, and they began to export raw cotton and to bring back to the States in return finished goods from England. Increasing foreign trade led them to seek headquarters nearer the seaboard, and in 1815 they moved to Baltimore, establishing branches in Philadelphia and New York seven years later. In 1827, Lancashire, England, opened negotiations for a crop of cotton from the Southern States, and to complete the transaction and buy merchandise with the profits thereof, Peabody made his first trip to Europe, sailing from New York on November 1, as one of twenty pas-sengers on the packet, *Florida*. A letter written to his sister Sophronia from Paris on April 16, 1828, relates that, after devoting three months to the business for which he had come, he spent six weeks in an extensive tour around Europe, in company with a friend from Baltimore. Only a single significant sentence or so need here be abstracted from this long letter. Speaking of Ireland, he says:

As soon as you leave this city [Dublin] the inhabitants of the smaller towns and villages are in the most deplorable state of Poverty and wretchedness. It was not unusual, on leaving a public house in a country town, to be [surrounded] by 20 or 30 beggars at a time, which always excited in my mind feelings of congratulation, that I lived in a country where such things are unknown, but where industry and economy never fail to procure the comforts of life.

Returning to America on September 2, 1828, after a forty-day passage that led him to say to Mary, "I have written mother to-day that I have given up all intention of being a sailor as I used to threaten when a boy," Peabody went again to Europe in 1832 and stayed two years. On his return in May, 1834, he reported to Mary that he had been "actively employed in buying and shipping goods to New York, Balt., New Orleans, Havannah, Pacific Ocean, China, etc. in all to amount of nearly *Seven Hundred Thousand Dollars.*"

In 1837, Peabody decided to establish himself in London, center of finance and commerce, and again his new move met with threat of disaster, through that same severe "revulsion of trade" that had depleted Caleb Marsh's resources in Haverhill. Peabody, however, had been watching the approaching storm, raised by the "rage for speculation," and had written his partners "to keep everything snug, and without reference to new sales or profits to get in outstanding debts and prepare for the emergency." There were days when, as he wrote his sister Judith, he feared each morning to hear that his fledgling business had succumbed, but, thanks to his precautions, the house of Peabody, Riggs, and Company rode out the storm; and by 1843 it had been reorganized, to become George Peabody and Company, merchants and bankers.

From this time on, there was no halt in George Peabody's progress along financial lines. But not only was he a highly successful banker; in addition, his name became a synonym for beneficence and uprightness on both sides of the Atlantic.

There is little direct evidence as to what training set his character into this mold, but it probably was derived from his mother, Judith Dodge, for whose comfort he was constantly solicitous, and whose memory was to him, Wilson says, "of a higher price than any gift, whether of Congress or of Queen." As a memorial to her, he rebuilt the church where she worshiped in Georgetown, her birthplace and the home of the Dodge and Spofford families; and he chose to lie at her side in the Danvers cemetery, when he might have rested with England's great in Westminster Abbey.

At the time when George Peabody first came into the life of Othniel Marsh directly, he was nearing the age of sixty, and he was known and revered as one of the great financial figures of the time. He had spent most of his middle years in England, and, in fact, his visit to Danvers in 1856 was the first in twenty years. He had in the meantime presented his native town with a Peabody Institute having a public library, a museum, and a lecture hall; and to Baltimore, scene of his early business success, he had given a similar but greater institution. His gift of $2,500,000 to the city of London to improve the housing conditions of the poor, and his refusal of a baronetcy from Queen Victoria had brought him world-wide acclaim. His quarters in London, on Queen Street, where he lived very simply with his partner, Sir C. Lampson, were the center of American gatherings, and his Fourth of July dinners were events even in the life of that great city. His service to this country in its difficult days gave him access to any circle in his own land, from the White House downward. But with all this widespread net of contacts, he never lost touch with his own family, and he held it his duty to see that the sons and daughters of his less prosperous brothers and sisters were provided for amply. His, however, was no largess carelessly given, to be spent in the same fashion. He had the banker's conception of money as something to be invested, to bring in a return, and he consequently insisted on an accounting of the allowances he made through his sister, Mrs. Russell. He had very definite ideas, also, as to the circles into which his money should be carried through marriage. He was kindly and benevolent to his young people as a rule, but his reprimands—and his commands—were at times most definite and unequivocal. We get the following glimpse of him from a letter written to Othniel by Mrs. Russell on the twenty-eighth of October, 1856:

Just before he left he took George and Russell [two of his nephews] and made to them the following declaration. That if they conducted well and were steady to their business, etc., they would, in a few years, be placed in a situation that would make hard labour unnecessary. He did not intend to make them rich, but, with their own efforts, they would have a handsome competence. On the other hand, if any of his nephews should in any way so conduct as to disgrace themselves and him, or (now *mind this*) should any of them form a marriage connection, or *even get engaged* before they had the means of supporting a family, they should *never have a cent of his money*, and if they ever had any benefit of it they should be dependent for it, on those, who had complied with his wishes. He desired me to communicate this conversation to all his nephews. . . . He is exceedingly displeased with H— and G— L—, says he will strike H's name off his will at once [it appears there, however].

Such was the personage whom young Marsh met for the first time at a family conclave at Mrs. Russell's home in the fall of 1856. When he learned from his aunt the date of Mr. Peabody's arrival in New York, Marsh's first impulse was to rush to that city and greet him at the boat. Mrs. Russell, wiser, counseled that this would be a poor time to make a first impression, "with so many people around," and suggested that they meet at her home, to which Marsh reluctantly agreed. All we know of this momentous meeting, however, is the record in Marsh's diary under date of October 12, 1856, which reads: "Reached Georgetown in the evening and found Uncle George there. Was much pleased with him."

During his visit to New Haven in July, 1857, Mr. Peabody had a call from another elderly gentleman of high ideals and beneficence. This was Prof. Benjamin Silliman, senior, then seventy-eight years old, a man as renowned in his own line of science as Peabody was in the world of banking. Silliman's call, duly recorded in a copy of a letter preserved in the Sterling Memorial Library at Yale, was doubtless one of courtesy only, but it had an aftermath in the form of a letter written to Mr. Peabody, seeking to interest the latter in the needs of the newly rising Scientific School, which was then striving by every means at its command to enlist the help of wealthy men to put it on a firm financial foundation. So far as we know, the immediate object of this letter was not obtained, but we may well speculate whether its effect was not far-reaching, when we remember that Professor Silliman was named as one of the original Trustees of the Peabody Museum, although he did not live to see the building actually erected.

Another leading exponent of science of whom Mr. Peabody must have heard during his visit to Yale was Professor James D. Dana, son-in-law of Professor Silliman and his successor in the chair of Natural History. Professor Dana already at this time had the idea of a museum in connection with the Scientific School clearly in mind, and spoke of it thus in his Commencement Address to the Yale alumni in 1856: "The museum . . . should be a spacious one, containing collections connected with all the subjects taught in the school": specimens in natural history; seeds, soils, implements of agriculture; engineering models; samples of materials for construction; models of machines; and collections illustrating mines and metallurgy. "In fact, the museum should lecture to the eye. . . . It should be a place where the public passing in and out, should gather something of the spirit, and much of the knowledge, of the institution." [2]

The year of Mr. Peabody's return to London was again one of financial panic, but Peabody and Company emerged from it even stronger than before, and shortly thereafter Mr. Peabody practically retired from active conduct of the business, the control coming more and more into the hands of Mr. Junius Spencer Morgan, who had been taken into partnership in 1854. When the war between the states broke out, Mr. Peabody, always a man of peace, was greatly disturbed, and he is credited with having played a large part in keeping Britain neutral. He refused to join in the condemnation of the South, however, and on one occasion declined to meet Harriet Beecher Stowe because, as Mrs. Russell wrote Marsh, he "never favors those, who go to England to berate their own country." As the war progressed, the Peabody firm was hotly criticized for sending

2. J. D. Dana, "Science and Scientific Schools," pp. 26–27. An address before the alumni of Yale College at the Commencement Anniversary, August, 1856. Published at the request of the alumni. S. H. Babcock, New Haven, 1856.

American securities home for resale, and thereby reaping great financial rewards. However, the sale of these securities abroad was no longer possible, since the war had led European investors to dispose almost completely of their American holdings, and the flow of capital to the States did not begin again until the assurance of Union victory in 1864. Mr. Peabody insisted to the end of his life that his course in this matter had in the long run tended to assist, and not to injure, the credit of the nation.[3]

Under these circumstances, Mr. Peabody was in a mood to consider his future donations in America with more than usual care. It was natural, therefore, that when his nephew arrived fresh from the States in the fall of 1862, they should have had a "long talk" about this very subject. Marsh, by this time a thorough devotee of the cause of science, and conversant with the needs of the young Scientific School at Yale, saw an opportunity to further his chosen field. His success was reported to Benjamin Silliman, Jr., as follows:

Berlin, Nov. 26, 1862.

I had a long talk with Mr. P. in regard to his future plans and donations and he told me very freely about those already arranged. Of course I can not repeat the conversation but I will tell you confidentially that Harvard will have her usual good fortune. So many of our family have been educated at Harvard that he naturally felt a greater interest in that institution than in Yale of which I am the only representative. I can assure you, however, that I did [not] allow the claims of my Alma Mater to be forgotten on that occasion and I have strong hopes that she may yet be equally favored although nothing is as yet definitely arranged. The donation to H. is a large one and for a School of Design.[4]

I did not recommend an endowment for a similar object at Yale, partly because I did not feel so much interest in Art as in Science and partly because Mr. P. manifested so much interest

---

3. Lewis Corey, *The House of Morgan* (1930), pp. 74–76.

4. The eventual gift to Harvard was $150,000, for a museum and a professorship of American Archeology and Ethnology, Jeffries Wyman being the first incumbent of the latter. The part that Marsh played in the shift from Astronomy to Art to Archeology is told in a letter written to his uncle on February 5, 1866, after a trip to Cambridge to consult with Asa Gray.

in my scientific studies that I thought it not unlikely that he
would be more inclined to favor that department. I did not propose
any definite plan to him, as I had then none to propose, but
shall hope to do so before long as I do not intend to let the matter
rest until something definite is decided upon one way or the other.
I should like much to have a talk with you on the subject but
as this is impossible at present I should be glad to have your
opinion of how a donation—we will suppose of $100,000—could be
best employed for the benefit of science at Yale. This case is at
least a supposition and is I think worth considering.

I judge from Mr. P's past donations that he prefers to have
those of large amount distinct in a measure from other endowments, and a plan of this kind would be more likely to strike him
favorably although he said nothing in regard to [it] and is too
liberal in opinion and in pocket in such matters to restrict the
advantages to be derived from his donations. . . .

I think for the present at least no direct applications should
be made for Yale to Mr. P., as he receives so many such from
institutions and personal friends that were he to grant them the
Bank of England could not supply the requisite funds.

As I have at present no interest in any institution except Yale
I shall use all my influence with Mr. P. in her favor and I think
there is a fair prospect of success.

I think for the present the matter better remain between you
and myself until something further is accomplished.

                    [From an unsigned pencil copy.]

Professor Silliman's reply, quoted below, is important as
containing the first mention of Yale's "Peabody Museum," as
well as a rough plan for its organization and endowment already worked out by himself and Professor Dana. He wrote
in part:

                    New Haven, Jan. 20, 1863.

My dear Marsh:

What you say of Mr. Peabody's future intentions interests me
very much—and I have observed (and shall) your caution in
respect to any hint relating to the matter—save only to Prof.
Dana with whom I feel at liberty to consult inasmuch as we had
three years ago prepared a scheme for a wealthy friend who it
was supposed was willing to listen to something of moment in

reference to the permanent endowments of science in Y[ale] C[ollege]. We agreed then, as now, that the most beneficial thing one could ask for was the erection and suitable endowment of a building designed to accommodate the departments of Natural History, Chemistry and Physics, with Lecture rooms, Recitation Rooms and museums. We have made a rough plan to show about what is needed. . . . To build such a building, fit it with suitable furniture and fixtures—and provide a fund to run it in working order would cost probably from $150,000 upward. . . .

Let the whole establishment bear the name of the founder in such terms as may be most permanent and expressive—e.g., "Peabody Museums" or "Peabody Hall." . . . You will obtain from this statement about what we esteem as most desirable. I think Mr. P. with his sound practical sense will see the value of such an establishment which involves no risk of failure in setting on foot untried schemes and which really turns to his credit all that has been done heretofore in the endowments and purchases of cabinets etc. . . . An important advantage of this plan is that while it is complete in itself it is upon such a scale as will meet the growing wants of the future—and it is so distinct from the other departments and outward presentments of the university that the name of the Donor is sure to be always prominent and gratefully remembered. . . .

You will understand readily that this plan will give a degree of permanency and prominence to the scientific departments of the College proper which they will never have as the result of their own development. There would be no interference between such a plan and the Scientific School—but on the contrary a mutual benefit.

> Yours very truly,
> [Signed] B. SILLIMAN, JR.

To which Marsh replied from Berlin on February 16:

> *Links Strasse 14.*

My dear Professor:

. . . .

I was much interested in the plan you and Prof. Dana proposed for the advancement of science in Yale College, and I think a better one in all respects could hardly be devised. Should Mr. P. decide on a donation to that institution I think it probable the plan would meet with his approbation. One of those I had in mind was similar, although not so comprehensive, the others were quite different. I shall see Mr. P. in the spring or early in the summer, and shall then try to bring the subject before him in a way best suited to ensure its success. . . .

The donation for the School of Design at Harvard is $100,000, which was the sum Edward Everett, who drew up the plans, thought necessary. Whether this amount will eventually be increased, I can not say, but judging from the Danvers donation I think it not unlikely. That donation has already been raised from $20 to 100,000. . . . The reasons I gave you why Mr. P. naturally felt a greater interest in Harvard than Yale, might be an objection to his giving the latter, especially at first, a greater sum than he has to the former. I have no particular reason for supposing that such will be the case, if he decides on a donation; but mention it for consideration. . . . I certainly would prefer to have Yale receive a much larger sum than the above, and shall do all in my power to accomplish it. . . .

I remain very truly yours,
[Signed] O. C. MARSH.

There the matter rested until the month of May, when Mr. Peabody, as was his wont, crossed the Channel to take the cure at Wiesbaden for the gout that was his chief affliction, and summoned his nephew to meet him at near-by Homburg. As a result of this conference, Marsh was able to write to the elder Silliman the letter below, enclosing a note of similar tenor from Mr. Peabody. A letter to the younger Silliman three days later gave more of the details of the conference. Reproduced below also are the replies which these letters elicited from Professor Silliman, Jr., and from Professor Dana and a further letter from Marsh to the former.

Homburg, May 25, 1863.

To Benjamin Silliman, Sr.
My Dear Sir:

I take great pleasure in announcing to you that Mr. George Peabody has decided to extend his generosity to Yale College, and will leave a legacy of *one hundred thousand dollars* to promote the interests of *Natural Science* in that Institution.

PLATE VII

George Peabody
The Friend of Maryland and Champion of her Faith

GEORGE PEABODY

FROM A RARE LITHOGRAPH MADE BY FABRONIUS AND
PUBLISHED IN 1857 BY A. HOEN & CO. BALTIMORE

Reproduced by permission of the Peabody Museum of Salem,
Massachusetts

PLATE VIII

FIRST MUSEUM 1876–1917

NEW MUSEUM OPENED TO THE PUBLIC IN 1926

THE PEABODY MUSEUM OF NATURAL HISTORY

He has expressed a wish that the five following persons should act as his Trustees in employing this legacy for the attainment of the above object:—

Prof. B. Silliman.

Hon. James Dixon.

Prof. J. D. Dana.

Prof. B. Silliman Jr.

O. C. Marsh.

In order that the matter may be definitely arranged, Mr. Peabody suggests that the Trustees, as soon as convenient, decide upon a plan which seems to them best adapted to promote the object proposed, and to embody the main features of this plan in a clause to be inserted in his will. . . .

About the first of August next Mr. Peabody intends to add another codicil to his present will, and it is desirable that the clause relating to this legacy should then be inserted. As soon, therefore, as it can be prepared, please send it to me, and I will transmit it to him.

As an illustration of the general form which this clause might assume, I enclose a copy of one prepared by the Trustees of a similar legacy to Harvard College. It stands in the will exactly as written by them last year; and as this will also be the case with the clause prepared by the present board of Trustees it is desirable that it should be arranged with care. . . .

With high respect, I remain

Very truly yours,
[Signed] O. C. MARSH.

Heidelberg, May 28, 1863.

[To Benjamin Silliman, Jr.]

My Dear Professor.

The enclosed letter [quoted on pages 49-50] was written about a fortnight since, but I delayed sending it in consequence of securing an invitation from Mr. Peabody to spend a few days with him at Wiesbaden, and I hoped that after seeing him I might be able to add a P. S. announcing at least some progress of a measure in which we both feel an interest. A letter which I wrote to Prof. Silliman Sr., a day or two since, has doubtless already informed you that my expectations were more than realized, and I am sure you will rejoice with me that Yale College is to be so highly favored. . . .

The general features of the plan you once mentioned to me I submitted to Mr. Peabody, and he appeared well satisfied with it. Should the Trustees decide upon this, or any similar plan, I have no doubt it would meet with his approval.

Although the present donation of $100,000 is given as a legacy, I think it not unlikely that Mr. Peabody, if his life and health should be spared, may be willing to have the fund applied to its object during his lifetime. This would perhaps be more satisfactory to him, and certainly more advantageous for the College. It *might*, moreover, result in an increase of the donation, especially, if the present amount was judiciously applied, and needed an enlargement to complete its usefulness. Mr. P. has never given me any intimation of such an enlargement, and I only judge from his previous donations, and some of his future bequests with which I am acquainted. This point may be worth considering in deciding on a plan for applying the present fund. . . .

Desiring a kind remembrance to Profs. Dana and Brush,

I remain
Very truly yours,
[Signed] O. C. MARSH.

New Haven, June 15, 1863.

My dear Marsh,

We were quite *electrified* by the receipt of yours of May 28th which came to hand by last mail. Yours to my father coming thro Mr. P. *via* Boston chanced to reach us at the same moment, covering also an autograph letter from Mr. Peabody to my father confirming all the tenor of your letter.

I can not tell you how much I am delighted at the success of our application to Mr. Peabody and his noble appreciation of my father's labors, crowning his life, in his last days, with a serene joy in view of the permanent endowment of those departments which he has created and cherished with so much zeal.

Enclosed I hand you the document you have asked for embodying in brief the general plan, and I hope in terms which your uncle will approve. At his request (to save time, as he said) a copy of what is now sent you, has gone to him at London. So it will not be needful that you should send this one, which you had better retain. I admire the wisdom of the Donor in naming a Board of Trust to manage the fund and direct its appropriation. It cuts away many difficulties which seemed to surround the subject, and will I believe be found to work well. . . . Meantime we shall go forward without delay to mature plans of a building to embrace the objects in view on a scale commensurate with the amt. named, but with such capability of expansion as will allow of enlargement. . . .

Believe me yours very faithfully,

[Signed] B. SILLIMAN, JR.

New Haven, June 16, 1863.

My dear Mr. Marsh.—

Your good words and Mr. Peabody's generous deeds have filled us with rejoicings. I can not let Prof. S's letter leave without adding a word of thanks and gratulation. I can almost see the grand structure standing in its place. May your suggestion be carried out and it soon be there. . . . We have already begun to shape our ideas with respect to a building and will soon send on a plan. Considering that such building must be made for the future as well as the present time, and that Yale will probably double her number of students in a century, the building can not properly be a small one; and it ought to be made to last at least 1,000 years, if time's wheels run so long. . . . It will be a great day for Yale when the building is completed! . . . I would add my warmest thanks to Mr. Peabody and have you assure him that he has made us all very happy.

Sincerely your friend,

[Signed] JAMES D. DANA.

Aug. 20, 1863.

[To Benjamin Silliman, Jr.]
My dear Sir,
Your letter enclosing those from your Father and Prof. Dana and a copy of the clause sent to London I received in due time and was glad to know that the proposed donation seemed likely to be so fully appreciated. . . .

In regard to the plan proposed for applying the donation I have no doubts Mr. P. will accept it as it stands, as he would be far from wishing to interfere with a plan drawn up by those who so well comprehend the wants of Natural Science.

There is one point which I fear I have not made sufficiently clear in my previous letters although I particularly endeavored to do so. Mr. P. considers and I think justly that Harvard has much greater claims on him than Yale, so that even after he had promised me a legacy for Yale he objected [to] making it so large as the Harvard donation, and it was only after I had strongly urged the special claims of Yale that he consented to make the sums equal. It would therefore in my opinion, be very unwise *for the present* to make any further applications either directly or indirectly in behalf of Yale. I am not without hope that at some future time with some prospect of success this may be done. . . .

I shall use my influence with Mr. P. to have the building completed as soon as possible, and I think it not unlikely that he may sanction it in a year or two, especially if he visits America as he intends to do. I hope the Faculty will provide a good site for the building. Has this yet been selected?

I hope also that the building itself, if it is to stand 1,000 years as Prof. Dana suggests, may be made an ornament to the city and not the reverse as many public buildings in America are. . . .

[Signed] O. C. Marsh.

As intimated in one of the junior Silliman's letters, the news of George Peabody's gift to Yale came at a time when the Connecticut legislature had just voted to allocate to the Sheffield Scientific School some of the funds accruing to agricultural schools under the Morrill Act, thus giving double cause for rejoicing to the small band of devoted men who were laboring to establish science on a firm foundation at Yale. These State funds, Dana writes, "will establish tolerably well the men that have been years on the ground, and give a salary for a Prof. of Practical Agriculture, but will afford nothing for additional departments. We live in hope." Within a year the College was to feel the first influx of a series of gifts that were to change its physical aspect almost as completely as it was altered in the present century. "The fact is," says jubilant Professor Dana, "that Yale is going to be largely rebuilt, and all at once! The time of her renaissance has come." The picture becomes even more familiar when he says: "With the erection of the new dormitories, there would be a pulling down of old ones, clearing off the old brick lines; and it would be very desirable to demolish the old Cabinet building at the same time." But—significantly—"the great objection to building now is high prices."

Because of this rather sudden increase in projected buildings, an architect was employed to lay out a comprehensive plan for structures and grounds; and the placing of the future buildings became a real problem, as reflected in the frequent letters to Marsh from Dana. These letters show that the Peabody Museum was a wanderer even in its prenatal days! The first site selected was the corner of Chapel and High streets, thought to be the best location on the College Square. However, this did not suit the Museum Trustees because it would require "fronts" on all four sides of the building, thus using up too much of the money. The Scientific School professors were in favor of the corner of Elm and College streets. President Woolsey and the College professors (Dana excluded), still insisting that it should go on the Square, suggested the corner of Chapel and College streets. The final decision was to leave the site to Mr. Peabody's preference.

From these letters, also, it is evident that Professor Dana must have spent a great deal of time and thought on the building itself at this stage, as he discusses detailed plans, especially for the interior, which he felt could not be left to the pleasure of an architect.

Of Marsh's part in this correspondence we have very little, but one fragmentary pencil copy retained by him has some significance:

Will the Museum, as at present designed, be large enough for the requirements of the future? It would certainly not be large enough for the present Berlin collections and why should not those of New Haven soon be as extensive? Would it not be possible to so lengthen the front of the building that eventually another wing (of the same size as that on College St.) might be added without injuring the proportions of the building? Or can the number of the departments included be eventually diminished when present space becomes insufficient for them all? I am sure Yale has a glorious future before her.

A letter from Dana in January, 1865, reports that Professors W. H. Brewer (Agriculture) and A. E. Verrill (Zoology) have been added to the Scientific School faculty, and that the latter,

bringing in collections rapidly for our museum . . . is beginning to be distressed for space. . . . Peabody Hall is needed exceedingly, and as soon as the stone and mortar can be put together; and we hope that our generous patron will carry out his plan of early coming to this country and giving it a start.

And on July 27, 1865:

We feel like the crab just ready to break loose from its old shell, and enjoy the freedom of space adapted to a new and higher condition. With the new Hall up, we shall take the new expansion for which we are ready.

There seems to have been no further move made in the matter of the Museum until Mr. Peabody's trip to America in 1866, and his visit to New Haven. Inasmuch as Marsh was also at home by that time, we can no longer turn to letters as a source of information. From subsequent events, however, it appears that the need of the College for the building persuaded the banker to alter his original plan of leaving the money as a legacy, and to turn it over at once. Furthermore, as Marsh had made clear to him during the summer, if the $100,000 was to be used entirely for the building, an additional sum of $50,000 would be required for its care and maintenance; and his gift was therefore increased by one half.

The actual deed of gift to the Trustees was dated October 22, 1866, and the order for "gold paying 5 per cent Mass^{tts} bonds" to the amount of $150,000 was enclosed in a letter to Professor Marsh on November 27. The specific purpose of the gift was "for the foundation and maintenance of a Museum of Natural History, especially of the departments of Zoology, Geology, and Mineralogy, in connection with Yale College." A part of this sum, not to exceed $100,000, was to be used for a fireproof Museum building, on land to be provided by the College; $20,000 was to be invested, to accumulate as a building fund until it should amount to at least $100,000, when it could be used for additions to the Museum; $30,000 was to be invested and the income used for care and increase of the Museum and its collections.

Of the Board of Trustees mentioned in the letter from Marsh to the senior Silliman announcing the gift, Professor Silliman himself, Professor Dana, and Professor Marsh served throughout the rest of their lifetime; Senator Dixon only until 1868; and Professor Silliman junior not at all, since he left Yale to teach Chemistry at Louisville, Kentucky. Other Trustees added within the next few years were the Honorable Robert C. Winthrop of Boston, a business associate and close friend of Mr. Peabody; Professor Brush; and Mr. George Peabody Wetmore, son of the Newport gentleman who had given the great reception for Mr. Peabody in 1857.

The first ten annual meetings of the Peabody Museum Trustees were held in the library of the Sheffield Scientific School. Because of the high cost of construction of which Dana's letters had complained, it was thought best, even with the Peabody money in hand, not to put up the Museum building at once but to allow the fund to accumulate. This delay, although necessarily disappointing to all concerned, gave plenty of time for the plans to mature under the supervision of the Yale members of the Board of Trustees. Whether or not the question of the site was settled during Mr. Peabody's visit is not clear, but at the eighth annual meeting of the Trustees, on June 29, 1873, the site fixed upon was the southwest corner of Elm and High streets, off the College Square, the frontage on Elm Street being 147 feet, and that on High Street 165 feet, to the corner of Library Street. Three plans for the building were submitted by architects and at a special meeting held on May 27, 1874, the one by Mr. J. Cleveland Cady of New York was accepted.

The construction of the north wing of the Museum was begun early in the summer of 1874 and completed in 1876, the cost, including cases, etc., totaling about $176,000. This expenditure still left intact the original reserve building fund of $20,000, and the "care and increase" fund of $30,000. The increase from the $100,000 originally given for the building to the $176,000 which it actually cost was made possible by converting the Massachusetts gold bonds of Mr. Peabody's gift into United States gold bonds, selling at about par, and then letting the interest on the entire fund accumulate until 1876.

As completed in that year, the Museum had about 34,000 square feet of floor space available for laboratories, study and exhibition collections, and a lecture hall. The Trustees met for the first time in the new building on June 19, 1876, for their eleventh annual session. The effectiveness with which they had done their work was humorously commented on in the New York *Tribune* for August 10, 1877, by W. C. Wyckoff,[5] who said:

The executive officers of the board to whom this trust was confided, are Profs. J. D. Dana, G. J. Brush and O. C. Marsh. It is needless to say that wiseacres in general wagged their beards ominously at the notion of college professors managing such a trust and putting up a building of original design. Much sage advice was gratuitously tendered by men who had had experience with trust funds and architecture, and on the rejection of outside counsel it was confidently predicted that the Trustees of the Peabody Fund would be passing around the hat for contributions long before the stonecutters departed. But the professors of natural science had not allowed their practical mathematics to rust; they had the building constructed just as they wished it, and when it was finished, and the cases to hold the collections were made and placed, all bills were paid, and the building opened to the public, there was still something left—less than $10—in the hands of the Treasurer. It adds a new chapter to the histories of neat financial management of scientific trust funds, of which the Smithsonian Institution has furnished a conspicuous example.

The basement of the new Museum building had nine rooms of various sizes, one each for storage of zoological, mineralogi-

5. Wyckoff, whose name appears in several places in this book in connection with press reports, was scientific editor of the New York *Tribune* from 1869 to 1878. The son and grandson of a minister, engaged in his early years as bookkeeper and clerk in various lines of business, he seems to have had no special training in science, but his reports of the meetings of the American Association for the Advancement of Science during his years with the *Tribune* won "wide recognition as the best scientific reports that were ever made for a daily paper" (Appleton's *Cyclopedia of American Biography*). After leaving the *Tribune,* he was for a time associate editor of *Science News* and editor of *The American Magazine.* He died in 1888.

cal, and paleobotanical collections, one for the janitor, and the other five for storage and preparation of fossil vertebrates. The first floor had a small lecture hall, an exhibition room for minerals, and four rooms for geological and mineralogical laboratories and offices. The second floor had an exhibition room for fossil vertebrates, another (with a gallery) for fossil invertebrates, and three other rooms for Paleontology, one being Marsh's study. The third floor housed four rooms devoted to the exhibition of zoological material, and another used by Professor Verrill as a laboratory.

It is interesting to note here that in 1864 Dana's idea was that "Paleontology will of course go into the Zoological Museum as well as the Geological. In the latter, its species should be stratigraphically arranged; in the former, zoologically," thus anticipating the arrangement in the present Museum. The original plan provided temporary space for Physics and Chemistry, but before the Museum was built, they had fortunately been housed elsewhere.

In the Instrument of Gift, Mr. Peabody had said that the Museum building should be fireproof. Marsh's European notebooks show that this matter of fireproofing was much in his mind and that he was studying the methods used in all the museums he visited; and he was the prime mover in all the precautions later taken. In 1898 he said, discussing type specimens and the need for their care, "I recall no less than five Museums of Natural History, in America, that have either been destroyed, or their contents consumed, or seriously damaged by fire, since I became actively interested in Natural Science." It must be admitted, however, that although Marsh made every effort to have the Yale Museum fireproof, all that he could do at the time was to make it a "slow burner." If fire had ever started among the zoological material preserved in alcohol on the third floor, the whole Museum would have been destroyed, and the same would have been true in the high-gabled attic, since all the roofing and the floor joists as well were of soft pine. In an attempt to make the building fireproof, $15,000 was allotted to the Fire-Proof Building Company of New York City. Their method was to make large tiles, an inch thick, of cement and cinders, hang them on long nails that held them about an inch away from the joists, and cover them over with lime plaster! In less than five years, the plastering and most of the tiles naturally began to fall to the floor.

So much for the building itself. What of its contents?

Natural history material had been accumulating at Yale for many years, chiefly around minerals as a nucleus. Shortly after Benjamin Silliman had been so happily chosen for the professorship of Chemistry and Mineralogy by President Timothy Dwight the first, in 1802, he took the entire Mineral Collection to Philadelphia with him in a candle box, to have the specimens identified by Adam Seybert, who had studied at Freiberg under that greatest of "Neptunian" geologists, Abraham Gottlob Werner. Under Silliman's efforts, however, the Mineral Collection increased notably, and by the winter of 1809–10, when the collection of Col. George Gibbs (of Newport) was loaned to the College for exhibition, the room in Old South Middle (now Connecticut Hall) where it was displayed was one of *the* places to be visited in New Haven. Purchased by the College some ten years later, the Gibbs Mineral Collection, with others, was moved to the new Commons Hall, to which a second story had been added for that purpose. When the idea of a common dining hall was given up in 1842, the building came to be known as the Cabinet, and was later called the Philosophical Building; it stood a little to the northwest of South Middle. In 1857, the Yale catalogue stated that the mineral and geological collections had about 30,000 specimens, and by the time the Peabody Museum was built the Mineral Collection was already the largest in America, thanks to the fostering care of the Sillimans, the Danas, and Brush.

Zoological material began to come to Yale, as already indicated, with the appointment of Professor Verrill in 1864, and it increased in amount rapidly after 1871 when he was placed in charge of one of the vessels of the United States Fish Commission, and allowed to keep at Yale a complete duplicate series of the marine collections made off the Atlantic coast. In this work he was much aided by Sydney I. Smith, Yale's first professor of Comparative Anatomy, appointed in the Scientific School in 1875. Up to the time of the erection of the Museum, the zoological material was housed in the Footprint Room in the Trumbull Gallery (or Treasury Building).

What the College had in the way of paleontological material at the time of Marsh's appointment to a professorship was mainly a collection of fossil invertebrates, brought together under Professor Dana's direction to illustrate his course in Geology. In 1863, this collection included 22 vertical cases of minerals, 25 of rocks, and 21 of fossils. With the prospect of a new building, Dana's thoughts turned to the acquisition of more material, and his instructions to Marsh in Europe stress the need for "*characteristic species* of each of the successive formations, from the Primordial upward—the Permian excepted, of which we are well supplied through Geinitz." He had been offered the collection of Colonel Jewett for $7,000 but saw no way of securing a purchaser for it, "because others are engaged obtaining moneys for the general interests of the college." Later, Colonel Jewett raised his price to $10,000, whereupon Dana "mentioned" to Mr. R. S. Fellowes of New Haven that he could secure as good a cabinet

for much less money—$5000 at the most—by employing the money for a series of summer excursions, and since then, Mr. F. has given me $500 to start off such a series of excursions, I having told him that $500 would keep a collector in the field for three months. [Frank H.] Bradley is now in New York State on this fund.

The Jewett cabinet was finally purchased at its owner's price by Ezra Cornell, for the college that was to bear his name, but Dana was partly consoled by the fact that he had another $500 with which to send Mr. Bradley into the field in 1865, a gift this time from Mr. Raphael Pumpelly, who "intimates that he may do as much for 4 or 5 succeeding years." This trip of Bradley's was mainly among the Carboniferous formations in the West.

Of fossil vertebrates, which were to be the most striking feature of the new Museum, Yale had, at the time of its erection, very little indeed. The collection included, according to one of Dana's letters, plaster casts of

the head and paddle of a large Ichthyosaur, a Plesiosaur . . . a Teleosaur, the head and tracks of the Labyrinthodon, cast of Pterodactylus cranirostris, casts (excellent) of head of Paleotherium crassum and of Anoplotherium; also cast (very fine) of a Machaerodus head. These are all.

When Marsh took up his new position, a future museum to house collections was an assured fact, and he threw himself joyously into the task of getting together material to fill its cases and trays. As stated in an earlier chapter, he had brought back with him from Europe collections and books to the weight of two-and-a-half tons. By 1875, the geological material was stored in thirteen different places in the College buildings, and the footprints were shown in the old State House, then standing on the Green.[6]

In the pre-Museum days, Marsh's office, like that of Verrill, was on the lower floor of the Trumbull Gallery, which stood on the old campus behind the present College Street dormitories. Upstairs, according to the reminiscences of T. Mitchell Prudden, were the offices of President Noah Porter and Treasurer Henry C. Kingsley, and

[the] maceration of great mammalian skeletons and the diverse pickling fluids used in the laboratories—not always sanitarily successful—gave rise to frequent and furious smells, and Prex Porter would now and then send a discreet messenger down to inquire if it were not practicable to "ameliorate" these "without detriment to the advancement of knowledge."[7]

Although the Museum was planned for the departments of Mineralogy, Geology, and Zoology only, Professor Marsh almost at once saw the wisdom of adding a fourth, Archeology, and this was recognized in 1877; it had probably been left out of the original plan because of the gift to Harvard of a museum specifically for Archeology and Ethnology.

Of the 34,000 square feet of floor space in the new Museum, Marsh and his interesting but bulky vertebrate material eventually occupied more than half, although only one room was devoted to its exhibition. Among the striking exhibits in this hall were footprints on Triassic sandstone slabs found in

6. Up to 1874, the sessions of the Connecticut legislature alternated between New Haven and Hartford.

7. *Biographical Sketches and Letters of T. Mitchell Prudden* (1927), p. 14. Yale University Press.

the Connecticut Valley, skulls and other bones and a replica
in papier-mâché of a large mammal, *Dinoceras mirabile*, which
Marsh had found in lower Eocene strata near Fort Bridger,
westernmost Wyoming. Other cases displayed single bones and
skulls of *Brontotherium, Mastodon, Oreodon*, etc. Most significant exhibit was the table case with the collection of fossil
horse remains, showing the essential stages in evolution from
the four-toed equines of the Eocene to the one-toed living horse.

From our present viewpoint regarding exhibition collections
of fossil vertebrates, we are bound to conclude that the show
made by Marsh for the public—seen by the senior author in
1892—was wholly unworthy of the Marsh Collections. It was,
however, in keeping with the ideas of the times, as exemplified
in other American museums. Reformation began with Henry
F. Osborn of the American Museum of Natural History, shortly
after his appointment in 1891. Following his example, there
began to appear in one museum after another articulated fossil
skeletons standing in lifelike poses, which fascinated the interested visitor, and which were great educators, not only for
the general public but even more for the paleontologist.

One of these restorations in the American Museum, a
brontothere mounted by Adam Hermann, for many years
Marsh's head preparator, was seen by the senior author on a
fine Sunday afternoon in 1896, and it so aroused his enthusiasm
that he then and there determined to have the same method
adopted in the United States National Museum, where he was
at that time employed. On his return to Washington, he laid
the matter before his chief, Director G. Brown Goode, describing in glowing terms the marvel he had seen and all that it had
taught him. Director Goode listened patiently, and then
smilingly replied: "Mr. Schuchert, I admire your enthusiasm,
but what you have seen is not Fine Paleontology, but Fine
Art." He suggested that the same story be told to Dr. Theodore
Gill of the Museum, to see what his reaction would be. Gill
agreed, crushingly, that such restorations were indeed Nothing
But Fine Art; furthermore, he held that fossil skeletons were
not for the understanding of the general public, but that the
bones should be left inarticulated in museum drawers or on
shelves for the edification of paleontologists alone! Those were
still the days of extreme conservatism in museum installation.

Marsh never ceased to hope that either Yale itself or some outside donor would build the central portion of the Peabody Museum as originally planned by Architect Cady, but nothing came of his endless efforts toward that end. In 1917, to make way for the Harkness Quadrangle, the Museum was torn down, with the expectation that a new one would shortly be built. The World War intervened, however, and the collections were in storage until 1924, when the present Museum was completed, affording for the first time an adequate setting for many of the treasures that Yale owes to Marsh's talents as a collector.

George Peabody's gift of a natural history museum helped to make possible the great growth of these sciences at Yale; but his indirect contributions, through his nephew, were much greater. By the time of the great philanthropist's death in 1869, his fortune of $12,000,000 had been reduced two thirds by his gifts. On his last visit to the States, in 1866, he made his most notable gift to education, in payment of what he liked to call "a debt due from present to future generations." This was the Peabody Education Fund of $1,000,000 (later doubled), to be devoted to education in the South, where he felt that the postwar need was the greatest. At this time, also, he established a trust fund (with headquarters in Boston) from which his sister, brother, and fourteen nephews and nieces received a definite income. His will, likewise made this year, distributed among his heirs a further $1,500,000. Of this, one nephew and one niece received $150,000 each, two nephews (one of them Marsh) $100,000 each, the others $50,000 apiece. Nine of these legacies had already been distributed in part, the advance as a rule going for the purchase of a house and furniture; but in Marsh's case there is no mention of previous gifts. His portion was to be divided as follows: $20,000 to be kept invested until he should require it for a house and furniture, $60,000 to yield him income half-yearly and half to be willed away as he chose, $20,000 to be kept invested for the benefit of his children until the oldest was twenty-one; if he left no heirs, this last portion was to revert to the estate.

The scale on which Marsh lived, and the money that he spent on his collections over a period of thirty-two years (1867–99), show that his income from the Peabody estate must have been very large. His financial history is analyzed more fully later in the book (Chapter XIII), but it should be said here that the amount of money that came to Yale University directly from George Peabody and indirectly from him through his bequests to Professor Marsh was but little short of half a million dollars.

CHAPTER V
YALE STUDENT EXPEDITIONS OF
1870–1873

EVEN after his establishment in the professorship of Paleontology at Yale, Marsh did not at once turn definitely into the channel that he was to follow for the rest of his life. Later in the summer following his appointment he attended the meeting of the American Association for the Advancement of Science at Buffalo, becoming a member of the Association; and when the autumn term began, he entered upon his academic duties, teaching Geology to the senior class in the absence of Professor Dana. His notebooks for 1866–67 indicate that he was visiting the museums of the country, partly for the purpose of acquiring information that would be useful in planning the Yale Museum, and partly to establish contacts with other workers in Paleontology. Thus he inspected the Philadelphia Academy Museum in December, 1866, and met Lea, Conrad, Leidy, and Hayden; and at the Smithsonian Institution in Washington he made the acquaintance of Meek and Gabb. Another trip took him to Montreal, where he arranged for exchanges with Principal Dawson of McGill University and with Elkanah Billings, paleontologist of the Geological Survey of Canada. In search of well-known invertebrate localities he went to Trenton Falls, New York, where he found William Rust, a local collector (and later a collector for the United States Geological Survey, under Walcott), to whom he sent Volumes I and II of the *Paleontology of New York* after his return; to Utica, then the home of Charles D. Walcott; and to Chazy on the west shore of Lake Champlain.

His part in the planning of the Peabody gift to Harvard had brought him to the attention of the Harvard scientists and he was offered a professorship there, but declined it. The offer was repeated in 1874, with no better success.

With the thought of the new Museum in his mind, his attention was attracted to two different fossil fields, each of which was to yield him important material, although he made

but slight contribution to its published description. The first
of these was in southwest New Jersey, where the excavation of
the Cretaceous greensands, then used as fertilizer, was bringing
to light a good many fossils, chiefly belemnites and bivalves,
rarely dinosaur bones, and somewhat more commonly birds
and mammals from the overlying Cenozoic deposits. Possibly
the immediate stimulus that led Marsh to explore these marls
was the description of the remains of an eighteen-foot carnivorous dinosaur, *Lælaps aquilunguis*—the seventh "huge saurian"
to come from these beds. On his visit there, Marsh collected
some material and made arrangements with farmers and
quarrymen that brought him considerably more in succeeding
years. In the early spring of 1868 he went on a collecting trip
through the area with Edward D. Cope, discoverer of *Lælaps*,
who was then living at Haddonfield, in the vicinity; and within
the next few years he described a number of the New Jersey
vertebrates, chiefly birds and mammals.

The second region to which Marsh turned in the first years
of his professorship was the Connecticut Valley near Green-
field, Massachusetts, where remarkable fossil footprints had
long been known, Edward Hitchcock, Amherst's benevolent
professor of Natural Science and the State Geologist of Massachusetts, having described 119 species. The larger foot impressions were at first thought to have been made by birds as
much as 20 feet tall, but, after some years, the possibility of
certain of the track-makers being dinosaurs began to be discussed. Dana was much interested in this question, and in 1866
he took Marsh to Turners Falls to see some of the famous tracks
in situ. Marsh at once set about building up a collection of
them for the new Museum, starting with a purchase of $1,000
worth at the time of the visit, and persuading the class of 1868
to buy an unusually fine large slab as a graduation gift to the
University. In 1867, he made arrangements with Mr. T. M.
Stoughton to have quarrying carried on intermittently at
the various localities, and four years later he bought the accumulated material—a carload—for $1,500. The final ship-
ment, sent in 1898, amounted to another carload. Even though
he had this abundance of material, Marsh never published anything about the footprints other than to give them a very brief
general discussion in his dinosaur monograph of 1896. He did,

however, succeed in finding remains of some of the dinosaurs that made the tracks, and described these.

His published papers during these first years on the faculty of the Sheffield Scientific School show that he was still feeling his way. The first one, appearing in July, 1866, was a description of the burial mound that he had explored during his trip to Ohio. In 1867, he recorded his observations on mastodon remains found near Cohoes, New York, described a new genus of Middle Ordovician sponges (*Brachiospongia*), and commented further on Nova Scotia minerals. Papers of the first part of 1868 treated of *Palæotrochis* (described by Emmons as a coral but later shown to be a mineral growth), of lignites, sponges, and weathering effects on fossils—subjects that he had discussed at the Burlington (Vermont) meeting of the American Association in August, 1867. It was the summer of 1868, however, that brought the event which crystallized his interest in fossil vertebrates.

In August, 1868, Marsh went to Chicago to attend the meeting of the American Association. During the meeting he read three papers, on the track of a limulid (*Protichnites*) found in the Potsdam sandstone on the shore of Lake Champlain, on the preservation of the original color in Paleozoic fossils, and on new vertebrate remains from New Jersey; and, notwithstanding his short term of membership, he was elected general secretary of the Association. At the close of the meeting, the *Proceedings* reports, "members of the Association were offered excursions to several points of scientific interest, to the Coal Valley near Rock Island, to the Lake Superior iron mines, or to the newly planted germs of a city on the Missouri River, Omaha." [1] Marsh chose the last of these, and a momentous choice it proved to be.

After visiting Omaha, the party proceeded further westward over the "whole length" of the Union Pacific, which, begun in 1865, had reached a point more than sixty miles beyond Benton, Wyoming; [2] and on the afternoon of August 17, "after

1. *Proc. Amer. Assoc. Adv. Sci.*, Chicago meeting, 1868, 1869, p. 360.
2. A town about fifteen miles east of Rawlins. "Its population numbered at one time, in the summer of 1868, 2,000 persons, among whom whisky-sellers and gamblers were plenty, but, as the road passed on, the people went with it, and nothing remains" (Appleton's *Hand-book of American Travel* [1872], p. 103).

dining in the construction train of General Casement, rode over a mile of road which had been finished with the rails which their own train had brought forward two hours before." [3]

Fortunately, we have on record Marsh's own impressions of what he saw on the trip, which he later spoke of as a "geological excursion." He says:[4]

"It was my first visit to the far West, and all was new and strange. I had a general idea of the geological features of the country I was to pass through in ascending the gradual slope towards the mountains, especially the great plains extending for hundreds of miles along my route, but the actual reality was far beyond my anticipations when I found myself thus surrounded, as far as the eye could reach in every direction, reminding me of mid ocean with its long rolling waves brought suddenly to rest. It was in fact the bottom of an ancient sea, and not the petrified waters, that I then saw, and I was not long in deciding that its past history and all connected with it would form a new study in geology, worthy of a student's best work, even if it required the labor of a lifetime.

"As we passed westward, ever ascending the sloping flanks of the Rocky Mountains, the plains continued, but the scene changed to even more gentle grades, and I saw we were crossing the former bed of a great fresh-water lake [Green River]. I was eager to explore it at once as I felt sure that entombed in the soft sandy clays . . . there must be remains of many strange animals new to science. . . . It has been well said that what one truly and earnestly desires in youth, he will have to the full when no longer young, and my own experience has proved no exception to this rule. My first lesson in investigating the wonderful region I was so rapidly passing over gave me the key to one chapter of its history, and from this other chapters opened one by one as year after year I returned West with ever-increasing zeal to continue the work."

In addition to his general interest in seeing the western country, Marsh had at least two specific quests in mind. The first of these had to do with a find of fossil "human remains" recently reported from Antelope Station, Nebraska, just

3. *Proceedings,* p. 361.
4. Sections of this chapter quoted from Marsh directly are taken from the Howe manuscript of which mention is made in the Preface.

east of the Wyoming line. Associated with these, according to
the newspapers, were bones of "elephants and tigers," a combination that led one correspondent to add: "I should think
this extraordinary circumstance . . . would attract the attention of geologists and scientific men." His final observation
was entirely correct, at least with regard to one scientific man.
Marsh had read these reports and was highly skeptical of them.
However, as he remarked, "I kept silent, as I had no facts."
But he had every intention of obtaining facts, and his account
of how he did so needs no paraphrase:

"Before we approached the small station where the alleged
primitive man had been unearthed, I made friends with our
conductor, and persuaded him to hold the train long enough
for me to glance over the earth thrown out of this well, thinking perchance that I might thus find some fragments, at least,
of our early ancestor. In one respect, I succeeded beyond my
wildest hopes. By rapid search over the huge mound of earth,
I soon found many fragments and a number of entire bones, not
of man, but of horses, diminutive indeed, but true equine ancestors. . . . But the horse was not alone. Other fragments
told of his contemporaries—a camel, a pig, and a turtle, at
least—and perhaps more to hear from when I could remove the
clay from the other remains secured. Absorbed in this work,
I took no note of time. The conductor's patience was at last
exhausted, and, watch in hand, he gave a final signal which I
was forced to heed. As the train started, I could only conclude
a hasty bargain with the station agent to have the whole pile
of earth dug over, and the bones found saved for me; then I
caught the rear end of the last car, and moved slowly west to
still more promising fields.

"A hatful of bones was my reward when I passed Antelope
returning East, for the station master had kept his promise.
As we shook hands, I left in his palm glittering coin of the
realm, and we parted good friends to meet again another day.
A hasty examination of my new fossil treasures as I showed
them to my fellow travellers, disclosed no trace of man, but
positive evidence of no less than eleven inferior animals, all
extinct, that lived around that lake in Pliocene times. The small
horse was strongly in evidence, and interested all observers.
He was then and there christened *Equus parvulus*. . . . During

life he was scarcely a yard in height, and each of his slender legs was terminated by three toes. Later researches proved him to be a veritable missing link in the genealogy of the modern horse. Recalling the old adage that 'truth lies hidden in the bottom of a well,' I could only wonder, if such scientific truths as I had now obtained were concealed in a single well, what untold treasure must there be in the whole Rocky Mountain region. This thought promised rich rewards to the enthusiastic explorer in this new field, and thus my own life work seemed laid out before me."

It is interesting to note that with the promptness to herald his discoveries that was to become one of his marked characteristics, Marsh presented a paper on the Antelope Springs fossils before the National Academy of Sciences, meeting in Northampton, Massachusetts, on August 31 to September 3. They were further described in the *American Journal of Science* for November, and *Equus* (now *Protohippus*) *parvulus* thus was the first in the long series of fossil horse remains that was to form one of the chief jewels in Marsh's scientific crown.

A second concrete result of this first trip West received possibly even wider attention than the fossils. Lake Como, a small shallow sheet of alkaline water not far from Medicine Bow, Wyoming, had for some time been known to be inhabited by peculiar tailed batrachians, locally called "devil-fish" or "fishes with legs," but known to zoologists as *Siredon lichenoides*. Another species of this genus, *Siredon mexicanus*, had been shown by the French savant Duméril (1865, 1867) to have undergone a remarkable metamorphosis. In an attempt to find out whether the Como species had a similar life story, Marsh persuaded General Snyder, then superintendent of the Union Pacific, to help him procure a number of specimens from Lake Como and these he kept alive during the week's trip back to New Haven, and later in his office. In due time the creatures altered in color, lost their external gills, lessened in size, and underwent other changes, emerging finally as unmistakable representatives of the species *Amblystoma mavortium* Baird.

When Marsh reached home in the late summer of 1868, he at once set about making plans for the systematic exploration of the western plains, convinced that in them lay riches comparable to the wealth of vertebrate remains on which he had been trained in Europe. It was his intention to lead a party into the field the succeeding summer, but this plan had to be given up because of the imminence of Indian wars. The delay was fortunate, however, because it gave him time to perfect a brilliant plan—that of taking into the West a party of Yale students and recent graduates who would not only assist him in collecting, but would help to defray the expenses of the expedition.[5]

George Bird Grinnell, telling the story of the expedition of 1870 many years later,[6] says that he was the first member of the party to be chosen, and that he thus had a good deal to do with its eventual make-up. When word of the proposed western trip spread about the campus, Grinnell, nearing graduation, determined to go, although he felt that he had no special qualifications. Mustering up courage, he went to Professor Marsh, explained that he had been fascinated since boyhood by tales of the Wild West, and asked if he could join the party in any capacity. The Professor, "less formidable" than he had feared, agreed to consider his application and later said that he could go. Grinnell then was able to suggest the names of other men who would be interested in such a trip; probably none of the lot, except the leader, he says, "had any motive for going other than the hope of an adventure with wild game or wild Indians."

The men finally selected are cited in the following list, with the number of described specimens found by each in parentheses after his name:[7]

Charles T. Ballard, '70 S., subsequently a manufacturer in Louisville, Kentucky (6, one of which is named after him).

Charles Wyllys Betts, '67, M.A. '71, Columbia LL.B. '69, later well known as a patent lawyer (3).

5. History shows that Marsh was the second to lead an expedition of college students and others interested in Geology into the western field, the first being Maj. J. W. Powell. His methods were soon followed by Scott and Osborn (1877), then students at Princeton, and now such expeditions are common practice among the geologists in American colleges.

6. "An old-time bone hunt," *Natural History,* XXIII (1923), 329–336.

7. Much of the account of these early expeditions is drawn from contemporary press articles and letters, an excellent summary of which was made by Professor Richard S. Lull in 1913 in a supplement to the *Yale Alumni Weekly* entitled "The Yale collection of fossil horses."

Alexander Hamilton Ewing, '69, in business with A. T. Stewart and Company, Chicago, until his death in 1890 (6).

George Bird Grinnell, '70, Ph.D. '80 (2). See Chapter XII.

John Wool Griswold, '71 S., an iron manufacturer until his death in 1902 (2).

John Reed Nicholson, '70, Columbia LL.B. '73, of Dover, Delaware, who gave years of notable service to his state as attorney general and as chancellor (1).

Charles McCormick Reeve, '70, M.A. '73, of Minneapolis. He served in the Minnesota state legislature, and was colonel in the Thirteenth Minnesota Volunteers during the Spanish War. He was made brigadier general in 1908 for service in the battle of Manila, and was deputy provost marshal and the first American chief of police in Manila.

James Matson Russell, '70, an agriculturist of Paris, Kentucky (2).

Henry Bradford Sargent, '71 S., M.A. '07, member of the Yale Corporation and head of the great hardware firm of Sargent and Company in New Haven until his death in 1927 (12).

James W. Wadsworth, M.A. '08, of Geneseo, New York. He prepared for Yale but entered the Union Army instead, and was brevetted major of volunteers after the battle of Five Forks. Later he served as comptroller of the state of New York and twice represented the state in Congress (1).

Eli Whitney, '69, M.A. '72, grandson of the inventor of the cotton gin, member of the Yale Corporation, and president of the New Haven Water Company until his death in 1924 (1).

Harry Degen Ziegler, '71 S., of New Haven, who was engaged in business until his death in 1909 (5).

Not only was it necessary to plan and supervise the equipment of this party, to lay out a route of march, to provide for transportation, and to arrange for the shipment of specimens, but careful arrangements had to be made for the expedition's protection, since the country to be traversed was full of Indians, most of them still resentful of their steadily narrowing hunting grounds and ready to harass any white man whom they might safely attack. Marsh's plan to guard against this latter hazard was to have his party under military escort at all times, and he asked the War Department's assistance to this end. The way in which this request was met proved to be a large factor in his success for many years, for he received from William Tecumseh Sherman, then commanding general of the Army, a letter which proved an open sesame to all army posts. The good will of the Army men in general, it may be said, was of considerable aid to Marsh throughout his exploration of the West, and in matters nonscientific as well. That he found favor in their eyes is not strange: he was preëminently an outdoor man in those early years, a crack shot, a fisherman of repute, a seasoned camper, at his best around a campfire where the swapping of tall stories is a highly appreciated art. His correspondence is full of friendly letters from such well-known military men as General Sherman, Gen. Phil Sheridan, Gen. E. O. C. Ord, and Col. T. H. Stanton; and he was often a guest in their homes.

The expedition's plans were so well laid out that Marsh must have given them much thought in the winter of 1869–70. That the 1870 party—and for that matter those that followed it—completed so hazardous a trip with no major accidents and no sickness is surely a tribute to his organizing ability.

The plan was to make the Union Pacific the base of operations, and to work out north and south of the railroad into the Rocky Mountain country. In fact, it is Grinnell's idea that some of the railroad officials were interested in the expedition, at least to the extent of either giving the party free transportation or substantially lowering the usual rates. The party, each "armed with a brace of trusty pistols and the all-essential knife, as well as the geological hammer and the appliances of science," left New Haven on the last day of June, 1870, and proceeded at once to the town of North Platte, Nebraska, the nearest station to Fort McPherson (six miles from the present town of Maxwell), where they were to acquire their military escort.

The commanding officer of Fort McPherson, Gen. Eugene A. Carr, helped provide the necessary equipment for the expedition and gave it as escort a troop of the Fifth Cavalry under command of Lieut. Bernard Reilly, Jr., and Lieut. (later Brigadier General) Earl D. Thomas. The party, which finally numbered seventy, had two Pawnee guides, Tuck-he-ge-louhs ("Duellist") and La-oodle-sock ("Best of all"), and, for still

PLATE IX

IN THE FIELD NEAR FORT BRIDGER, WYOMING. STANDING
(LEFT TO RIGHT): GRISWOLD, SARGENT, GRINNELL, BETTS,
MARSH, BALLARD, NICHOLSON, RUSSELL. SITTING: WHIT-
NEY, EWING, ZIEGLER, AND BILL, THE COOK

AT CHICAGO. STANDING (LEFT TO RIGHT): NICHOLSON,
GRINNELL, WADSWORTH, MARSH, BETTS, ZIEGLER, SAR-
GENT. SITTING: GRISWOLD, EWING, WHITNEY, REEVE,
RUSSELL

YALE EXPEDITION OF 1870

PLATE X

MAJ. FRANK NORTH

Buffalo Bill 1871

COL. WILLIAM F. CODY (BUFFALO BILL)

THE TWO ARMY SCOUTS WITH THE EXPEDITION OF 1870

further good measure, two of the best known of the many Army scouts whose exploits were famous along the frontier. The more spectacular of these was William F. Cody, who had recently been transferred to Nebraska from the Kansas territory where he had earned his sobriquet of "Buffalo Bill." Cody was with the expedition one day only, but the boys credited him with one of the choicest yarns brought back, which is:

The first day out, the Professor, "all aglow with the achievements his imagination pictured as in store for him," related to the open-mouthed company as they rode along that the Rocky Mountains were once the bottom of a shallow sea, that the region in front of them was then covered by a fresh-water lake, and that the fossils he hoped to find had been buried on its bottom or along its shores. In the evening Buffalo Bill remarked: "The Professor told the boys some pretty tall yarns today, but he tipped me a wink as much as to say, 'You know how it is yourself, Bill!' "

Cody accompanied Marsh on later trips and the friendship between the two lasted into the years when he entered the show business and became a familiar figure to the youth of the whole country. When his Wild West show came to New Haven, he always called on Marsh, and it was probably fine advertisement for show and museum alike when he rode up to the ornate iron gates of the latter, with his long locks flowing out from under his ten-gallon hat, and went in to see the Professor.

The second Army scout was Maj. Frank North, who had lived for many years among the savages and who had commanded a Pawnee regiment in the recent wars. The Pawnees were as a rule well disposed toward the whites, but battles between them and the warlike Sioux were frequent, the level areas between the Platte and Republican Rivers being the scene of many a bloody skirmish. Major North, whose exploits have been brought together in most readable fashion by Mr. Robert Bruce,[8] had more influence with the Pawnees than any man of his time, but he was described by one of the boys as "quite modest and retiring—a good shot, and, contrary to the idea that the eastern people hold of the western frontiersmen, drinks no liquor."

Two reports sent in by members of the party give a lively

8. *The Fighting Norths and Pawnee Scouts.* New York, 1932.

picture of its doings, one (by Ziegler) written for the New York *Weekly Herald* and published on December 24, 1870, the other (by Betts) appearing in *Harpers New Monthly Magazine* for October, 1871 (pages 663–671).[9] From the second of these we may quote the following account:

"The guides rode about a mile in advance of the column. The major pointed out the least difficult paths; while the Indians, with movements characteristic of their wary race, crept up each high bluff, and from behind a bunch of grass peered over the top for signs of hostile savages. Next in line of march came the company of cavalry . . . and with them rode the Yale party, mounted on Indian ponies, and armed with rifle, revolver, geological hammer, and bowie-knife. Six army wagons, loaded with provisions, forage, tents, and ammunition, and accompanied by a small guard of soldiers, formed the rear.

"As night closed over our geologists, cut off from civilization, in a country infested by hostile Indians, and they saw around them the tents, the bivouac fires, the soldiers standing in picturesque groups, the horses cropping in the twilight, the corral of wagons and pacing sentinels beyond, they felt 'in for' something more than science. This fact was more forcibly impressed by day, as hour after hour they marched over burning sand hills, without rocks, or trees, or sign of water, while the thermometer stood at 110° in the shade of the wagons. After fourteen hours in the saddle, one of the soldiers, exhausted with heat and thirst, finally exclaimed, 'What *did* God Almighty make such a country as this for?' 'Why,' replied another more devout trooper, 'God Almighty made the country good enough, but it's this deuced geology the professor talks about that spoiled it all!' . . .

"After five days of such trials we hailed with joy the fresh running water of the Loup Fork. . . . Our geological labors now commenced. The sides of the river were indented with cañons, in which were exposed the strata of the ancient lake, weathered into the formation known as *mauvaises terres*, and full of fossil remains. A strong guard was each day detailed to accompany our party, while the main body marched up the

9. It was this account, Scott tells us, that inspired him to take out similar parties from Princeton, beginning in 1877.

river. The soldiers not only relieved us from all fear of surprise, but soon became interested and successful assistants; but the superstition of the Pawnees deterred them for a time from scientific pursuits; for Indians believe that the petrified bones of their country are the remains of an extinct race of giants. They refused to collect until the professor, picking up the fossil jaw of a horse, showed how it corresponded with their own horses' mouths. From that time they rarely returned to camp without bringing fossils for the 'Bone Medicine-man'. . . .

"So far we had not been molested by live Indians; but the threatening column of smoke far up the river each night was

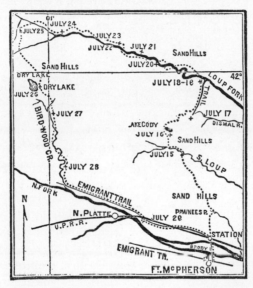

Fig. 1. Route followed by the Expedition of
1870 on its first trip, out of Ft. McPherson.

nearer and wider; and at length we found close upon us a prairie fire which the Sioux had lighted on both sides of the river. . . . From this point we marched over the burned prairie that stretched on every side as far as the eye could reach, studded with roasted cactus and dead grasshoppers; and it was with great difficulty that isolated patches of grass were found for the stock. The river soon dwindled to a little stream, and then to a slender rivulet and half-stagnant pools. We had reached its headwaters—the goal of our first expedition. . . .

On reaching the Platte, the Pawnees led us across the treacherous quicksands of the river in a mock raid on the city of North Platte, whose terrified inhabitants mistook us for a party of Sioux, and rose in arms to repel the invader."

The provisions not lasting quite as long as expected—could it be that the Professor had underestimated the capacity of college boys? Ziegler remarks that "getting up at five in the morning, starting at seven, marching until four in the afternoon, eating dinner at about six or seven makes a person ready

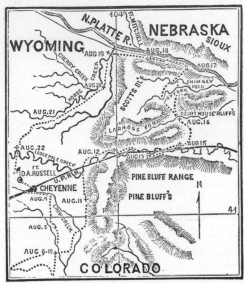

Fig. 2. Route followed by the Expedition of 1870 on its second trip, out of Ft. D. A. Russell.

to appreciate his meals"—the party turned back to Fort McPherson.

The scientific results of this first trip were noteworthy especially for their addition to the knowledge of fossil horses. The sandy bluffs of the Loup Fork yielded the remains of no fewer than six species in abundance, as well as two kinds of rhinoceroses, and other extinct types.

After a short rest, the expedition moved still further westward to Fort D. A. Russell, three miles north of Cheyenne, Wyoming, with the intention of preparing to visit the region between the North and South Platte Rivers, which had never been carefully explored. Again the escort, assigned by the commandant, Gen. John H. King, was a detachment of thirty men from Company I, Fifth Cavalry,[10] under Capt. Robert H. Montgomery and Lieut. James McB. Stembel. First marching south into northern Colorado, the party discovered, at the mouth of a canyon opening on one of the broad plains, an outcrop of the true *mauvaises terres* or badlands of White River (Oligocene) age, here nearly two hundred miles south of the Dakota region in which they had first been identified. The White River beds contained quantities of fossil turtles and rhinoceroses, a few rodents and birds, and that remarkable animal which seems to be a combination of the sheep, pig, and deer—the oreodont. The bird and rodent bones being very tiny, the Professor, according to Betts, "showed us that the only way to find such small specimens was to lie flat on the ground with the nose about six inches from it; but the boys too often obeyed these instructions with the nose pointing upward."

Among the most significant fossils found on this trip were many remains of a beast of fabulous size, which had been named *Palæotherium* (later *Titanotherium*) *prouti* after Dr. Hiram A. Prout of St. Louis, who first described it from a large molar in 1846, and which was to become the first recognized representative of the strange group of mammals known as brontotheres (Chapter XIX).

From the badlands the party went to Antelope Springs, Nebraska, to re-examine the locality already visited by Marsh in 1868. The excavation of the well had been carried ten feet deeper, and yielded three other horses in addition to the one of 1868.

Although thus successful in paleontological research, the reporter in *Harper's* goes on to say,

"Fortune did not smile upon us in the affairs of every-day life. At Antelope one of our cavalry horses was accidentally shot dead, and three draught animals were bitten by rattlesnakes. . . . The country swarmed with the reptiles. Numbers of them were killed every day among the horses' feet; and while we were bathing they would bask upon the bank of the stream

10. "The very company," according to Betts, "which in 1861 opened the ball on the Potomac by a brilliant dash into Fairfax courthouse."

beside our clothes. Their humming soon became an old tune; and the charm of shooting the wretches wore away for all but one, who was collecting their rattles as a necklace for his lady-love.

"On reaching the North Platte we followed the old California emigrant trail, in whose deep-worn ruts the grass is now growing. The column left us at an extensive fossil locality; and so absorbing is the practical study of paleontology that sunset

Fig. 3. The rattlesnake peril. From a woodcut in *Harper's New Monthly Magazine*.

surprised us still at work. Here we were found by some soldiers, who had been sent back to guide us through a labyrinth of shale and sandstone known as Scott's Bluff. It was pitch-dark when we began to pick our way through these narrow and rugged defiles. . . . Fitted by nature for ambush and surprise, this had been the Indians' favorite spot to fall upon the emigrants; and those dim bluffs, that towered so gray and ghostly silent, could tell many a tale of lurking savages, of desperate fights and massacres. Guards were posted to watch the borders of the

river, and many an anxious glance was cast across into the
Sioux reservation. 'The bishop,' a corresponding member of
the American Tract Society, here gladdened our hearts by
emerging from a gully with an immense petrified turtle lashed
upon his horse's back. . . . It soon became a vital question
which he should abandon, the turtle or the horse. The professor protested that it be not the former, and painted in vivid
colors the future position of this grand specimen in the Yale
collection. . . . But . . . the thought of Indians was too
much for the bishop. So the turtle still lies in nature's museum.''

Fig. 4. The "bishop" and the turtle. From a woodcut in *Harper's New Monthly
Magazine*.

The third and by far the most important trip made by this
party of 1870 was outfitted at Fort Bridger in the southwest
corner of Wyoming. In their preparation they were aided
greatly by the commandant, Maj. R. S. LaMotte, and by
Judge William A. Carter, both of whom were to have considerable to do with Marsh's later collections. Detailed as escort
was a detachment of the Thirteenth Infantry commanded by
Lieut. W. N. Wann, and the guide was a Mexican named Joe
Talemans. Horses not being obtainable at the post, the entire

party was mounted on mules, save for one or two of the Yale
boys who purchased Indian ponies from neighboring ranchmen.

Taking up the story from this point, the published account
goes on to say:

"Our main object . . . was to reach the junction of the
Green and White rivers in Utah, and to examine the surrounding country. No exploration of this region had ever been made;
but hunters and Indians had brought back fabulous stories of

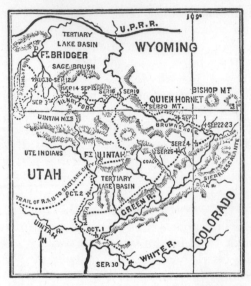

Fig. 5. Route followed by the Expedition of
1870 on its third trip, out of Ft. Bridger.

valleys strewn with gigantic petrified bones. To this geological
paradise the shortest route lay across the Uintah Mountains,
the altitude of whose lowest pass is eleven thousand feet; but
we could find no guide through these rugged defiles, and were
obliged to follow the circuitous course of the rivers. . . .

"The rough bottom-lands of Henry's Fork made terrible
work with [the wagons], and we were at last compelled to lighten
them by 'caching' a large quantity of grain. Notwithstanding
this relief, they again broke down so hopelessly that we determined to abandon them, and to make the rest of our journey
with pack-mules. Our Mexican guide, Joe, was therefore sent

back to the fort with instructions to obtain pack-saddles and ropes, and to meet us at the mouth of the river. During this delay we were overtaken by a party in pursuit of a desperate band of horse-thieves, who have their head-quarters at Brown's Hole, on the Green River. Our route lay of necessity through their haunt; and we were startled by the report that two suspicious characters, supposed to be in league with them, and who knew of our expedition, had left the fort just before us. . . .

"By dint of continual packing we made fair progress, and entered the much-dreaded Hole—a narrow valley, with high mountains on either hand. . . . Our scouts examined the various trails leading to the south, and found that it was impossible to continue our course down the left bank of the river. We therefore forded just above the mouth of Vermilion Creek, and ascended the eastern end of the Uintah Mountains to the altitude of snow. After crossing an extensive tableland a grand scene burst upon us. Fifteen hundred feet below us lay the beds of another great tertiary lake. We stood upon the brink of a vast basin so desolate, wild, and broken, so lifeless and silent, that it seemed like the ruins of a world. . . .

"At the White River we had ample reward for all the hardships we had experienced in reaching this goal of our journey. Though we found none of the gigantic bones of which we had heard so much from hunters and Indians, yet, as we ascended the river, the fossils increased in number, until from one point of view we counted eleven shells of pliocene tortoises which had weathered from the bluffs. After making collections in this region to the satisfaction of even our enthusiastic professor, we reforded the Green River and followed a trail to Fort Uintah. . . . Here we engaged a guide through the wild ravines and dense pine forests of the Uintah Mountains. . . . The ground in the forest was often heaped with fallen trunks; and for mile after mile a path for the pack-mules had to be cut with hatchets through the tangled thickets. After great difficulties we reached Henry's Fork, picked up the abandoned wagons, and came to the spot where the grain was cached. Here we found in possession a party of men . . . professing to be ranchmen, but the lieutenant commanding our escort assured us they were the identical horse-thieves of whom we had been already warned. They had appropriated the grain, and Professor Marsh went to the hut to claim our property. He was ushered into the presence of the party, each of whom was armed to the teeth. . . . Endeavoring to control his embarrassment by speaking as to ordinary ranchmen, our illustrious chief remarked, blandly, 'Well, where are your squaws?' 'Sir,' replied a dignified ruffian, 'this crowd is virtuous.' "

After these three trips, which were often difficult in the extreme, the Yale party devoted a few weeks to sightseeing about Salt Lake City, where the boys "flirted with twenty-two daughters of Brigham Young in a box at the theatre, and, overcome by the effort, immediately crossed the Sierra Nevada to San Francisco." From there they visited the Yosemite and the Mariposa big trees, and some of the mining regions. This brief vacation over, they returned by rail to a locality near the Green River in Wyoming, where they collected fossil fishes and insects.

It might seem as if this particular expedition had by this time had enough of adventure, even for youth, but they were to make yet one more foray into fossil fields. Professor Marsh's attention had been directed by Army officers to the possibility of rich fossils in the Cretaceous beds along the Smoky Hill River in western Kansas, the Smoky Hill trail having been in existence since before 1859. Accordingly, he took his party to Fort Wallace, near the western boundary of Kansas, from which they started out with an escort on the twentieth of November. Here, instead of the heat of the plain, they had to contend with nights of bitter cold, and the threat of snow soon forced them in from the field. Not, however, before they had enjoyed a Thanksgiving dinner on the plains under somewhat unusual circumstances, the tale of which was probably told and retold until it became a family legend in the homes of the members of the expedition. Professor Marsh's own version of it was as follows:

"We . . . pitched our tents under the lea of a high bluff near the river, in order to protect ourselves as far as possible from the cold northerly winds that then prevailed. . . . From fear of Indians, we had our wagons put in a half circle at the foot of the bluff, with our tents and all the equine animals inside, the latter tied at night to the wagons for greater safety.

Thus secure, we slept the sleep of the just, and dreamed only of fossils and the Thanksgiving dinner we hoped to enjoy in camp the next day.

"Some time during that cold, windy night, however, we were suddenly aroused by fearful noises of clashing wagons, snorting horses, and falling tents, as if an earthquake were in progress directly under our camp, or, as we first of all thought, that the Indians had made a night attack upon us. As the noise increased, and greater destruction came to our tents, we heard one shot, apparently from our own sentinel, and rushing out into the darkness, we feared most of all the silent but deadly Indian arrows. At last all was still, and we found that no one was killed or seriously wounded. As we lighted our lantern, however, and looked around where our quiet camp had been the evening before, we found our animals gone and everything left in confusion. A council of war was held, and gradually the true cause of our disaster became evident. The coyotes, who were often sneaking around our camp at night for stray bits of food, had now been especially attracted by the fresh buffalo meat that hung outside our cooking tent; but for some time none of them had dared a nearer approach, especially through the circle of mules, whose heels guarded the camp, although their heads were lashed to the wagons. One coyote, however, bolder than the rest, had leaped from the top of the high bluff directly into the magic circle, and all the army mules, taken thus by surprise, had stampeded, breaking away from their fastenings and tearing down the tents as they dashed out into the darkness. It was this and nothing more. We could do little until morning came, when we searched our surroundings and found that one ancient mule, known as 'Crazy Jane,' belying her name, but true to her nature, had, from sheer obstinacy, refused to desert us, and was soon caught near camp. . . .

"A soldier was soon selected to look up the missing mules if possible, and mounted on the only one left, he started out from camp to follow the trail. It was some time before he could make out the fact that the mules had finally got together some miles from camp, and had started with rapid gait back to Fort Wallace, a dozen or fifteen miles away to the westward. Concluding that they were probably safe at the post, as no Indian signs were seen, he rode leisurely back along the old stage road to the Fort.

"Meanwhile, the band of frightened mules with their broken halters and dragging lariats had already arrived at the Fort, and produced great consternation. General Bankhead, the commanding officer, felt at once the full responsibility of the situation, and exclaimed, 'Great God, the Indians have jumped the Professor. We must save the party if possible!' and an order was promptly given to have a company of troops start at once to our rescue. Lieutenant [Charles] Braden was placed in command, and with his troop and accompanying wagons, was soon pushing eastward with special orders for haste, to rescue us if we were surrounded, and if too late, to bring our remains back to the Fort.

"While the command was making good progress toward our camp, the solitary soldier that we had sent after the mules, rode slowly into Fort Wallace. Before he could tell his tale, General Bankhead saw him and sharply inquired, 'Where is your gun?' 'I left it at camp,' the man replied. 'Well,' said the General, 'if you are d——d fool enough to risk your own life in this Indian country, you shan't risk a Government mule. Officer of the day, put that man in the guardhouse.'

.   .   .   .

"Of all this we knew nothing at the time, and waited for the return of the soldier to report about our animals. Although it was Thanksgiving, we spent the greater part of it in fossil hunting, but made good preparation for our feast that evening. Before the hour arrived, just as the sun was going down, we heard the rattle of wagons, and looking up the river, saw Lieutenant Braden and his troops hurrying toward us. He seemed greatly surprised at the quiet greeting we gave him and his men, and inquired feelingly if we were all safe. We told him we were all right, but were rather short of mules. Explanations followed, and we invited the Lieutenant and his fellow officers to our Thanksgiving dinner, while his men received a similar invitation to dine with our escort.

"This dinner was a memorable feast, under the circumstances. Our bill of fare for the game courses included buffalo tongue, steak, and roast rib; antelope in various forms, and stewed jack rabbit; with pork and beans, canned fruit, and vegetables, from the Commissary Department, as side dishes. Our beverages were limited, but good army coffee, and the 'wine' of Kentucky were in abundance. As the feast progressed, the fun became fast and furious. I was requested to make a speech, thanking the Lieutenant and his comrades for our rescue, and he replied in feeling terms. Yale songs were sung by our party, and western stories were told by the army officers. The November wind howled through our camp, and the coyotes, sniffing the feast, serenaded us from the orchestra bluff above, but we heeded them not, for we were safe and happy, and that Thanksgiving dinner on the plains of Kansas will, I am sure, never be forgotten by any one present."

Fort Wallace was at that time in the midst of the buffalo range, and it was on this expedition that Professor Marsh staged the spectacular buffalo hunt that established his reputation, once and for all, as a hunter endowed not only with plenty of courage, but with an almost uncanny ability to send a bullet from a rifle exactly where he wanted it to go. Fortunately, his own story of this memorable event has been preserved:

"A large ambulance drawn by four stalwart mules, the pride of the garrison, was provided for my party, while Captain R., the master of the hunt, joined us, his horse being tied behind so as to be fresh when the hunting ground was reached. A small escort, with one or two mounted officers, accompanied us, with an army wagon to carry back the buffalo meat they felt sure of securing. On the way out, the Captain regaled us with stories of his own previous buffalo hunts, and as we were all supposed to be tenderfeet, he gave us much instruction as to how success was to be won. . . .

"On arriving at the table land where the buffalo were to be found, great numbers were in sight, mainly in two vast herds, one to the West on our right, and the other farther away to the South-east. Captain R. suggested that the best place for us to see the hunt was from the ambulance, but if we preferred, we might take our chances on foot, as the main hunt would probably be in plain sight, although extending over several miles of territory. With this advice, he mounted his horse and joined the rest of the escort, giving general directions to the ambulance driver and other teamsters to keep in the rear, so as not to disturb the hunt more than was necessary. Some of the Yale party used strong language about being invited to see a buffalo hunt without being mounted, but hoped to get a stray shot on foot at some straggler during the day. I remained in the ambulance, and from my seat beside the driver, watched the fray, as the officers and mounted soldiers dashed after individual buffalo that were nearest to them, and continued the chase far afield. This was tame sport for me, who had had considerable experience with other large game, and after watching the hunt awhile, I rebelled, and made friends with the ambulance driver by means of some good cigars.

"One large division of the herd was on our right, and seeing three buffalo start to cross from there to the main herd on the left, several miles away, in a direction that would apparently lead them athwart our course at some distance from where we were, I decided that my chance had come. Turning to the driver, who was watching the same animals, I said excitedly, 'Driver, do you want a Five Dollar bill?' 'Mighty bad,' he replied. 'Then put me alongside of those three buffalo, where I can get a fair shot, and here is your money.' 'I'll do it, or bust these mules,' he replied, and in a moment his long black-snake-whip cracked over the leaders, and the four sturdy animals were all at full speed; the ambulance swaying from side to side, as it dashed over the rough prairie.

"Knowing that the buffalo would not rapidly turn from their course, I directed the driver to go straight ahead, feeling sure that he would thus reach a point that would give me a shot at the buffalo as they passed. They were going at an easy but rapid lope and in single file, and as we came nearer, I saw through my field-glass, that the leader, by his darker color and more vigorous action, was a young bull in the prime of life, while the other two were older, but yet almost his equals in speed. As we drew yet nearer on our converging course, I saw that the rear animal, who was somewhat behind us, was much the oldest, his short, blunt, curved horns, and his lighter color, telling his age. As we drew closer, I singled him out as my victim, and telling the driver to keep his eye on him and look out for his mules, I drew up my Winchester and aiming low, just behind the fore-leg, where his heart should be, I fired, and down he came. I saw nothing more, for the frightened mules were in the air, each plunging for himself, and the driver could not hold them. The ambulance rocked fearfully, and I thought every moment it would go over, but I was willing to take the chance, and only lost my hat.

"The other two buffalo maintained their course, while we had lost ours by the sudden shying of the mules. Time was short, and elated by my first shot, I said again to the driver, 'Do you want another V?' He had only breath enough to say, 'You bet!' and I replied, 'Then give me another shot at Number Two.' With a great effort he swung the team back to their course, and the race went on, becoming still more exciting, as we had lost considerable ground while the mules were plunging each on his own account.

"We again drew near to the flying buffalo, whose heavy gait had perceptibly slackened, and just when I hoped to get in my second shot the team again broke away and tried to pull off, but the driver this time kept them in hand; and we were soon so close to the two buffalo that I had my choice between them for my next shot. The leader was clearly the prize animal, and if I could secure him, I should be happy. But, hoping that I might have a chance at him later, if I first disabled his comrade, and the mules held out, I fired at Number Two, and again the team was in the air. I merely saw that my shot had taken effect, for the animal halted, but the leader was defiant and kept bravely on with renewed vigor.

"As the team once more settled down to work, I said to the driver—'I have one more V for you; help me get that fine fellow, and we'll turn back.' A hundred yards rapid dash, a quick shot at close range, and the buffalo was on his knees. The mules were not—and it was some minutes before the driver obtained the upper hand, and swung them around where I could see my prize. I jumped from the ambulance and approached him. He was done, but there was blood in his eye, as well as on the ground where he lay. As I walked slowly toward him, with my rifle in hand, the driver suddenly exclaimed, 'Look out, he's going for you!' The bull sprang to his feet, and with head down and eyes and nostrils flaming, made a dash for me. I had just time to jump aside, and before he could turn, gave him another shot, which pinned him to the ground, and victory was mine. . . .

"Our chase had led us far away from the rendezvous of the hunt, and the mules showed only a slight resemblance to the sleek spirited animals we had started out with that morning. The other buffalo I had shot were two or three miles at least in the rear, but I cared not for them with the monarch of the herd at my feet. I must save what I could, as my time was brief, and taking out my hunting knife, I was soon at work. I determined, if possible, first, to cut off his magnificent head, as a trophy; next, to save his dark chocolate robe for a memento, as it recorded the position of both my shots; third, to cut off the fore and hind feet at the joint, as another evidence of what a fine animal I had slain. All this was hard work, but a labor of love. As I had lost my hat in the first mad dash of the mules, and the chilly November air of the afternoon now made me feel the want of it, I tied a white handkerchief around my head, and with rolled up sleeves, began at my bloody work.

"Before this was finished, Captain R. rode up. He had seen the chase after buffalo with the ambulance, and looking at the mules, reproved the driver. I took all the blame, and covered with blood as I was, with my hunting knife in hand, he was polite enough not to reprove me, and even helped me load my gory trophies into the ambulance, then getting in with me, and tying his own exhausted steed to the rear, we started slowly to pick up the rest of our party and return to the Fort. The driver had meanwhile said nothing in his own defense, except to intimate that the mules, frightened at the buffalo, had thrice run away with him; a little pleasantry that I did not dispute, as he tipped me a sly wink at the time, and touching his vest pocket where three greenbacks were safely deposited, he sat silent except to urge onward his tired mules. . . . Around camp fires in various parts of the West, I have since heard the story of that ambulance hunt with many variations, but what I give here is the official account."

The major fossil trophies of this Kansas trip were remains of the great sea serpents or mosasaurs of the seas that covered the region in Cretaceous time. Some of them reached a length of 35 feet, but one small bone picked up by Professor Marsh was of more importance to him than all the great sea serpents, and the story of its discovery was told by him as follows:

"One day I had been especially fortunate in my fossil discoveries, and thus remained behind the party till late in the afternoon, with only a single soldier as my companion. . . . It was after sunset when we left the bluffs and pushed down to the river bottom, following some old buffalo trails, which were deeply worn in the soft chalk that formed the river bank. As we rode down one of these, with our stirrups touching the rock on either side, I saw on my right, about a dozen feet from the trail, a fossil bone; and dismounting and giving my horse in charge of my companion, I picked it up. It was hollow, about six inches long and one inch in diameter, with one end perfect and containing a peculiar joint that I had never seen before. An hour earlier and I should have searched the locality for the rest of the bone and others that might go with it, but it was already twilight, and I could only wrap up carefully the specimen I had found, put it away in one of my softest pockets, and before mounting, cut a deep cross in the gray chalk rock beside the trail, so that I could be sure to find the spot again. . . .

"Even before I had my supper, I took another look at the fossil bone I had found, but it was as great a puzzle as before. It looked so much like the tibia of a gigantic bird, that I at first thought it might prove to belong to that class; and in my tent that night, I thought over the possibilities that view offered, but still in vain. The bird characters were there, but such a joint no known bird possessed, as it indicated a freedom of motion in one direction that no well-constructed bird could use on land or water.

"The specimen was carefully packed, and later reached New Haven with my other fossil treasures, and there the chances for comparison were greater. The bone was very hollow, and corresponded in many respects anatomically with the first joint of the little finger of the human hand. So far I felt sure that my determination was correct. The only joint much like it that I could find in any animal, living or extinct, was in the wing finger of the Pterodactyle, or flying dragon, but these reptiles, so far as known, were only diminutive creatures, not one-twentieth the size or one-hundredth the bulk this bone indicated, if it belonged to a creature of that type.

"After further comparison, however, I could only return

to the dragon's wing for the nearest resemblance, and believing in my science, as taught by Cuvier, I determined to make a scientific announcement of what the fossil indicated, and trust to future discoveries to prove whether I was right or wrong. I therefore made a careful calculation of how large a Pterodactyle must be to have a wing finger corresponding to the fragment I had found, and ascertained that its spread of wings would be about twenty feet—truly a gigantic dragon even in this country of big things, where hitherto no Pterodactyle large or small had yet been discovered. I therefore, with the courage of my convictions, announced the discovery, and published a description, naming the new animal after my friend, Professor Owen of London [*Pterodactylus oweni*], who had already written much on this group of fossil reptiles."

The Yale College Expedition of 1870 reached New Haven on the eighteenth of December, "after six eventful months, during which no serious accident or illness had happened to any of the party." Its success was far-reaching. Directly, it gave to the Museum thirty-six boxes of material that included many an important specimen destined to become the type of a new genus or species. Indirectly, the wide publicity it received from newspapers in the East and in the West focused attention both on the market for fossil vertebrates and on Professor Marsh as the most active figure in that market; moreover, it resulted in the army friendships that were to be of so much assistance to him throughout his career, and it made the gathering of personnel for succeeding expeditions an easy matter.

The next year's expedition (1871) had ten men, two less than in 1870, Ziegler being the only repeater. The personnel was as follows:

John Jay DuBois, '67, M.A. '72, Columbia LL.B '69, who practised law for some time, then returned to New Haven to engage in literary pursuits and philosophical research until his death in 1898 (2).

Oscar Harger, '68, Marsh's able assistant in Paleontology for seventeen years (10). See Chapter XII.

George M. Keasbey, '71 S., who served on the Government survey of the One Hundredth Meridian, and later was a lawyer in Newark, New Jersey (6).

George G. Lobdell, Jr., '71 S., a manufacturer, of Wilmington, Delaware (15).

Alfred Bishop Mason, '71, M.A. '74, vice-president of the Jacksonville, Tampa, and Key West Railway, president of the Vera Cruz and Pacific Railway in Mexico and of the Cauca Railway in Colombia. Author of a *Primer of political economy*, and of works on constitutional history and law (1).

Frederick Mead, '71, M.A. '74, a New York businessman (5).

Joseph French Page, '71, a real estate lawyer in Philadelphia (3).

Theodore Gordon Peck, '71, M.A. '93, a brick manufacturer in Haverstraw, New York (3).

John F. Quigley, '71 S., manufacturer and civil engineer (6).

Harry D. Ziegler.

Again we are fortunate in having two firsthand accounts, one (by MEM) in the New York *Times* for October 17, 1871, and the other (unsigned) in the Yale *College Courant* for February 3, 1872. During the winter, Professor Marsh had learned that one of the 1870 prizes from Kansas was indeed part of the first known American pterodactyl, and he was in a hurry to get the rest of the animal. It may be for this reason that the party went immediately to Fort Wallace and started where that of the previous year had left off. It may be, too, that, having had a taste of Kansas cold, they thought its heat might be preferable, a mistaken notion, as appears later. They rode out of Fort Wallace on July 2, accompanied by five army wagons and the usual escort (apparently in charge of Lieut. H. Romeyn), and on July 6 Marsh and Harger found six saurians five miles south of the post. The *Courant* correspondent continues:

"The march was in a south easterly direction, along a belt of sand, which was called Smoky River, but which required a stretch of courtesy to be so regarded, at least, at this season of the year. . . . The line of this river was followed in general on this trip, and of necessity, for the whole country was almost entirely destitute of water. . . . The country traversed consisted of a series of ridges varying in width from a few feet to two or three miles; separated by valleys of the same unequal extent. The ridges, called 'divides,' were often intersected by deep cañons, where the water has washed off the covering of earth and hollowed out a channel, often from fifty to a hundred feet deep, in the blue and yellow Cretaceous shale beneath. Some of these cañons extended but a short distance; while others stretched out for miles and often branched off into labyrinthian passages which confused and perplexed the unaccustomed explorer.

"The fossil-hunting was done in the cañons before described. As the explorer slowly rode along on his faithful mule or horse, with scientific instinct sharpened by curiosity to see the relics of ages so long gone by, and by ambition to discover something new, he would occasionally perceive upon a shelf of rock a skeleton fully exposed to view. To dismount, examine and secure the prize was the work of but a short time. But not always did these objects of search so readily reveal themselves. Sometimes it was only a projecting vertebra or rib, or bone of the foot or tail, that revealed the presence of the fossil within; and more often a piece of bone had become detached and having rolled a few feet down the cañon, was discovered quietly lying where the storms and gravitation had left it. When such a piece was found, the work of trailing began. The discoverer crept on hands and knees up the slopes, minutely scanning every inch of the rock. Usually his labors were rewarded by finding one or more other pieces which had become detached like the first. The location of each piece was carefully marked, and after thorough search had shown that no more were exposed to view, hammer, and chisel, and knife, and spade, and pickaxe were in turn, when necessary, brought to bear upon the highest point where a bone had been found. Sometimes the search was a fruitless one, but more often, a few strokes would reveal another bone and continued exertion lay bare the whole skeleton. If the specimen was a common one, only the more characteristic bones were exhumed, but if it was rare, the soft rock was dug away by the cubic yard, until every part and particle even to tooth and jaws, if they could be found, was disinterred. Then, when the earth had yielded up her dead, each separated bone was carefully wrapped in paper, or in cotton, or in both, and the whole put in a gunny sack, and sewed up, and in this condition taken to camp."

The scientific yield from this second trip to western Kansas included more bones of the pterodactyl located the previous season by Professor Marsh; describing the second find, the latter said:

"I confess that during the long winter that followed [1870–71], I at times had my misgivings, at least as to my calculations of the size the animal should have had, and I longed for spring to come that I might go back to the Kansas locality. . . . The opportunity did not occur, however, until June, 1871. . . .

"As soon as our tents were pitched, I started with two or three companions to seek the locality. . . . My remembrance of localities did not fail me, and I soon was near the very spot, and riding down a deep trail which I seemed to recognize, I found the cross nearly as distinct as when I cut it. A moment later I was at the spot where I discovered the fossil bone, and soon detected fragments of it lying near, partially covered up by the loose chalk that had been washed over it by the winter storms. More important still, I found the impression of the bone itself in the rock, and following this up with great care, I obtained the upper end of the same bone, and made out the exact shape and length of the whole from the impression and remaining part. My determination of the bone was thus confirmed. But how about the size?

"With my hunting knife and a small brush made from buffalo grass, I slowly and carefully cleared away the place where the upper end of the bone lay, and to my great joy, found another one which had fitted on to it when the animal was alive. Following this up with breathless anxiety, but with caution that long experience had given me, I uncovered still another bone, and at last the whole series that supported the gigantic wing of the ancient dragon. These I measured roughly as I took them up one by one, and making a sketch of them all as they were found, I was soon able to determine that my calculations based on the fragments were essentially correct, and that this first found American dragon was fully as large as my fancy had painted him.

"My journey from New Haven was amply repaid, but greater rewards were to come, for during the month that I spent at hard work in this region, other dragons came to light, even more gigantic and much more wonderful than I had before imagined. For, unlike all other dragons, living or extinct, known to science or mythology, these reptiles, notwithstanding their gigantic size and vast spread of wings—from twenty to twenty-five feet . . . were without teeth, and hence comparatively harmless. This feature was especially strange. The birds, who were their contemporaries in this region ages before, were all well supplied with teeth, although no modern birds possessed them."

Conditions in western Kansas were so bad that year that the party was glad to leave for Denver for a four-day rest. Then they went on to Cheyenne, their ultimate destination being western Wyoming, where "trips were as agreeable and pleasant as the other was hard." Outfitting again at Fort Bridger, which they reached on August 22, and which was then commanded by Col. Albert G. Brackett, they set out on a six weeks' exploration of the Green River Basin. Here, says the *Courant:*

"The country consisted of desert plains, too sterile to produce grass, but thickly overgrown with sage brush. The plains were occasionally varied by buttes or eminences which were entirely bare. The streams of water were more abundant than in Kansas, and their banks were fringed with cotton-wood trees and a narrow strip of rich deep grass which formed an agreeable relief from the gray expanse either side. The views presented in the Uintah Mountains were magnificent. . . .

"A large part of the collection in this region was of the remains of small animals. The fossils were generally found in the buttes, and on account of their minuteness their discovery was attended with much difficulty. Instead of riding along on the sure-footed mule and looking for a gigantic tell-tale vertebra or ribs, it was necessary to literally crawl over the country on hands and knees. . . . Often a quarter of a mile of the most inviting country would be carefully gone over with no result, and then again some one would chance upon a butte which seemed almost made of fossils. When two or three found such a prize at nearly the same time, lines would be drawn around each claim with as much care as when valuable mineral land is located; for it must be remembered that each man had full credit for all his discoveries, and the thought of having one's name attached to some rare specimen in the Yale Museum led to sharp competition."

From this basin, 7,000 feet above the sea, eleven boxes of material were shipped to the Museum to swell the collection from the Bridger beds of the Eocene, which includes such important specimens as the types of the horses *Orohippus uintanus* and *O. pumilis*.

Again resting for a few days in Salt Lake City, the party prepared to invade a new field, that of the John Day Basin in western central Oregon, which lay far from any railway. Leaving the line of the Pacific Railroad at Kelton, Utah, on October 5, they proceeded six hundred miles by stage[11] over the old emigrant trail, stopping on the way to visit Shoshone Falls and Boise, thence over the difficult route across the Blue Mountains to the headwaters of the John Day River, then down the river to Canyon City, Oregon, which they reached on October 17. Here they waited for a military escort sent from Fort Harney, seventy-five miles to the south; and when this outfit arrived, they set out to explore a still different type of country, one which, the party's chronicler says,

"showed everywhere evidence of former volcanic action on a stupendous scale. The lake deposits of clay and sand in which the remains of extinct animals were found embedded had been covered by thousands of feet of basaltic lava, and it was only where the present streams have cut deep cañons through this lava covering that the underlying beds and their fossil treasures could be reached. . . . The upper lake bed contained the remains of the elephant, rhinoceros, lion, and other tropical animals, with several species of fossil horses. In the lower and older basin many new fossil mammals and some reptiles were discovered."

Their guide to the John Day area was the Reverend Thomas Condon, pioneer geologist of Oregon, with whom Marsh had been in correspondence, and who is spoken of more at length in a later chapter. Under his leadership they collected eleven boxes of material between October 31 and November 8—the beginning of another notable Yale collection—and on November 12 they attended Condon's church in Dalles City. It was getting late in the season, however, and oncoming winter forced a halt to fossil collecting. The party therefore took ship down the Columbia River to Portland, where they rested from November

11. The receipt for this trip, still preserved, shows that its cost to the Yale party was $825.

18 to 22. Professor Marsh and most of the men then went on to San Francisco by steamer and the others went overland, both methods of travel being rendered hazardous by a severe storm. Two weeks in San Francisco seeing the sights brought the year down to the middle of December, and the group again divided, some returning East directly by rail and others electing to sail with Professor Marsh by way of Panama, reaching home the fourteenth of January. Incidentally, on the Isthmus, Professor Marsh secured the first of the valuable Chiriqui antiquities that he was subsequently to acquire by the thousands.

The 1871 Expedition, exclusive of the assistance received from the Government in the way of escort and provisions, cost in the neighborhood of $15,000, which was contributed by its members.

The 1872 party was a small one, its members being *Charles D. Hill* of Calais, Maine; *Benjamin Hoppin*, '72, who later was three times in the Arctic, the last time with Peary; *James MacNaughton* of Albany, New York; and *Thomas H. Russell*, '72 S., M.D. '75, later professor of Clinical Surgery in the Yale School of Medicine. Its time was divided between Kansas and Wyoming, the escort from Fort Wallace being in command of Lieut. James W. Pope, with Ed Lane as guide, and that from Fort D. A. Russell consisting of a detachment of the Ninth Infantry headed by Lieut. (later Maj. Gen.) Jesse M. Lee. The Kansas trip was especially successful, as it added more material to the Yale collection of Cretaceous toothed birds, one of the groups that brought Marsh world-wide fame. In fact, the specimen of the great diving bird, *Hesperornis regalis*, with the skull, which proved the existence of teeth in this form as well as in the smaller, ternlike *Ichthyornis*, was found on this expedition by Marsh and Russell (see Chapter XVIII).

Less is known of the experiences of this expedition than of any of the other three, but out of it came at least one good story, and what is by all means the best of the chapters written by Professor Marsh for his unfinished book of adventure. The story has to do with an adventure that befel Benjamin Hoppin, and as written down for this book by the late Professor Henry W. Farnam of Yale it reads as follows:

"Marsh's party was moving across Kansas and Hoppin was attracted by some animal (possibly an antelope) which he wished to shoot. He left the outfit on foot with a rifle and one cartridge, but with no coat and no matches in his pocket. He failed to get his game, and on starting to return found that he had lost the outfit. Being unable to see it anywhere, he realized that the best way to get back to civilization would be to follow the meridian in a due southerly direction until he should hit the Kansas Pacific Railroad. Once there he knew that by following the rails he would soon come to a station. At that time the buffalo of the plains had been slaughtered recklessly by the Western Union Telegraph Company, which used stuffed buffalo heads as a sign to be placed over their local offices. I can well remember when the buffalo head was as typical of the Western Union as the blue bell is now of the telephone company. As the day passed without any sight of the railroad, Hoppin found the remains of one of the buffalo of which the skin was still in good condition though the body was dried up. He shook the bones out of the skin and crawled in to spend the night. The next day he reached the track and started to walk along the rails. In the meantime, Professor Marsh had, of course, sent word all through the state that one of his men was lost, and offered fifty dollars reward for anyone who would find him. The telegraph operator in one of the stations saw a man walking along the track with a rifle and no coat, and, without waiting to identify the refugee, at once telegraphed along the line, 'Your man is found, send on the fifty dollars.' "

Marsh's own story was called "A ride for life in a herd of buffalo," and it runs thus:

"One afternoon, when returning from a long fossil hunt, the guide, Lieutenant Pope, and myself were riding slowly abreast, discussing the day's fossil hunt and the prospect for the morrow, from which I expected important results. As I glanced at my companions on either side of me, I was struck by the contrast they presented, and the three different types represented in our small party. The guide [Ed Lane] with his wide sombrero, his picturesque buckskin suit and his jangling Mexican spurs, naturally first drew my attention, as with keen eye, ever alert for signs of Indians, he said but little and that always to the point. The Lieutenant, in his army cap and trim blue uniform, was more socially inclined; greatly enjoying his first experience of army life on the plains; eager to learn all he could from the guide and ready to do his duty whenever occasion offered. The Professor, I regret to say, suffered by contrast with his two companions, as he wore a slouch hat, and an ancient suit of corduroy, with the capacious pockets of the shooting-jacket bulging with fossils, while a pair of high hunting boots, guaranteed rattlesnake proof, completed his costume, thus making him the disreputable looking member of the party. He fully realized this himself, and also thought sadly of the remark his striker, a soldier from Connecticut, made to him that morning as he was starting out from camp—'Professor, I would give a month's pay, with rations, just to see you in that rig ride down Chapel Street in New Haven, by the College, when the students are out on the fence. Wouldn't there be a racket! Wouldn't the horns blow!'

"As we rode to the crest of a high ridge, the guide, now slightly ahead, as is usual in an Indian country, suddenly called out, 'Great God, look at the buffalo!,' and we saw a sight that I shall never forget, and one that no mortal eye will ever see again. The broad valley before us, perhaps six or eight miles wide, was black with buffalo, the herd extending a dozen miles, up and down the valley, and quietly grazing, showing that no Indians were near. The animals were headed to the South, and slowly moving up the valley in the direction of the great table land where pasturage for the night was to be found. The sight was so wonderful that we sat on our horses for some time, watching the countless throng, and endeavoring to make some estimate of how many buffalo were in sight before us. The lowest estimate was that of the guide, who placed the number at 50,000. I thought there were more; and our military comrade, with his mathematics fresh from West Point, made a rapid calculation of the square miles covered, and the number of animals to the mile, making his total nearly one hundred thousand. While we were thus engaged, the slowly declining sun behind us shed a golden light over the valley, the black moving masses being in strong relief, while our own lengthening shadows pointed toward the herd, that thus far had not deigned to notice us, all forming together a panorama of surpassing interest.

"While wrapped in the wonderful prospect before us, the guide quietly remarked, 'We must have one of those fellows for supper.' This broke the spell and brought a practical question directly before us. The guide was mounted on a large mule, January by name, which had a long army record for nearly everything except buffalo hunting. Lieutenant Pope was on a tall cavalry horse, a new recruit, that was gazing timidly on a herd of buffalo for the first time. My steed was a fleet Indian pony, known as Pawnee, said to have been stolen from that tribe by a Sioux warrior, and well-trained for the hunt by his former owners. He had proved his mettle in the two expeditions I had ridden him, and in several chases I had given the buffalo then encountered. It was therefore at once decided that I must provide for our supper, and shifting my fossil treasures into the guide's saddle-bags, and tightening the cinch of my pony and my own cartridge belt, I was soon ready for the fray. My hunting weapons consisted of a cavalry carbine and a pair of navy revolvers, not too many for an Indian country, and I hoped soon to bring down a young buffalo that would give our camp the wished-for meal. I rode slowly down toward the herd, avoiding a few old bulls outside the main body, so as not to disturb them. The wind was in my favor, and I soon was near the herd. Selecting the animal, I promptly gave chase, hoping to get in my shot before the herd started, which I knew would soon be the case. The animal selected, a young cow, proved especially fleet, and it was some minutes before I was along side, ready to shoot, in the exact manner my first guide, Buffalo Bill, had taught me long before. While the chase was still going on, I had heard one or two shots behind me in the distance, and concluded that my comrades were firing at some straggling animal, but I had no time to look around, as my pony, knowing what was wanted, made a direct chase for the buffalo selected, and soon carried me, where a shot from my carbine brought the animal to the ground. I then had a chance to look back.

"To my amazement, I saw that the main herd, alarmed by the shots of my comrades, had started and was moving rapidly southward. I saw also what I had not before surmised; that in my eagerness I had pushed well into the herd without noticing it, and as the great mass of animals in the rear started, they began to lap around me, and I would soon be enclosed in the rapidly moving throng liable at any moment to be trampled to death if my pony should fail me. My only chance of escape

was evidently to keep moving with the buffalo and press towards
the edge of the herd, and thinking thus to cut my way out, I
began shooting at animals nearest to me, to open the way.
Each shot gave me some gain, as those near pushed away, and
when one went down, others stumbled over him. The whole
mighty herd was now at full speed, the earth seemed fairly to
shake under the moving mass, which with tongues out, and
flaming eyes and nostrils, were hurrying onward, pressed by
those behind, up the broad valley, which narrowed as it
approached the higher land in the distance. My horse was
greatly excited by his surroundings, and at first seemed to think
I wanted some particular animal, and was thus inclined to make
chase after it, but he soon came to understand the serious problem before him, and acted accordingly.

"A new danger suddenly confronted me. The prairie bottom
had hitherto been so even that my only thought was of the buffalo around me and the danger of being overwhelmed by them,
if my pony could not keep up the race. The new terror was a
large prairie dog village, extending for half a mile or more
up the valley. As the herd dashed into it, some of the animals
stepped into the deep burrows, and near where I was riding,
I saw quite a number come to earth and now and then a comrade from behind fall over them. My trained buffalo horse here
showed his wonderful sagacity. While running at full speed
along with the herd, he kept his head down, and whenever a
dangerous dog hole was in his path, he either stepped short
or leaped over it and thus brought me through this new danger
in safety. The race had now been kept up for several miles, and
my carbine ammunition was nearly exhausted; while my pony,
after his long day's work and rapid run, showed unmistakable
signs of fatigue. My only hope was that he could hold out until
we reached rougher ground, where the herd might divide. This
came sooner than I expected.

"As the valley narrowed, the side ravines came closer together at the bottom, and our course soon led us among them.
The smaller gullies were leaped with ease by the buffalo close
around me, and my pony held his own with the best of them.
As the ravines became deeper, longer leaps were necessary, and
my brave steed refused none of them. Soon the ravines became
too wide for a single leap, and the buffalo plunged into them

and scrambled up the opposite bank. My pony did the same, and several times I could have touched with my extended hands the buffalo on either side of me as we clambered together up the yielding sides of the narrow canyons we were crossing. This was hard work for all, and the buffalo showed the greater signs of fatigue, but no intentions of stopping in their mad career, except those that were disabled and went down in the fierce struggle to keep out of the way of those behind them.

"As the valley [still] narrowed, I saw ahead, perhaps a mile distant, a low butte, a little to the left of the course we were taking. This gave me new courage, for if I could only reach it, it would afford shelter, as the herd must pass on either side of it. Drawing a revolver, I began to shoot at the nearest buffalo on my left, and this caused them to draw away as far as the others would let them, and when one went down, I gained so much ground. They were now really more afraid of me and my horse than we were of them, and for this reason did not charge, as a single wounded buffalo might have done. Continuing my shooting more rapidly as we approached the butte, I gradually swung to the left, and when we came to it, I pulled my pony sharp around behind it, and let the great herd pass on.

"Dismounting, I saw why my pony had seemed so foot-heavy during the last mile. He was covered with dust, nearly exhausted, and with bleeding flanks, distended forelegs, and blazing nostrils, he stood there quivering and breathing heavily, while the buffalo were passing within a few feet. We could not move until the herd had gone by, and it was more than an hour before the last of them left us alone. . . .

"The danger was now over, and the pangs of hunger reminded me of the supper I had promised to secure for my comrades. One of the last stragglers of the herd in the twilight was a young heifer, and a shot brought her to my feet. To draw my hunting knife and remove the tongue and hump steaks, sufficient for our small party, was the work of a few minutes; and thus laden, I was ready to start for camp, some half a dozen miles to the eastward.

"Meanwhile, I had not forgotten my faithful Indian pony. He had saved my life, and I did all I could for him. I took off his saddle, and rubbed him down with the saddle blanket. My canteen was empty, but I offered him the scanty contents of my pocket flask, but this he declined, although needing it more than myself. I started to lead him slowly in the direction of camp, but he soon made me understand that he was himself again, and, after mounting, I gave him his head, and he hurried on in the darkness to where he knew our comrades were waiting for us. It was late as we approached camp, and the signal guns to guide us had for some time been flashing in the distance. My first duty on arriving was again to my pony, and for once my striker was not permitted to relieve me. I sang Pawnee's praises around the camp fire that night, and have told the story of his gallant run many times since.

"Poor Pawnee! He deserved a better fate than overtook him in his first campaign the next year. Grazing at night, he was bitten on the nose by a large rattlesnake. When found in the morning, his head was fearfully swollen, and all the whisky in camp could not save him. He was buried with military honors, and a double salute fired over his remains. If, in the happy hunting ground above, Pawnee does not have a place of honor, I shall lose all faith in the belief of the untutored Indian, who thinks,—

> 'admitted to that equal sky,
> His faithful dog shall bear him company.' "

The Yale Expedition of 1873 was the last of the four student parties. It included among its members two, at least, who were to have distinguished careers, one in medicine, and one in economics, and it is from these two that we have most of our information about the expedition. The personnel was:

William Constantine Beecher, '72, Columbia LL.B. '75, son of Henry Ward Beecher, lawyer, and sometime assistant district attorney for New York County.

Henry Grant Cheney, ex-'75 S., of the Cheney Silk Mills in South Manchester, Connecticut.

Clark Dewing, '74, a broker.

Henry W. Farnam, '74, M.A. '76, Strasbourg R.P.D. '78, professor of Economics at Yale for many years, and chairman of the Department of Economics and Sociology of the Carnegie Institution of Washington. He died in 1934.

Oscar Harger, a member of the 1871 party.

PLATE XI

YALE EXPEDITION OF 1872

SITTING (LEFT TO RIGHT): HILL, HOPPIN, MACNAUGHTON, RUSSELL. IDENTITY OF THE MEN STANDING ON EITHER SIDE OF PROFESSOR MARSH NOT KNOWN

YALE EXPEDITION OF 1873

IDENTIFICATIONS FOR THE MOST PART TENTATIVE. STANDING (LEFT TO RIGHT): DEWING, KNOX, ?, MARSH, ?NEWHALL, ?HUNTINGTON. SITTING: OAKS, ?, HARGER, PRUDDEN, BEECHER, ?

PLATE XII

CHIEF RED CLOUD AND PROFESSOR MARSH
WITH THE PIPE OF PEACE AND BELT OF WAMPUM. TAKEN
DURING RED CLOUD'S VISIT TO NEW HAVEN IN 1883

Dwight H. Huntington, '73, of Yonkers, New York, artist, and editor of *Amateur Sportsman*.

H. Evelyn Kinney, '71, Columbia LL.B. '74, member of the legal staff of the New York Central Railroad, later a farmer in Norwich, Connecticut.

Reuben Knox, '73, who practiced law for some time in Plainfield, New Jersey.

William Mayo Newhall, '76 S., Columbia LL.B. '79, sometime lawyer, later manager of the Newhall Land and Farming Company in San Francisco.

Henry A. Oaks, '75, Columbia M.D. '78, a doctor in New Haven and later in Southington, Connecticut.

T. Mitchell Prudden, '72 S., M.D. '75, LL.D. '97, for many years professor of Pathology in Columbia University, and a director of the Rockefeller Institute for Medical Research. His services to the expedition were such that Professor Marsh would gladly have retained him in paleontological work had his interests not lain along other lines. He died in 1924. His diary of the expedition is now in the Sterling Memorial Library at Yale.

A. B. Waring of Yonkers, New York, a special student at Yale the following year.

Frederick S. Wicks, '73, Columbia LL.B. '76, who later engaged in the practice of law in Syracuse, New York.

From Professor Farnam, who was good enough to write down his recollections of the trip for the authors in 1931, we learn that the students, before starting, "received full instructions from Marsh regarding . . . outfit, etc. We were told to buy a copy of and carefully read a book called 'The prairie traveler.' This gave complete instructions for crossing the plains, telling how to make backfires in case of a prairie fire, how to camp, how to place the wagons as a protection against the Indians, how to make temporary boats for crossing rivers, etc. We were required to carry a Sharp's carbine, 50 caliber, as then used by the Cavalry, a Smith and Wesson's 36 caliber six shooter, and a large hunting knife. We also had to have waterproof match boxes of a special type."

This party outfitted, as did that of 1870, at Fort McPherson, whence they set out for the Niobrara country with two companies of the Third Cavalry under Capt. (later Brigadier

General) Anson T. Mills, with Lieuts. Frederick Schwatka and
Albert D. King as aides; and with a supporting column of the
Eighth Cavalry under Col. J. H. Gregg, bringing the total to
about 150 men and 200 horses.[12] The guides were Ed Lane and
Hank Clifford, the latter destined to become one of Marsh's
most successful collectors, the former distinguished by his habit
of beginning the day with a long volley of profanity when he
crawled out of his tent in the morning, "doubtless to put his
mind in tune for the work before him."

Says Prudden in a letter to the New York *Tribune:*

"We then struck directly north-west into the sand hills,
and with our last look at the railroad and the North Platte
[June 14], we bade goodbye to civilization for a month's hot,
desert march. . . . We were nine days in reaching the Niobrara, and every day taxed men and animals to the utmost.
The country is made up of great sand ranges trending northwest and south-east, some of them hundreds of feet high, and
only very scantily clad in spots with dry grass, scarcely sufficient to keep the sand from drifting with every wind. In other
parts it is broken up into high knolls, basins, and sharp ridges,
like great waves in a chopping sea. . . . Not a tree or shrub
to break the smooth brown curve of the hills, or afford the least
protection from the hottest of July suns. Nearly every day of
our outward march the thermometer indicated from 98 to 104
degrees in the shade, where that could be procured from a
blanket or pony. The swamps and streams afforded along their
banks a verdure which was most refreshing in comparison with
the hills. But great musketoes lurked in myriads among the
long grass, and at the slightest movement came forth to their
work of torture. . . .

"It was with extreme joy that we rode down to the banks of
the Niobrara, which we reached near the mouth of Antelope
Creek [June 27], not only because we were to go no further
into the wilderness, but because here, for the first time, nature
left her dull platitudes of sand, and gave us some really fine
river scenery; and here were trees, the blessing of whose shade

12. Another account of this trip, recorded in the diary of Dr. Thomas G.
Maghee, "contract doctor" detached from Omaha Barracks to accompany the
expedition, appears under the editorship of Charles L. Lindsey in the *Nebraska
History Magazine,* Vol. XII (July-September, 1929 [July, 1931]), No. 3, pp.
252–263.

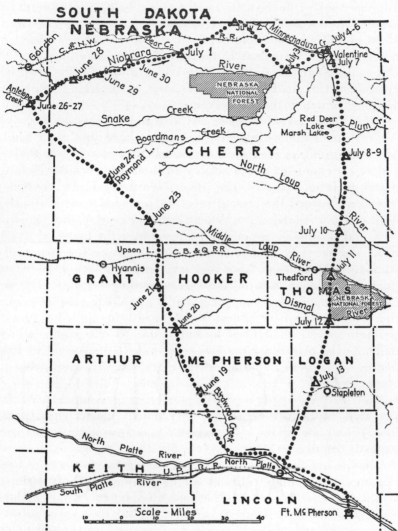

Fig. 6. Route of the Expedition of 1873. Reproduced, by permission of the Nebraska State Historical Society, from *Nebraska History Magazine,* July-September, 1929.

we had never realized before. The Niobrara is a broad winding river which has channeled deeply through the white rocks, and in some parts the bed has widened so as to form beautiful wooded parks at the bottom of the cañon, often from three to five hundred feet deep. . . .

"We spent twelve days of hard work on the river, and on the 7th of July turned back for the homeward march. The weather up to this time had been very hot, and we had but little rain. On our return march, however, we were blessed with cloudy weather, and a few of those little prairie episodes known as hail-storms. I know of nothing in nature more absolutely fiendish than great jagged hail-stones, when they come pounding out of the clouds on men's heads and shoulders, unprotected by roofs or trees. Saddles, tin basins, blankets, pails, anything which can afford the least protection, are madly snatched and held over the heads. . . . When the hail was over, and bruised, wet, and disgusted, we crawled from under the heaps of draggled canvas which had once been tents, and realized that our animals were gone we knew not whither, and that we were on foot in the desert, our dismay was beyond description. Thanks to the promptitude and efficiency of Capt. Mills, and the shelter which a near cañon afforded, our animals were finally brought back. . . . The enormous size of the stones which fell may be inferred from the fact that 16 hours afterwards lumps of ice were found among the grass nearly two inches in diameter."

The second trip started from Fort Bridger on July 25 for ten days' work in the Eocene formations from which Yale already had an abundant harvest. The Indians of the area (mostly Shoshones) were so friendly that only a small escort was needed. The first locality for collecting was Grizzly Buttes, a range of badlands running for many miles along the north slope of the Uintas, and the second was Henry's Fork, twenty miles away, both destined to become familiar names in Peabody Museum records. The trip was highly productive, adding in considerable amount to the total of five tons of material collected by the expedition. Among its prizes were a perfect *Dinoceras* skull, and many good horse skulls.

For some reason not stated, the next trip, from Fort Bridger to Salt Lake City, presented hardships that were "exceptionally severe," but these were soon forgotten in the welcome offered the Professor and his party by the disciples of Brigham Young, which seemed to be even more marked than in former years. This unusual cordiality was explained only when Professor Marsh called by special appointment on Brigham Young and found assembled to meet him the prominent members of the Mormon church. To quote further from a contemporary press report:

"After the conversation opened, Brigham Young bent his inquiries especially to the subject of fossil horses. . . . He made it a point to ascertain minutely where fossil remains of the horse family were found; he asked particularly as to the facts developed respecting this peculiar group. . . . When at length his curiosity on all these points was satisfied, Brigham Young explained its cause. Some years ago, during a public discussion in London, the point was raised against the authority of the Book of Mormon as a revelation, that it spoke of horses as existing in America in the prehistoric era in which it describes certain events. It is well known that there were no horses in this country at the time of its discovery, and that the Spaniards were the first to introduce these animals. So it seems that while most theologians are regarding the developments of the natural sciences with fear and trembling, the chiefs of the Mormon religion are prepared to hail the discoveries of palaeontology as an aid in establishing their peculiar beliefs. . . . And thus Prof. Marsh, one of the warmest advocates of the development theory, is raised to the rank of a defender of the faith." [13]

At Salt Lake City the party divided, part of them going to the John Day Basin over the stage route followed by the Expedition of 1871. After several weeks' collecting here, they went on down the Columbia River to Portland and thence to San Francisco by steamer, reaching it on October 8, after narrowly escaping shipwreck on the voyage. Coming back from California they made a brief stop in Kansas before pushing on to New Haven. The summer's yield of fossils filled 49 boxes.

This Expedition of 1873 was the last on which student assistants were used, changed conditions making this type of personnel inadvisable. It must be written down, however, that the foundation of Yale's great collection of fossil vertebrates was

13. New York *Tribune*, November 17, 1873. Probably also by Prudden.

laid by these four student parties, and that Yale and the world of science in general owe a very great debt to the men who made them possible, both by the money they contributed and by the long hours they spent in the saddle, blistered by heat, pelted by hail, plagued by mosquitoes, or at the backbreaking labor of excavating fossil bones in the midst of a country where game beckoned on every hand.

CHAPTER VI

THE EXPEDITION OF 1874 AND ITS RED CLOUD SEQUEL[1]

"I like a master standing firm on legs of iron."

EMERSON.

NOT only was the Expedition of 1874 different in character from those that preceded it, but it was to bring Marsh into national prominence in another rôle than that of "Big Bone Chief," as well as to make his courage and resourcefulness almost legendary.

It had not been Marsh's intention to take a party into the field in the summer of 1874, because a beginning had been made in the construction of the Peabody Museum and he was needed in New Haven for consultation. He did, however, have at least twelve parties of "bone diggers" at work for him in the West under various financial arrangements and under his constant instructions. In June, word came to him from Col. T. H. Stanton at Cheyenne, telling of the discovery of a most promising fossil region in the Big Badlands south of the Black Hills, near the Red Cloud and Spotted Tail Indian agencies, and suggesting that he come out and join a party soon to start for that part of the country. He declined the invitation, and asked that a collection be made for him from the new field. In October, however, when a further invitation from Colonel Stanton, seconded by General Ord, proposed a trip into the Dakota country, he wired his acceptance.

Anticipating special hardship and danger on this trip, both

1. The reconstruction of this old story has been possible in large part because of Professor Marsh's ingrained habit of collecting. The Yale Peabody Museum has at least three good-sized scrapbooks filled with newspaper clippings bearing on the Red Cloud controversy, and a small wooden box containing copies of many of the documents concerning it. There are also many letters, not only from his friends and acquaintances, but from strangers who were interested in the Indian cause. Because the interest of these records is historical rather than scientific, they are to be transferred to the Sterling Memorial Library of Yale University.

because of the lateness of the season and because of Indian unrest, he took no party with him from New Haven, but planned to rely on frontiersmen who had formerly been in his employ, among them Hank Clifford, his head guide on the Niobrara trip the preceding year. When he reached the Red Cloud Agency early in November, he proceeded to assemble men and materials for his party, his military escort being M Company of the Second Cavalry, under command of Capt. John Mix. General L. P. Bradley, Colonel Stanton, and Lieutenant Hay came from Laramie to join the expedition, and other members of it were Lieut. W. L. Carpenter and Maj. A. S. Burt.

The time was a particularly parlous one for a trip into that particular Indian country. By the treaty signed in 1868, following Red Cloud's War, all of what is now South Dakota west of the Missouri had become a "permanent reservation" for the Sioux. The region north of the North Platte and east of the summit of the Big Horns was to be considered "unceded Indian territory," and as no northern limit was set to this tract, the Sioux held that their land extended to the Yellowstone. On this land, so loosely delimited, no white man was to be permitted to settle, or even to pass through without consent of the Indians. The main object of the treaty, of course, was to keep the Indians away from the proposed line of the railroads and bring them into reservations, where they were to be fed by the Government.

After the signing of the treaty, Red Cloud, in accordance with its terms, sought to lead his people into the new reservations, but those who had followed the great Sioux warrior, when he fought, now gave less heed to his voice; many of them chose to remain unreconstructed patriots and, under the leadership of Sitting Bull, Gall, and Crazy Horse, to range free in the country drained by the Powder and the Bighorn and other tributaries of the Yellowstone. As a result, four months after the treaty was proclaimed, General Sherman issued an order that all Indians who were not on their reservations were to be regarded as hostiles.

In 1871, the already restless Sioux learned that the land they considered theirs was not to be kept free of whites, as had been agreed, but that a railroad—the Northern Pacific—was to be driven through the heart of it. The Government sent emissaries to the hostiles to try to persuade them to allow the railroad to cross their territory, but the Sioux were unanimous in their refusal. Their reply was reported by the commission, but with the comment that the Indians would hardly be able to offer "combined resistance" to the railroad construction, because they had "neither ammunition or subsistence to undertake a general war." This opinion was evidently justified, for a surveying expedition, under military escort, built a base camp on the south bank of the Yellowstone eight miles above the mouth of Glendive Creek, and ran a survey successfully from the north bank of the river at this point to Pompey's Pillar, without any Indian trouble, save for two skirmishes. But if there was no "general war" with the savages, there continued to be trouble in plenty among the whites themselves, as the War Department, faced with the practical necessity of keeping the Indians in check, came into conflict with the determination of the Indian Bureau to treat the nation's wards with kindness and conciliation. Finally, General Sheridan, sensing the direction from which trouble was likely to develop, urged that a large fort be built near the base of the Black Hills.

Why the Black Hills? Because out of this almost legendary region, known to none but a few intrepid explorers, the winds had for some years been bringing the magic whisper, "Gold!" But here was no "unceded land"; here was land "set apart for the absolute and undisturbed use and occupation of the Indians." Well, what matter? What need have savages for gold? Sheridan's demand for a fort near the Black Hills fell on responsive ears, and in the summer of 1874 an exploring expedition, headed by General Custer, was ordered to proceed into the area.[2]

Custer the bright haired, already known as one of the most ruthless of Indian fighters, was accompanied on this expedition by a force of about 1,000 men (including, as a complete innovation in western travel, a military band, mounted on white horses, which played the troops out of camp every morning!). The chief guide was Charley Reynolds, a well-known scout, and

2. For a fine account of this expedition, with reproductions of many of the pictures taken by W. H. Illingworth, its official photographer, see C. C. O'Harra, "Custer's Black Hills Expedition of 1874," *Black Hills Engineer*, Vol. XVII, No. 4, November, 1929.

on Custer's personal staff rode Lieut. Frederick Dent Grant, the President's son. The scientific staff consisted of Capt. William Ludlow as chief engineer; N. H. Winchell as geologist, and Professor A. B. Donaldson as assistant; George Bird Grinnell as naturalist, and L. H. North as assistant;[3] and Dr. J. W. Williams as chief medical officer and botanist. Two "practical miners" went along to look for gold, and a number of newspaper correspondents to spread the news, should it be found.

On August 2–3, Custer sent Scout Reynolds out from his camp near Harney Peak with dispatches containing long and vivid descriptions of the fertility of the region, and—more significant in the present connection—these words: "I have upon my table 40 to 50 small particles of pure gold . . . most of it obtained today from one panful of earth. . . . Veins of what the geologists term gold-bearing quartz crop out on almost every hillside." On August 15 another dispatch said: "Subsequent examination at numerous points confirms and strengthens the fact of the existence of gold. . . . Men without former experience in mining have discovered it at an expense of but little time or labor." Reynolds was interviewed when he reached Fort Laramie, and his statement was the first intimation to the outside world that the Custer party had found gold. William Ellery Curtis, accompanying the expedition as correspondent for the Chicago *Inter-Ocean*, had made arrangements for Reynolds to telegraph the golden tidings to his paper, and his own letters fed the general excitement, which increased until it was fanned into veritable gold fever by an interview given by Custer after his return—an interview, be it said, which contained statements about gold that were not approved by the geologists of the party.

As a result of this stir over gold in the Black Hills, the Indians at the Red Cloud Agency, which was only a short day's ride southeast of the Hills,[4] were in an ugly temper this fall

3. General Sheridan wrote Marsh about this expedition on May 15, 1874, saying that its route would pass over rich fossil country, and adding: "I do not intend to let Gen'l Custer be embarrassed by any outside people except yourself if you should desire to go, and extend to you an invitation. . . . I do not know when you will have such an opportunity." Marsh refused the invitation, but sent Grinnell and North in his stead.

4. About halfway between the present town of Crawford, Nebraska, and the military post, Fort Robinson.

of 1874, the news of Custer's expedition coming to them from the "wild Sioux" who were moving into the reservation with the onset of winter. Moreover, this influx of hostiles as cold weather came on was, as usual, causing friction with the Indian agents, since it upset their estimates of supplies needed; and this year the Red Cloud agent, Dr. J. J. Saville, had finally issued the ultimatum that rations would be withheld at Washington unless the Indians would allow themselves to be counted —something that they had hitherto steadfastly refused to permit, "as if being counted was a dreadful matter, like getting cholera or smallpox." In the meantime, Red Cloud, attempting to regain prestige by showing his people that he was a bigger man than the agent, had been complaining to the soldiers at Fort Robinson that the rations, blankets, etc., given the Indians by Saville were of poor quality, to which charges the military men probably lent a willing ear. Saville, on the other hand, had countered by writing to the Indian Bureau that the Army was interfering with his business.

It was into this general and particular love feast that Professor Marsh unwittingly stepped that morning of November 4, 1874, when he arrived at the Agency—the very day on which the council of chiefs had decided against the census demanded by Saville. It was ascertained that the fossil field which he wished to explore was not within any of the reservations, and hence that the Indians would have no right to object to his expedition. Nevertheless, to avoid trouble, Saville recommended that a guard to accompany the party should be assembled from the Indians themselves, and he brought a council of chiefs together to discuss this matter. It was at once evident that the chiefs had no faith in the idea that the Marsh party would be going into the Black Hills at the beginning of winter to look for anything of so little value as old bones; but when the Professor, speaking through an interpreter, assured them that he had no interest whatever in anything else, that he would pay for Indian services in collecting fossils, and that he would take back to Washington such complaints as they cared to make to him about their food or blankets, consent was given for him to proceed with a guard of selected young warriors.

The start of the expedition, set for the next day, was delayed by a snowfall. In the meantime, the Oglalas, hard pressed for rations, capitulated in the matter of the population count and started a census landslide, which showed that the number of Indians then present at the Agency was about 12,000. The rations issued as a result of this capitulation changed the complexion of things: with food and blankets once more in their hands, the Indians no longer needed to be on their good behavior, and the sentiment regarding the Marsh expedition once more swung to hostility. Unaware of this fact, on the second morning after the Government annuities had been issued, Marsh and his military escort came into the Agency to pick up their Indian guard. The sight of the soldiers and the wagons, actually drawn up in marching order, excited the Indians greatly, and they gathered around in great numbers, armed quite as well as the small band of soldiers, with breech-loading rifles and revolvers of the most recent pattern.[5] Red Cloud, appealed to by Professor Marsh for an explanation of the change of heart, said that his people could not be convinced that the party was not in search of gold. In this tense situation, when a single shot, or an order to advance, would probably have precipitated a massacre, there was nothing to do but direct the soldiers to go back to Fort Robinson.

After many consultations between Marsh and the officers and Saville, it was decided that the best way to win the consent of the Indians again would be to give the chiefs a feast, to which Marsh rather disgustedly consented. The feast was given in a big tent and every detail of Indian etiquette scrupulously observed. Presents to the important chiefs were distributed, the Professor made another speech, and a reluctant consent was again given. Marsh, however, had his own ideas about the good faith behind this agreement and, resolving to test it, sent word that the expedition would start next morning. Not a single Indian scout, guide, or interpreter would go!

Exasperated by these delays, Marsh made up his mind to give the Indians the slip, and gave the order to start shortly after midnight. The soldiers made their way with extreme caution through the Indian villages, which lay between the Agency and the only spot for fifteen miles where the White River could be crossed. The dogs barked furiously as they went past the

5. Acquired from the traders at the Agencies in exchange for the hides of the beef issued as Government rations!

lodges, but, contrary to the usual idea of Indian alertness, the warriors slept peacefully on and the stolen march was not discovered until daylight. Before the fossil region was reached, the party was under the surveillance of Indian sentinels, posted on the high buttes. On arrival at the desired locality, Lieutenant Carpenter chose a camp site well flanked by ravines, although the fossils were well scattered over a ten-mile circuit.

The weather was so intensely cold that no encouragement was needed to begin work at once, and soon fossils were piled up in heaps and their position marked by stones, in the event of a snowstorm. When the collecting was nearly completed, it was feared that an impending storm would halt the packing. Moreover, there was still more serious reason for apprehension in the news brought by a party of friendly Indians, who had been sent out (reputedly by Red Cloud) to warn Marsh that the hostile northern Indians were planning an attack, which might come the same night. Again Marsh was faced with a difficult decision: to throw the specimens into the wagons unpacked was simply to have them broken in pieces; to attempt to pack them at night would be folly, since no better target for a long-range shot could be asked for than a lighted tent. A second time he took the long chance, and won. Remaining one more day, to pack his treasures properly, the expedition left the region less than twenty-four hours before it was scoured by a large war party in search of the Big Bone Chief.

Daring as was the march of the 1874 Expedition, and valuable as were its scientific results, the sequel to which it led was even more dramatic and far-reaching. When Marsh returned to the Agency, highly pleased with the success of his trip, Red Cloud poured more of his story into the Professor's sympathetic ear. Marsh had seen considerable of Indian agents in his western expeditions, in all probability, and he had had many hours of talk with Army men. He questioned Red Cloud at some length, and, shocked at what he heard, he asked the latter to give him samples of the food. Red Cloud brought him coffee, beans, tobacco, and pork, all of very poor quality indeed. Also, he showed Professor Marsh the scrawny cattle in the recent beef issue. Then the Professor and the Indian Chief parted, the latter doubtless with little faith that this white man would keep his promises any better than the others with whom he had come into contact. But this was a white man of a different stripe, "standing firm on legs of iron."

When Marsh went to Washington in April, 1875, to attend the meetings of the National Academy of Sciences, he took with him most of the exhibits that Red Cloud had furnished, and on April 24 he showed them to E. P. Smith, then Commissioner for Indian Affairs, describing the circumstances under which he had obtained them. Smith conceded that the quality was bad, but thought they might have been "picked" samples. Professor Marsh then added that in his opinion Saville was not a proper man to have charge of so many Indians, to which the commissioner's reply was in partial agreement, qualified by the remark that he couldn't get a better one for $1,500 a year. Feeling that this was a rather unsatisfactory interview, Marsh next day called on President Grant, accompanied by Postmaster General Jewell (a Connecticut man), and repeated his story.

It should be said at this point that the matter of frauds in the Indian service was nothing new; they were, indeed, but one phase of the general corruption that hung over Washington like a miasma in the days of the Grant administration, as has been so brilliantly pictured by Allan Nevins in his recent book on Grant's Secretary of State, Hamilton Fish. In 1870, Jacob D. Cox, Secretary of the Interior, had fallen afoul of the spoilsmen, after gallant attempts to resist their demands in the Indian Bureau, the Patent Office, and other departments, and he had resigned. His place was taken, Nevins says, by "a dry, baldish clerical-looking man with a sly, contriving air— Columbus Delano, old-time Ohio criminal lawyer, who had gotten into Congress, and had then become head in 1869, of that tainted department, the Bureau of Internal Revenue. His appointment marked a sad step in the deliquescence of the Administration."[6]

Taking cognizance of the outcry about Indian frauds, the Forty-second Congress had instructed its Committee on Indian Affairs to proceed with an investigation. The committee in its report on March 3, 1873, "expresses its surprise and regret that the authorities controlling Indian affairs have heretofore

6. Allan Nevins, *Hamilton Fish; the Inner History of the Grant Administration* (1936), p. 467. Dodd, Mead & Company.

neither directed their own attention nor called the attention of Congress to the great and revolting waste of the patrimony of the Indians."[7] However, this attempt to mend matters was promptly nullified by a similar committee of the next Congress, who, after a long investigation, stated that they found no such evidence of fraud, circumstances which appeared suspicious being found capable of complete explanation![8]

Details of Marsh's interview with Commissioner Smith and the President in the spring of 1875 found their way into print, and the gathering storm led the Board of Indian Commissioners [9] to ask Marsh to meet them at the Fifth Avenue Hotel in New York City on April 28. In spite of the fact that no arrangements had been made for reporting the meeting, a full account of it appeared in the *Tribune* on the thirtieth. This account was written by William Wyckoff, whom Marsh had taken with him into the meeting.[10] Charged with bad faith in so doing, Marsh stated to the Commission later that he had had no reason to suppose that the meeting was to be a private one, that no objections were made at the time to Wyckoff's presence, and that the latter's report, written from memory and not from shorthand notes, was published only when no other account of the meeting was given to the papers, as was customary.

Marsh had not brought the already famous samples with him to the meeting, but at the request of the Board he went to his hotel and got them; after close inspection, the Board agreed that there was no doubt as to their inferior quality. "Something must be done to reform this business," exclaimed

7. 42d Congress, 3d Session, House Report No. 98, p. 3.
8. 43d Congress, 1st Session, House Report No. 778.
9. A board appointed by the President to have joint control with the Interior Department over expenditures for the Indian Service. It served without compensation. See further, page 160.
10. The backing that Marsh received from the *Tribune* throughout his career has an interesting bit of history behind it. When Horace Greeley died in the early 'seventies, there was a struggle for the editorship, which finally went to Whitelaw Reid, who had been in charge of the paper during Greeley's losing campaign for the presidency. One of Reid's strongest supporters, according to the *Dictionary of American Biography,* was William Walter Phelps, later Minister to Hungary and to Germany, who was not only a member of Marsh's class at Yale, but who had married the daughter of Joseph Sheffield. In addition, Isaac H. Bromley, Yale '53, well-known Connecticut journalist, was a member of the *Tribune* editorial staff from 1873 to 1883.

one of the more impulsive commissioners, "even if it is necessary to put a special agent on every barrel of flour!" "You forget," retorted one of his more cynical companions, "that he would eat up the flour on the way." This brought up the matter of the traders at the various agencies, whom Marsh was inclined to defend as a class, citing J. W. Deer at the Red Cloud Agency as "an instance of the best sort." As for the agents, he said that these posts were greatly sought after, especially among the religious denominations, and that thus men with little previous experience were called upon to handle hundreds of thousands of dollars annually, and on a very small salary. "Do you mean to say that they become dishonest?" asked a commissioner. "I do not say that," was Marsh's reply, "but I do say that the kind of men that can be hired to take their life in their hands . . . for $1,500 a year, is not the kind that should be trusted without watching them when, as at the Red Cloud Agency, they have to distribute more than $400,000 annually. They may not be dishonest, but they are likely to be lacking in the business capacity for such a trust." He contrasted the haphazard, hurried distribution of rations to the 12,000 Indians in one day, such as he had witnessed, with the orderly system in use in the Army, with its elaborate checks and counterchecks.

The *Tribune's* Bright Young Men, it must be admitted, were only too happy to have this ammunition to use against the Grant administration, of which the paper had long been a severe critic. The *Tribune*, therefore, in editorials on May 1 and again on May 3 further underlined the points brought out at the meeting, laying the matter squarely on the doorstep of the President and his Secretary of the Interior, and ending its polemic thus: "Under such circumstances the saving of Mr. Delano's character is quite out of the question."

The next move in the drama came from the Honorable W. R. Steel, member of Congress from Wyoming, who asked the Indian Commissioners for an opportunity to be heard. Appearing before them on May 4, he took issue with Marsh on practically all his statements regarding Indian rations, their methods of distribution, etc., and concluded by saying that, when he had called on the Professor and had been shown the samples, the latter admitted to him that "Red Cloud lied to him every morning for seven months." This last remark and several of the others struck fire from Marsh at once, and he replied, at some length, in letters appearing in the *Tribune* and the *Times* on May 7. Mr. Steel, in turn, favored the *Times* with a communication defending his appearance before the Indian Commissioners, on the ground that certain of Marsh's charges tended to reflect upon the business integrity of many of his constituents in Cheyenne, the community from which most of the supplies were delivered to the agencies.

This exchange of letters delighted the press of the country, and its repercussions naturally reached Cheyenne, where the *Daily News* commented on the matter editorially, with a warning to Mr. Steel that he should be sure of his facts before he undertook to defend Saville. The widespread publicity drove Secretary Delano to action, and his next move supplied what might be termed the comic relief in a strained situation, for on May 10 he wrote the following letter to Chairman Fisk of the Board of Indian Commissioners:

Department of the Interior, Washington, D. C., May 10.
Hon. Clinton B. Fisk, President Board of Indian Commissioners:

Sir: I am desirous of appointing a commission from the members of your Board, to investigate certain reports put in circulation by a Mr. Marsh, relative to the Indian service at Red Cloud agency, and I write you to request that you will consult with your Board and name to me such members of it as may be designated to make the investigation. It would be well to have the commission consist of three members. Should you be unable to designate them from your Board, will you do me the favor to recommend some other suitable persons as commissioners. I desire to have the commission named by yourself or the Board of which you are president.

Yours, etc.
[Signed] C. DELANO.

The New York *Evening Post*, in a note beneath its copy of this letter, rebuked Secretary Delano for venting his spite by so childish a trick as referring to a man of Professor Marsh's standing as "a Mr. Marsh"; the *Tribune* practically burst into flames at the insult; editorial writers and reporters had a field day; and thousands who knew little about Indian frauds, and cared less, laughed at the controversy raging over "a Mr. Marsh." [11] The *Tribune*, meantime, began calling loudly for Secretary Delano's resignation. Delano's friends stated promptly that he would not resign, and a defense of certain of his alleged irregularities came from Washington, evidently inspired by the White House.

COLUMBUS D. DISCOVERS "A MR. MARSH!"
BUT THE GREAT PROFESSOR KNOWS NOT WHAT LILLIPUTIAN IS TREADING ON HIS TOES.

Fig. 7. "A Mr. Marsh" and Secretary Delano, as seen by a cartoonist in *Frank Leslie's Illustrated Newspaper,* May 29, 1875.

While all this had been going on, the larger matter of which it was but a part was slowly proceeding on its course. By constant pressure all along the line, the Indian chiefs had been brought at least to discuss the possibility of selling the Black Hills, and a group of them started for Washington to confer with the Government about this matter. On May 18,

11. A similar incident which must have at once suggested itself to Professor Marsh was the London *Times's* reference to "a Mr. Huxley," when that eminent exponent of evolution had his celebrated tilt with Bishop Wilberforce at the Oxford meeting of the British Association for the Advancement of Science in 1860.

the Indian delegation made a formal call on Commissioner Smith at the Interior Department, Secretary Delano being in Ohio. The commissioner made them a speech of welcome, introduced them to Governor Thayer of Wyoming, told them the Great Father would see them presently, and then sent them off to see the wonders of the Patent Office. The next day they were sent for by the President, who received them pleasantly but would not let them discuss the matter for which they had come specifically to Washington, bidding them state their business to Secretary Delano and Commissioner Smith. This disappointed the Indians much, for they had confidence in neither of those two men and wanted assurance from the Great Father himself. This feeling was aggravated because they were not allowed to have their own interpreters, but had to speak through young halfbreeds selected by the agents. Also annoying, from their point of view, was the fact that they were lodged at the Tremont House instead of at the Washington House as on former visits (and where, according to reports, the proprietor had provided them with plenty of entertainment, liquid and otherwise, and did not insist on their wearing the ridiculous white man's garb).

This same day Marsh also called on the commissioner and discussed the matter of the Red Cloud rations. Newspaper reports said that he had tried to see Red Cloud and Spotted Tail, but that the chiefs had refused, saying that they had been told not to talk to any white men except in the presence of Delano and Smith. With his usual determination to keep the record straight, Marsh wrote a letter to the *Times* (published on the twenty-second), pointing out that the move for a meeting between himself and the chiefs had been made at the instigation of the latter; that they were, however, prevented by Saville from coming to see him; and that he had been permitted to call on them at their hotel only in the presence of the agent and the official interpreter.

On May 28, some of the chiefs sent word to Secretary Delano that they wanted to talk with the Great Father himself about another matter not connected with the Black Hills. The President agreed to see them at three o'clock in Secretary Delano's office, but when Red Cloud, Spotted Tail, and several other chiefs appeared at that time, neither the President nor the

Secretary was present, and they were met by Assistant Secretary Cowan, Commissioner Smith, and Professor Marsh. Red Cloud made complaint about the quality of the rations issued to his people, and then was cross-questioned by both the Government officials and by Marsh. Thus confronted with Government men, however, his replies became evasive, and he was not certain at all about several of the points on which he had been very emphatic to Professor Marsh in 1874. This failure of Red Cloud to back up his statements left Professor Marsh in a very embarrassing position, even when Red Cloud later blamed some of his evasiveness on the interpreters, whom he claimed not to have understood. Marsh stayed on in Washington, however, and attended several more of the fruitless councils, which finally resulted in a stalemate, the chiefs refusing to accept $25,000 for the cession of their hunting rights until they had gone home and consulted their people.

The next step in the story with which we are immediately concerned came from Agent Saville, who sent two letters to Commissioner Smith on June 18, one demanding an investigation of the charges against him and the other tendering his resignation. Smith forwarded these to Secretary Delano, recommending that Marsh be requested to put his formal charges in writing. He notified Marsh, on July 1, that Secretary Delano, upon nomination from the Board of Indian Commissioners, had appointed a "Committee to Investigate the Affairs at Red Cloud Agency," consisting of former Governor T. C. Fletcher of Missouri, the Honorable A. H. Bullock of Massachusetts, and the Honorable George W. Lane of New York. (The two latter declined to serve and were replaced by the Honorable B. W. Harris of Massachusetts and the Honorable C. J. Faulkner of West Virginia.)

This letter of Commissioner Smith's appeared in the newspapers before it reached Professor Marsh, as did also Mr. Smith's letter of instructions to the committee. Marsh acknowledged receipt of Smith's letter under date of July 3, and added:

I have as yet received no communication from the gentlemen named, but I will at once proceed to prepare a detailed statement, embodying the evidence on this subject, now in my possession, a copy of which I will with pleasure lay before the committee, so soon as they inform me that they have organized, and are ready to act.

He was even better than his word. Possibly his days with the Army had taught him the value of a surprise attack. Most certainly he was aware of the value of wide publicity. In any event, his next move was a bold one. On July 13 he sent to President Grant and five of his Cabinet the letter reproduced below, accompanied by a mass of printed evidence that (in digest) covered 8 full newspaper columns, and that *in extenso* occupied 36 pages of a pamphlet entitled: "A statement of affairs at Red Cloud Agency made to the President of the United States." This document was released to the press the next day, and four days later a copy of it was mailed to no fewer than 1,500 prominent persons in the country—statesmen, military officers, ministers, editors, etc. "A Mr. Marsh" had again made the headlines!

To the President of the United States:

Sir: In the two interviews I have had with you on Indian Affairs, I was impressed with your earnest desire to do justice to the Indians, and with your broad and philanthropic views on the whole Indian Question. This must be my excuse, as a private citizen, for coming again to you, to lay before you a statement of wrongs committed on the Sioux Indians, mainly under my own observation, during a recent visit to their country. My visit to this region was wholly in the interests of Science, with no intention or wish to investigate Indian affairs. The frauds I observed were brought to my notice by Red Cloud, who refused to allow my party to enter the "Bad Lands," until I had promised to submit his complaints to you, in person.

Since my last interview with you upon this subject, I have been informed by the Commissioner of Indian Affairs of the appointment of a committee to investigate affairs at the Red Cloud Agency, and invited to lay a statement of the facts before them. This I am quite ready to do whenever the committee request it. I must decline, however, to give my statement to the Interior Department alone, for the following reasons:

1st. I have no confidence whatever in the sincerity of the Secretary of the Interior or the Commissioner of Indian Affairs, when they publicly announce their wish and determination to correct the present abuses in Indian management, because I have reason to know that they have long been aware of these abuses, and have made no sincere effort to reform them. 2d. In all my intercourse with these two officials, their object has manifestly been to find out, not so much what the frauds actually were, as the extent of my information concerning them, so as to prevent, by every means in their power, all publicity or exposure of them. 3d. The evidence now in my possession reflects unfavorably on both Secretary Delano and Commissioner Smith.

For these reasons, I have thought best to lay before you, to whom, in accordance with my promise to Red Cloud, I made my first communication, the accompanying statement in detail, in full confidence that the evidence presented will meet with the consideration its importance demands.

In the Statement which accompanies this letter, I have given the results of my investigation into the affairs of Red Cloud Agency, the largest and most important in the West. These results clearly indicate both mismanagement and fraud, especially in the following particulars:

1st. The Agent, J. J. Saville, is wholly unfitted for his position, and guilty of gross frauds upon the Indians in his charge.

2d. The number of Indians at this Agency has been systematically overstated, for purposes which can only contemplate fraud.

3d. The last issue of Annuity Goods, which I witnessed, was a suspicious transaction, and, in part, at least, fraudulent.

4th. The beef cattle given to the Indians have been very inferior, owing to systematic frauds practiced by the agent and beef contractors.

5th. The pork issued to the Indians during my visit was not suitable for human food.

6th. The flour was very inferior, and the evidence of fraud in this article is conclusive.

7th. The sugar and coffee issued were not good, although better than the other supplies.

8th. The tobacco observed was rotten, and of little or no use to the Indians.

9th. In consequence of fraud and mismanagement, the Indians suffered greatly during the past winter for want of food and clothing.

10th. The contract for freight from Cheyenne to Red Cloud Agency was fraudulent, as the true distance is 145 miles, while the contractor was paid for 212 miles. . . .

The statement I have prepared is supported in all its essential parts by the testimony of officers of the Army, who were with me on my expedition, or at the Red Cloud Agency. Among these officers are several personally known to you, and all are gentlemen of high character. Should any part of my statement be seriously questioned, I trust you will allow these gentlemen to be heard. If the commanding officers of all posts near Indian agencies, or other equally trustworthy and disinterested observers there, could likewise testify, I think it would be found that I have but faintly indicated the corruption pervading Indian affairs.

I have purposely confined myself in this statement to a single agency, and mainly to the time of my visit, without reference to much other testimony, which has come to me incidentally in the prosecution of my inquiries, showing frauds of equal magnitude at other points. This corruption, which is a constant source of discontent and hostility among the Indians themselves, is, in my judgment, a natural result of the present loose and irresponsible system of furnishing the Indians with goods and supplies, a system that tends directly to invite fraud. I do not believe that anything but a radical change in this respect will prevent the continued demoralization of the Indian service. You alone have the will and the power to destroy that combination of bad men, known as the Indian Ring, who are debasing this service and thwarting the efforts of all who endeavor to bring to a full consummation your noble policy of peace.

> Very respectfully,
> Your obedient servant,
> O. C. MARSH.

Yale College, July 10th, 1875.

The storm of censure that followed the publication of the Marsh charges drove the Administration back on that good old line of defense, abuse of the enemy. The criticism of Marsh now took a personal turn, accusing him (1) of raising all this fuss to get notoriety and turn an honest penny by writing long articles for the *Tribune;* (2) of being the catspaw of the

Tribune, whose editor, Whitelaw Reid, had a personal grudge of long standing against Secretary Delano; (3) of being bribed to submit the complaints of Red Cloud; (4) of being "impetuous but not very practical—a nervous, impulsive, credulous man, naturally combative"; and (5) of holding "sculking [sic] interviews" with the Indians while they were in Washington. In answer to charges by the Albany *Journal* that he had been guilty of "a violation of common decorum in presenting his charges in this irresponsible way, instead of presenting them directly to the President," Marsh stated that the document was finished on July 10 and that he had intended to take it to the President that same day. Learning, however, that the latter was in Cape May, he waited until the thirteenth and then started to deliver it. Upon arriving in New York, he was unable to ascertain whether or not the President had come back to the summer White House at Long Branch, and so had mailed the letter in time to reach that place the same afternoon. Copies of it were given "to the only two newspapers who asked for it," the *Tribune* and the *Evening Post,* on the afternoon of the thirteenth, and printed by them on the next day. On the fourteenth, hearing that the President was again at Long Branch, Marsh called on Mr. Grant there and explained his statement more fully.

Perhaps best representing at least an attempt at a judicial view of the situation is an editorial in Henry Ward Beecher's *Christian Union* for July, 1875, not improbably written by the great preacher himself. It says in part:

THE PROFESSOR AND THE SECRETARY

It is ingeniously insinuated that Secretary Delano's contemptuous use of the indefinite article in referring to "a Mr. Marsh" as the author of certain charges against the Indian Ring may have affected the equanimity of that gentleman, and influenced him to deliver his latest and most telling blow against prevailing abuses; but that it is a telling blow there is ample evidence. There is something fascinating to the average intellect in the way in which this climax has been reached. The Professor with his party of retainers and a small cavalry escort, trying to penetrate the remotest wilds of our territory, and caring little for the red man unless he might chance to be found in a fossil state; the encounter

with the unwilling and unscientific savages in a state of activity
not in the least suggestive of fossils; the tedious "talk" about
the council fire; the final conviction of the Professor that in order
to get at his beloved hipparions and pterodactyles he must covenant
with the legitimate owners thereof; then the circumlocutions and
evasions of the Washington officials, and finally the formal appeal
to the President—all these combine to make a passage of departmental history that shall be a warning to future Secretaries of
the Interior and Indian Commissioners.

That he should have become the champion of the unpleasant
Indian of the Period, and, as it were, be providentially forced to
take up the cudgels on his behalf, was probably as far from the
Professor's mind six months ago as it was when he used to pull
a sturdy waist oar in the *Nautilus,* a generation ago. Even in
those days he was pottering about New Haven harbor at low
tide, hunting the fugacious crab, making long vacation trips to
rich geological regions, and in a hundred ways developing those
tastes and qualities which have enabled him so successfully to
pursue his favorite science in the face of dangers and difficulties
which would have discouraged many a man engaged in a more
widely appreciated cause.

The indirect benefits which mankind may derive from investigation have always afforded the votaries of science their most telling
arguments. . . . It were perhaps a somewhat circuitous course
of reasoning which should trace the reform of the Indian Bureau
back to the immature interest of a college boy in trilobites, or
more remotely still to those prehistoric crustaceans themselves,
but it cannot be altogether denied that this departmental hornet's
nest would not have been stirred up had it not been for the fossil
deposits of the Great Plains.

Very shocking is it to the properly constituted official mind to
have things done irregularly. The papers in the case, with the
specimen rations, ought to have been left with the Secretary,
who would have sent them to a clerk, who would have endorsed
them, "Marsh, O. C.—Makes statement, etc., etc." and there
would have been rulings with red ink and references to letter-
book No. 10,375, Series X, and at last tying up with red-tape and
final consignment to the pigeon-hole, whence no document returns;
but Providence had ordered otherwise. It had decreed that the
Professor, with tantalizing visions of many-toed fossil horses before

his spectacles, should be compelled, *nolens volens*, to hobnob with a pack of grumbling savages until an unwilling promise was extorted from him to bear dispatches to the Great Father in person. So he had a distinct pledge to keep and he was not a man to let himself off with a mere perfunctory performance of his word. He went to the Secretary, but he went to the President too, and finding the last more approachable than the first, he kept it up. . . .

Commissioner Smith has taken direct issue with Professor Marsh, meeting some of his statements with explicit denials, and promising prompt and thorough investigation. We have strong confidence in Mr. Smith's personal integrity, and we shall certainly not be in haste to pronounce against him. But it must be said that there are several weighty reasons for scrutinizing very closely the course of his Department. In the first place, the disclosures of the past two or three years have revealed an amount of corruption in the civil service which fully justifies a vigilant and even suspicious attitude on the part of the public. The existence of a strong and mischievous "Indian Ring" is a fact already established to a moral certainty. In the present case, Professor Marsh has all the qualifications of a first-class witness: unimpeachable character; uncommon intelligence, the absence of any personal motive—the whole business being a distraction from the professional pursuits to which he is devoted—and excellent opportunities for personal observation. Besides, he brings forward witnesses entitled to peculiar credit, in the army officers who corroborated his statements. These gentlemen belong to a class little given to criticism of governmental proceedings, and whose words always carry weight. On the other hand, Mr. Smith is entitled to the strongest presumption of personal integrity, by the record of his honorable and useful life; and we are the most disposed in his favor because he has previously been the object of attacks which we considered alike malicious and unfounded. Yet such specific and weighty evidence as Mr. Marsh has brought forward cannot be offset merely by the good character of the Commissioner, nor even by his personal assurances that everything is right. We have had abundant experience of honest officials whose subordinates used their chiefs' honesty as a figure-head to hide their own knavery. The public will watch most closely the action of the Indian Department; and we believe that no "vindication" which does not include a vigorous rooting-out of abuses will be accepted.

With the publication of the Marsh charges, and their implication that Secretary Delano and Commissioner Smith were at least cognizant of the frauds in the Indian Service, Secretary Delano recommended to the President that three additional members of White House selection be added to the Red Cloud investigation committee. The President chose Senator Morrill of Maine, Senator Howe of Wisconsin, and the Honorable Wayne McVeagh of Pennsylvania. Senator Morrill and Mr. McVeagh also declined to serve, and the place of one of them was taken by Professor George M. Atherton of Rutgers College. Senator Howe was present during only a small part of the investigation, had no hand in preparing the report of it, and his name does not appear among the signers. The committee began its investigations in July, summoning Professor Marsh before it in New York on July 21. It then transferred its labors to the West, arriving at Omaha on July 26, where it interviewed several witnesses.[12] Needless to say, it was accompanied by a special correspondent of the *Tribune*, probably *not* Mr. Wyckoff!

From Omaha the committee went to Cheyenne, which was a center for Indian contracts and the home of many members of the Indian Ring; this made it difficult to get accurate testimony, and the *Tribune* writer reports his hotel proprietor as saying that "there will be more lying in this town while your commission is here than there has been since it was settled." From Cheyenne the committee went to Fort Laramie, and after questioning Army officers there, traveled on to the Red Cloud and Spotted Tail Agencies. The Army men kept Marsh informed of its progress, Colonel Stanton writing him under dates of August 12 and 20:

12. A letter to Marsh from a Washington correspondent says that the committee was preceded westward by a "secret agent," dispatched by Secretary Delano to see that things were in order for the investigation. At the committee's request, Marsh had supplied it with a long list of witnesses to be interviewed. It must be noted, however, that it had no legal power to compel witnesses to appear before it, or to receive testimony given under oath; such an investigation could be conducted only by Congress.

We met them [the committee] on our way down from Red Cloud, being convoyed by Mr. Saville and Mr. Bosler, the beef contractor, and thought it a little singular that the court and prisoners should be such good company. . . . Look out for a first-class white-wash. . . . There are only two members of the Committee who desire to get at the bottom of things. These are Senator Howe, and Prof. Atherton.

Back on the home front, Professor Marsh received strong support early in August from an unexpected source. He had already been in receipt of letters from Mr. William Welsh, one of the great merchants of Philadelphia, who had long been concerned with Indian affairs—had been, in fact, chairman of a committee of citizens who went to President Grant twenty days after his inauguration and suggested that an unpaid commission for Indian affairs should be appointed, in order to reform the "flagrant abuses" in the Indian Bureau, which they attributed to pressure for political patronage. The President listened to their suggestion and appointed such a board, of which Mr. Welsh was chairman, but they had found their efforts to clean up the Ring so thwarted on every hand that they resigned in a body in 1874. Mr. Welsh, therefore, was greatly interested in Marsh's attempt to succeed where his committee had failed; and, although reluctant to become involved in the affair, he wrote Marsh that he probably would not be able to stay out if the pressure became too strong. His entrance into the fray was precipitated by the attempt of one of the then Board of Indian Commissioners to drag a red herring across the already odoriferous trail. A letter from "Charity," appearing in the Providence *Journal*, the Washington *Chronicle*, the Philadelphia *Bulletin*, and the Chicago *Inter-Ocean* (but rejected, according to Mr. Welsh, by the Associated Press), referred to the *Tribune's* "deadly war" on the Interior Department and Secretary Delano, and intimated that one of its sources of information was a discharged Government clerk ("discharged for the best of reasons") in its employ. The man so described was Mr. Samuel Walker, confidential clerk of the first Indian Board, who had, in its service, revealed so many Indian frauds that he became "dangerous," was found guilty of "intoxication," and was removed from his subsequent

OUR INDIAN POLICY

Fig. 8. Cartoon from *Frank Leslie's Illustrated Newspaper* for September 18, 1875, during the Red Cloud investigation. The caption read: "Indian Agent— 'Here, my red brothers, is a case of rifles . . . Also, fifty sides of beef and two thousand blankets. The amount seems small, compared with the invoice, but, remember, 'tis a day of small things. All this is the gift of your Great White Father, Ulysses, and of Columbus, his profit!'"

position in the Treasury Department. This mention of Walker was a most unfortunate move. Mr. Welsh, now that the battle had begun to infringe on his own terrain, sent to Marsh (and the press) the first of a series of long letters telling of his own experiences with the Indian Ring. He also sent an open letter to the President on August 11, stating that he had in his possession letters that would prove Marsh's statements with regard to Delano and the Interior Department; and he followed this letter with four others, addressed to Professor Marsh, and appearing at intervals up to September 18. His action started a veritable flood of open letters, and of course brought down a shower of abuse on him which included such choice epithets as "blackmailer" and "slaveholder." As the Springfield *Republican* remarked: "The Indian literature is become absolutely oppressive and not all of it is in the choice style of New Haven professors."

In addition to the heavy artillery brought up by Mr. Welsh, the maligned Mr. Walker came rushing to the attack with a battery of machine guns. His letters to Marsh leave no doubt that he was enjoying himself highly, and his peppery notes to the press showed that he had plenty of ammunition in reserve. Living in Washington, with friends in many a Government bureau, and with a knowledge of exactly where to lay his hands on reports that had been filed and when to shout aloud about reports that should have been in the files and were not, Mr. Walker was as busy as the proverbial bee.

That Marsh himself was finding it difficult to keep quiet under the barrage directed against him from Washington goes without saying, but it is evident that he listened to the advice of his friends and held himself in check. One of these friends, Isaac H. Bromley, then on the editorial board of the *Tribune*, wrote him on August 23, 1875:

My Dear Marsh—

I received your telegram from Newport. . . . My first advice holds good. *Keep still.* The very best people understand your position now precisely—that you have discharged your duty thoroughly and conscientiously and that it is no longer your fight. You can't improve it by rushing into print to answer Saville, Smith, Delano or any of that crowd. Consider the matter calmly a moment and you will see that these fellows are in a death struggle and are spattering everybody who has attacked them. Public attention is directed not to the men whom they spatter but to their own squirming. Don't interrupt the death rattle, but "stand still and see the salvation of the Lord."

Of course Saville lies. What else could you expect him to do? But it has been a very pretty fight and you have all the credit of making it. And all you have to do now is to keep perfectly quiet and let 'em wriggle. . . . The whole gang of them are doing now the very worst things they can for themselves and the best for the country. Let them keep at it. Cultivate patience, and don't be disturbed at being lied about. Everybody who is anybody or does anything has to have that experience. . . .

Yrs truly,
[Signed] Isaac H. Bromley.

The investigating committee, returning to Washington, listened on September 9 to a long statement from Professor Marsh, in which he dealt in detail with "falsehoods" appearing during the summer in documents that he claimed were prepared and circulated by the Interior Department. This statement appeared duly in the *Tribune*.

The following morning Delano chose to breakfast at Wormley's, where Marsh regularly stopped, and an exchange of good mornings between the two was followed by other, less courteous sentiments, the majority of which proceeded from one man or the other, depending upon which paper was reporting the incident. One account says that, during the Secretary's onslaught, Marsh sat calmly at his table with pencil and paper, taking notes of it. "Exhibit A" in proof of this is a small orange-colored envelope (enclosed in a large one marked "Mr. Delano's attack, Sept. 10th"), which, evidently hastily pulled from the professor's pocket that morning, bears the penciled notes that he scribbled about the encounter. Unfortunately—shall we say?—the only witness to the altercation, aside from the waiters, was Secretary Delano's son, who was breakfasting with him that morning.

This attack by the Secretary in person, however, was a small affair in comparison with the floods of vilification that Administration papers, notably the Washington *National*

Republican, poured out upon Professor Marsh, reflecting not only upon his sincerity of purpose in bringing the Red Cloud charges, but upon the manner in which he obtained some of his evidence, and finally, upon his personal character. Again the Springfield *Republican's* comment is succinct:

A whole day has passed without bringing us any of those familiar vindicatory proof slips from the Interior Dept. Society for the Propagation of Useful Knowledge about Prof. Marsh, Mr. William Welsh, and the other depraved members of the Christian religion who have said things about Messrs. Delano and Smith. What has happened?

Before the committee could prepare its report, and while the press was openly prophesying that the report would white-wash the Indian Ring, basing its surmise on the manner in which Professor Marsh had been "investigated" rather than the Ring, the President made public his acceptance of Secretary Delano's resignation. When the committee report was released to the press, on October 18, it followed the lines already foreshadowed. Signed by Professor Atherton, the long unanimous report, covering 929 pages, dealt in detail with the charges brought by Marsh, acknowledged that certain irregularities had existed, but stated the committee's belief that Secretary Delano and Commissioner Smith were not implicated in them. It recommended, however, that Saville be removed and that several of the contractors be excluded from further Indian business; and suggested a number of changes in Indian administration. The opinion of the country about the report may be gathered from the following excerpts:

The Boston *Transcript* of October 19 said, in part:

THE INTERIOR DEPARTMENT

Professor Marsh let daylight into a section of this department. The President's commission has illuminated another portion of the same. Whatever delinquencies are unearthed by the commission should be passed to the credit of the professor. It was his trenchant criticism which forced the Government into an investigating mood. It was his persistent accusations of cheating that compelled the national authorities to uncover fraudulent practices—deeds whereby contractors constantly enriched themselves, while the aboriginal people, with whom the contractors dealt, were just as continually swindled. There would have been no inquiry if the professor had not entered the lists. He is really the author of the commission, the result of whose scrutiny is made known today. The public will commend the document issued by it while laughing at the studied efforts to screen the principal officers inculpated by the vigorous Yale professor. It is apparent that the commissioners believe in contractors obtaining "living" profits. On the beef contract, amounting to $700,000, the net sum accruing to the individual obtaining the opportunity of supplying the article was $117,000, which is pronounced perfectly "fair and legitimate" gain by the representatives of the Government. In these times of cutting down prices the amount has a somewhat overgrown look. . . . Professor Marsh's allegations that the secretary was aware of abuses without endeavoring to reform them are declared to be unsustained by the facts. But it is noteworthy how hard the commissioners are upon some unfortunate subordinates intrusted with furnishing Indian supplies. . . . The tenor of this report of the commission appointed by the President shows what a great public service Professor Marsh performed when he held up to general condemnation the manner in which the Indians are treated by the agents of the General Government.

Under the heading, "The Red-Cloud Report," the *Nation* had this to say on October 28:

The report itself is fair enough. The Commissioners seem to have gone to work in a painstaking manner to sift to the bottom all accusations against Indian officials, and they have sifted them, and have thrown a good deal of light upon Indian affairs. Considering the extra-legal character of the enquiry, and the fact that instead of a prosecuting officer with an able staff of assistants to get at the truth, with all the machinery of the criminal courts behind them, and the hope of professional distinction and public rewards to urge them on, there was only on the side of the Indians and the people of the United States a college professor doing work to which he had never been trained, and incited only by the desire to do his duty, and having against him the united forces of all the corruption, all the ignorance, and all the prejudice of the "practical men" of the Plains—the results are startling. They may be generally summed up as the removal of the head of one of the Departments at Washington, the dismissal of half a dozen subordinate officials or employes, and the probable removal of the head of the Indian office [Commissioner Smith's resignation followed that of Secretary Delano]. . . .

What, then, is the reason, in view of the externally respectable character of the report and the success of the investigation in unearthing abuses, that the report has fallen so flat and attracted so little attention? The real answer, is the very simple one that the Commission was appointed by the very men whose official conduct was to be investigated, and the instructions issued to the court thus constituted were drawn up by the accused themselves. The whole affair was such an insult to the common-sense of the public that it is difficult to write with moderation about it.[13]

It remained for Samuel Walker to write Secretary Delano's political epitaph, which appeared in the Washington *Capital* of October 9:

R. I. P.

Not a drum was heard, not a funeral note
As the corpse to Ohio was hurried;
Not an Injun discharged a farewell shot
O'er the grave where Columbus lies buried.

For a modern résumé of the Red Cloud committee's investigations in the West, the reader is referred to Chapter XIII of George E. Hyde's interesting book called *Red Cloud's Folk* (University of Oklahoma Press, 1937), which the present authors have found very useful indeed in the preparation of this account.

Red Cloud's friendship with Professor Marsh lasted for many years. Early in 1877 the chief came to Lieutenant Carpenter at Fort Robinson and asked him to transmit his peace pipe to Marsh as a gift. Carpenter's letter of January 31 read:

13. As a further sidelight on the committee, it might be added that the *Nation* on November 11, 1875, had declared that it had evidence to show that former Governor Fletcher, while serving on the committee, had been writing letters to western newspapers, under an assumed name, defending Delano. Representative Harris, furthermore, could hardly be said to have started his work on the committee without bias, as he was a member of the House Committee which had so vigorously whitewashed the conduct of Indian affairs in the 43d Congress.

I today send by express, Red Cloud's pipe and hope it will arrive all right.

Mr. Red Cloud came to my quarters and said he wanted to give it to you, and wished me to, at the same time, tell you something. This is his speech, as translated by an Interpreter. "I remember the wise chief. He came here and I asked him to tell the Great Father something. He promised to do so, and I thought he would do like all white men, and forget me when he went away. But he did not. He told the Great Father everything just as he promised he would, and I think he is the best white man I ever saw. I like him. I want you to tell him this. . . ." I showed the old fellow your photograph which he at once proceeded to pocket. . . .

In middle January, 1883, Chief Red Cloud came to New Haven on a visit, spending three days in seeing the sights of the city and meeting its prominent folk. When he reached the station, escorted by his interpreter and by Thomas A. Bostwick, Professor Marsh's assistant, who had been sent to meet him at Jersey City, he was awaited not only by the Professor but by an interested crowd of 300 or 400 other citizens. He spent the morning in the Peabody Museum and in the Yale Art Museum, but none of these wonders elicited from him more than a very faint show of interest—"not even a grunt of appreciation," according to the reporter for the New Haven *Register*. The next day, Sunday, he received nearly a hundred visitors at Professor Marsh's home. On Monday morning he faced a real ordeal—a series of eight to ten sittings for a local photographer; reporters were excluded for fear they would make the chief nervous, this being reputedly only his second experience with the camera. However, the photographer told them afterward that Red Cloud was a most docile subject, readily posing as directed. The series of photographs included the well-known one of Red Cloud and Professor Marsh with the belt of wampum passing between them. Incidentally, a painting of the chief in full regalia was one of the ornaments of Marsh's home.

Monday proved a brighter day for the chief, because it included a visit to the Winchester factory, where the sight of the rifles piled together in the assembling rooms "awakened a grim smile of pleasure." Even more delightful was a visit to City Hall, and to one of the firehouses, on special invitation of Mayor Lewis, where the hitching of the horses and the sliding of the firemen down the pole made him "laugh and drop his hands with delight." After another evening devoted to visitors, Red Cloud went back to Washington, accompanied by his erstwhile champion, Professor Marsh.

CHAPTER VII

MARSH AND HIS "BONE-DIGGERS"

IMPORTANT as were Marsh's published contributions to Vertebrate Paleontology, the science was benefited almost as much by his remarkable ability as a collector. The collections that he amassed during the last thirty years of his life, Beecher says,

form a lasting monument to his perseverance and foresight. . . . He not only had the means and the inclination, but entered every field of acquisition with the dominating ambition to obtain everything there was in it, and leave not a single scrap behind. Every avenue of approach was made use of, and cost was often a secondary consideration. The nine-tenths, when attained, were only an additional stimulus for securing the remaining one-tenth.

This preëminence of Marsh as a collector rests not only on the amount of material that he acquired, but equally on the improvements in collecting technique that he brought about. At the time when he began to collect vertebrates, the material that had been described was nearly all of a fragmentary nature, usually consisting of teeth, parts of jaws, and other isolated and broken bones, as is evident at once in the early publications. Such fragmentary material Marsh would have none of, if better could possibly be found. As John Bell Hatcher, the best of his many field men, put it, Marsh was after "the choicest plums," with the result that

Where a generation ago the extinct vertebrate life of America was but poorly represented in our museums by imperfect series of teeth and isolated bones, we are now able to study many of these extinct animals from more or less complete skeletons. For these improved conditions we are mainly indebted to the late Professor Marsh, either directly by reason of the vast collections acquired by him, or indirectly through the improved laboratory and field methods developed by him and his assistants.[1]

1. John Bell Hatcher, *"Diplodocus* (Marsh): its osteology, taxonomy, and probable habits, with a restoration of the skeleton," *Mem. Carnegie Mus.,* Vol. I, No. 4 (1901), p. 1.

Along these same lines, we have the further testimony of Jacob L. Wortman, who was in a position to observe the changes in methods, inasmuch as he was for a long time assistant to Cope and later a member of Osborn's large staff in the American Museum of Natural History. In his memorial of Marsh, he says:

The record of his discoveries . . . is one of almost continual triumph in the bringing to light of new and strange forms of life that had inhabited the western hemisphere in the distant past. . . . The methods of collecting and preparing these fossils for study and exhibition which he has introduced in the course of his long experience form the basis very largely of all similar work in almost every paleontological laboratory of the world, and it is a matter of common remark that nearly all the noted collectors and preparateurs have received their training under his immediate influence.[2]

Another matter on which Marsh held progressive views, and one which has direct connection with his insistence on the collection of good material, was the importance of type specimens, those on which species or genera are based. He recognized early in his career that such specimens are the final court for the adjusting of species and genera, and toward the end of his life he presented his matured views before the International Congress of Zoology, in a paper entitled "The value of type specimens and importance of their preservation." A type, he said, should be "a characteristic specimen, worthy of being the representative of a new group of individuals." It should be neither an immature individual, nor a very old animal, since these tend to have the essential features obscured. Its value

may depend largely upon its completeness . . . the records of Paleontology are burdened with the names of many fragmentary fossils, types of species practically unknown. . . . [In Vertebrate Paleontology] especially reform in methods is a pressing necessity. . . . I recall one collection of types of extinct vertebrates, described in a single volume, and nearly a hundred in number, the greater part of which are uncharacteristic fragments, well fitted to burden

2. Jacob L. Wortman, "Othniel Charles Marsh," *Science* (new ser.), IX (1899), 562, 565.

science for all time with a legacy of uncertainty and doubt. . . .
A type in Paleontology should consist of the remains of a single
individual, and this should stand as the original representative
of the name given. A second specimen, or even more, may be used
later to supplement the first, but not to supplant it. This sub-
stitution, however, has been made by some authors, with the natural
result of causing endless confusion in the nomenclature.[3]

In conclusion, he said:

In all branches of Natural Science, type specimens are the lights
that mark the present boundaries of knowledge. They should be,
therefore, not will-o-the-wisps, leading unwary votaries of science
astray, but fixed beacon lights to guide and encourage investigators
in their search for new truth.[4]

In regard to the loan of type specimens—a subject about
which there is still disagreement—he felt that the danger
from injury or loss in transit is so serious that it is wise not
to allow types to leave the building in which they are preserved,
and he enforced this rule in the Peabody Museum. Furthermore,
his dislike of having skeletons freed entirely from the rock,
if they lay in natural position, was well known.

In order to get the better material which he desired, Marsh
not only had to keep urging his collectors to search more
diligently, but he had to train them to get the bones out of
the rock with less breakage. The first period of collecting fossil
vertebrates might be called the *pick-rake-sack stage.* As Marsh
said in a conversation with the senior author in 1892, the usual
method in those days was to drive the pick under the bone,
pull it up, rake all the pieces together and throw them into
a sack, in the hope that the preparators at the laboratory would
be able to fit the puzzle together. Or, as Williston commented:
"Modern methods were impracticable with rifle in one hand
and pick in the other." How much better Marsh and his
collectors came to do their work may be seen from a perusal
of the plates in his monographs on the toothed birds (1880),
the Dinocerata (1885), and the dinosaurs (1896), and in his
many papers that give lifelike restorations of extinct reptiles

3. *Amer. Jour. Sci.* (4), VI (1898), 401–403.
4. *Ibid.,* p. 405.

and mammals, even though, as is well understood, these restorations have been more or less "perfected."

From 1870 to the close of 1874, Marsh was for the most part with his collectors in the field, and thus was able to demonstrate to them how fossil bones should be handled; but his paid collectors increased rapidly in numbers after that year, and so he had a set of directions printed early in 1875 and gave or sent a copy to each of his field men. These directions read:

DIRECTIONS FOR COLLECTING VERTEBRATE FOSSILS FOR YALE COLLEGE MUSEUM

1st. On leaving camp to collect, always take proper tools, and also sacks, paper, cotton and twine, so as to pack specimens where found. Otherwise they may be badly injured in getting them to camp.

2d. The best way to find fossils is to go over all the ground on foot, slowly and carefully. Haste makes waste in collecting, as the best specimens may be easily overlooked.

3d. It is of the greatest importance to keep the bones of each animal by themselves, separate from all others, and to save all the pieces, however small or weathered.

4th. Collect carefully all the loose bones and fragments, on the surface or covered with earth, before beginning to dig out the rest of a skeleton. Otherwise valuable pieces are sure to be lost.

5th. Never remove all the rock from a skull, foot, or other delicate specimen. The more valuable the fossil, the more rock should be left to protect it. Better send 100 pounds of rock, than leave a tool mark on a good specimen.

6th. When an entire foot is found, keep the bones of each toe together, and separate from the rest; then the foot can be put together again with certainty. A complete foot is often more valuable than a skull.

7th. Get all the bones of every good specimen, if it takes a week to dig them out. The absence of a single tooth or toe bone may greatly lessen the value of a skeleton.

8th. When a rare bone cannot be got out of the rock entire, it is important to measure its exact length on a piece of thick paper, and pack this, properly marked, with the pieces saved. A drawing of such a bone, however rude, may prove of value.

9th. Small specimens are often more valuable than large ones, and should always be carefully sought for, when a good locality is found. Bird bones, which are usually small, and very hollow, are among the rarest of fossils, and should be preserved with great care.

10th. Single bones, if one end is perfect, are worth saving. If freshly broken, look carefully for all the pieces. When two or three bones are found together, they should always be kept together.

11th. In packing, a skull should be rolled up in cotton, and then in one or more sacks, closely tied or sewed up. Teeth and other delicate specimens should be put in cotton, and if very fragile also in cigar-boxes, or tin cans. Every bone should be wrapped separately in paper. If broken, the ends should never be together when packed.

12th. Each skeleton, or part of a skeleton, should be put in one sack, with a label inside, and a tag outside, giving locality, formation, collector, and date. If one sack is not large enough, use two or more, properly marked, and tied together when packed in the box.

13th. Pack fossils in boxes of moderate size, and made of inch boards. Plenty of hay or straw should be put on the bottom, and closely around the sacks of fossils, so that they cannot move when the box is turned over. Always put a large label inside, just under the cover, stating number of box, contents, locality and collector. Hoop all boxes at both ends, with iron, wood, rawhide, or leather.

14th. All boxes should be numbered, and plainly directed, not on a card, but with *marking ink* on the cover, as follows:

YALE COLLEGE MUSEUM,

WITH CARE   NEW HAVEN, CONN.

15th. Send boxes as freight. Small boxes with very valuable contents should be sent by express. Keep full list of boxes sent, but always send the R.R. receipts direct by mail to

PROF. O. C. MARSH,
Yale College, New Haven, Conn.

Although many of these directions are still valid after a lapse of sixty years, it is apparent that at the time they were drawn up, the method of preserving bones in the field by bandaging, now so commonly in use, was not known. We may, therefore, digress a little here to add some facts to the history of this great improvement in collecting technique. In 1892, when the senior author was at work in the Yale Museum as preparator of fossil invertebrates, he frequently saw masses of rock and bone coming in from the field, held together by gunny sacking that had been cut in strips, saturated with plaster of Paris, wrapped over the fossils before they were lifted out of the ground, and again when they could be turned over. He saw these packages, small or large, being opened little by little by the skilful "bone-setters" with no disturbance of the much fractured contents. As each specimen was un-wrapped, thin shellac or liquid glue was poured into all the crevices, or the pieces were lifted one after another and reset in plaster of Paris, so that when dried out they were held firmly in place. Such resurrection of ancient bones and their preservation for the edification of paleontologists were fasci-nating processes to watch. Having heard that Marsh was the inventor of the bandaging technique, the writer asked him one day how this came about. Marsh replied that he got the idea from seeing medical men set broken bones in splints and hold them together with strips of cloth soaked in plaster of Paris. This may be true, but rumor has it that one of the first steps in this method was invented by Samuel W. Williston, who had studied medicine before coming into Marsh's service as a collector. In the late summer of 1877, Williston and M. P. Felch were trying to take up the nearly complete rear half of a skeleton of the dinosaur *Diplodocus* found near Cañon City, Colorado. The skeleton had been largely exposed at the surface, and the weathering processes had broken and fractured it badly, so that finally, in despair of being able to take up the bones, they threw most of them into the dump pile. This failure to collect the skeleton worried Williston, as it naturally should have, and on September 21, in a letter to Marsh, he asked: "Will it do to paste strips of strong paper on fractured bones before removing?" Five days later he added: "The bones are getting better as we get farther away from the atmosphere. . . . Those strips are put on with ordinary flour-paste and can be removed I think easily." It is pleasant to be able to relate that there is still extant in the Peabody Museum a bone protected in this way by Williston and Mudge near Garden Park, Colorado, late in 1877.

Cope and Sternberg, faced with the problem of salvaging brittle bones on their trip to Montana in 1876, solved it by boiling rice into a thick paste, dipping flour bags and burlap into it, and using them to hold the bones together.[5]

Another of Marsh's collectors, David Baldwin, working in the Eocene of New Mexico in 1876 and 1877, sent in mammalian foot bones held together by a coating of plastic gumbo. And in January, 1878—at a time when Williston was in the Museum—Baldwin sent in a jaw (*Coryphodon*) imbedded in gumbo, laid between two hollowed-out pieces of soft wood cut to fit, and then wound about with hemp—as nice a "bandage" as one could wish! This specimen was shown to the writers by Chief Preparator Fred W. Darby in the spring of 1939, so there seems to be no doubt that Baldwin was, so far as we know, the initiator of the method of bandaging fossil bones with splints, while Williston, about the same time, was beginning to use strips of strong paper with flour paste. From the latter, it would have been but a short step to strips of gunny sacking soaked in liquid plaster of Paris—an improvement that Marsh may have suggested.

Still another bit of evidence that must be taken into account comes from a letter written to Marsh in this same month of September, 1877, by Arthur Lakes, who was then taking up dinosaur bones at Morrison, Colorado. Lakes says:

I do not know whether you wish us to use plaster of paris but if it is not an obstacle in your final clearing up of the bones it would be often a great assistance to us in keeping together very fragmentary bones. The rock is so intensely hard, so destitute of good cleavage and seamed in every direction that it is next to impossible to prevent fractures and not infrequently the seam breaking right across the bone has a tendency to break it up into minute fragments. To obviate this I have occasionally laid on a strong coat of plaster of paris on the outside of the bone to preserve it whilst the rest of the rock was being jarred by the hammer.

5. Charles H. Sternberg, *Life of a Fossil Hunter* (1931), p. 88.

In any event, by 1880 this surgical device was in use by nearly all Marsh's collectors.

By 1875, it was becoming apparent to Marsh that if the wealth of material brought back to Yale by the four student expeditions of 1870 to 1873 and the Red Cloud party of 1874 was to be adequately installed in the new Museum and to be properly presented to the world of science, he himself could no longer spend from two to six months each year in the field. It might occur to a layman, of course, that his collections were already large enough so that no further field work would be necessary, at least for a time. But the word "enough" is in no paleontologist's vocabulary—so far at least as collections are concerned—and Marsh was never to have fossils "enough." Even with almost every box opened at the Museum yielding a new species, or throwing new light on an old one, he saw need for more and yet more material. In the further prosecution of western field work, he had two main purposes in view: to explore and preëmpt at once every promising new field that came to his attention; and to promote intensive collecting in certain localities (or beds) from which he needed more material to complete his knowledge of the groups of animals which he intended to monograph. To develop these two lines of field work, he turned to paid collectors, who worked under his direction. For this reason, the story of the later 'seventies is largely the story of these collectors and their discoveries.

In the beginning, Marsh employed men whom he had met in his early trips to the West, and who might be said to be of the genus *prospector:* men accustomed to frontier work and to the somewhat sporadic sort of labor involved; men who could pick up a grubstake, a horse or two, and a rifle, and set off into the fields to stay until their provisions were exhausted; men to whom the regular arrival of a pay envelope was not an essential. Typical of this group were H. C. ("Hank") Clifford, a handsome squaw man, son-in-law of Red Cloud, Sam Smith, John W. Chew, E. S. ("Ed") Lane, Sam Snook, E. Defendorf, B. D. Smith, and others.

Another type of collector employed by Marsh was the college-trained man, who had some knowledge of Geology and Paleontology, and who could be sent out to develop a locality and bring in the material that was specifically needed. Included in this group were Benjamin F. Mudge, Samuel W. Williston, Arthur Lakes, and, above all, John B. Hatcher. Both groups made important contributions to the Yale Collections.

Still a third source of fossil material for Marsh were his many friends and acquaintances at the various Army posts in the West, who not only sent him word of promising fields but often purchased material for him from local collectors. Lieut. W. L. Carpenter, mentioned in the Red Cloud chapter, was one of these. The son of a country editor in New York State, the lieutenant had come up to his commission from the ranks; he was an enthusiastic "bug-hunter" and was of help to Marsh in a number of ways. Also of great assistance to Marsh were the Carters at Fort Bridger, where Judge William A. Carter— "postmaster, post-trader, cattle owner, and capitalist generally," as Scott describes him—had come to be the presiding genius. This soft-spoken Virginian, so picturesque a figure in Wyoming's early history, wrote to Marsh at Fort D. A. Russell on August 1, 1870, acknowledging the receipt of several of the latter's articles, and offering to give him all the help possible when he came to

that portion of Wyoming Territory . . . that is so entirely free from the dread of Indians and whose silence has so seldom been broken by the foot of Science. . . . The Uinta spur of the Wasatch Range [30 miles distant] is probably the last upheaval on the American Continent. Its history is still distinctly legible, time having scarcely obliterated a single character.

There is but one other letter from Judge Carter to Marsh, referred to later, the correspondence being continued by Dr. James Van A. Carter, a relative, who acted as intermediary and banker for Marsh in his dealings with various collectors until the evacuation of the post in 1878.

The hundreds of letters from the "bone-diggers" who formed the first two of these groups give one a curious picture of the relations between Marsh and his men. At the outset, the arrangements as to wages, allowances for assistants, living expenses, etc., seem to be quite definite; but at some stage in the work there is almost sure to be a conflict over these matters, usually because the wages fail to appear when they should. The lack of system and promptness in financial matters, of which Marsh's Aunt Judith complained in his student days, seems never to have been outgrown by him. His absorption in the fascinating work of describing his new material was so great that he had no vision of an angry collector, returning to town after weeks in the field, with wages due an assistant or two and supplies for the party to be replenished, and hearing from the postmaster, "Nothing for you today." And probably nothing tomorrow, or the next day, and nothing until the collector's letters of protest finally penetrated through the scientific haze at New Haven and the necessary money was rushed off by telegraph. Not niggardliness, but carelessness, rather, was seemingly at the root of this haphazard method of carrying out Marsh's agreements with his men. Curiously, however, in spite of this propensity of his, which must have been well known in many a frontier town, he seldom lost a collector to a rival, and he could always find one ready to undertake a new task for him. For some reason, the group of western men, particularly, seemed to prefer to work for him, despite financial difficulties and despite his tendency to give them insufficient credit for their work.

Any discussion of these collectors of Marsh's must take into account the fact that their work was done at a period when the struggle between Marsh and Cope to control the field of western Vertebrate Paleontology was at its hottest. All the field men collecting for these two ambitious and wealthy paleontologists were drilled in the triple duty of (1) finding and excavating fossils; (2) preventing news of their finds from reaching Philadelphia or New Haven, as the case might be; and (3) seeing to it that rival parties had access to none of the quarries in operation. This situation is dealt with further in Chapter X.

Of the personal history of the first group of collectors, we know little. The Museum records preserve their names as the finders of many a valuable specimen, but of the manner in which it was collected we know next to nothing. They belong to the type that is seldom eloquent with the pen. One, only, of these minor collectors reaches across the years as a real personality. This was Sam Smith, "Sam Smith of the Rocky Mountains," as he occasionally subscribed himself, who collected for Marsh off and on from 1873 to 1876 and again in

PLATE XIII

COL. T. H. STANTON

JUDGE WILLIAM A. CARTER

LIEUT. W. L. CARPENTER

"SAM SMITH OF THE ROCKY
MOUNTAINS"

THREE OF THE MEN WHO HELPED MARSH ON HIS
WESTERN EXPLORATIONS AND ONE OF HIS COLLECTORS

PLATE XIV

ARTHUR LAKES

BENJAMIN F. MUDGE

S. W. WILLISTON 1876

W. H. REED 1879

FOUR OF MARSH'S MOST SUCCESSFUL COLLECTORS

1882. He was with one of the student expeditions and probably was among its brighter memories for the boys. It is to him that we are indebted for the information that Cope, Marsh's great rival, *persona non grata* at Fort Bridger, slept "in the Government hay yard [and] took his meals at Manleys—hitoned for a bone sharp." A letter from Judge Carter in 1872 expresses his chagrin that Smith, whom he had introduced to Marsh, "had hired himself to Cope and was going out with him and that he had showed him some of the fossils gathered for you." However, Marsh apparently forgave Sam and rehired him, for in 1874, when informed by Marsh that the skeleton of a Shoshone Indian sent in by him was lacking in certain important particulars, Smith replied: "Sorrow to hear that the noble red man was not complete. When I have time I will go and see what I can do for him. I was in a big hurry for I had but little time for raising the dead."

Marsh's appeal to men of this sort was doubtless his own knowledge of camp life and his prowess as a hunter and fisherman. In many instances he delighted them with the gift of a rifle, as he did Sam Smith, bringing from that worthy the comment: "I never mist a shot with my new gun yet. I can beat the man that made the gun. I will get you a grisly next Spring or bust."

Smith vanished in the late 'eighties, according to Scott, and his bones, found later, indicated that he had been murdered.

Intermediate between the group of prospector-collectors and the group with some training along scientific lines, comes the David Baldwin already mentioned. He was highly recommended to Marsh by Lieutenant Carpenter, with whom he had worked in the Eocene of New Mexico for the Wheeler Survey in 1875; Carpenter said that, when he first met Baldwin, the latter "was equipped like a Mexican with a burro, some corn meal, and a pickaxe. These were his worldly possessions." Baldwin had a little knowledge of Geology but described himself as a greenhorn at collecting bones. He began to collect for Marsh in New Mexico in May, 1876, and continued intermittently until 1880. Marsh was then concentrating on Eocene mammals and the material of that age sent in by Baldwin—34 boxes and 20 packages—did not please him; moreover, with his customary absorption in the work in hand, he failed to appre-

ciate the value of the bones (14 boxes) collected by Baldwin
from red beds supposed to be of Triassic age but later determined to be Permian. The terms under which Baldwin was to
work were evidently not clearly defined by Marsh at the start,
and a long wrangle resulted. The two finally agreed to submit
their differences to Lieutenant Carpenter. The officer censured
them both for "an absence of proper business terms," and ruled
that the amount still due Baldwin was $400 instead of the
$1,400 that the latter claimed. He had written Marsh earlier
that Baldwin "cannot help collecting for the rest of his days,"
and so it turned out. The next year Baldwin began to collect
for Cope in the same region, and he was the real discoverer of
the highly significant archaic vertebrates of the early Eocene
Torrejon and Puerco formations.

Marsh published but 1 short paper on Baldwin's Permian
material, in May, 1878, naming 3 remarkable genera (1 lost
to Cope) and 4 new species. Many years later, the Permian
part of the Baldwin collection was restudied by Williston and
described in 6 papers appearing between 1911 and 1918; it
yielded at least 10 genera of amphibians and reptiles, the
new forms being *Platyhystrix, Aspidosaurus novamexicanus,*
and *Limnoscelis paludis.* The last-named species is based on
a marvelously complete seven-foot-long individual found by
Baldwin in El Cobre Canyon, and said by Williston to be one
of the most notable reptile specimens ever obtained from the
Permian rocks of America. The box containing it had never
been unpacked by Marsh.

It would seem, therefore, as if Marsh's seeming neglect
of David Baldwin and his collections were in part compensated
for, even if the rectification came too late to benefit that
worthy collector.

Passing, now, to the group of scientifically trained men who
collected for Marsh, we come to another figure who has frequently been said to have received shabby treatment from the
Yale professor. This was the Reverend Thomas Condon, pioneer
geologist of Oregon, whose story has been interestingly told
by his daughter.[6] Condon had been the first to find fossil bones
on the John Day River—forerunners of the rich faunas that

6. Ellen Condon McCornack, *Thomas Condon, Pioneer Geologist of Oregon.*
University of Oregon Press, 1928.

were to come from this Oligocene basin, in which volcanic ash had buried thousands of skeletal remains. Told of these finds by W. P. Blake of the Smithsonian Institution and by Clarence King, then engaged on his survey of the Fortieth Parallel, Marsh had hoped to include a visit to Oregon in his 1870 itinerary. Not being able to do this, he sent Condon $100 to be used in securing specimens for him, and followed it presently with another check for an equal amount. Condon's reply stated that he had already placed considerable late Cenozoic material in the hands of Leidy at Philadelphia for description, but he sent Marsh a small lot and promised him more.

The following year Marsh and his party made the difficult stage trip from Kelton, Utah, to Canyon City, Oregon, and spent some time in the field with Condon. With Condon's consent, Marsh also made arrangements at this time to have collections gathered for him by Leander S. Davis, who had collected for Condon, and who, with Sam Snook and William S. Day, sent to the Museum during 1873 to 1877 its superb collection of John Day vertebrates.

The difficulty between Marsh and Condon, therefore, was not with regard to field work, but over Marsh's failure to return material which Condon believed he had loaned him, but which Marsh thought he had paid for. Some of the material Condon had expected would remain at Yale, but as he was hoping to build up a collection within Oregon itself, he began shortly to send Marsh only duplicate material; and in order to complete research already begun, Marsh had to pay a second visit to Condon after the field work of the 1873 Expedition was finished, to study the latter's collection with the help of Oscar Harger and a photographer.

Included in the shipment received from the 1871 Expedition's collecting in Oregon was one box of "loaned fossils from Condon's collection." Apparently this was the box that Marsh never got around to return—not, however, because he was making use of the fossils in his own work, since there was no evidence that they had ever been studied or named. They were finally returned by the senior author in 1906. It is to be hoped that Condon's daughter echoed her father's kindly forbearance when she wrote: "Professor Marsh was so buried in the avalanche of specimens that it was impossible, with all his other arduous duties, even to begin serious work on the Oregon fossils . . . so that camels and horses and other animals waited patiently for years at Yale without even learning their own names." [7]

On the score of Marsh's recognition of Condon's work, it should be said that in his description of the type of the new equine species *Anchitherium* [*Miohippus*] *anceps*, in 1874, he wrote: "The specimens on which the above description is based, were presented to the Yale College Museum by the Rev. Thomas Condon, of Oregon." [8] And again in the same paper, the description of another new species, *Protohippus* [*Parahippus*] *avus*, closes with this acknowledgment: "For the type specimen of the species, I am indebted to Rev. Thomas Condon, of Oregon, who first explored the Pliocene strata of that State." [9]

Mr. Condon, after transferring his field of activity from the ministry to education, was appointed to the chair of Natural Science in the newly established University of Oregon in 1876, under its first president, J. W. Johnson, Yale 1862. He continued to teach there until he was past eighty years of age, and probably the most distinguished of his pupils, at least in science, was Dr. Jacob L. Wortman, whose name appears a number of times in these pages.

The roster of college-trained men whom Marsh actually employed as collectors over any length of time is headed by Professor Benjamin F. Mudge, whose acquaintance he had made during his Andover days, as a result of a common enthusiasm for minerals. Mudge, a down-easter, with a bachelor's degree from Wesleyan University, was then practicing law in the city of Lynn, Massachusetts. However, he had always been interested in natural history and served as curator of the local natural history society. In 1860, he was employed as a chemist in oil refineries in Breckenridge, Kentucky, but his pronounced antislavery views led him to move to Kansas, where, becoming well known as a lecturer and teacher, he held the office of State Geologist for one year, and was then elected to the

7. *Op. cit.*, p. 153.
8. O. C. Marsh, "Notice of new equine mammals from the Tertiary formation," *Amer. Jour. Sci.* (3), VII (1874), 251.
9. *Ibid.*, p. 254.

professorship of Natural History in the Kansas Agricultural College at Manhattan.

His first letter to Marsh that is preserved relates to late Paleozoic and Cretaceous fossils, and was written from Manhattan in December, 1866, in response to one from Marsh announcing his appointment at Yale and accompanied by his paper on the Ohio burial mounds. Letters continued to pass between them, with mention of "saurian" bones and the statement that the beds containing them were in the extreme western portion of Kansas. Marsh may have had this in mind when he took the Yale expedition into that region in 1870 and the two succeeding years, and saw their labors richly rewarded by the discovery of flying and swimming reptiles and marvelous toothed birds. In the discovery of the last-named group Mudge was inadvertently concerned. The Expedition of 1872 had numbered among its trophies a fine, though headless, skeleton of the great Cretaceous diving bird, *Hesperornis regalis.* Eager for more of this rare bird material from Kansas, Marsh wrote Mudge after the return of the expedition, asking what the results of his summer's collecting had been. In response, Mudge sent to New Haven a box of fossils which he had collected in 1871, and which included, Marsh reported to him, several hollow bird bones and two "saurian" jaws. These remains Marsh described as *Ichthyornis dispar*, a small bird, and *Colonosaurus mudgei*, a reptile, respectively. However, further removal of the rock matrix from the specimens revealed a skull and more parts of the jaws, which showed conclusively that all the bones belonged to one animal, and that that animal was a *bird with teeth*—one of the most important contributions to Vertebrate Paleontology made by Marsh. Mudge's share in this discovery was briefly acknowledged in the paper describing the fossil.

Marsh visited Mudge at Manhattan in the fall of 1873, with the immediate object of inspecting a collection of Upper Carboniferous footprints that Mudge had been making at his request (they were not described until 1894); and in the course of the visit he expressed a desire to find one or more young men whom he could set to collecting fossils in western Kansas. In February, 1874, Mudge recalled this conversation to his attention, and suggested that, inasmuch as he (and other professors)

had been "summarily discharged" from the college because of
differences of opinion with the president, he might do as well
at the collecting job as a younger man. This proposal interested
Marsh, and on April 9 he agreed to pay Mudge $250 a month
for himself and two assistants, sending a check for $100 in
advance.

The party was in the field from April to November, 1874,
sending in mainly remains of marine reptiles; and that Marsh
was pleased with their results is evident from the fact that
he added $200 to the $1,500 agreed upon, and asked Mudge
to reserve his assistants for the next season. These assistants
were E. W. Guild, H. A. Brous, G. Cooper, and S. W. Williston.

Early in 1875, Cope approached Mudge with an offer to
collect for him in western Kansas, but Mudge replied that he
was engaged by Marsh. Starting in April, Mudge reported to
Marsh that he found "the Northwest part of Ellis Co. and the
N. E. of Trego the best hunting ground for fossils I have ever
seen. We have now the best mosasaurian head I think that
has ever been found west." Marsh's payments to Mudge for
the season of 1875 totaled just short of $1,800.

Valuable as were the Kansas Chalk fossils gathered in 1875,
they nevertheless were not the most important result of the year
for Marsh. The idea had evidently been developing in his mind
that he would get better material from his collectors if the field
parties included someone trained in his own methods and conversant with his immediate needs. In answer to an inquiry as
to a possible candidate for such training, Mudge wrote from
Manhattan on October 3, 1875:

In relation to an assistant "capable of making Science a study,"
I think Mr. S. W. Williston will answer your purpose. He was a
student in some of my classes for several years and has taken his
degree of A.B. He is 24 years old, and has just gone to attend
medical lectures at Chicago [he went instead to the medical college
at Iowa City]. He excels in Mathematics and the Natural Sciences.
Has not paid much attention to paleontology till the past year or
a little more, but is now quite interested in comparative anatomy.
He has said to me that he only made medicine a study, hoping to
become a professor of Natural Science. He made all the drawings
which were sent you this summer.

This recommendation from Mudge pleased Marsh and he therefore extended an invitation to Williston to come to New Haven for a time before the 1876 field season.

Samuel Wendell Williston was the son of a Boston blacksmith who took his family to Kansas when the four boys were quite young.[10] The mother, determined that her sons should not be handicapped by illiteracy as their father had been, kept them in school at every opportunity. In 1866, Wendell entered the State Agricultural College at Manhattan, where he came under the influence of Professor Mudge, his first teacher in science. It took him until 1872 to finish his college course, partly due to his restlessness and partly to his lack of funds. The independence of thought that marked his whole life was already apparent: although Professor Mudge was opposed to evolution to the day of his death, he placed in Williston's hands Lyell's book, *Antiquity of Man,* and the student, from his wider reading, embraced the theory wholeheartedly and, in fact, gave in February, 1874, what is believed to have been the first public lecture on evolution ever delivered west of the Mississippi River.

Williston finally decided to be a civil engineer, but when the hard times of 1873–74 made it impossible for him to obtain employment along that line, he turned to the study of medicine, pursuing it under the direction of the family physician. His connection with the subject to which he was to devote most of his life came about rather casually. Mudge's first assistant in the Marsh party had succumbed to fear of the Indians, and another of Mudge's students, H. A. Brous, was invited to take his place. Brous, in turn, asked Williston to go with him, and the latter did so, after meeting an engagement to play the cornet in a Fourth of July band concert. Soon after getting into the field, Williston says, he "found a good specimen of pterodactyl and became an enthusiastic lover of the sport of collecting fossils—for sport it seemed to me."

In his unpublished autobiography, Williston thus retails the manner of his arrival at Yale:

10. Much of what follows about Williston is abstracted from "Biographical memoir of Samuel Wendell Williston, 1852–1918," by Richard S. Lull, *Mem. Nat. Acad. Sci.,* XVII (1924), 113–141; and "Memorial of Samuel Wendell Williston," by Henry F. Osborn, *Bull. Geol. Soc. America,* XXX (1919), 66–76.

I promptly accepted the invitation and sold my watch and borrowed enough to take me there in March. . . . My heart was in my mouth when I knocked at the basement door of the old Treasury Building and heard the not very pleasant invitation to "come in." There was a frown on Marsh's face, accentuated by his near-sightedness, as he waited for me to state my business. No doubt he thought me a wild and woolly westerner in my military cloak, slouch hat, and cowboy boots, as I stammered my name. But he quickly made me feel more at ease. He found me quarters in a little building in the rear of Peabody Museum then approaching completion. The next day he set me at work studying bird skeletons with Owen's Comparative Anatomy as a guide. He was then deeply interested in his Odontornithes.

Williston was in New Haven for about a month, and by April, 1876, he was again in the field with Mudge, Cooper, and Brous. His letters show him to have been a voluble youth, filled with enthusiasm and ambition, determined to remember every instruction given him by Marsh and to profit thereby, and throwing himself wholeheartedly into the game of check-mating collectors engaged by Cope. That he was putting into practice what he had learned appears from one of his first letters, which reads in part:

Hill Gove, Buffalo, K.T., April 21, 1876.

. . . .

I followed your directions strictly—marking out the spot and looking over it inch by inch lying flat on the ground, and afterwards working over the wash and loose soil as thoroughly with the knife. I think we have gotten *every* fragment . . . the other fragments that you expected must be irrevocably lost in the sand stream. . . . I looked for them as if they were diamonds.

This intensive search produced immediate results, Mudge writing on April 27 that two *Hesperornis* specimens had been found, and another came to light on May 14. Supplementing Mudge's letters about this summer's field trip were the more breezy ones of Williston, who was being paid directly by Marsh. It is from Williston that we learn of another attempt on the part of Cope to persuade Mudge to collect for him in Kansas, which went so far as to place "a month's salary subject to his

order." Not being able to dislodge Mudge, Cope engaged
Charles H. Sternberg, then new at the collecting business, and
at times the two parties were working only a half-mile apart.
According to Sternberg's description of this summer's field
work, written after he had become one of the country's successful collectors, the town of Buffalo Park had

a great windmill and a well of pure water [which] made it a
mecca for us fossil-hunters after two weeks of slimy alkali water.
At this place Professor Mudge's party and my own used to meet
in peace after our fierce rivalry in the field as collectors for our
respective paleontologists.[11]

Williston's letters mention no such fraternizing, but they
show the zest with which Mudge's assistants were trying to
outwit the other party. Sternberg, he says, "has orders from
Cope to collect all vertebrates and we will take pains to leave
him plenty of fishes." (Most of the Kansas Cretaceous fishes, as
a result, were named by Cope.) By July 27 the Sternberg
party had given up the struggle and left the field.

It is already evident, from the letters of this year, how valuable Williston's few weeks of training in New Haven had been
in equipping him to find the fossils in which Marsh was at
that time most interested; i.e., small and delicate bird and
pterodactyl bones. It was, indeed, this training, plus Williston's
enthusiasm, that made it possible for Marsh to have to his
hand, when he was preparing his memoir on the toothed birds,
parts of 50 different individuals of *Hesperornis* and 77 of
Ichthyornis; and this despite the fact that bird bones, because
of their fragility, are amongst the rarest of fossils. Pterodactyl
bones, also rare, he likewise had in quantity; and of the marine
reptiles known as mosasaurs, his collection, made largely by
Williston, included partial remains of no fewer than 1,400
individuals. Both these latter groups were later to form the
subject of valuable scientific contributions by Williston himself,
but his papers were based on material that he collected after
leaving Marsh.

The superior results obtained by Williston, and the rather
strained situation of the year before, when the command of
the party was nominally in Mudge's hands and yet Williston

11. C. H. Sternberg, *Life of a Fossil Hunter* (1931), p. 34.

was paid directly by Marsh, evidently left the latter in something of a quandary about the plans for 1877. Williston had spent the winter in New Haven and was thus still better trained to handle the Kansas work. On the other hand, Mudge, if not reëngaged, would surely go to work for Cope. In an attempt to solve the problem, Marsh decided to put Williston in charge of the Kansas party, and to send Mudge to the Red River region of Texas to report on its fossil prospects. However, the latter were not at all bright, according to Mudge's report when he returned in June, and Marsh's dilemma was still on his hands when it was solved by the news of the discovery of large dinosaurs in Colorado.

To block in the background for what might be called Marsh's three-ring dinosaur circus of 1877, it may be said that not so many years ago dinosaurs were far from being the household word that they have since become. Although dinosaurs had been known to scientific men since the early part of the last century, both in Europe and in the United States, the first visualization of a dinosaur as a living beast was brought to the public in general by a motion picture based on Conan Doyle's story, "The lost world." Incorrect as the restorations were in detail, and especially in the assumed coexistence of the dinosaurs with man, they nevertheless left the impression of creatures of tremendous size, and of kinds totally unlike any now on the earth. The next major step in America's education on the subject of dinosaurs was provided by the Sinclair Oil Company's exhibit at the Century of Progress Exposition in Chicago, and by the company's subsequent use of a dinosaur for a trademark. Indeed, so dinosaur-minded have the Sinclair people become that they have provided funds which enable the American Museum to "spot" dinosaur burials from an airplane.

The statement has been made that when Professor Marsh first went West, in 1868, he saw a weathered dinosaur bone at Como, Wyoming, and this is corroborated by Mr. W. E. Carlin, as appears later in this chapter. However, Marsh was then so much interested in other things that evidently the sight did not impress him. Just who deserves credit for first discovering and bringing into public notice the huge bones that were to place the American dinosaurs very much in the scientific limelight is difficult to decide sixty years later. In any event, the gods that direct men's actions must have been in a prankish mood in the spring of 1877, when they led two Colorado schoolmasters to these great bones within a few weeks of each other and less than a hundred miles apart, suggested to one of them that he report his find to Professor Marsh, and whispered in the ear of the other that the proper person to approach would be Professor Cope!

Arthur Lakes, the first of these schoolmasters, was an English clergyman, a graduate of Queen's College, Oxford. He came to Canada shortly after leaving the university, and in the 'seventies was teaching in Jarvis Hall College (apparently a mission school) in Golden City, shortly to the west of Denver. He was deeply interested in natural history and had had some training in Geology. One day in March, 1877, as he and a friend, Capt. H. C. Beckwith, U.S.N., were hunting for fossil leaves in the hard Dakota (Cretaceous) sandstone making one of the hogbacks so characteristic of parts of Colorado and Wyoming, they came upon an enormous vertebra, lying in bas-relief upon a block of older sandstone near the town of Morrison. Feeling sure, from what he knew of fossil vertebrates in England, that this discovery was of importance, and having had some correspondence with Marsh the year previous, Lakes wrote the latter about his discovery on April 2, 1877, enclosing a rough sketch of the bones. To Marsh's offer to identify them he replied on April 20 that he wanted to find more before he decided as to their disposition; he reported, also, that he had already discovered another huge bone, apparently a femur, which measured 14 inches across near the base, indicating an animal with a length of "not less than sixty to seventy feet."

It seems astonishing that Marsh was not stirred into immediate activity by these letters, with their sketches showing plainly the size and character of the great bones. He apparently made no reply to Lakes's second letter, but, nevertheless, the latter on May 19 shipped to New Haven 10 boxes of his dinosaur bones, weighing some 1,500 pounds. They did not reach their destination until June 12, almost a month later. Before their arrival, Marsh had found time to reply to Lakes and had sent him $100. In the meantime, his procrastination, if such it was, had had an unfortunate consequence; Lakes, not having heard from Marsh, had sent some of his specimens to Cope, "for the privilege of first examination only," as he stated in his letter to Marsh on June 20. To Marsh's suggestion that he let no one know about the locality, he replied, ruefully, that the discovery had already been well written up in the newspapers.

It is not difficult to picture the lively scene that Professor Marsh's office presented the morning this letter arrived, with its revelation that Cope also knew about the huge Morrison fossils and that, indeed, some of them were in all probability on the way to him or already in his hands. One telegram went to Lakes, evidently intended to keep him from sending the bones to Cope; it was sent to Golden City instead of to Morrison and he did not receive it for several days; in any event, the bones had already gone to Philadelphia. A second telegram to Mudge in Kansas directed him to proceed at once to Morrison and to make arrangements with Lakes to secure all the rest of the bones. Mudge, reaching Morrison on June 28, wrote Marsh next day that he had been unable as yet to see Lakes, who was "camping along the 'hog-back,'" but he had acquired enough information to cause him to add, "I have a strong impression that this locality is valuable." The day following, a second message from Mudge must have set Marsh's mind partly at rest: "Satisfactory arrangements made for two months [it read]. Jones [Cope] cannot interfere." A letter of the same date shows that Mudge had engaged Lakes's services for two months at $100 a month, or $125 "if we are very successful," the arrangement to include, furthermore, "all his knowledge of the region and apparent localities." Mudge indicated, also, that the bones sent to Cope could probably be retrieved.

Lakes was inclined to welcome Mudge's arrival to take over the work of excavation and wrote Marsh that after he had "trotted out the menagerie," Mudge had seemed "exceedingly delighted and in amazement almost at what he considers the very largest bones of dinosaurians or any other saurians he has ever seen."

Once Marsh realized the importance of the discovery at Morrison, he lost no time in describing the bones that Lakes had already sent him, and the *American Journal of Science* on July 1, 1877, carried a one-page "Notice of a new and gigantic dinosaur." The great dinosaur to which these bones belong, estimated by Marsh to have had a length of 50 to 60 feet, and thus surpassing in magnitude "any land animal hitherto discovered," was fittingly named *Titanosaurus montanus*, and Lakes and Beckwith were given credit for the discovery.[12]

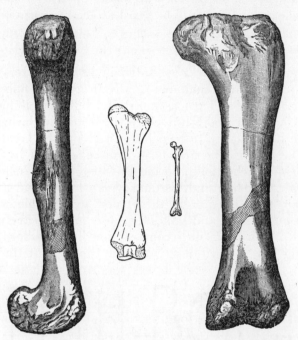

Fig. 9. Two views of the left femur of *Atlantosaurus immanis*, found by Arthur Lakes at Morrison, Colorado, in 1877 or 1878. Original slightly over 6 feet long. Between, for comparison, femur of a living elephant and a human femur, drawn to the same scale.

Marsh shortly afterward learned that the generic name *Titanosaurus* had been previously used, and replaced it in December by *Atlantosaurus*.

With a trained collector in charge, the work at Morrison went ahead more rapidly, and the richness of the find became

12. Lakes wrote Marsh on September 17 that his father, a clergyman in Cornwall, had recently attended a picnic of the British Association for the Advancement of Science at which one of the younger Lakes's letters was read, together with Marsh's article about "our Titan," and "made quite a sensation among the fossil hunters."

more apparent. Mudge saw almost at once the great difficulty in the collector's way, writing to Marsh:

The more I see of these vertebrates, the more I am impressed with the value of the "find," and equally impressed with the bad condition of most of the bones. They are badly broken—seldom do we find one whole. . . . You will be vexed at the fragmentary condition of the bones but this is . . . mostly Nature's doings and not Prof. Lakes'.

The bone-bearing rock, as stated in Lakes's letters (which were frequent and voluminous), was in part a fine-grained sandstone, almost as hard as quartzite, but above this was a layer of clay shale; both beds were tilted at a high angle, and this made it necessary to trench down along the layers which carried the bones. The first large bone excavated by Mudge, a humerus 55 inches long, 25 inches wide, and 10 inches thick at one end, took him and his quarryman a day and a half of hard labor to extricate. It threatened to crumble when removed from the rock, and Lakes therefore made a careful drawing of it to be used in its reconstruction in the laboratory—a proceeding that proved of great value throughout the collecting from these beds, since Lakes was an excellent sketcher, and worked also with water colors. By July 14, Mudge and Lakes had another 10 boxes to send, weighing 2,500 pounds, at least half the bones belonging to the skeleton of which part had been sent to Cope *(Apatosaurus)*.

Leaving Mudge and Lakes for the present busy at Morrison, we may turn to the other Colorado schoolmaster who had discovered "saurian bones." This was O. W. Lucas, superintendent of schools for Fremont County. Lucas, an amateur botanist, was roaming the hills in Garden Park near Cañon City one day (probably) in March, 1877, when he stumbled upon some fragments of fossil bones, which were large enough to excite his curiosity. He had heard of Professor Cope, and therefore sent some of the bones to him for identification, although at what date is not known; when Cope described the bones in a paper appearing August 23, 1877, he said that he had learned of their discovery "not long since." A fragmentary jaw that was included among these bones was attributed by Cope to his dinosaurian genus *Lælaps*. The vertebrae of a second specimen, he said, apparently represent a much more gigantic animal, "which exceeds in proportions any other land animal hitherto described, including the one found near Golden City by Professor Lakes." [13] Cope named his new dinosaur *Camarasaurus supremus*, the first name having reference to the cavernous structure of certain of the bones.

Before this specimen was received from Lucas, Cope had been examining the bones sent him by Lakes, and, expecting to purchase them, had "made some remarks on their character" at a meeting of the American Philosophical Society in Philadelphia on July 20; but before he had his proposed article in print, he received an order from Lakes to send the bones to Professor Marsh, as the latter had purchased them.

In the meantime, Lucas was continuing his excavations near Cañon City, and reported at least one femur five feet in length. News of these discoveries reached Marsh, and he telegraphed Mudge to go to Cañon City and look over the situation. Mudge wrote in August that the bones had already been secured by Cope, "at cost, a low sum." He commented on the fact that David Baldwin could have secured the bones for Marsh before they were sent to Cope. Reference to Baldwin's letters reveals the interesting fact that he had written Marsh, as early as February, 1877: "There are bones of large animals in the Jura near here"; and in another letter: "I had found [them] in the Jurassic in several places two or three months before Lucas . . . but I did not dig on them on account of not hearing from you that you wanted them." In April, hearing of the finding of a "bird" in the Jurassic near Cañon City, Baldwin visited the locality and, he says,

found nothing but some very large bones all reptilian I guess. In all the vertebrae I saw the centrum was biconcave. There are the bones of one tremendous big animal laying on a flat about 15 feet higher than the strata where this [the "bird"] was found. One limb joint that I saw . . . measured 20 inches across and broken off, two feet long.

Baldwin went to the Curiosity Shop in Colorado Springs to see the "bird" bones and there bought them through a friend

13. E. D. Cope, "On a gigantic saurian from the Dakota epoch of Colorado," *Paleontological Bull. No. 25* (1877), p. 10.

for $3. They were described by Marsh in September as belonging to a very small dinosaur, the size of a fox, which he named *Nanosaurus* [*Hallopus*] *victor*. Another dinosaur, only half as large, was later found near-by by Lucas and sent to Marsh, who called it *Nanosaurus agilis*. These specimens remain unique, no other remains of the two species having been discovered. They are exceedingly interesting, but, for the present narrative, the letters concerning them are more significant, as showing how easily Marsh might have preceded Cope at Cañon City also, had he paid heed to the casual remark in Baldwin's letter of February, 1877.

Mudge carefully examined the gigantic bones being taken out by Lucas for Cope, and wrote Marsh that they were all "on a larger scale than T [*itanosaurus*] m [*ontanus*], from 10 to 30 per cent"—disturbing news! Prospecting the near-by area, he found bones in half-a-dozen places from a few rods to two miles distant from Lucas' quarry. Presently he learned that Lucas, feeling that he had sold his big bones "too cheap," was not averse to overtures from other sources, and he whetted Marsh's appetite still further by reporting that the sacrum already taken up by Lucas was "3 feet 1½ inches long and one 10/12 feet high (!). The femur six feet long, largest vertebra (centrum) fourteen inches in diameter. Length of the scapula five 5/12 feet—width three 2/12." In answer to Marsh's urgent telegram, "Secure all possible . . . Jones has violated all agreements," Mudge replied that Lucas would send to Cope all the remainder of the saurian represented by his first shipment to Philadelphia, but that in the case of subsequent specimens he might be willing to come to terms with Marsh.

The dinosaur material obtained here at Cañon City by Cope was very great in amount, but not much of it was described by him. When this task was undertaken many years later by H. F. Osborn and C. C. Mook, it was found to be a very difficult one because all the quarry records had been lost. Their memoir of 1921 [14] states that most of the bones were evidently sent in by O. W. Lucas in 1877, and by his brother, Ira H.

14. H. F. Osborn and C. C. Mook, "*Camarasaurus, Amphicœlias,* and other sauropods of Cope," *Mem. Amer. Mus. Nat. Hist.* (new ser.), Vol. III, Pt. 3 (1921), pp. 251–387.

Lucas, in 1880. The shipments included the huge *Camarasaurus*, already mentioned, of which Cope presented a reconstruction at the American Philosophical Society meeting in December, 1877, and eight other genera. Cope's two quarries were at a much higher geologic level than the "Marsh quarry."

Mudge continued to send Marsh material from Cañon City and early in September he wrote that he could use Williston to advantage in the "delicate work," and especially in making drawings of the bones, which had a distressing tendency to crumble when taken out. Williston, instructed by Marsh, went to Cañon City and was left in charge there while Mudge made a trip East. The shipments made by Williston did not, however, prove altogether satisfactory, the reason therefor appearing in his letter of September 21, 1877, which says in part:

8-Mile Park, Oil Creek [*Colo.*]

I am very sorry to find that Cope is getting by far the best lot of fossils. The locality that the man Lucas first discovered is in a heavy clay or shale and the bones are well preserved. . . . Where we are at work the sandstone renders the bones less accessible and when uncovered they are so extremely friable and broken that it seems almost useless to send them. . . . They [Lucas] have a man out prospecting all the time. Fragments of bones are scattered all through the hills—the point is to find them in good material. And I don't propose to see Cope get better specimens . . . than we can get. Prof. Mudge thinks we had better work out these than use time in the risk of not finding better. But I *am* going to find better.

Marsh, however, thought best to abandon the work at Cañon City and ordered Williston back to Morrison. He had been there only a few weeks when there was an accident in the quarry, caused by the fall of many tons of rock, which nearly wiped out the whole party and put a stop to the work for the season. Williston, not in the best of health, started for his home in Kansas, thus missing a telegram from Marsh bidding him go immediately to Wyoming.

This brings us to the third of the famous dinosaur localities that were to yield Marsh so striking a harvest. His first intimation of this new field came in the following letter:

UNION PACIFIC RAILROAD COMPANY

Agent's Office, Laramie Station [Wyoming], July 19th, 1877.
Prof. C. Marsh, Geologist.
Yale College.
Dear Sir:

I write to announce to you the discovery not far from this place, of a large number of fossils, supposed to be those of the Megatherium, although there is no one here sufficient of a geologist to state for a certainty. We have excavated one (1) partly, and know where there is several others that we have not, as yet, done any work upon. The formation in which they are found is that of the Tertiary Period.

We are desirous of disposing of what fossils we have, and also, the secret of the others. We are working men and are not able to present them as a gift, and if we can sell the secret of the fossil bed, and procure work in excavating others we would like to do so.

We have said nothing to any-one as yet.

We measured one shoulder blade and found it to measure four feet eight inches 4 ft. 8 in. in length.

One joint of the vertebrae measures two feet and one half 2½ in circumference and ten inches (10) in length.

As a proof of our sincerity and truth, we will send you a few fossils, at what they cost us in time and money in unearthing.

We would be pleased to hear from you, as you are well known as an enthusiastic geologist, and a man of means, both of which we are desirous of finding—more especially the latter.

Hoping to hear from you very soon, before the snows of winter set in,

We remain,
Very respectfully
Your Obedient Servants
[Signed] HARLOW & EDWARDS
Laramie City,
Wyoming Territory.

Marsh asked the writers of this letter to ship him the bones, which they did on September 19. The shipment was delayed in transit, Marsh acknowledging its receipt on October 20, wiring Harlow and Edwards to "send rest, with all small pieces," and enclosing a check for $75 in a letter of the same date. However, the discoverers of the bones could not cash this check, for reasons that will appear presently, and they wrote Marsh to that effect. The latter, in the meantime, had seen from his examination of the fossils already received that the "Laramie Station" field was worth investigating, and had wired Williston to go there. Williston's first letter, on November 14, cleared up the matter of the uncashable check. "Harlow and Edwards," he told Marsh, were names assumed by W. E. Carlin, station agent at Como, 65 miles west of Laramie, and W. H. Reed, the section foreman, in an attempt to keep their identity concealed and thus avoid attracting attention to the bone field which they had discovered. The bones, he wrote excitedly, "extend for *seven* miles and are by the ton. . . . The bones are right by the station but there are only 4 or 5 persons that know about them. . . . The bones are very thick, well preserved, and easy to get out. . . . I will send a ton a week gotten out good." Another letter two days later confirms the impression that the Como region is a bone-hunters' paradise. The bones are not in hard sandstone, as at Morrison and in the Marsh quarry near Cañon City, but in clay shales, which, in addition to yielding up big bones readily, "*will be the grandest place imaginable to hunt for small specimens.*" The dip of the rocks from the horizontal is much less than in Colorado, and the bones, "magnificently preserved," can be taken out whole. Moreover, by starting work in sheltered places with a southern exposure, excavating can be carried on all winter. Board can be had at the section house, not far away, and the fossils can be taken to the track on a wheelbarrow and thence to the station on a handcar. In short, he wound up, "Cañon City and Morrison are simply nowhere in comparison with this locality both as regards perfection, accessibility and quantity."

Thus started the development of the Como dinosaur field, which was to prove the greatest the world has so far known. And here again, Marsh might have learned of it much earlier. For Williston has stated in print that it was Carlin who showed a dinosaur bone to Marsh when he stopped off at Lake Como in 1868 to obtain specimens of siredons. In the years since Williston opened "Quarry No. 1" at Como, his prophecy that "hundreds of tons" of bones would be taken from this area has been amply fulfilled.

Lakes remarks in one of his letters that when Mudge rode into his camp one day in the summer of 1877, he "trotted out the menagerie" to show him. This expression might be used to

PROFESSOR MARSH'S PRIMEVAL TROUPE.

Fig. 10. "Ringmaster Marsh." Published in *Punch* on September 13, 1890, during the Leeds meeting of the British Association, at which Marsh delivered a paper on the Ceratopsia. Reproduced by permission of the Proprietors of *Punch. See* page 342.

characterize the last two papers in the *American Journal of Science* for December of that year, in which Ringmaster Marsh "trotted out" some of the amazing animals in his three-ring dinosaur circus of 1877: *Stegosaurus*, most bizarre of land animals, with small head, body heavily armored with large bony plates, two rows of huge plates standing erect along its back, and tail bristling with huge spikes—an impressive defensive armament for a harmless plant-eating creature; *Apatosaurus*, a dinosaur of the same general type as *Atlantosaurus*, between 50 and 60 feet long; *Allosaurus*, a fierce carnivore, half the size of the foregoing, but much more terrible in claw and tooth; and, in striking contrast, the graceful little *Nanosaurus* and the tiny "leaping" *Hallopus*.

Dinosaur collecting at Como went rather slowly at the beginning of 1878, the yield from Quarries 2 to 5 not equaling that from the first quarry opened (Quarry No. 1). However, Williston's idea that the rock would prove productive of small bones as well as large received important confirmation in May, when Marsh telegraphed him to search for the remainder of a tiny jaw forwarded by Reed in an earlier shipment, and which, when duly found, proved to belong to the first mammal known in this country from the very remote Jurassic period. Described by Marsh in June, 1878, as *Dryolestes*, it represents a contribution fully as important as that of the dinosaurs, even if less spectacular.

Williston was recalled to New Haven from Como in July, 1878, and except for a few weeks in the summer of 1884, he did no more collecting for Marsh. The further relations between the two are discussed in the chapter on Marsh's assistants at the Museum. With Williston's departure, Reed took charge of the work at Como and continued it through 1882, becoming one of the most valuable of Marsh's many field men. In the early part of 1879, despite constant work, he found little that was of comparable interest to the 1877 yield, and yet Marsh kept him on the ground to guard against poachers, there being Cope parties in the vicinity in 1879 and 1880. It was possibly with the thought of speeding up the work that Marsh transferred Lakes from Morrison to Como in May, 1879. From this time on, the mention of small mammalian jaws and teeth becomes more frequent in the letters, and evidently Marsh had impressed the value of these tiny fossils upon the party, which now consisted of Reed, Lakes, E. Kennedy, and H. G. Ashley. The first mention of what was to prove the banner mammal quarry at Como, the famous "Quarry 9," was in Reed's letter of July 10, 1879; with the exception of the first specimen

found, from Quarry 1, of another tooth from Quarry 11, and
of three from Cañon City, the 250 known specimens of
Jurassic (Morrison) mammals all came from this quarry.

As might have been expected, the Lakes-Reed combination
proved to be anything but successful, the former's "Oxford
ideas" and the latter's rough-and-ready plainsman make-up
producing so much friction that they were soon working
separately in different quarries. Reed opened "Quarry 13 East"
and found it productive,[15] but news of greater importance,
although unappreciated at the time, was contained in his letter
of November 5, which said: "We are at work in No. 10 but
have not done any more in the small bones yet. We uncovered
a femur today that is over six feet long. The bone is in good
preservation but broken up considerably. There seems to be
quite a lot of bone directly under it." Such was the laconic
announcement of what was to prove Reed's masterpiece of
excavation—the removal from the rock of the mighty "thunder
saurian," *Brontosaurus excelsus*, the most perfect sauropod
skeleton ever collected. Marsh had the description of this new
dinosaur in print in the *American Journal of Science* in December, noting especially the lightness of the sacrum. More
boxes from Quarry 10, coming in over a period of some months,
brought other parts of the skeleton, until *Brontosaurus* was
practically complete, and Marsh presented a restoration of it
in 1891. The earlier descriptions gave the locality only as
"Atlantosaurus beds of Wyoming," or "Wyoming west of the
Rocky Mountain range," and mentioned no collector's name,
but credit for the discovery is given to Reed in Marsh's dinosaur
monograph of 1896. It is interesting to imagine "Bill" Reed's
feelings if he could today stand beside this great skeleton as
it stretches to a length of 67 feet in the Great Hall of the
Peabody Museum, and rears its head to the level of the gallery
floor.

Reed's record of six-and-a-half years' steady collecting at
Como was a remarkable one. He had been at one time a professional game hunter for the railroad, and was therefore well
acquainted with outdoor work. He was quick to learn the names

15. One of the most important of the Como quarries, No. 13 yielded types of
Camptosaurus browni, C. dispar, and *C. medius, Dryosaurus altus, Stegosaurus
sulcatus, Diracodon laticeps, Cœlurus fragilis*, and *Morosaurus lentus*.

of the various bones and to recognize them as they turned up
in the rock; he kept accurate accounts of the excavations and
the shipments; and he managed his men with no apparent difficulty except in the case of Lakes and Kennedy, both of whom
Marsh made the mistake of hiring independently, thus removing them from Reed's control. He worked day in and day out
for $75 a month, and the fossils from Como—huge boxes of
dinosaur bones and small cans of mammal teeth and jaws—
traveled eastward in a never-ending stream. Although his
erstwhile partner, Carlin, went over into Cope's employ, Reed
never wavered in loyalty to Marsh. In short, his services were
invaluable. The Museum records show that the number of shipments sent in from Como between November, 1877, and March,
1883, totaled 152 boxes and 84 cans. During these years Marsh
paid Reed and his assistants (Kennedy, Kenney, Fred Brown,
Phelps, LeRoy, Dixon, Ashley, and C. B. Reed), upwards of
$8,000. Whether it was Reed's conspicuous success that made
Marsh careful to keep financial arrangements between them
going smoothly, or whether he sensed that here was a man with
whom he would have to do so, their relation during these years
forms an agreeable interlude among the complaints that fill
so many of the letters from other collectors.

Reed's last letter from Como was dated April 2, 1883, when
he left the bone business to go into sheepherding, turning the
Como equipment over to Kennedy and Fred Brown. He collected for Marsh at intervals in later years, and was in correspondence with him as late as 1898. He was then assistant in
Paleontology at the University of Wyoming at Laramie, and
was later curator at that institution.

During the early development of the new field at Como,
Lakes continued to collect at Morrison in his spare time. In
June, 1878, Jarvis Hall College burned, leaving him out of
employment, and in November, at Marsh's suggestion, he came
to New Haven and was evidently at the Museum all winter.
April of 1879 found him back at Morrison, proposing to concentrate on finding parts of the *Atlantosaurus* that he had seen
to be missing during his stay at the Museum. After a month
of this work, he was sent to join Reed at Como, from which
field he forwarded to Marsh a daily journal, with sketches. As
a matter of fact, it was these sketches that were partly to blame

for the trouble between him and Reed. Lakes clearly loved to sketch, and Reed felt that instead of confining himself to drawings of bones, Lakes was adding embellishments; Lakes, however, protested to Marsh that he put in the "fancy touches" only in his leisure hours. Marsh at this time complained that the bones were reaching him in so confused a state that he could make nothing of them—a not-too-surprising result when one considers the friction between Reed and Lakes. Many of the bones broke badly when they were taken up, and as Lakes usually sketched them as they lay in the rock, it is quite possible that Marsh received sketches of bones that had crumpled to fragments and had been thrown on the quarry dump!

After the two received orders from Marsh to work separately, Lakes collected straight through the winter of 1879–80 at Como, sending in some valuable stegosaur material; and his letters give a much more vivid idea of the field work than do the matter-of-fact ones of Reed. In spite of the hard work under difficult conditions, his health improved, and when he got an offer to teach at the School of Mines in Golden, he was reluctant to give up "a life and work which has been growing increasingly enjoyable and interesting to me and to go into a life that will be tame and less congenial." He finally made the change, however, and had a long and successful career at the School of Mines. He was associated with S. F. Emmons of the United States Geological Survey in the survey of the Leadville district, and he wrote several textbooks on mining, as well as a good many papers, his bibliography listing 51 titles. Leaving Golden in 1892, he worked as a mining engineer in Denver until about 1910, and then moved to Nelson, British Columbia, to join a son engaged in the same profession. He died in 1917.[16]

The station at Como (later called Aurora) was originally less than ten miles east of the village of Medicine Bow, along the line of track; but when E. H. Harriman, the modernizer of the Union Pacific, straightened out some of the extraordinary digressions of its roadbed, the station house was left far to the north of the present railway. A mile or more south of the station the Como Bluffs extend east for many miles, and it was along the foot of these bluffs that the various quarries operated

16. From information kindly supplied by another son, Mr. Harold Lakes of Nelson.

by Marsh were located. So many bones were taken away by his men that subsequent collectors found little of value. This was the experience of Walter Granger of the American Museum of Natural History in 1897; he reported "numbers of massive bones strewn along the base of these bluffs, tumbled from their stratum above; too weather-worn to attract collectors"; and this was also the experience of the Harriman Union Pacific excursion of geologists in 1899, of which the senior author was a member.

Granger did, however, find another extraordinary locality for dinosaur bones that same summer about ten miles northwest of Como. This was the famous "Bone-Cabin quarry," so called from the sheepherders' cabin with the foundation made of dinosaur bones, which first attracted Granger's attention to the spot. The quarry covered an area of about 170 by 100 feet, and from it in six summers of excavation the American Museum took out more than 50 partial skeletons of giant dinosaurs, weighing when boxed about 50 tons. Rarely, however, was an entire skeleton found, and more frequently a third or a half of an individual lay together. The Bone-Cabin quarry was "a veritable Noah's ark deposit, a perfect museum of all the animals of the period," including dinosaurs of many kinds, crocodiles, and turtles.[17]

In the 'eighties, still another collector whose work was of great value to Marsh was M. P. Felch, who had helped Mudge and Williston at Cañon City in 1877. When Marsh's appointment as vertebrate paleontologist to the United States Geological Survey in 1882 placed more money at his disposal, Felch was one of the men whom he set to work, and their association continued until 1889. Felch, like Reed, was a methodical worker, who kept detailed records of his finds and sent frequent reports to New Haven. His letters have a peculiar interest, moreover, because they show that he and Marsh were working out, between them, a gigantic jigsaw puzzle, with dinosaur bones for pieces. The collecting of 1877 had been done when the dinosaur fever was in its first stages, and species were made on limb bones or on vertebrae or on other incomplete material. By 1882, Marsh, with his usual thoroughness, wanted

17. H. F. Osborn in W. D. Matthew, "Dinosaurs," *Amer. Mus. Nat. Hist.* (1915), p. 136.

to complete the picture of these great beasts, and he therefore
needed the missing parts to add to those he already had. After
considerable prospecting about the Cañon City region, it was
thought wise to reopen the old quarry that had been worked
in 1877, and a wise choice it proved to be; for out of this so-
called "Marsh quarry" came detailed knowledge of many of
the great dinosaurs that Marsh had made known to the
world from partial skeletons only, and not only those whose
remains were originally found at Cañon City but others from
Como as well: *Allosaurus, Ceratosaurus, Stegosaurus, Brontosaurus, Diplodocus, Morosaurus,* and *Laosaurus.* The quarry
was restricted in area to a few hundred square feet, and the bone-
bearing horizon was not more than three feet thick. Nevertheless, from it came representatives of at least a dozen genera and
species, and two or three times that number of individual
skeletons. It would seem difficult, Hatcher remarks,

to overestimate the wealth of the reptilian fauna of this region
in Jurassic times or to exaggerate the total number of genera and
species that must have existed throughout the period of time required for the deposition of the several hundred feet of sandstones
and shales that here constitute that formation.[18]

One of the best known of the Marsh dinosaur types that
came from Cañon City was the huge whiptailed sauropod,
Diplodocus. Williston, its discoverer, many years later told
how the hind leg, pelvis, and much of the tail

lay in very orderly arrangement in the sandstone near the edge
of the quarry, but the bones were broken into innumerable pieces.
After consultation we decided that they were too much broken to
be worth saving—and so most of them went over the dump. . . .
We were in too much of a hurry [one of Williston's field character-
istics] to get the new discoveries to Yale College to take much
pains with them.[19]

Williston did note, however, that the vertebrae in the tail
had peculiar double chevrons, or V-shaped arches, such as

18. J. B. Hatcher, "Osteology of *Haplocanthosaurus," Mem. Carnegie Mus.,*
Vol. II, No. 1 (1903), p. 2.
19. In W. D. Matthew, "Dinosaurs," *Amer. Mus. Nat. Hist.* (1915), pp.
129–130.

he had not seen before, and he saved samples of these. Marsh confirmed his impression that these belonged to a new dinosaur, and in 1878 gave it a name based on this feature (*diplos,* double), the genus and species *(D. longus)* being described from a hind limb and a part of the tail. He amplified the description of *Diplodocus* in his later papers, but complete knowledge of this great whiptailed dinosaur came much later, as a result of collecting by the American Museum in New York and the Carnegie Museum in Pittsburgh, whose specimens were from the Bone-Cabin Quarry and from near Sheep Creek, Albany County, Wyoming, respectively. After the Pittsburgh skeleton was mounted, Andrew Carnegie sent replicas of it to museums in other parts of the world, and it has become the most widely known dinosaur.

The dump referred to by Williston in connection with *Diplodocus* was to give Felch and his men plenty of trouble a few years later, as Marsh demanded that they search it over and over for bones that were missing from this or that dinosaur complex. Felch comments on this as follows in his letters of April 4 and 11, 1884:

Working this dump over is more of a job than I expected. All the rock and earth from above was thrown over into the narrow bottom of the gulch, filling it in places 12 to 15 feet deep several rods long, and we are cramped for room to work. . . . The wonder is that we have been able to find and restore the half we have found, and if you should ever visit this quarry you will think so too. Had the earth and rock removed in stripping [for *Allosaurus*] been only thrown behind us it would have been comparatively easy . . . but for all the material to be dumped over a cliff the first fall of which is 40 or 50 feet and then down again still farther to the bottom of a narrow gulch was a different matter. Nothing but an interest in the work on this particular skeleton and a feeling that I was in a measure responsible for its loss would have induced me to have undertaken it.

Felch was of New England stock, and a man of some education, as is apparent from many of his letters to Marsh. His last letter is dated January 2, 1893, two years after he had paid a visit to his old home back East and had called on Marsh at the Peabody Museum. He died about 1894–95.

In the matter of priority of discovery of these Colorado and Wyoming dinosaur fields, Reed's letter of June 15, 1898, says that he has two witnesses to prove that he found Quarry 1 at Como on (or by) March 7, 1877; whereas Lakes's first letter, written on April 2, 1877, says that he and Captain Beckwith made their discovery "a few days ago." The bones at Cañon City, on the other hand, judging from notes made by Marsh at the time of his visit to the locality in 1880, were found by Henry Felch, a brother of M. P. Felch, in 1869 or 1870, and were later determined to be bones by Dr. J. F. Lewis of Cañon City. It is apparent, from letters to Marsh, that the Curiosity Shop in that place was selling chunks of bone to tourists as fossil wood in the winter of 1876–77, and at this time the local and Denver papers had accounts of the finding of large fossil bones. As for the bone said to have been shown to Marsh by Carlin in 1868, at Como, nothing further is known about it.

CHAPTER VIII
JOHN BELL HATCHER, KING OF COLLECTORS

ONE DAY in the early summer of 1884, Marsh looked up from his desk to see before him a member of the class just graduated from the Sheffield Scientific School, John Bell Hatcher by name, whom he had already met through Professor Brush. Queried as to his errand, the young man said that he wanted a job collecting fossils, anywhere, at any salary. Marsh knew that Hatcher came from the Middle West, and that he had worked in coal mines before coming to Yale; knew, also, that he had made a small collection of Carboniferous fossils. This June morning, something in Hatcher's quiet manner, his wiry physique, or the look in his steady gray-blue eyes, must have further impressed him. In any event, the outcome of the interview bore evidence to Marsh's ability to pick men, for the association begun that morning was to be of inestimable benefit, not only to both Marsh and Hatcher, but to the science of Vertebrate Paleontology.[1]

In this year of 1884, Marsh had Federal money at his disposal, and shortly after Commencement he sent Hatcher out to Long Island, Kansas, where Charles H. Sternberg had found a quarry of Pliocene rhinoceros bones that he regarded as the greatest fossil deposit he had discovered in nearly a decade. The bones lay along both sides of a ravine for a quarter of a mile in great profusion, although the individuals were exceedingly intermingled, the whole possibly representing the wash from a disastrous flood. Marsh, with his instinct for the spectacular in collecting, had engaged Sternberg to work this region, and to him Hatcher was sent as assistant. The young man spent only one night with his parents in Iowa before going on to Alma, Kansas, to look for Sternberg, whom he

---

1. For other biographical sketches, see "John Bell Hatcher," by Charles Schuchert, *Amer. Geol.*, XXXV (1905), 131–141; and "John Bell Hatcher," by W. J. Holland, *Ann. Carnegie Mus.*, II (1904), 597–604. Also see Scott's *Some Memories of a Paleontologist*, 1939, especially p. 261.

finally joined, after several unsuccessful attempts, on July 8. When he wrote to Marsh two days later, he already had three important things to report. First, the locality was "by no means exhausted," as Sternberg had thought. Second, he could not comply with Marsh's request for a weekly report of his collections, because it was Sternberg's policy to have the whole party work together; "I would be glad to keep such a report," he said, "if I could work somewhat independently." Third, and most significant, he thought much better specimens could be obtained "by taking more pains in raising the bones after they have been uncovered."

Three days later, the last two thoughts were reiterated: "I found a set of rhinoceros teeth together the other day and Mr. Sternberg sent them to you by mail yesterday. I hope he packed them all right. Yesterday I found all the toe and foot bones of one foot together . . . he broke some of them a little getting them out . . . I hope it will be so after a while that I can take out what I find myself."

By the thirty-first he was still more emphatic: "If you keep me with Mr. Sternberg this season I should either like the privilege of *taking out* and *packing* what specimens I find myself, or if you can't grant me this privilege please do not estimate my work by his. He is a hard-working, industrious man but quite careless, and in a hurry about taking out and packing specimens"; and then he added, as if conscious of his short apprenticeship, "at least in my opinion."

Early in August, difficulties arose over the continued exploration of the beds. The owner of the land, a Mr. Overton, had been trying to make trouble for Sternberg all season, and had finally refused to allow him to proceed. Williston was sent out by Marsh to try to adjust the matter, with instructions to have Hatcher continue work if possible. While Sternberg was away on a trip to another town, Hatcher solved the problem himself by hiring Overton to work with the party, and when Sternberg returned, it was arranged that he and Hatcher should excavate on opposite sides of the ravine. In other words, the apprentice had in a month become an independent collector. In his report of the deal, he wrote Marsh that he proposed to use a team and scraper to get down to the bone levels, asked for money at once to purchase packing material,

PLATE XV

JOHN BELL HATCHER 1861–1904

FROM A PHOTOGRAPH TAKEN IN THE EARLY DAYS
OF HIS COLLECTING FOR MARSH

PLATE XVI

OFFICERS OF THE
AMERICAN ASSOCIATION FOR THE ADVANCEMENT OF SCIENCE
PHOTOGRAPHED AT NASHVILLE IN 1877

STANDING (LEFT TO RIGHT): ?, A. R. GROTE, GENERAL SECRETARY; N. T. LUPTON, CHAIRMAN, SUBSECTION OF CHEMISTRY; W. H. DALL, SECRETARY, SECTION B; H. C. BOLTON, SECRETARY, SECTION A; ?. SITTING (LEFT TO RIGHT): O. C. MARSH, VICE-PRESIDENT, SECTION B; SIMON NEWCOMB, PRESIDENT; F. W. PUTNAM, PERMANENT SECRETARY planned to keep accurate accounts and send in monthly reports, and announced that he would not hurry, because he thought that "this sort of work depends more for its success on care than haste": a young man with progressive ideas and a definite mind.

Hatcher's first independent report, dated Sunday, August 17, must have shown Marsh what a prize he had secured. He had then been at work on his own for four days. He had divided the quarry into numbered sections each 5 feet square, had taken the bones out of 3 of these, and stripped the dirt from 4 more. Out of section 77 alone he had taken 67 bones. He sent Marsh a diagram of the quarry with the sections marked, made a large diagram of each section, and located on it every bone found—a very important advance. From all of which it appears that Hatcher and the business of collecting fossil bones were affinities from the start.

Marsh visited the party in Kansas some time in September, and the work for the year was finished the first of November, the boxes sent in numbering 143. Of this number, 117 reached New Haven on November 25, probably the Museum's largest single shipment up to that date.

On December 23, Hatcher was in Wichita Falls, Texas, in a supposedly milder climate, ready to start on a prospecting trip after Permian vertebrates with team and wagon, the driver being one of the oldest settlers of the country, and, still more important, one who knew many of the places where Professor W. F. Cummins had collected for Cope. By January 3, he had located three fossil beds. Settlements, he reported, were fifty to sixty miles apart, the thermometer was 12 degrees below zero, and as for law and order, when two men quarreled and one was killed the authorities arrested and imprisoned the dead man! As the days went on, he could get no word of instruction from Marsh—not strange, perhaps, in view of the fact that, as he says, "the present postmaster has been arrested for destroying the mail." By February 3 he "had not money enough to buy a postal card" and had had to come into town to outfit because someone had stolen his blankets and provisions. A week later, in spite of destructive postmasters, he had received funds from Marsh. He used none of these for blankets, however; he had borrowed some to replace the stolen ones and now proposed to visit all the cow camps in the neighborhood, and "if the boys have the blankets I will have them or *something else!*" Such was the environment in which one collected Permian fossils in central Texas in 1885.

Hatcher had written Marsh that he would be in the town of Seymour for mail on March 8. When he had walked sixteen miles and waded the ice-filled Big Wichita River to fulfil this appointment, and found no letter there with funds, he sent a vigorous message to New Haven which said: "Unless there can be a change I had rather stop work"—a sentiment that he was to repeat many times in the next eight years. A telegram followed the letter, but the check from Marsh did not arrive until the seventeenth, and with it the news that the latter had been ill. The enforced idleness while waiting for funds was far harder for Hatcher than any field work, however difficult, and probably confirmed his opinion that Texas was "the worst place outside of Hades."

By the end of March he was again working on the rhinoceros quarry in Kansas, remarking laconically on April 12: "Already have out 727 bones including 4 skulls three of them perfect and one perfect jaw of mastodon. . . . You wanted to see some hyoid bones [very rare] of rhinoceros last Fall. I will send some by mail today."

His success in collecting led him to ask for an advance in wages a few weeks later; he had agreed to stay with Marsh for two years at $50 a month, but now thought he should have $75 in the field and $50 while at the Museum. Throughout these months his letters show impatience at the irregular arrival of money from Marsh, protesting more on account of his men than for himself. On the other hand, he was active in "sewing up," by contracts, land that might be expected to yield fossils, so as to give Marsh "absolute control of the Pliocene fossil beds of this locality."

The 1885 field season ended in October, with a total of 115 boxes, and presumably Hatcher spent the winter at the Museum. In the spring of 1886, his wish for increased wages was more than met by an agreement with the United States Geological Survey, which gave him $90 a month until July 1, 1887, and $100 a month for the following four years. Shortly after the signing of this agreement he went out to Long Island, ap-

parently to inspect "Bone Mound," a locality at which Cope
had worked for a few months some years previous. His real
objective this year, however, was the Brontotherium beds in
Nebraska and Dakota, and his immediate destination the town
of Chadron, Nebraska, where he was to obtain from Hank
Clifford, its discoverer, information about missing parts of
Marsh's type specimen of the brontothere, *Brontops robustus*.

Among the monographs then projected by Marsh was one
on this strange race of hoofed and horned mammals, of which
the Yale Expedition of 1870 had found some magnificent
specimens in Colorado. Cope was not far behind Marsh in finding brontotheres, beginning in 1872. Both authors had continued to describe genera and species, but had developed no
idea of the phyletic relations between them, and it was at this
stage that Hatcher was sent into the badlands to collect more
material.

He established connection with Clifford, but the latter could
not take the field until a month later. Hatcher therefore went
to work near Chadron with a young man named Drury, and by
May 5 had 4 boxes of "*good*" specimens packed and 1,200
pounds more ready to pack, including 4 skulls and limb bones
"much better" than any he had seen in the Museum. Two weeks
later he had 18 boxes packed, totaling 4,000 pounds, and he
aimed to get a carload by fall. In pursuit of this goal he and
Drury left for the badlands, with the avowed intention of not
coming in until it was too cold to work longer; and by October
he had 118 boxes of brontothere material ready to ship, with a
total weight of 24,136 pounds, which he feels sure is "by far
the largest shipment of fossils ever made to the government."

The length of this field season of 1886 and the great amount
of work done were probably responsible for the long siege of
inflammatory rheumatism which held Hatcher in the hospital in
New Haven much of the succeeding winter. However, there
is no mention of hardships in his letters from the field, only one
remark that the weather was hot; and in March, 1887, he was
back at Chadron preparing for another attack on the Brontotherium beds, although his writing, penned with his "lame
hand," was exceedingly shaky. This year the weather was even
less favorable, with heavy storms and mud knee-deep. Digging
began early in April in the Hat Creek country, which Marsh

had seen in 1874, and the shipment early in June amounted to 22 boxes, including 11 *Brontotherium* skulls. At the end of June, camp was transferred to the vicinity of Hermosa, South Dakota. In the beginning, the party did not strike luck, reporting on June 28 that they had so far found only one skull. "I can work as hard as anyone," Hatcher says, "but I must find something." This state of affairs was transitory, however, for a letter of July 12 says: "Now I am going to surprise and I hope at the same time please you. On the last trip we took out and packed 13 skulls. . . . The 4th of July was the banner day, on that day we got three skulls. You will have no chance to complain this winter about my skulls all being small for some of them are the largest I ever saw." The Dakota brontotheres, he reports, show a greater variety of forms than he has hitherto noted.

The first few months of the winter of 1887 Hatcher spent on a collecting trip around Washington and to the south in Virginia and North Carolina. This was the time when the Potomac formation was a subject of controversy among the Federal geologists, Marsh holding it to be of one age (Jurassic), and others thinking it was younger (Cretaceous); and it was hoped that Hatcher, by finding vertebrates in these beds, might help to settle the question. Also, the milder climate of the region promised to be more favorable to his rheumatism. Under the direction of W J McGee of the Federal Survey he started work in a ditch beside a road "as much traveled as Elm St. in New Haven"; fossils were abundant but "quite small, so you must not expect any carload lots." It is clear, however, that this sort of "civilized" collecting was not to Hatcher's taste, for he burst out to Marsh on November 6:

I don't believe these people here know which is Potomac and which is not. When I came here a month ago Mr. McGee drove me around and showed me what he said was Potomac and what Quaternary, and showed me the only place where fossils had been found in the *Potomac*. Now I have made a large collection from that very spot and the fossils seem to show conclusively that it is Eocene. . . . I had Mr. McGee walking the floor yesterday at a very rapid pace. . . . There is considerable fireside geology in the country.

Marsh, on receipt of the fossils, confirmed the Eocene age, and Hatcher then went to work on localities "which Mr. McGee says are really Potomac." This time, after a slow start, he began to get dinosaur bones, which Marsh pronounced to be Jurassic.

April, 1888, found Hatcher again in Chadron for a third season, and two weeks later he was back at work in the Hat Creek country. He was apparently getting tired of brontotheres, however, and in the middle of May he persuaded Marsh to let him go up into the Judith River region of Montana where late Cretaceous beds rich in dinosaurs had been reported. This trip was not a success, at least quantitatively, to Hatcher's chagrin, its yield being but 15 boxes of fragmentary material. He therefore returned to the brontotheres and during the months of October and November sent to New Haven 71 boxes, weighing 15,140 pounds.

The Judith River trip, although producing mainly fragmentary material, did have at least one important consequence. Among its fossils was part of a skull with horn cores which Marsh recognized as new and described in December, 1888, as that of a dinosaur, *Ceratops* ("horned face"), belonging in the new family Ceratopsidae. The previous year, however, Whitman Cross of the Federal Survey, working out the age of the Denver formation, had sent to Professor Marsh for determination a pair of large fossil horn cores, found by George L. Cannon, Jr., on the banks of Green Mountain Creek, near Denver. Marsh had at once (October, 1887) concluded that they belonged to "one of the largest American bovines and one differing widely from those already described," and named them *Bison alticornis*. He reported to Cross that these fossils were "probably late Pliocene" in age, a conclusion to which he was led by the fact that he himself had collected mastodon remains and other Pliocene fossils near the same locality. The age thus postulated, however, was wholly at variance with Cross's field studies, which indicated that the Denver beds containing the "bison" were much older, either early Cenozoic or more probably Cretaceous.

Hatcher, on his way back from the Judith River field, went to southern Wyoming to look at some bones owned by one Louis Lamothe. These seemed to him at the time of little value—they later turned out to be ceratopsian—but while he was in the town of Douglas he was introduced to a Mr. Charles A. Guernsey, owner of the Three-Nine cattle ranch, who had, as Hatcher reported to Marsh,

a considerable collection of fossils. . . . Among the many interesting things in this collection I was at once struck with the fragment of a very large horn core. . . . On inquiry Mr. Guernsey informed me that the specimen had been taken from a skull several feet in length which had been found by his ranch foreman, Mr. Edmund B. Wilson, completely embedded in a hard sandstone concretion, weighing not less than 2,000 pounds, that lay in the bottom of a deep canyon about 35 miles north of Lusk, east-central Wyoming.[2]

This was surprising news. However, Marsh had already become suspicious of his "*Bison alticornis*," because Cross and Cannon had been finding undoubted dinosaur remains in the Denver beds. On Hatcher's return to New Haven and his instant recognition of the similarity between the "bison" horn cores and the one he had seen in the Guernsey collection, the isolated parts of the puzzle clicked into place: the horn cores on the skull of *Ceratops* from the Judith River, the horn cores owned by Mr. Guernsey, and the Denver horn cores of "*Bison alticornis*," all belonging to the same type of dinosaur. Something new and exciting was in the wind! Guernsey, on request, sent his horn cores to New Haven for comparison, and Marsh immediately became "possessed with a burning desire" to secure the skull and learn the exact geological horizon from which it came. He sent Hatcher back to the field, with instructions to go after the skull at the earliest possible moment, but his patience was tried by a series of delays. First, Hatcher was held at his home in Long Pine, Nebraska, by illness in his family. When he finally reached Lusk, Guernsey was absent in Chicago. By the time the latter returned, Wilson, the man who had actually found the skull, was away and he did not get back until the middle of April. It was not until May 7 that Hatcher was able to report to Marsh: "The big skull is ours. . . . It is badly broken up, but was in good condition when found three

2. J. B. Hatcher, O. C. Marsh, and R. S. Lull, "The Ceratopsia," *U. S. Geol. Surv. Mon.* 49 (1907), p. 7.

years ago. They [the discoverers] broke the horncores off it [with a lariat] and rolled it down the bluff and broke lots of it into small pieces some of which we found over 100 yards below . . . lower jaws were there . . . when packed [in four boxes] it will weigh 1,000 lbs. or over." [3] The prize was hurried to New Haven by fast freight. When studied, the skull proved to have had a horn on the nose in addition to two on top of the head, and Marsh accordingly named it *Triceratops.* Unfortunately, Guernsey refused to let Marsh keep his horn cores and they were returned to him and subsequently lost. The historic skull that once bore them is now being restored in the laboratories of the Yale Peabody Museum.

This was the beginning of a Hatcher collection which was to rival in importance, if not in number of specimens, that of the brontotheres. In the field seasons from 1889 to 1892, Hatcher sent in remains of 50 ceratopsians, 33 being represented by more or less perfect skulls—the most striking results of his many years of collecting. Moreover, this collecting was of a much more difficult nature than any he had done before, both because of the nature of the country and because of the weight of the material. (Even so, Marsh was wont to grumble at the slow progress!) The largest skull sent to New Haven (No. 24), weighing 6,850 pounds, had to be lifted out of a 50 foot ravine, and then hauled more than forty miles to the railroad over trackless country and through streams; when it was safely on board a train, Hatcher exulted: "I would not be afraid to tackle one now that weighed ten thousand pounds." Charles E. Beecher, then an assistant of Marsh's, who had been sent out to help Hatcher, testified that this feat "is really a monument to the collecting skill of Mr. Hatcher. I do not believe any other collector would attempt to take up such a large and fragile specimen whole." The abundance of material cleared

3. Mr. Guernsey tells his own story of the finding of this skull in his book, *Wyoming. Cowboy Days,* 1936. Wilson, he says, had reported to him excitedly that during a beef roundup the boys had seen a large head "sticking out midway of a high bank on one side of a deep dry gulch, with 'horns as long as a hoe handle and eye holes big as your hat.'" After the roundup was finished, he and Wilson went back to the skull, and Mr. Guernsey started to dig it out. He succeeded, however, in only undermining it so that it broke loose and rolled to the bottom of the gulch, nearly taking him with it. The horn cores and lower jaw broke off in the fall and were taken back to the Three-Nine ranch.

up all doubts about this new type of dinosaur, for which Marsh established in 1890 the new suborder Ceratopsia.

Nearly all the best ceratopsians came from beds of Laramie (late Cretaceous) age in an area about fifteen by thirty-five miles in the east-central part of Converse (now Niobrara) County, Wyoming. In this area Hatcher worked for most of four years, aided by O. A. Peterson, W. H. Utterback, A. L. Sullins, W. H. Burwell, and C. E. Beecher, shipping to Marsh more than 300 large boxes, containing 31 "big skulls," several fairly complete skeletons of horned dinosaurs, 2 quite complete skeletons of the bipedal dinosaur, *Claosaurus annectens*, besides other material among which were more than 5,000 small mammal teeth and jaws.[4] Has any other collector equaled this?

With his customary energy, Hatcher continued to collect ceratopsian skulls summer and winter, and not until he was forced to desist in July, 1892, because of the Congressional cut in appropriations for Paleontology did the ceratopsian stream cease to flow to New Haven.

As indicated above, the collecting at Lusk had other important issues besides the horned ceratopsians. One of the two remarkably complete skeletons of the web-footed dinosaur, *Claosaurus*, was the first dinosaur to be mounted in the United States, achieving that distinction after Beecher succeeded Marsh as head of the Yale Museum. Even more important than the collecting of these dinosaurs was the discovery of mammals in the Laramie beds, the first Cretaceous mammals to be recognized as such, except for Cope's *Meniscoëssus conquistus*, founded in 1882 on two teeth (one later shown to be reptilian), and a humerus collected by Wortman in South Dakota, not in place but apparently from the Laramie formation. (Leidy in 1856 had described as mammalian certain vertebrae found by Hayden in the Judith River Basin, but these later proved to be reptilian; and twenty years later Cope had described a "reptilian" tooth from Montana (*Paronychodon*) which is now known to be mammalian.) Hatcher had been charged by Marsh to keep a lookout for tiny mammals in the Laramie beds, and he made a special search for them in Dakota and Wyoming, but without success. On March 28, 1889, he

4. See J. B. Hatcher, "Some localities for Laramie mammals and horned dinosaurs," *Amer. Nat.*, XXX (1896), 112–120.

wrote Marsh that, when he was after the big ceratopsian skull, he had seen a basin of Laramie badlands several miles in extent on Buck Creek, Wyoming; and on May 20, the same day that the big skull was dispatched, he sent by registered mail "a package containing some 4 or 5 species of Laramie mammals. . . . I hope you will be pleased. . . . They are by no means abundant, the few I send you requiring several days careful search after the localities were discovered. I hope you will not despise them because they are few in number [!] and will make the best of them." Marsh's reply was a telegram telling him to stop work on the Ceratopsia and go after mammals altogether. That he continued to shout for Cretaceous mammals is apparent from Hatcher's remark of July 27: "You seem to think that Laramie mammals are everywhere abundant out here and that all that is necessary is to go out and scoop them, notwithstanding what I have said to the contrary. They are very rare and about two teeth represents an average patient day's work. They are getting more rare every day and unless we find a new locality you need not expect many more." Despite this gloomy prophecy, Marsh was in print in July, with a description of 12 new "genera" and 18 "species" of Cretaceous mammals, and with the announcement that he had in preparation for the United States Geological Survey a memoir on this "rich mammalian fauna." In this paper he gives credit to Hatcher for the discovery of "material for a new chapter in paleontology. Mr. J. B. Hatcher, the writer's valued assistant, had entire charge of the field work, and to him belongs the main credit of the fortunate discoveries made." [5]

A copy of this paper was in Hatcher's hands by July 6, and he was pleased at the credit thus given him. His answer to Marsh's optimistic statement regarding a projected monograph on Cretaceous mammals was to send him more than 500 mammal teeth, making the total to date in excess of 800. "I broke the record yesterday," he says, "by finding 87." In this letter, also, he speaks for the first time of the anthill method of hunting small mammal remains, described by him in 1896.[6]

5. O. C. Marsh, "Discovery of Cretaceous *Mammalia*," *Amer. Jour. Sci.* (3), XXXVIII, 82.

6. J. B. Hatcher, *op. cit.*, p. 119. See also R. S. Lull, "Ant-hill fossils," *Pop. Sci. Mo.*, LXXXVII (1915), 236–243.

Hatcher's letters this summer of 1889 show more than his usual impatience over delay in receiving checks from Marsh. He felt, correctly, that Marsh did not appreciate the difficulties and consequent expense involved in getting out the huge ceratopsian skulls and transporting them to the railroad; the cost of thus transporting to Lusk two boxes, each with a ceratopsian skull, he figured as close to $100.

Field work for the season closed on December 3, 1889, and Hatcher came back East, spending a third winter in the South, partly at Gulf, North Carolina, in search for Triassic mammals, and partly in northwestern peninsular Florida around Archer and Williston, from which he was recalled at the end of February to start for Wyoming. At most, he could have been in New Haven about a month, in spite of the fact that he had written Marsh very heatedly on November 21 that he wanted to get out of the field for a time, since he had had no respite from it for almost three years. "The past month," he remarked, "is enough to take the enthusiasm out of any one. I have had nothing but wet feet, sore throat and colds."

Marsh's instructions for the field season of 1890 included a number of different items connected with the roundup of additional material belonging to remains already in the Museum. After these details, the general admonitions were (on March 7, 1890): "First of all, go for the big skulls, *Ceratops* and *Hadrosaurus*, and don't let any other party get away with you on that point. . . . Next push on the mammal hunt. . . . With your party as a whole, and with every member of it, your word is law."

Hatcher's complaint that he had been kept in the field for too long a time has less weight in view of the fact that his letters show, over and over again, that he was of too restless a disposition to be content anywhere but in the field, whether it was at his home in Long Pine or in New Haven. The last remark quoted in the foregoing paragraph, however, has reference to a source of trouble which had been growing since the previous year, and which probably had its origin in Hatcher's resentment at what he thought was Marsh's favoritism for Beecher. The two men were as opposite in type as could be imagined: Hatcher restless, impetuous, delighting to match his strength and ingenuity against seemingly unconquerable field problems; Beecher quiet, reserved, capable of the immense patience needed to tool out of the rock the most delicate limb of a tiny trilobite. It was probably because of this patience and skill with small specimens that Marsh sent Beecher (and his far less gifted brother) to help Hatcher with the collecting of mammal teeth and jaws in the Laramie beds, both in 1889 and 1890.

Beecher, a graduate of the University of Michigan, and for ten years assistant to James Hall in the New York State Museum, had been with Marsh since 1888, his special work being with invertebrate fossils. Through Marsh's efforts, he was given the Ph.D. degree in course at the Yale Commencement of 1889. Hatcher, although his relations with Beecher seem to have been cordial enough, was possibly justified in feeling that he was as well qualified for such a degree as the latter, although at that time he had had little chance to display any ability other than for field work. At any rate, he began to press Marsh to give him a permanent position, such as, he says, Marsh had promised him if he did well. His skill as a collector was by that time becoming so well known that he was receiving offers from other places, and his discontent was reflected in the following letter:

Camp on Lance Creek, Wyo., March 30, 1890.
It is with a great deal of reluctance that I have thought of closing my connections with you, for I have much to be thankful to you for. But during the past matters have so shaped themselves that I no longer feel contented. Perhaps I am too sensitive but I feel sore over some things, and if I am, it is my fault, and I will have to suffer for it. You no longer have a place for me in the Museum winters, and at times I think you are only waiting for an opportune moment to get rid of me in the field.

In justice to Marsh, it must be said that Hatcher was of the wrong make-up to work successfully with bones in the laboratory, where patience is the most shining virtue. Within the senior author's experience, Hatcher attempted to demonstrate that he could clean one of the great ceratopsian skulls in much less time than the other preparators, whose slowness he often derided. He was working in a room by himself, but Hugh Gibb, then Marsh's head preparator, knowing, from the hollow sounds made by the hearty blows of Hatcher's mallet, that he was approaching a danger zone, warned him to temper his strokes if he would avert disaster. The warning went unheeded, and one day there came an appalling crash of rock. No one dared to go into the room to see what had happened, and presently Hatcher, black of mien, came striding out without a word and made for the street. The skull was badly broken, and Gibb had the job of putting together the wreckage.

As a result of Hatcher's continued protests, Marsh met him in Chadron in October, 1891, for a conference, and at the end of the year a new five-year contract was signed between them, giving Hatcher $2,000 a year, with the title "Assistant in Geology," with only six months a year field work, five months at New Haven, and one month's vacation, and with the further proviso that the geology of the Brontotherium beds and of the Ceratops beds was to be worked out by him and published under his name.

Somewhere in this year of 1890–91, Hatcher had been in correspondence with Professor Henry F. Osborn of the American Museum of Natural History with regard to a position, and Osborn telegraphed him in the field in April, 1891, that he had been appointed assistant in Paleontology in that institution, in spite of the fact that Hatcher had given him a "final answer" in January. Whatever the truth about this three-cornered bargaining, Hatcher worked for Marsh throughout the summer, although he was at times so crippled with rheumatism that he could not get on and off a horse alone.

In June, in the midst of details about ceratopsian skulls, Hatcher paused long enough to deliver to Marsh the following surprising homily:

Lance Creek, Wyo., June 20, 1891.

. . . .

I think you are a long way ahead of Cope so far as material is concerned and do not see why you should let him get ahead of you on the literary part of the work, with all your assistants back there to help you. I will certainly try to keep the end out here a good, long pull ahead of any party that attempts to come in. I think the idea of keeping a corner on fossils of any kind should be given up and the work of cleaning up and describing pushed more vigorously. You certainly have an abundance of material and much more already than Cope can ever have. Of course it is the proper thing to go on collecting for only by such work are the new things brought out. But if Osborn or Cope or any one else see fit to send collectors into this rich field (which they have a right to do) there are bones here for the millions and it would be the utmost folly for me to attempt to keep them from getting some of them. I should not have written as I have only for the repeated mentions you have made in your letters about poachers, etc., insinuating that everything rested with me.

As the end of the field season approached, Hatcher felt that he must spend as much of the winter as possible indoors, because of his rheumatism. Nevertheless, he stayed out until January in order to get the mammal localities cleaned up—an American Museum party being expected in the region in the spring—and after only a month at home he was restless for the field again. Rheumatism defeated his hopes, however, and kept him in until the first of March. His letter of June 17, 1892, shows that, under his new agreement, he was working out the stratigraphy of the Ceratops beds. "I find," he says, "that the beds are not so discontinuous as I had supposed. Have been able to make out several distinct horizons and on the whole I think I shall be able to write a very fairly creditable paper on the geology of this region." A month later, he makes the following very important comment on an article by Whitman Cross that Marsh had sent him:

Long Pine, Neb., July 22, 1892.

Before leaving camp I went carefully over the sections showing the Triceratops beds and those underlying and overlying them with Cross' article in my hand. Whatever may be the section at Denver, I nowhere find such a section as he described there in our region. Our Triceratops beds in Converse Co., Wyo., came entirely within the Laramie [Ceratops beds=Lance] as described by King and Hayden. There is in no instance observed the slightest unconformity between the Triceratops beds and the underlying beds right down through to the Jura which is well represented in one locality in the southeast.

As intimated here by Hatcher, the Converse County ceratopsian material was of much help in the solution of the controversial "Laramie question," in which was involved the drawing of the boundary line between the Mesozoic and Cenozoic eras. At the time he and Marsh were working on these beds, however, no one had enough information to settle the age of these beds, and the actual age determination has come only recently.[7]

Under his contract, Hatcher would have stayed with Marsh until 1896, but in July, 1892, for reasons dealt with elsewhere in this book, the United States Geological Survey's appropriation for paleontological work was cut by Congress, and Hatcher's salary had to be assumed by Marsh himself, at a time when the latter's own finances were in a bad state. Hatcher finally spent the summer working on the Laramie beds in Wyoming and Montana, but his collections were mainly of the dinosaur *Hadrosaurus*, then not one of Marsh's major interests. To the latter's protests, Hatcher replied:

Willow Creek, Aug. 26, 1892.

I can not agree with you that we had "such poor success at our old localities this season." I am well pleased with my work done there. I shipped you over 15,000 lbs. of *good* bones from there besides many hundred mammal teeth and other small things. . . . Ten years ago you would have considered our success phenomenal. . . . A collector in this country has some hardships to bear, but neither bad water, hot weather, cold, chilly rains or anything else affects me as it does to find my efforts have not been appreciated by you. . . . I do not know that I care whether I ever work in the field again or not after this year. Of course I want to do whatever suits you best, during the continuance of our contract. But if as you say in your last letter you do not know as you will ever do any more field work after this year it will work no misfortune to me I think. For I had quite as soon be in New Haven with my family.

The contract between Marsh and Hatcher was finally dissolved at the end of 1892, the abrogation, drawn up in legal form, being signed on January 10, 1893. Marsh's recommendation of Hatcher, of the same date, read:

Mr. J. B. Hatcher, a graduate of the Sheffield Scientific School, has for nearly nine years been in my employ as assistant in

7. See, further, Chapter XVII, under ceratopsian dinosaurs.

Paleontology engaged in collecting vertebrate fossils and in museum work. During all this time he has shown great ability and industry, and has given entire satisfaction. The discoveries he has made are known to all paleontologists. I regret that for financial reasons I can not retain his services, and heartily recommend him to any institution needing such an assistant.

Leaving Marsh's employ thus early in 1893, Hatcher went to Princeton as curator of Vertebrate Paleontology and assistant in Geology, conducting field parties (and for a part of each summer, graduate students) through Utah, Wyoming, and South Dakota in 1893–95, and continuing to make fine collections, although hampered by lack of resources. The Princeton Patagonian expeditions, carried out in 1896 to 1899, were his own plan, even to the method of publishing the results, and were in part financed from his slender funds. During these expeditions he suffered many hardships, among them a violent attack of his old enemy, inflammatory rheumatism. He left Princeton in 1900 for the Carnegie Museum at Pittsburgh. For four more summers he pursued his western explorations and in these years he wrote most of the 48 publications that make up his bibliography. At the time of his death he was happily engaged in completing the Ceratopsia monograph, assigned to him by the United States Geological Survey. An attack of typhoid fever, with which his previous illnesses and his long summers of hardship in the West and in Patagonia left him little vitality to cope, brought his life to a premature end on July 5, 1904, six months after that of his old colleague, Beecher.

Hatcher's letters showed little of the adventurous nature of the work in which he was engaged, but this was not for any lack of color in his own personality. Quite the contrary, for in whatever part of the world his collecting took him, he became almost a legendary figure. He had all the hard-bitten recklessness that went with the frontier. In the field, he drove himself and his men without stint, whether it were scouring the plains on horseback in search for fossil outcrops, for which he had the uncanny sixth sense that makes the great collector, or whether it were pitting his skill against the forces of nature, as exemplified in the tenacity with which a huge skull will cling to the bottom of a canyon. When he rode into town for his pay check, his idea of respite from the field was to test his skill against the best poker players that the place afforded. If a telegram arrived at the Museum, saying, "Send two hundred ammunition. Hatcher," everyone there knew what was happening; that the money was sent, regardless, is a tribute to the scrupulous honesty with which Hatcher's business was always conducted. Tales of his poker exploits reëchoed from Montana to Patagonia, testimony to their almost traditional character coming recently into print in a short sketch by James Terry Duce in the *Atlantic Monthly*. Duce says:

One trick Fate played on the Patagonians was to send a rather subdued-looking American scientist from Princeton to collect fossil bones. . . . He came for a few months, stayed three years, and taught the Patagonians poker. The professor passed through every hamlet from Bahia Blanca to the Straits; the lessons were always the same . . . but as a rule the loose change of the community passed on to the bone hunter to be spent on science. When the famous night finally arrived on which Hatcher was to leave San Julian the whole countryside dropped in to exact revenge. The game started early and was one of those friendly Western games with everybody's sixshooter on the table. The stacks of pesos in front of Hatcher climbed up and up until he was almost hidden behind them; the whistle of the steamer sounded down the harbor. Hatcher announced that he must go. Someone suggested that they would not let him. He picked up his gun and his pesos and backed through the door with a "Good night, gentlemen!" No one made a move. The wind whooped round the eaves and Patagonia went back to its sheepshearing with a wry smile on its face.[8]

The story of Hatcher's work has been told thus fully for two chief reasons: first, to show what a remarkable collector he was; and, second, to show that his widely rumored difficulties with Marsh had their origin, at least in part, in his own rather difficult nature. He was, as the senior author said in 1905, "a very plain, unassuming, hard working, resourceful man,— honest, devoted, fearless, determined, and strenuous to a

8. James Terry Duce, "Patter-gonia," *Atlantic Monthly*, September, 1937, p. 372.

remarkable degree. He hated pretense of any sort." After his bitterness toward Marsh had died away, Hatcher was willing to grant the greatness of the man to whom he owed the opportunity to make the magnificent collections that stand as an eternal monument to them both. The first volume of reports of the Princeton Patagonian expeditions, written by Hatcher and published in 1904, is dedicated "To the memory of Othniel Charles Marsh, student and lover of nature"; and the senior author can bear witness that, when questioned in later years about Marsh and the other paleontologists with whom he had been associated, Hatcher replied, with feeling, "Marsh was the best of them all!"

CHAPTER IX

MARSH'S CONTRIBUTIONS TO THE EVOLUTION THEORY

ONE result of Marsh's late intellectual maturity was that his professional training took place during the years when Darwin's *Origin of Species* was bringing the creationist and evolution theories sharply into conflict. That he was already familiar with creationist ideas in his early days at Andover seems likely, since the Peabody Museum Library has a copy of the 1851 edition of the Agassiz-Gould *Principles of Zoology*, which is marked on the fly-leaf, "O. C. Marsh, Lowell, Mass." At the end of this book the authors make their position regarding evolution entirely clear in the following words:

From the above sketch it is evident that there is a manifest progress in the succession of beings on the surface of the earth. This progress consists in an increasing similarity to the living fauna, and among the Vertebrates, especially, in their increasing resemblance to Man. But this connection is not the consequence of a direct lineage between the faunas of different ages. There is nothing like parental descent connecting them. The Fishes of the Palaeozoic age are in no respect the ancestors of the Reptiles of the Secondary age, nor does Man descend from the Mammals which preceded him in the Tertiary age. The link by which they are connected is of a higher and immaterial nature [pp. 237–238].

Marsh's first contact with a distinguished exponent of the creationist theory probably was on a Monday afternoon and evening in November, 1855, when he listened to two lectures given in the Andover chapel by the Swiss geologist, Arnold Guyot, then newly transplanted to Princeton. Guyot was an ardent creationist, a follower of Cuvier and of Louis Agassiz, and his ideas in all probability fitted in well with those that Marsh had been absorbing at the Academy. When he came to Yale in 1856, Marsh was to find much the same views reflected by Professor Dana, who was Guyot's companion-in-arms in defense of the creationist theory, at least insofar as it applied to man, having assured the Yale alumni gathered for the preceding Commencement that "no senseless development principle evolved the beasts of the field out of monads, and men out of monkeys, but . . . all can alike claim parentage in the Infinite Author." [1]

Darwin's book appeared on November 24, 1859, early in Marsh's senior year in Yale College. The heated controversy over it spread shortly to America, and its new ideas as to the methods by which evolution progressed were naturally discussed in academic classrooms. Of its effect on Harvard, historian Morison says:

When Darwin's "Origin of Species" began to rock the western world in 1859, his friends Asa Gray and Jeffries Wyman who were already evolutionists, became (with some reservations) converts to natural selection, but Louis Agassiz continued to assert the permanence of type inculcated by his master Cuvier. Agassiz promptly became a hero of the clergy, and until his death in 1873 he remained the rallying point of the opposition. [2]

All that Morison says is true, and yet, curiously, Agassiz is said by one of his biographers to have

paved the way for the prompt acceptance of the theory of evolution—first, because he familiarized the great public with a structural knowledge of the animal kingdom and the affinities existing between the different groups, and, second, because he demonstrated the recapitulation theory [i.e., that each individual species repeats more or less of its ancestral history] . . . and added the great conception that the history of the animal kingdom from the earliest geological horizons added further proof of these principles. [3]

At Princeton, Professor Guyot, as stated earlier, had long been a creationist. His reactions to the evolution theory, and

1. J. D. Dana, "Science and Scientific Schools," p. 18. An address before the alumni of Yale College, at the Commencement Anniversary, August, 1856.

2. S. E. Morison, *Three Centuries of Harvard* (1936), p. 308. Harvard University Press. Reprinted by permission of the President and Fellows of Harvard College.

3. E. S. Morse, "Jean Louis Rudolphe Agassiz," *Pop. Sci. Mo.,* LXXI (1907), 546.

found a separate department, and they suggested a "Museum of American Archæology." With the idea of ascertaining the Harvard reaction to this plan, Marsh had gone to see Asa Gray, and had found him highly in favor of it. When the professorship (or curatorship) of Archeology that was eventually founded under the Peabody gift became vacant through the death of Jeffries Wyman in 1874, it was Gray who offered Marsh the chair.

Whether Marsh's thinking along evolutionary lines was influenced by Gray, or whether he found other supporters of Darwin's theories among his Scientific School instructors, is not definitely known; and it may be that he was not entirely converted to the evolutionary doctrine until the years of his study abroad. On his first visit to England, in 1862, he made the acquaintance of a number of the leading workers in science, notably Lyell, whose *Principles of Geology* had had so strong an influence on Darwin. It is not certain whether his new acquaintances of this year included Thomas Huxley, the brilliant zoologist who had become the leading exponent of the Darwinian ideas, but their meeting could not have been long delayed, because he spoke of Huxley in after years as one who had been "guide, philosopher, and friend, almost from the time I made choice of science as my life work." We also know that as early as 1865 he had been at the country home of Darwin, and his library has a copy of the fourth English edition of the *Origin of Species*, dated June, 1866. However it came about, by the early 'seventies he was seeking for lines of descent among various groups of vertebrates.

The demonstration of the truth of the evolution theory can come only, as it now appears, through the study of fossils, and Marsh's well-preserved and carefully collected material played a large part in the establishment of the hypothesis. It was, indeed, his specimens from the region to the east of the Rocky Mountains, where there exists an unrivaled record of dinosaurs, birds, and mammals, that helped to take the entire question of evolution out of the realm of hypothesis and to demonstrate that it is a living truth.

Marsh's first major contribution to the evidence for the evolution theory—and in some ways his most important one—was his discovery in 1872–73 of Cretaceous birds which, by

their possession of teeth and other reptilian characters, proved
the genetic relationship between these two classes of animals
that had been foreshadowed by Huxley. This relationship had
already been suggested by the earliest-known bird, *Archæopteryx*, which was reptilian in so many respects that it had
originally been described as belonging to that class; at the
time of Marsh's discoveries, however, the presence of teeth had
not been detected in this famous bird from the Jurassic of
Bavaria. Commenting on this matter in 1877, Marsh said:

Fig. 11. Marsh restorations of the famous toothed birds from the Cretaceous of
Kansas. Left, *Ichthyornis dispar;* right, *Hesperornis regalis.* Although here
drawn as of the same height, *Ichthyornis* stood less than a foot high, as
against 4½ feet for *Hesperornis.*

The classes of Birds and Reptiles, as now living, are separated
by a gulf so profound that a few years since it was cited by the
opponents of evolution as the most important break in the animal
series, and one which that doctrine could not bridge over. Since
then, as Huxley has clearly shown, this gap has been virtually
filled by the discovery of bird-like reptiles and reptilian birds.
[The dinosaur] *Compsognathus* and [the toothed birds] *Archæopteryx* of the Old World, and *Ichthyornis* and *Hesperornis* of the

New, are the stepping-stones by which the evolutionist of to-day leads the doubting brother across the shallow remnant of the gulf once thought impassable.[8]

The anatomical features which show the connection between the toothed birds and the reptiles were discussed by Marsh in much detail in his monograph, *Odontornithes,* in 1880, and they are reviewed briefly in Chapter XVIII of the present book. In that same year, Huxley paid tribute to the value of Marsh's discovery thus:

The discovery of the toothed birds of the cretaceous formation in North America by Professor Marsh completed the series of transitional forms between birds and reptiles, and removed Mr. Darwin's proposition that "many animal forms of life have been utterly lost, through which the early progenitors of birds were formerly connected with the early progenitors of the other vertebrate classes," from the region of hypothesis to that of demonstrable fact.[9]

With the dinosaurs, Marsh's work was in general descriptive rather than genetic in character. He concerned himself with their classification, but not primarily from the standpoint of evolution. With regard to the group as a whole, he commented in 1878 that the sauropods, which he regarded as the least specialized of the dinosaurian orders, showed enough approach to the Mesozoic crocodiles "to suggest a common ancestry at no very remote period." [10] In 1896, he said: "Some of the large, earlier forms are apparently related to the Crocodilia, while some of the later, small specialized ones have various points of resemblance to birds." [11] The one dinosaurian feature which he studied from the evolutionary standpoint was the brain.

It was, however, Marsh's magnificent collection of fossil horses, and his accurate and careful tracing of the progress

8. O. C. Marsh, "Introduction and Succession of Vertebrate Life in North America" (1877), p. 17.

9. T. H. Huxley, "The Coming of Age of 'The Origin of Species,' " 1880. In *Collected Essays,* II (1893), 235. Macmillan & Co., Ltd.

10. "Principal characters of American Jurassic dinosaurs, Pt. I," *Amer. Jour. Sci.* (3), XVI (1878), 412.

11. "The dinosaurs of North America," U. S. Geol. Surv., *16th Ann. Rept.,* Pt. I (1896), p. 143.

of the horses through geologic time, that tended to give him a greater reputation than any of his other evolutionary discoveries. As Wortman pointed out, Marsh

was the first to show that the fossil forms of the American Continent furnished every conceivable link between the small polydactyl species of the Eocene and the modern horse. So strong, indeed, is the evidence of this descent that were there no other evidences of evolution to be found among the fossils this would be quite sufficient of itself to establish its truth.[12]

In March, 1874, writing of new forms of fossil horses found in the United States, Marsh said: "The line of descent appears to have been direct, and the remains now known supply every important form." [13] Amplifying this statement two months later, he continued:

The large number of equine mammals now known from the Tertiary deposits of this country, and their regular distribution through the subdivisions of this formation, afford a good opportunity to ascertain the probable lineal descent of the modern horse. The American representative of the latter is the extinct *Equus fraternus* Leidy, a species almost, if not entirely, identical with the old world *Equus caballus* Linn., to which our recent horse belongs. Huxley has traced successfully the later genealogy of the horse through European extinct forms [1870], but the line in America was probably a more direct one, and the record is more complete. Taking, then, as the extremes of a series, *Orohippus agilis* Marsh, from the Eocene [Bridger] and *Equus fraternus* Leidy, from the Quaternary [Pleistocene], intermediate forms may be intercalated with considerable certainty from the thirty or more well marked species that lived in the intervening periods. The natural line of descent would seem to be through the following genera:—*Orohippus*, of the Eocene; *Miohippus* and *Anchitherium*, of the [Oligocene and] Miocene; *Anchippus, Hipparion, Protohippus* and *Pliohippus*, of the Pliocene; and *Equus* [of the Pleistocene and Recent]. . . .

12. J. L. Wortman, "Othniel Charles Marsh," *Science* (new ser.), IX (1899), 564.

13. "Notice of new equine mammals from the Tertiary formation," *Amer. Jour. Sci.* (3), VII (1874), 258.

The most marked changes undergone by the successive equine genera are as follows: 1st, increase in size; 2d, increase in speed, through concentration of limb bones; 3d, elongation of head and neck, and modifications of skull. The increase in size is remarkable. The Eocene *Orohippus* was about the size of a fox. *Miohippus* and *Anchitherium*, from the Miocene [Oligocene] were about as large as a sheep. *Hipparion* and *Pliohippus*, of the Pliocene, equalled the ass in height; while the size of the Quaternary *Equus* was fully up to that of the modern horse. . . .

The ancient *Orohippus* had all four digits of the fore feet well developed. In *Miohippus* . . . the fifth toe had disappeared, or is only represented by a rudiment, and the limb is supported by the second, third and fourth, the middle one being the largest. *Hipparion* . . . still has three digits, but the third is much stouter, and the outer ones have ceased to be of use, as they do not touch the ground. In *Equus*, the last of the series, the lateral hoofs are gone, and the digits themselves are represented only by the rudimentary splint bones. The middle, or third, digit supports the limb, and its size has increased accordingly.[14]

Although Marsh knew at least thirty kinds of American fossil horses in 1874, it was in the year 1876 that these fossil mammals came into their own as documentary evidences of the progress of evolution. Huxley, visiting this country for a period of seven weeks, was met by Marsh on his arrival in New York, and stayed with him for a week in New Haven, examining his general collection, which he wished to see before delivering a series of lectures in New York City and elsewhere. To his wife, who did not accompany him to New Haven, he wrote, excitedly: "The collection of fossils is the most wonderful thing I ever saw. I wish I could spare three weeks to study it"; and Leonard Huxley, in the *Life and Letters* of his father, adds the further comment:

At each inquiry, whether he had a specimen to illustrate such and such a point or exemplify a transition from earlier and less specialized forms to later and more specialized ones, Professor Marsh would simply turn to his assistant and bid him fetch box number so and so, until Huxley turned upon him and said: "I be-

14. "Fossil horses in America," *Amer. Nat.,* VIII (1874), 291–292, 293.

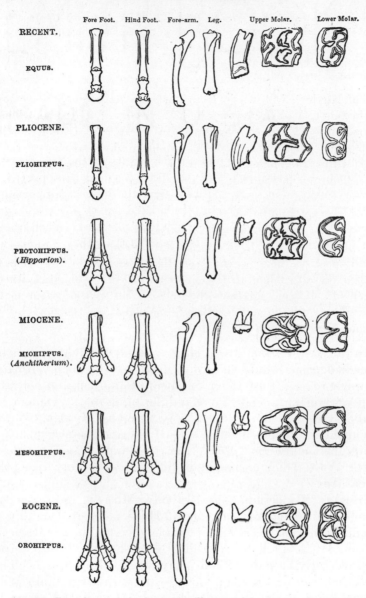

Fig. 12. Genealogy of the horse, as illustrated by Marsh. This drawing was made for Huxley's use in 1876, and published by Marsh in
1879. It shows the evolution from the four-toed foot (at bottom)
to the foot with the single toe of the living horse, and certain
changes in tooth pattern.

lieve you are a magician; whatever I want, you just conjure it up." [15]

The result of Huxley's visit to New Haven was summarized later by Marsh, thus:

One of Huxley's lectures in New York was to be on the genealogy of the horse, a subject which he had already written about, based entirely upon European specimens. My own explorations had led me to conclusions quite different from his, and my specimens seemed to me to prove conclusively that the horse originated in the New World and not in the Old, and that its genealogy must be worked out here. With some hesitation, I laid the whole matter frankly before Huxley, and he spent nearly two days going over my specimens with me, and testing each point I made. He then informed me that all this was new to him, and that my facts demonstrated the evolution of the horse beyond question, and for the first time indicated the direct line of descent of an existing animal. With the generosity of true greatness, he gave up his own opinions in the face of new truth, and took my conclusions as the basis of his famous New York lecture on the horse.[16]

In the New York address, Huxley predicted that still earlier Eocene deposits would some day yield a fossil horse with four complete toes in front and a rudiment of another, and probably with a rudimentary fifth toe on the hind foot. "Seldom has prophecy been sooner fulfilled," says Leonard Huxley. "Within two months, Professor Marsh had described a new genus of equine mammals, *Eohippus*, from the lowest Eocene deposits of the West, which corresponds very nearly to the description given above." [17]

In this connection, the Peabody Museum possesses one valuable and amusing souvenir of Huxley's visit. One day, as he and Marsh sat discussing possible ancestral horses, then unknown, Huxley fell to sketching on a sheet of brown paper, and presently he said: "That is my idea of 'Eohippus.'" Then he added, "But he needs a rider," and with a few more pencil strokes he supplied the lack. He and Marsh joked about the

15. Leonard Huxley, *The Life and Letters of Thomas H. Huxley* (1901), I, 495. D. Appleton-Century Company.
16. "Thomas Henry Huxley," *Amer. Jour. Sci.* (3), L (1895), 181.
17. Leonard Huxley, *op. cit.,* p. 501.

sketch, and finally Marsh said: "The rider also must have a name. What shall we call him?" "Call him 'Eohomo,'" said Huxley, and Marsh wrote the names underneath the sketch. When Marsh came to describe the Eocene horse that Huxley's sketch had foreshadowed, he gave it the name that had been coined in jest, adding the specific name *validus*, in token of his

Eohippus + Eohomo

Fig. 13. "Eohippus and Eohomo," as drawn by Huxley. The original drawing was in pencil on brown paper. The present reproduction is from an inked copy given to the authors by Dr. George F. Eaton.

belief that this oldest-known American equine was, indeed, "the true dawn horse."

It is possible that Huxley's view of the Marsh Collection had another important result besides the modification of his New York lectures. During a stay at Newport he met Clarence King, then in charge of the United States Geological Survey of the Fortieth Parallel, and their conversation naturally turned to Marsh, who had been King's classmate in the Sheffield Scientific School. Four years later, the King Survey published, as Volume VII of its reports, Marsh's memoir on the toothed birds, and it seems quite likely that the reason for the inclusion of this seemingly unrelated memoir is indicated in the following letter from Huxley to King:

Newport, August 19, 1876.

My dear Sir,—

In accordance with your wish, I very willingly put into writing the substance of the opinion as to the importance of Prof. Marsh's collection of fossils which I expressed to you yesterday. . . .

I am disposed to think that whether we regard the abundance of material, the number of complete skeletons of the various species, or the extent of geological time covered by the collection, . . . there is no collection of fossil vertebrata in existence which can be compared to it. . . .

And I think that I am quite safe in adding that no collection which has hitherto been formed approaches that made by Prof. Marsh in the completeness of the chain of evidence by which certain existing mammals are connected with their older tertiary ancestry.

It is of the highest importance to the progress of biological sciences that the publication of this evidence, accompanied by illustrations of such fulness as to enable palaeontologists to form their own judgment as to its value, should take place without delay.

I am

Yours very sincerely,
[Signed] THOMAS H. HUXLEY.

Huxley's friendship with Marsh continued throughout his life, and a short time before he died he sent Marsh a complete set of his works. The latter's sketch of the great English scientist was his only contribution to biography.

Huxley's lectures in America, well publicized and published under the title, *American Addresses*, spread the gospel of evolution widely, but there were still places in which it was not encouraged. Noah Porter, president of Yale from 1871 to 1886, was one of the noted champions of conservative thinking, and more especially of conservatism in teaching. However, that his objections to evolution were only to a theory that denied any divine architect of the evolutionary plan seems apparent from a speech made by him in 1877 at the annual banquet of the New England Society of New York, at which Marsh was also a speaker. Dr. Porter said in part:

I deem it proper here to remind you, that Yale College was foremost among the American colleges in cherishing the taste for physical science, and that these sciences, in all their forms, have received from us the most liberal attention and care. If any of you doubt this, we would like to show you our museum, with its collections, which represent all that the most recent explorations have been able to gather. In these well-ordered collections you would find as satisfactory an exhibition of results as you could ask for. You need not fear, however, that, because we believe in science, we have learned any more to disbelieve in the living God. As we stand in the midst of one of the halls of our splendid museum, and see arrayed before us all the forms of vertebrate life, from man down to the lowest type, and see how one and the other suggests the progress—the evolution, if you please—during we care not how many centuries of advancing life; the more closely we study these indications, the more distinctly do we see lines of thought, of intelligence and goodness reflected from one structure to another, and all declaring that a divine thought and love has ordered each and all. Hence we find no inconsistency between the teachings of this museum on the one corner and the teachings of the college chapel on the other.[18]

Marsh's first chance to make a strong public stand in favor of evolution came in August of the year following Huxley's visit, during the meeting of the American Association for the Advancement of Science at Nashville, Tennessee. This gathering was of unusual importance, since it was the Association's first meeting in the South since the Civil War. The southern members had been slow to come back into the organization, and it was hoped that the Nashville meeting would prove a long step toward restoring its national character. These circumstances, combined with the fact that Nashville has long been a center of culture and education, led the people of the city to outdo even their own repute for hospitality. The members of the Association were, indeed, well-nigh overwhelmed with entertainment. After the meeting, more than 100 of the 173 present were given a free excursion to Chattanooga by the Chattanooga Railway Company, and 20 to 30 of them spent an additional three weeks in a free trip as far west and south as San Antonio, under the leadership of Professor Cope.

Marsh was at that time one of the vice-presidents of the American Association, and since the retiring president, William B. Rogers, was unable to be present and deliver the usual presidential address, Marsh's vice-presidential address turned out to be the major one of the meeting. The occasion therefore provided just the sort of setting that he liked, and he embraced it by making a long and brilliant summation of what was then

Fig. 14. "Adam and Eve, after Marsh," another sketch by Huxley, drawn in the guest book at the summer home of John Fiske, at Petersham, Mass., in August, 1876.

known of American fossil vertebrates, which, as Dana later said, "set forth the succession of vertebrate life, with a fulness, as regards mammals, before unequalled." In the very first paragraph of this important address, Marsh said:

To doubt evolution to-day is to doubt science, and science is only another name for truth. Taking, then, evolution as the key to the

18. *Seventy-second Anniversary Celebration of the New England Society in the City of New York, at Delmonico's, December 22, 1877*, p. 51.

mysteries of past life on the earth, I invite your attention to the subject I have chosen.

The address was privately printed in the same month in which it was delivered, and more than 1,000 copies of it were sent out by Marsh. It also appeared in *Nature* for September 20 and 27 and October 4, in the *American Journal of Science* for November, in *Popular Science Monthly* for March and April of 1878, and in the Parisian *Revue Scientifique* for May 4 and May 11.

Remarkable as this address was in itself, it gains heightened significance from two facts. In the first place, the year previous, Huxley had paid a visit to his sister, who lived in Nashville, and in response to public demand had delivered an address, which was listened to with deep interest. He spoke of the "slow, constant and gradual change, one species giving way to another," which science shows to have taken place in the history of the earth's inhabitants, but, as a recent biographer says, he "did not labor this issue, and the audience was apparently not disturbed." [19] However, although there seems to have been no open criticism of Huxley's speech, the subject of evolution was a strongly contested one in that part of the country, so much so that in 1877 Alexander Winchell, dividing his teaching of Geology between Syracuse University and the newly established Vanderbilt University at Nashville, was under fire from the Methodist authorities in charge of the latter institution because of his attempts to reconcile religion and science. He had published a book on evolution in 1874, but it was an article by him on "Preadamites," appearing in McClintock and Strong's *Cyclopedia of Biblical, Theological, and Ecclesiastical Literature* in 1877, that had aroused the special ire of the churchmen and led to the abolition of his professorial chair early in 1878, after he had refused to resign. To assume that Marsh went to Nashville in 1877 and made a strong defense of evolution without knowing of the Winchell affair would be stretching coincidence too far, although there is no evidence on this point in the shape of letters from Winchell.

In any event, Marsh's lengthy address was delivered before the largest audience of the sessions on Thursday evening, August 30, in the Hall of Representatives at the State Capitol,

19. Houston Peterson, *Huxley, Prophet of Science* (1932), p. 202.

"the intelligent and cultured element of Nashville's population being well represented." Moreover, it was printed verbatim in the Nashville *Daily American*, occupying a full page of fine type and spilling over slightly onto a second. This newspaper also later gave Winchell space in which to defend himself on the charges brought against him by the Vanderbilt authorities. Its admirable editorial comment on the Marsh address ran thus:[20]

The address of Professor O. C. Marsh at the Capitol last evening is given verbatim and entire in this issue. Notwithstanding its length and the great proportion of it which is devoted to scientific detail and technicalities, familiar only to the advanced student, it possesses an interest to the ordinary reader, as having a direct bearing upon the accepted theory of evolution, of the utmost importance at this time. For in this field, the work which Professor Marsh has accomplished in this country is hardly second in importance to that of Darwin in the mother country. . . . The address we lay before our readers this morning is a comprehensive review of the results of the labors and researches of the eminent palaeontologist of Yale . . . a condensed history of the development of the higher vertebrates of this entire continent. . . .

The necessarily unpopular style of treatment and extensive Latin and Greek terminology should not deter the reader from following the array of evidence closely, in justice to the author and the more intelligent and satisfactory comprehension of his deductions. It is no light weight which is here cast into the scale in favor of the doctrine of filiation. It will be hailed as the most valuable of recent contributions to the Descent Theory, and a most timely and potent auxiliary in the determination of the position of man in nature. It is the mechanical and monistic view of an investigator, as calm, earnest and unbiased as might be some scientific visitant from a neighbor planet, who is recounting his observations of terrestrial phenomena, and does not exclude from the fauna of the planet inspected a race of mammals, simply for showing a higher type of development. It is the revelation of a bold discoverer, whose services to the science of paleontology in our western wilder-

20. Through the kindness of the Nashville Public Library the authors learn that this editorial was in all probability written by Mr. Albert Roberts, editor of the *Daily American* at the time and related to Huxley by marriage.

nesses have been more heroic and not less important than those of Cuvier, in his researches in Parisian suburbs.

Guyot, acknowledging a copy of the Nashville address under date of October 16, 1877, wrote Marsh as follows:

Your Nashville address has reached me in due time and I thank you for it very much. The great array of new facts in our American Geology, which you have exposed with great clearness, is of the most intense interest. As to their interpretation it must be left to the best judgment of every one conversant with the subject; for every one judges with the amount of light he possesses from all quarters and all domains of Science, which amount depends in great measure upon the nature and degree of our individual growth.

I always have believed, from facts observed, in development. Without such a law, an organizing idea, in Nature, science would not be possible, and Nature would lose its interest for our own minds.

Evolution from an individual germ is the law of the individual being—whether it is the law of a system of organic forms is not so clear. The formula of development is identical in both; the evolution by transmutation of species is quite another question, which the Darwinian hypothesis entirely fails to demonstrate. It is utterly inadequate to account for the facts. An internal organic law alone is sufficient for the purpose, a law with a pre-established aim, as all true law is.

You truly say that *Science* is another name for *truth*.

But what is *Science?* Is not this the same question as what is truth?

In his presidential address delivered to the American Association at Saratoga in August, 1879, Marsh said that Darwin's *Origin of Species* had in two decades "changed the whole course of scientific thought. . . . Darwin spoke the magic word—'*Natural Selection*,' and a new epoch in science began." [21] These were strong words indeed from one who, as Mr. Paradise has commented,

spent his early, impressionable years on Zions Hill [Andover], who had experienced religious revivals under "Uncle Sam" Taylor,

21. O. C. Marsh, "History and Methods of Palaeontological Discovery," author's ed., p. 35.

and who had listened to the threats of eternal damnation thundered from the pulpit of [Yale's] Battell Chapel.[22]

As to the method by which evolution works, Marsh was a follower of Darwin rather than of Lamarck, believing that, out of the constant changes in life, Nature selects those found best for the individual in a given environment; and that in the struggle for existence those individuals best fitted to carry on the battle of life are selected. His position on this point was thus defined in his Saratoga address:

The difference between Lamarck and Darwin is essentially this: Lamarck proposed the theory of Evolution; Darwin changed this into a doctrine, which is now guiding the investigations in all departments of biology. Lamarck failed to realize the importance of time, and the interaction of life on life. Darwin, by combining these influences with those also shown by Lamarck, has shown *how* the existing forms on the earth may have been derived from those of the past.[23]

Five years after Huxley's visit, Herbert Spencer, that other mighty exponent of evolutionary principles, came to America, remaining from late August into November. He visited a number of cities, but the state of his health prevented him from meeting many people; however, he lunched at Professor Marsh's home on October 21, and was shown the sights in the Peabody Museum. Two days before he sailed back to England he was tendered a banquet at Delmonico's in New York City, which was attended by some 200 of the country's leading intellectuals. Marsh was one of an illustrious group of speakers, which included William Evarts, William Graham Sumner, Carl Schurz, John Fiske, and Henry Ward Beecher. In response to the sentiment: "Evolution—once an hypothesis, now the established doctrine of the scientific world," his speech was a notable one, even for that distinguished company.

Whether or not it was Spencer's visit that was responsible, such modern doctrines as he professed ran into heavy weather at Yale about this time, President Porter objecting to Professor Sumner's use of Spencer's *Study of Sociology* as a text-

22. Scott H. Paradise, "Othniel Charles Marsh, 1831–1899," *Phillips Bull.* (January, 1930), p. 16.
23. Marsh, *op. cit.*, p. 36.

book, on the ground that it was "materialistic in view and hence unsuited to an institution like Yale, with its Christian background and belief." The fiery Sumner—who, incidentally, had been appointed by President Porter in the face of considerable opposition—was loud in protest, and was supported by his colleagues Dana, Marsh, Thacher, Beers, and others, while President Porter's hands were upheld by former President Woolsey, Cyrus K. Northrop (later of Minnesota), and Franklin Carter. The argument reached the outside world and "highly spiced articles" appeared in the New York *Times* and *Evening Post*. President Porter finally went to the Yale Corporation with the question: "Should a professor be allowed to choose textbooks for his classes without reference to the opinion of the president and the general policy of the institution?" The Corporation considered passing a resolution giving veto power over textbooks to the president, but in the end it was not presented and Sumner voluntarily withdrew the offending textbook on the ground that, because of the agitation, its usefulness was gone.[24]

In closing this chapter, we may well quote a few paragraphs from Marsh's address at the dinner to Herbert Spencer, of which mention has already been made. He said in part:

In meeting here to-night, to do honor to our distinguished guest, who is one of the great Apostles of Evolution, it seems especially fitting to the occasion, that we should, for a moment, at least, glance back to the past, and recall briefly the progress of a doctrine which has so rapidly brought about a revolution in scientific thought. . . .

When the second half of the century began, the accumulation of scientific knowledge was sufficient for the foundation of a doctrine of Evolution which no authority could suppress, and no objections overthrow. The material on which it was to be based was not preserved alone in the great centers of scientific thought, but a thousand quiet workers in science, many of them in remote localities, had now the facts before them to suggest a solution of that mystery of mysteries, the Origin of Species.

Our guest of to-night did not stop to solve the difficulties of organic evolution, but with that profound philosophic insight

24. C. H. Patton and W. T. Field, *Eight O'clock Chapel* (1927), pp. 100–102. Houghton Mifflin Company.

which has made him read and honored by all intelligent men, he made [in 1857] the grand generalization that the law of organic progress is the law of all progress. . . . "Whether it be in the development of the Earth, in the development of Life upon its surface, in the development of Society, of Government, of Manufactures, of Commerce, of Language, Literature, Science, Art,

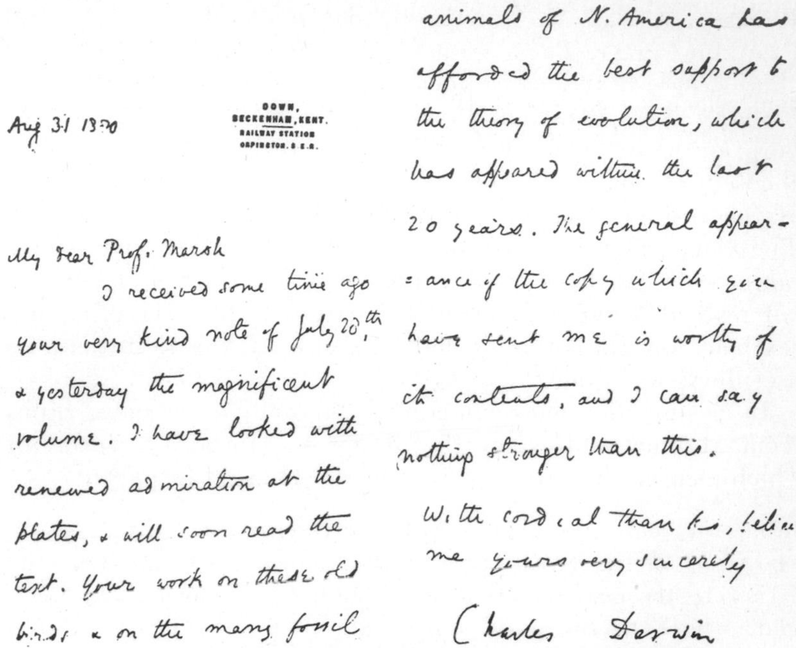

Aug 31 1880

DOWN,
BECKENHAM, KENT.
RAILWAY STATION
ORPINGTON. S.E.R.

My dear Prof. Marsh

I received some time ago your very kind note of July 20th & yesterday the magnificent volume. I have looked with renewed admiration at the plates, & will soon read the text. Your work on these old birds & on the many fossil

animals of N. America has afforded the best support to the theory of evolution, which has appeared within the last 20 years. The general appearance of the copy which you have sent me is worthy of its contents, and I can say nothing stronger than this.

With cordial thanks, believe me yours very sincerely

Charles Darwin

Fig. 15. Letter from Charles Darwin to Marsh, August 31, 1880.

this same evolution of the simple into the complex, through a process of continuous differentiation, holds throughout." . . .

If . . . I may venture to answer briefly the question, What of Evolution to-day? I can only reply: the battle has been fought and won.[25]

"Won," yes! And as to the part that Marsh played in the winning of the battle for evolution, we have striking testimony

25. O. C. Marsh, "Evolution," reprinted from *Herbert Spencer and the Americans, and the Americans and Herbert Spencer* (New York, 1882), pp. 1, 3.

in the form of a holograph letter treasured in the Peabody Museum archives, which reads:

Down, Kent, August 31, 1880.

My dear Prof. Marsh,—

I received some time ago your very kind note of July 28th, and yesterday the magnificent volume [*Odontornithes*]. I have looked with renewed admiration at the plates, and will soon read the text. Your work on these old birds and on the many fossil animals of N. America has afforded the best support to the theory of evolution, which has appeared within the last 20 years [i.e., since the publishing of the *Origin of Species*]. . . .

With cordial thanks, believe me

Yours very sincerely,

[Signed] CHARLES DARWIN.

CHAPTER X

ORGANIZATION OF THE UNITED STATES GEOLOGICAL SURVEY, AND ITS EFFECT ON THE MARSH–COPE RIVALRY

T HE year 1874 was one of the most important in Professor Marsh's life, not altogether for the events of the year itself, but rather for the results to which they led. He was then in his forty-third year, and the eighth of his Yale professorship; he had conducted four highly successful fossil-collecting expeditions to the West, receiving much popular recognition therefor; and the number of papers giving brief descriptions of his striking new discoveries was just short of fifty-five. At New Haven, construction of the new Peabody Museum, with money given to Yale by George Peabody in 1866, had been begun. Harvard made him a second offer of a professorship, this time to succeed Jeffries Wyman. A fourth expedition to the West, featured by a daring night march through bands of hostile Indians, laid the fuse that was to explode under Secretary Delano of the Interior Department the following year. And on April 22, he received a telegram from Professor John Strong Newberry of Columbia which read: "Elected you triumphantly to the [National] Academy [of Sciences] today." A day or so later a letter from Theodore N. Gill, the zoologist, then serving as chief assistant librarian of Congress, showed that he also had been instrumental in bringing about Marsh's election to the Academy, at the meeting in Philadelphia. On the final vote, according to this letter, Marsh received thirty-seven out of thirty-eight votes; remembering the rising heat of the Marsh-Cope quarrel at this time, it is not difficult to figure out who was the lone dissenter.

Marsh was greatly elated over his election to the National Academy at so early a stage in his professional career, as he might well have been. The geologists in the Academy at this time were a strong and influential group, including as they did Cope, Dana, Guyot, James Hall, Hayden, E. W. Hilgard, T.

Sterry Hunt, Leidy, Lesquereux, Meek, Newberry, Pumpelly, W. B. Rogers, and Worthen. Only three of these men were younger than Marsh—Cope, Hilgard, and Pumpelly, whose elections had preceded his by two years.

Marsh became an officer of the Academy in April, 1878, when he was elected vice-president. The very next month its president, Joseph Henry, died, and Marsh thus found himself acting president of the Academy only four years after he had been elected to membership. This might have involved little more than attention to routine administrative duties until the election of a new president the following spring. However, it so happened that Congress placed in the hands of the Academy in June, 1878, the settlement of a controversy that was to have a crucial bearing on Marsh's own career, as appears later in this chapter.

At the spring meeting of 1879, W. B. Rogers was elected president of the Academy and Marsh resumed his status as vice-president. Curiously, however, the third president of the Academy, like the other two, was not destined to fill out his elected term. Rogers died in 1882, and once more Marsh was acting president. At the April meeting of 1883, Wolcott Gibbs was chosen to succeed Rogers, but as he could not serve, the presidency was given to Marsh. As a result of this odd chain of circumstances, Marsh was no stranger to the Academy's administrative duties when he became its president, and he was an efficient and active leader during his two six-year terms. Testimony to this is included in a statement by Professor Russell H. Chittenden, a member of the Academy since 1890, who set down the recollections here quoted, at the writers' request:

As president of the Academy during a period of twelve years, 1883–1895, Professor Marsh through his strong personality exerted an influence on the meetings of the Academy which resulted in a dignified formality in keeping with its high standing. Somewhat stern in appearance, rather punctilious in intercourse with his associates, and with a stiffness of bearing frequently misunderstood, Marsh nevertheless possessed an innate courtesy and kindness of heart which softened his apparent hardness and made him a friend and colleague to be respected and admired.

His interest in the Academy was deep and sincere. By many

means, both direct and indirect, he sought to promote its standing with the administration at Washington, even suggesting to the Government specific ways in which the Academy could be of service to the Government. Whenever possible at the annual meeting in Washington he arranged for a formal call of the Academy on the President at the White House, this at a time when there was laxity in this custom. In these and other ways he used his office to enhance the standing of the Academy as an efficient servant of the Government of the United States.

As I have already stated, he was a strong advocate of reasonable formality in the scientific sessions of the Academy, and I recall especially the interest aroused by the procedure he instituted for the introduction of new members; a procedure which seemed to many at least more in keeping with a National Academy of Sciences than the very informal method such as now prevails. The introduction of new members was made at the opening of the first session, and I remember that in 1890, when I was presented, there were four of us new members gathered at the rear of the hall. Each in turn was escorted to the platform by some colleague or friend and introduced to the President who shook hands and said a few words of welcome, after which the new member faced the audience and was presented by the President to the other members of the Academy. It was a dignified and sensible procedure.

Professor Marsh's connection with the National Academy has been more fully discussed by the senior author in a memorial prepared for that organization and appearing in Volume XX of its biographical memoirs. In the present book, therefore, it seems desirable to give further attention only to what was probably the most important, and certainly the most controversial, affair that came before the Academy in Marsh's administration; namely, the reorganization of the various Federal geological surveys.

On June 30, 1878, Congress approved and set upon its records, as part of the Sundry Civil Act, the following vote:

And the National Academy of Sciences is hereby required at their next meeting to take into consideration the method and expenses of conducting all surveys of a scientific character under the War or Interior Department, and the surveys of the Land Office, and to report to Congress as soon thereafter as may be practicable, a plan for surveying and mapping the Territories of the United States on such general system as will, in their judgment, secure the best results at the least possible cost; and also to recommend to Congress a suitable plan for the publication and distribution of reports, maps, and documents, and other results of the said surveys.

Behind this act lay almost ten years of discussion as to the relative merits of military and civilian control of public enterprises, particularly those connected with the public domain —a discussion which by 1878 had become animated, acrid, and widespread. The circumstances that led to the action by Congress are described by George P. Merrill, historian of American Geology, as follows:

The period of the Civil War had brought to light a considerable number of men for whom the piping times of peace, even when varied by Indian outbreaks in the West, afforded insufficient opportunities. They were men in whom the times had developed a power of organization and command. They were, moreover, men of great physical and moral courage. It was but natural, therefore, particularly when the necessity for military routes in the West and public land questions were taken into consideration, that such should turn their attention toward western exploration. . . . Willing workers were abundant and Congress not difficult to persuade into granting the necessary funds. Hence expedition after expedition was organized and sent out, some purely military, some military and geographic, with geology only incidental, and others for the avowed purpose of geological and natural history research.[1]

As a result of this condition, six separate surveys of the western territories were functioning in 1874—two geological surveys under the Engineer Corps of the Army and two under the Department of the Interior, a land-parceling survey under the latter Department, and the Coast and Geodetic Survey under the Treasury Department. There was, moreover, little or no attempt at mutual collaboration, more or less overlapping, and consequent wasteful expenditure of time and of public funds.

When the Congressional act was approved, Marsh was in

1. George P. Merrill, *The First One Hundred Years of American Geology* (1924), p. 500. Yale University Press.

Europe. Upon his return in August, after consulting members of the Academy council and others, he at once set about fulfilling the mandate of Congress. In his own words, as given in his annual report for that year:

I was required to appoint a special committee to consider the subject. The report of the committee, when completed, could, in accordance with the constitution of the Academy . . . be transmitted directly to the government, and afterward to the academy at its next stated session. Inasmuch, however, as the subject to be considered was of great importance, I thought it better to have the report submitted first to the Academy before transmission to Congress.

In the appointment of this special committee it was obvious that I could not properly select as members any of those who had taken part in the controversy between the then existing government surveys; which contention, it was said, had resulted in the passage of the law for the proposed reorganization. Again, the subjects to be considered by the committee pertained to mensuration, geology, and natural history, and I therefore selected those who were familiar with these branches of science, namely: Prof. James D. Dana, whose long experience as geologist and naturalist of the Wilkes exploring expedition, and subsequent residence at Washington, while preparing his report, had especially fitted him to advise on government work; Prof. William B. Rogers, the Nestor of American geology, who had had long and varied experience with [state] geological and geographical surveys; Prof. J. S. Newberry, the State Geologist of Ohio, who had spent several years in the West on government exploring expeditions under the War Department; Prof. W. P. Trowbridge, a graduate of West Point, who, while a member of the Corps of Engineers, served for several years on the Coast Survey; Prof. Simon Newcomb, whose knowledge of mathematics and astronomy rendered his advice most valuable; and Prof. Alexander Agassiz, whose experience both in mining engineering and biology made him a fit representative of those departments.[2]

These appointments led to a protest by General Humphreys, Chief of Engineers, who asserted that "a properly constituted committee should have had among its members those officers in

2. *Ann. Rept., Nat. Acad. Sci.,* for 1878, 1879, p. 7.

the Government service whose duties consisted in part or in whole in making geodetic, topographic, or other scientific surveys in the different departments of the government."

Marsh next addressed letters to the Secretary of War and the Secretary of the Interior, informing them that the Academy committee had been appointed, and requesting any information as to their plans or wishes in regard to the scientific surveys under their departments that they might think proper to lay before it. Replies were received from the acting Chief of Engineers of the Army, from the Commissioner of the General Land Office, and from F. V. Hayden and J. W. Powell, both of whom had been in charge of Federal surveys.

The committee deliberated nearly three months, then handed in a report of about 2,000 words which was brought before a special meeting of the Academy at the autumn session in New York City. After three hours' discussion, the report was adopted, 31 members voting in the affirmative and one in the negative. The one dissenting vote was cast by Cope, who had been a member of the Government surveys conducted by Lieutenant Wheeler and Professor Hayden. Cope stated in the *American Naturalist* early in 1879 that, although he favored the adoption of the Academy report insofar as the unification of all geodetic work was concerned, and also in respect to the plan for the conduct of the Land Office, he felt that

as regards the geological work proper of the country, there is no such reason for consolidation. If the work be well done, it matters not to how many organizations it be confided, provided it be not duplicated, and of this there is now no danger.[3]

Early in December, Acting President Marsh transmitted to Congress the report of the committee, as approved by the Academy, and it was printed as Appendix D to the Report of the Academy for 1878–1879, pages 19–22.

The report recommended the recombination of the various surveys into three: (1) Coast and Geodetic Survey, "whose function will embrace all questions of position and mensuration." (2) United States Geological Survey, to determine "all questions relating to the geological structure and natural re-

3. *Amer. Nat.,* XIII (1879), 36.

sources of the public domain." (3) Land Office, to control "the disposition and sale of the public lands." All three organizations were to be within the Department of the Interior.

When the report was printed, the chief opposition to it came, as was to be expected, from the Engineers, and especially from their chief, General Humphreys, who, as Simon Newcomb wrote to Marsh, "opens the fight by a sort of hari-kari," resigning from the Academy. (It should be noted here that the two members of the Engineer Corps who were present at the special meeting to consider the reorganization plan, General Meigs and Professor Trowbridge, apparently voted in favor of it.) Despite the opposition, the House Committee on Appropriations incorporated the whole plan in a bill (House Resolution 6140) which was duly reported to Congress.

That Marsh was actively working in favor of the passage of the bill appears from the letter below:

> *Yale College Museum, New Haven, Connecticut,*
> *November 19, 1878.*

Dear Professor Rogers,—

You will be pleased to know that our Report was as well received in Washington as it was by the Academy. I telegraphed you that there was only one dissenting vote. The discussion went on for about two [three] hours, but no valid point was made against our Report.

I went to Washington on the 9th inst., and in less than two days got the approval of Secretary Schurz, Secretary Sherman, General Sherman, the President (so far as he had the plan before him), and Supt. Patterson of the Coast Survey. Professor Baird thinks the Report a very strong one, and that it will go through Congress without difficulty.

Altogether, I think we have done a grand piece of work, and one that will help the Academy very much.

I remain,

> Yours very truly,
> [Signed] O. C. MARSH.[4]

The final action by Congress accepted only that portion of the Academy's plan relating to the establishment of a single

4. *Life and Letters of William Barton Rogers* (1896), II, 358. Houghton Mifflin Company.

geological survey under the Department of the Interior. A commission was appointed to consider the codification of laws relating to the survey and disposition of the public domain, but the matter of the mensuration surveys was left for the present in abeyance.

Once the unified survey was established, the next important question to be decided was: Who is to be its director? Prominent in the struggle for this position were three of the men who had headed the earlier surveys, all three able and each backed by a strong following.[5] These men—F. V. Hayden, J. W. Powell, and Clarence King—offer an interesting study in contrasts.

Ferdinand Vandeveer Hayden (1829–87), born in Massachusetts, worked his way through Oberlin College and was graduated there in 1850, taking a degree in medicine at Albany, New York, three years later. While in that city, he made the acquaintance of James Hall, who sent him out to the badlands of the upper Missouri to collect fossils with F. B. Meek, then one of his assistants. He was in the West again in 1854, with Lieutenant Warren of the Engineers in the Dakotas and Montana in 1856 and 1857, with Meek in Kansas in 1858, with the Raynolds expedition to the upper Yellowstone region in 1859, and in the Dakota-Nebraska badlands for the Philadelphia Academy in 1866. During the Civil War he served as surgeon, rising to the rank of brevet lieutenant colonel. In June, 1865, he was appointed professor of Geology and Mineralogy in the University of Pennsylvania and remained there until 1872. In 1867, the value of his western work was recognized by Congress, which gave him an appropriation for a survey of his own, called the United States Geological and Geographical Survey of the Territories. As director of this survey, Hayden's administrative powers came into full swing, and the twelve volumes of reports of the so-called Hayden Survey, representing its work through 1878, are guideposts in American pioneer Geology.

John Wesley Powell (1834–1902), born in New York State, was almost wholly self-taught. He served with much gallantry

5. Lieut. G. M. Wheeler of the U. S. Engineers, who had headed the valuable United States Geographical Surveys West of the One Hundredth Meridian (1869–79), was out of the running once the principle of civil rather than military control was established.

in the Civil War, losing his right arm at Pittsburgh Landing, and at the end of the war held the rank of major. After the war he taught Geology in Illinois Wesleyan College at Bloomington, and he is said to have been the first college professor to combine field teaching with western exploration, taking a party of sixteen "naturalists, students, and amateurs" across the plains to the Colorado Rockies in 1867 and getting his supplies at government rates at military posts. In May-August, 1869, he made a trip through the Grand Canyon in a small boat, one of the most hazardous adventures in the field of exploration, which brought him much public acclaim. In 1871 to 1875 he returned to the Plateau region, first with a division of the Hayden Survey, and later with his own organization, the United States Geographical and Geological Survey of the Rocky Mountain Region. He displayed marked leadership and organizing ability, and his survey, like that of Hayden, did important work and published a series of valuable reports. It may be noted, in passing, that one of the members of his expeditions of 1874–76 was the able geologist, Capt. Clarence E. Dutton of the Ordnance Department, United States Army, graduate of Yale College with the class of 1860.

Clarence King (1842–1901), born at Newport, Rhode Island, and educated in classics and modern languages by his young and widowed mother, showed an early aptitude for natural science that finally led him to Yale, where he was graduated from the Sheffield Scientific School in 1862, in the same class with Marsh. At the age of twenty-five, after serving for some time with the Whitney Geological Survey of California,[6] he conceived the project of making a geological section across the entire Cordilleran system, and won an appropriation from Congress for this purpose. His organization, known as the United States Geological Exploration of the Fortieth Parallel, continued for ten years, and established once and for all King's fame as an organizer and a geologist. The last volume of seven in its final reports was a monograph by Marsh on the toothed birds of the Kansas Cretaceous.

6. King's popular book on his work in California, *Mountaineering in the Sierra Nevada,* is famous for its beauty of style as well as for the interest of its observations. First published in 1871, it went through several editions, and was reprinted in 1935.

Insofar as the qualifications of these three men for the post of director of the new Geological Survey were concerned, they seemed to stand about on equal footing. But before long the contest left the ground of qualifications and resolved itself into a struggle between rival camps. It became known shortly that there were two camps instead of three, and that Hayden was the odd man against the other two. It was indeed an epic struggle, and its final solution is one more tribute to the power of personality.

In the Indian country, Hayden often worked alone and unarmed, and the story is told that when the Indians, suspicious of his strange actions, took him captive, they were so puzzled by his lack of firearms that they concluded he must be a madman, and therefore not to be molested. He was, moreover, an able and experienced leader, as the success of his expeditions showed. Nevertheless, because of a diffidence that had handicapped him since his college days, he was bound to impress the casual acquaintance with doubts as to his administrative ability. Sir Archibald Geikie, director of the Geological Survey of Great Britain, one of his friends and admirers, later described him as having "a quiet enthusiasm for science, supported by an undemonstrative but indomitable courage, and a determination to gain the proposed end, cost what it might in bodily and mental endurance." At the same time, he said, Hayden had a tendency to keep himself in the background and to push forward his coworkers.[7]

Hayden and Marsh had been in occasional correspondence on scientific matters since 1867. The first letter from Hayden to Marsh that has a bearing on the present situation, dated December 8, 1873, shows that the latter had protested to Hayden about certain of the statements of Cope, who was then attached to the Hayden Survey. Hayden's reply was, in part:

Washington, D. C., Dec. 8, 1873.

My dear Professor Marsh:

Your letter of December 3d came to hand in due time. I have consulted with Prof. Baird and Mr. S. H. Scudder who happened to be here and they both agree with my own decision that I can

7. A. Geikie, "Ferdinand Vandeveer Hayden," *Nature* (February 2, 1888), pp. 326–327.

do nothing in the case except where Prof. Cope uses personalities. I insisted on that and obtained a promise to that effect, and I do not now know of a single personal allusion to you that could be offensive in the report for 1873. As to dates, claims for species or discoveries, those matters should be settled by the parties and they will be undoubtedly in due time. I do not consider myself competent to decide disputed claims. Prof. Cope presents me with a report. If I were to cut out such matter he would have a right to censure me much. He is alone responsible for the matter therein, and your way will be, to take up the report and review it, making the corrections. Cope's 4to report is not ready for publication yet. The Cretaceous of Kansas will appear first, but as long as he does not allude to you personally in an offensive way, I can do nothing. If he claims your species you must reclaim them and present your evidence.

Prof. Cope is one of the collaborators of the Survey, you are not, and have refused to become such though requested by me to become so many times within the last three years. You call upon me to decide against Cope in a matter [in] which Cope claims to be as much in the right as yourself, and which must be settled by experts. . . . I am sorry of course, but the above view is the only one I could take under any circumstances. . . .

Now in this matter you must take any course you see fit. My course is as plain as anything can be. Your disputed scientific claims must be wholly settled between yourselves (Cope and Marsh) and such experts as you can agree on. . . . The whole affair is a struggle in which I wish you well, but can do nothing more than I have done.

Yours sincerely,
[Signed] F. V. HAYDEN.

Two days before Marsh's election to the National Academy, he received the following note from Hayden.

Washington, D. C., April 20th, 1874.

My dear Marsh.

Your name is being used extensively here at this time by certain parties to sanction a statement that the survey of which I have charge is a fraud, etc. It is working to your disadvantage. Is the use of your name in such a connection authorized by you? Please write or telegraph me on receipt of this at my expense. I wish to make use of your reply for your own good.

Yours sincerely,

[Signed] F. V. HAYDEN.

Marsh's reply was:

[No date. From a pencil copy.]

My dear Hayden:

Your letter of the 20th came duly, and I regretted extremely to receive it. Your language could admit of only one interpretation, and that was an implied threat, that if I did not at once endorse your survey, I should suffer for it at the Academy. As no personal considerations whatever, could induce me to yield in such a case, I made no reply, leaving it for you to act as you saw fit. As the Academy will probably adjourn before this reaches you, I now answer your letter, with the same candor, but hardly with the kind feelings, that I should have done had you written me a straightforward letter about the rumors you allude to.

In contrast to Hayden, Major Powell was bluff, impetuous, vigorous, at times intolerant, making warm friends and equally warm enemies. He had seen the waste of effort and money in the rival surveys, and as early as 1874 had tried to reach an adjustment among them by mutual consent. When the consolidation came, therefore, he was in a strong position, and his active mind had already formulated a plan of organization for the new bureau, which he set before the investigating Academy Committee. It was because of this activity during the deliberation over the Academy plan that Powell felt he should not be a candidate for the directorship, and he put his support squarely behind King.

Simon Newcomb, the gifted mathematician connected with the Naval Observatory who was long one of Marsh's most active counselors on Washington affairs, wrote the latter on December 7, 1878, that the fight over the Academy report would apparently be won or lost in the Senate, "and there is where we want King." Which brings us to the one outstanding factor in the situation—the brilliant and captivating personality of Clarence King, of whom it was said that

Senators, representatives, and government officials of every grade
became at once his admiring friends. Fessenden, of Maine, after an
evening's companionship with King at Sam Hooper's genial dinner-
table, was himself almost persuaded to be a scientist, and professed
his conversion in saying, "If I were not United States Senator I
would be United States Geologist." Another senator, on the same
occasion, was so charmed by King's descriptive powers that he con-
fessed a strong desire to actually see with his own eyes "those
marvelous isothermal lines" which King had pictured to him with
the fascinating effect of an Aurora Borealis. . . .

When the Secretary of War handed King his letter of appointment, immediately after the accomplishment of the first necessary
legislation, authorizing the work [of the King Survey of the
Fortieth Parallel], he said, "Now, Mr. King, the sooner you get
out of Washington, the better—you are too young a man to be
seen about town with this appointment in your pocket—there are
four major-generals who want your place." [8]

It was not only senators and representatives who felt King's
charm, however, but any circle into which he stepped. He was a
favorite at the Century Club in New York, whose members published a special booklet in his memory. In Washington, his most
intimate friends were the John Hays and the Henry Adamses,
with whom he formed a group that was called "The Five of
Hearts." [9] The famous *Education of Henry Adams* contains
this passage:

King had everything to interest and delight Adams. He knew more
than Adams did of art and poetry; he knew America, especially
west of the hundredth meridian, better than anyone; he knew the
professor by heart, and he knew the congressman better than he
did the professor. . . . Incidentally he knew more practical
geology than was good for him, and saw ahead at least one generation further than the text-books. . . . His wit and humor;
his bubbling energy which swept everyone into the current of his
interest; his personal charm of youth and manners; his faculty of
giving and taking, profusely, lavishly, whether in thought or in

8. James D. Hague, "Memorabilia," in *Clarence King Memoirs* (1904),
pp. 382, 385. G. P. Putnam's Sons.
9. Mrs. Adams's letters, edited by Ward Thoron in 1936, show that Professor
Marsh was also a frequent visitor at her Washington home.

PLATE XVII

CLARENCE KING
FROM A PORTRAIT
IN THE SHEFFIELD SCIENTIFIC
SCHOOL

F. V. HAYDEN   J. W. POWELL

PLATE XVIII

MARSH ABOUT 1880   SPENCER F. BAIRD

"THE FOUR DIRECTORS"

LEFT TO RIGHT: CHARLES D. WALCOTT, J. W. POWELL, SIR ARCHIBALD GEIKIE, WILLIAM BULLOCK CLARK

TAKEN AT HARPERS FERRY IN 1896 BY PROFESSOR H. F. REID

money, as though he were nature herself, marked him almost alone among Americans. . . . One Clarence King only existed in the world . . . whatever prize he wanted lay ready for him—scientific, social, literary, political—and he knew how to take them in turn.[10]

When the smoke of battle cleared away that year of 1879, it is not surprising, therefore, that the first director of the new United States Geological Survey was Clarence King, appointed at a salary of $6,000 a year. Powell was made head of the Bureau of Ethnology, and Hayden, retained as a member of the new Survey, was given a large appropriation to complete his reports. King, however, served as director of the Survey but a single year, his resignation being ascribed to several reasons: in the first place, his health was not robust; in the second, he felt that he could render greater service to the science of Geology by continuing his theoretical research into its deeper problems than by devoting his time and strength to administrative work; and third, the official position made it impossible for him to take any of the remuneration that could easily have come to him as the result of his extensive mining experience, and that he much needed for financial obligations he had assumed. He was succeeded in 1881 by Major Powell, who retained the position until 1894. Later in life King suffered a mental breakdown, and after spending some time in Cuba with Henry Adams, in search of health, he died in California at the age of fifty-nine.

The organizing of the United States Geological Survey in accordance with the provisions of the National Academy report, the consequent abandonment of the several other surveys that had been enjoying Federal support, and the appointment of King to the directorship of the new organization established Marsh in a very strong position at Washington. In the struggle for the directorship he had taken a very active part, marshaling behind King the influence of many notable Yale alumni, as well as of scientists at other universities. The appointment of King therefore marked the first step in Marsh's ascendancy over his rival Cope, who had been the favored vertebrate paleontologist in the earlier surveys.

The rivalry between these two leading vertebrate paleontolo-

10. Henry Adams, *The Education of Henry Adams* (1918), p. 416. Houghton Mifflin Company.

gists had been increasing rapidly since the summer of 1871, but up to the time of the Survey reorganization it had been concerned chiefly with attempts to find new and striking fossil material and to describe and name the extinct animals that it represented. They had met in Berlin in Marsh's student days, and apparently their first impression of each other had not been especially favorable, although their respective accounts of the meeting, given later, were undoubtedly colored by what followed. In the early days of Marsh's professorship their correspondence was friendly—five to seven letters a year—and they made at least one collecting trip together in New Jersey. But in 1871, when Cope decided to invade one of Marsh's boneyards and collect vertebrates in the Bridger Basin of Wyoming, their relations ceased to be amicable. Marsh regarded as his own any fossil field that he discovered, and he had no intention of having it entered by a rival. This was a principle that Cope would not admit, and one that is not in the collectors' code of today, except within the limits set by the modern spirit of coöperation in scientific matters. But these were pioneer days, when astonishing discoveries were constantly being made, and such a spirit was far less existent. The years that followed saw a fight for supremacy in the western fossil fields that had many comic aspects, although it led to much bitterness. Information about new fields was sought by both from every possible quarter, collectors were lured away from one "bone sharp" only to reappear the next year on the payroll of the other, great precautions were taken to keep excavations secret, and there were as many false trails and "salted" clues as one might find in a lusty melodrama, the whole reaching its climax in the "dinosaur year" of 1877.

With rival parties collecting in rocks of the same age, often in adjacent areas, bones of the same sort of fossil animal were sure to be found, and in the race to name the animal first, more than one of the ancient western vertebrates received two baptisms, sometimes only a month apart, at times only a week, and on several occasions only a few days. Late in 1872, Marsh began to charge that Cope was predating certain of the publications in which his new species of animals were being named, so as to insure their priority under the rules of nomenclature. He hammered away at this point in at least four different papers during that year, presenting documentary evidence, and meeting with denials and countercharges from Cope.

Cope, as a member of the Hayden and Wheeler surveys, had made large collections of fossil vertebrates, mostly of fragmentary material, and had described the remains in many reports or monographs, culminating in one so large that it was usually known as "Cope's Bible." His position at Washington had seemed secure, and his opportunities for vertebrate work unlimited. Like Marsh, he had at his disposal a considerable fortune. However, his expenditures for collectors to compete with Marsh, his purchase of a periodical (*American Naturalist*) to ensure immediate publication of his results,[11] and his ill-judged investments in Mexican silver mines, led him into financial difficulty at the end of the decade. The change in Survey affairs which placed Marsh in the favored position was therefore a severe blow, not only to his prestige, but to his finances as well. It meant that he could look for no further support from the Government in his field work, which was extremely expensive, and that funds would be forthcoming only to complete the publication of what he had in hand—and this at a time when his own fortune had largely disappeared. Thus hampered in his work, he never ceased to try to regain the ground lost at Washington. The ways in which he went about this are indicated in considerable detail in Professor Osborn's story of Cope's life,[12] especially in the exchange of letters between the

11. In the matter of a publication medium, Marsh was of course fortunate, with the pages of the *American Journal of Science*, appearing the first of each month, always open to him. The "mutual assistance pact" between the two was of much value to both, since the *Journal* gained added interest and prestige from the notices and descriptions of Marsh's striking discoveries, and Marsh could rush these into print with at most a few weeks' delay. During the four decades covered by his publications, the *Journal* printed 204 of his papers, with a total of a few less than 1,000 pages. In the year 1872, when results from the first two student expeditions were coming thick and fast, and when the race with Cope for priority was on in earnest, Marsh papers in the *Journal* numbered 20 (7 in the October number alone), with a total of 85 pages. Many of his papers were only a page or so long, but their qualitative importance was often great.

It must be admitted that Marsh's habit of doing things at the last possible moment gave the editors and printers of the *Journal* many moments of exasperation. This resulted in an arrangement whereby his papers could appear as an appendix, and thus not disturb the make-up of the rest of the issue.

12. H. F. Osborn, *Cope: Master Naturalist* (1931). Princeton University Press.

two which appears on pages 378–394. He made little headway, however, and in 1890 a newspaper writer by the name of W. H. Ballou persuaded him to tell his grievances to the world through the medium of the press. His sensational attack on Marsh, transcribed and headlined by Ballou, and including statements from a number of Marsh's assistants, was launched in the New York *Herald* on Sunday, January 12, 1890; and was met, a week later, by an even more detailed reply from Marsh, with retractions from some of the men quoted by Cope, the whole furnishing an unparalleled public washing of dirty paleontological linen. The quarrel became a *cause célèbre,* into which were drawn almost all the vertebrate paleontologists of the decade, and the echoes have not even yet entirely died away.

Marsh has been charged with being an unscrupulous pirate in matters paleontological—there is abundant evidence in letters at Yale to show that such methods were not confined to either party. And that this is true for other aspects of the controversy is only too apparent from the astonishing Cope-Osborn correspondence. Nevertheless, the present writers feel that enough time and space have been devoted to the personal aspects of this quarrel of long ago, and that nothing is to be gained by discussing them in further detail.

There is, however, another aspect of the dispute which, inasmuch as it involves the National Academy, should be dealt with briefly. In his newspaper attack on Marsh, Cope said:

There is attached to the government, and authorized by an act of Congress, an institution called the "National Academy of Sciences." Professor O. C. Marsh is president of it and its functions are chiefly to investigate scientific questions authorized by Congress. . . .

One of the first acts of Major Powell and Professor Marsh was to get practical control of this Academy for their mutual uses. As many as possible of the staff of the Geological Survey were elected members, and many members of the academy were given pap in the survey. By these means Professor Marsh has been retained at the head of the society.

An analysis of the elections to the Academy from the annual reports—a source as available to Cope as to the present writers, presumably—shows that in the twelve years of Marsh's presidency, five members of the United States Geological Survey were elected: G. K. Gilbert (1883), C. E. Dutton (1884), Arnold Hague (1885), C. A. White (1889), and S. F. Emmons (1892). Hayden's membership dated from 1873, King was elected in 1876, and Powell in 1880. Furthermore, of the thirty-seven Academicians elected to all divisions of the Academy during Marsh's term, but eight were Washingtonians. Professor Marsh's strength lay, of course, in the fact that he had support not only from Washington but from many of the college Academicians as well, Alexander Agassiz of Harvard being a notable exception.

Cope then went on to say:

All questions relating to the survey that Congress has referred to the academy have been controlled by Professor Marsh, who appointed committees with majorities composed of members of the survey, such committees reporting as instructed by Marsh and Powell. When the question of a consolidation of the scientific departments of the government came before the academy its subsidized committee rendered a cut and dried report by which the Geological Survey was made more powerful rather than curtailed. When the academy was ordered to investigate [in 1884] in connection with a committee of Congress the Geological Survey, friends and members of the survey were put on the committee appointed by Marsh, and again the survey profited.

The composition of the 1878 committee has already been discussed; it contained no member of the "Washington group," strictly speaking. Simon Newcomb, although connected with the Naval Observatory, had strong academic affiliations, and he was, moreover, a notable free lance. Newberry had been on one of the early surveys for a while, but at the time of the report he was teaching in Columbia College. Professor Trowbridge, a West Pointer, and a member of the Engineer Corps, had served for several years on the Coast Survey, but was likewise teaching at Columbia in 1878.

The 1884 Academy committee, requested to confer with Congress on the organization of the Signal Service, the Geological Survey, the Coast and Geodetic Survey, and the Hydrographic Office, consisted of General Meigs, W. H. Brewer of Yale, Gen. Cyrus B. Comstock, Samuel P. Langley (not then at Washington), Simon Newcomb, E. C. Pickering of Harvard, W. P. Trowbridge, Francis A. Walker of the Massachusetts Institute of Technology, and Charles A. Young of Princeton. Subsequently, Newcomb and Comstock resigned.

By his ill-judged attack on the Survey and the Academy, as well as on Marsh, Osborn admits,

Cope arrayed against himself not only the entire staff of the Geological Survey, but the entire group of anti-Cope members of the National Academy of Sciences; the officers of the Department of the Interior under which the Survey was operated; Marsh's colleagues in Yale College, and Marsh's numerous friends and acquaintances abroad and in America.[13]

Powell, in reply to this same charge, said that the Academy committee appointed in 1878 called on Hayden and himself and others for opinions and suggestions, which were presented in writing and later published. He continued:

At that time Professor Marsh was acting as president of the Academy, but I was not a member of that body and had no official relations with Professor Marsh and only a slight acquaintance with him. . . . At the time I wrote my letter I did not expect to become connected with it when it was organized. Clarence King was made its first director, and I at once engaged in other work [Ethnology] under the Smithsonian Institution, to which work I expected and hoped to devote my life.

In 1881 Clarence King resigned in order to engage in great mining enterprises, and my nomination as director of the survey was thereupon sent to the Senate without my solicitation and without my knowledge. A few days after this President Garfield said to the members of the National Academy that he had consulted but one man in relation to my nomination; that when Mr. King sent in his resignation he sent for him and asked him to withdraw it, and that when assured that that was impossible he immediately sent for Professor Baird, by whose advice he immediately sent my name to the Senate.[14]

13. H. F. Osborn, *op. cit.*, p. 403.
14. An interesting sidelight on this appears in the letters of Mrs. Henry Adams, who wrote her father on April 24, 1881, that "King beams with joy at being out of office. He and Mr. Hay were as eager to get out as most fools to get in." And on March 27, 1881, she says that King is about to leave for a trip,

The facts which I have stated constitute all the basis there is for any charge of intrigue between the Academy and myself.

Professor Marsh, in his reply to Cope's attack, likewise vigorously defended himself and the Academy.

Cope and Theodore Gill opposed Marsh's election to the presidency of the Academy in 1883, persuading James Hall to run against him; and President Barnard of Columbia was the candidate of another group. When Marsh was reëlected in 1889, Cope wrote Osborn: "You see that the National Academy has disgraced itself again." According to Henry Shaler Williams, as quoted in the New York *Herald* for January 13, 1890, Cope at this election again endeavored to defeat Marsh. However, Williams adds,

The fact is, Professor Marsh had been president of the Academy for six years and it was generally considered that it was time for some one else to be elected. Mr. Cope's strenuous opposition had such a reflex action that the other members elected Marsh a second time, showing that the National Academy supported him against the attacks of Mr. Cope.

"having got out of office, named and seen confirmed his successor, Powell of Illinois, in whom he has great confidence. He did it so noiselessly that Professor Hayden, who would have done his best to upset it, knew nothing of it till it was done." (*Letters of Mrs. Henry Adams* [1936], pp. 286, 278. Little, Brown & Company.)

CHAPTER XI

MARSH AS VERTEBRATE PALEONTOLO-
GIST OF THE UNITED STATES
GEOLOGICAL SURVEY

WHEN Spencer F. Baird was appointed assistant secretary of the Smithsonian Institution in 1850, he was confronted with an entire lack of natural history material, and yet he was expected *to build up a national museum on an allowance of about $2,000 a year for research studies,* one fourth the amount appropriated for guards and for governmental red tape; i.e., administration. Nevertheless, he did somehow get together a fine foundation for a national collection, and he became the leading fructifier of the Smithson bequest, for in his time the Smithsonian grew into one of the greatest biological laboratories in the world. In his quest for specimens of living plants and animals, he laid his hands on every American naturalist of his time, and many of them became "Baird's missionaries"; Audubon was one of these, and from him Baird received a considerable part of his collection of birds. Within Washington, Baird's friendly nature had made him liked by most of the leaders, in and out of Congress, and he was very influential both in scientific and in Government circles.

Previous to 1870, Baird's only method of acquiring fossil vertebrates for the Smithsonian was through the several Federal surveys operating in the Rocky Mountain country. Gifts of specimens from other sources were rare and usually of little scientific value. But when Marsh's spectacular success as a collector came to his attention, he thought he saw a chance to build up the national collections as well, and letters were frequent between them beginning as early as 1870. In 1881, when Baird's good friend, Major Powell, was made director of the newly organized Geological Survey, he, too, turned to Marsh for help in securing fossil vertebrates, preferring to deal with him rather than with the trouble-making Cope. Moreover, aside from assistance along scientific lines, Powell knew very well that

Marsh could be of much help in easing the annual Survey appropriations through Congress, by means of his Yale influence, his wide personal acquaintance with important men, and his leadership in the National Academy.

Marsh's official connection with the Survey was established in August, 1882, his appointment as Vertebrate Paleontologist lying on his desk when he returned from Europe early in September. On May 10, 1887, Baird appointed him Honorary Curator of the Department of Vertebrate Paleontology in the United States National Museum. This position he held until the time of his death, although his active field work for the Survey was terminated in 1892, as told in Chapter XIII.

In Beecher's biography of Marsh, the statement is made that Marsh accepted this Survey appointment only "after repeated solicitations and with promises of material aid in the way of publications and collections." Why was Marsh so reluctant to accept the offer of a Government position? This question was answered fully by Marsh himself in a letter to Walcott in 1898, quoted in later pages, but it seems desirable at this point to attempt to explain the circumstances that lay behind his statements, even at the risk of a lengthy digression. Between 1868 and 1882, Marsh had carried on his explorations at his own expense, spending in this way, he says, about $200,000. All the collections thus accumulated were indisputably his own. By joining the Federal Survey, he would no longer be able to claim or control the fossils collected by his staff, and it was this aspect that made him hesitate, especially when he considered the possibility of "type specimens." In his statement he says that Baird, confronted with this first objection, promised verbally that he "should also have a series of the specimens thus secured . . . an agreement he made with other scientific branches of the Government, and still in force." Regarding type specimens, "Professor Baird endeavored to remove this objection . . . also, but without success. The new law of 1879, relating to Government collections, required that all specimens, 'when no longer needed for investigations in progress, shall be deposited in the National Museum,' a provision I myself had placed in the law." The pressure from Washington continued, however, and finally, Marsh says, "the proposal made to me to aid the Government was *more favorably presented* [italics ours] by both the Director of the Geological Survey and Professor Baird, and the position of Paleontologist in the Survey was accepted by me, July 1st, 1882."

None of these "more favorable" aspects of the agreement were put in writing, as subsequent search through the files in Washington demonstrated. Nevertheless, the present authors believe that there was a "gentlemen's agreement" between Marsh and Baird and between Marsh and Powell as to the distribution of the material to be collected by Marsh. In fact, Professor A. E. Verrill of Yale told the senior author that he had a similar "understanding" with Baird in regard to the marine invertebrates collected for the Fish Commission.[1]

Why were these supposed verbal "promises" made? In Verrill's case, because the Fish Commission had no money with which to pay salaries to him and to his coworker, Professor Sydney I. Smith. By coöperation with these two zoologists, however, Baird was getting for the National Museum an abundance of authenticated material, identified as to species; and through their publications on this material, the basic principle of the Smithson bequest—"for the increase and diffusion of knowledge among men"—was being made a reality. In Marsh's case, because Baird wanted the superior kind of fossil material that Marsh was getting; Marsh himself relates that when Baird was shown one small drawer of his collection in 1871, he remarked that it contained fossils of more scientific value than all previous expeditions had brought back from the West and deposited in the National Museum.

1. It is interesting to recall that Professor Bache of the Coast Survey had somewhat similar arrangements with Louis Agassiz. In 1851, the Survey wanted Agassiz' help in charting the constantly changing geography of the Florida Keys, which stretch for more than 150 miles from Biscayne Bay to beyond Key West. These changes are due to the rapid growth of reef-making corals, and Agassiz spent ten weeks studying these colorful animal gardens, with their menace to the mariner. During the investigation, he was allowed to collect the corals in great quantities, and these collections, it appears, were regarded by the contracting parties as compensation for his otherwise unpaid services.

The Coast Survey called on Agassiz again in 1871–72, and he and his assistants spent a year on the *Hassler,* cruising along the coasts of the Americas from Boston to San Francisco, and studying the life dredged up by the vessel. In his Museum Report for 1872 (pp. 6–8), Agassiz states, however, that this opportunity for making "magnificent collections . . . did not provide in any way for the expenses incident upon the making of the collections, their preservation or their transportation to Cambridge." These further expenses were met by friends of Agassiz, who raised $17,450 for that purpose.

On this matter of the growth of the fossil collections in the National Museum, we have testimony from W. H. Dall, conchologist of the Smithsonian Institution from 1866 to 1927. Speaking at the memorial meeting to G. Brown Goode, Baird's successor in charge of the National Museum, Dall had this to say:

To Baird and Goode's untiring labors we are indebted for the National Museum. . . . [Secretary Joseph] Henry was determined that the "increase and diffusion of knowledge among men" in the highest and broadest sense of the words should be the object to be attained, and that nothing local and special should absorb the funds or the energies of the Institution. . . . Professor Henry knew that the resources of the Smithsonian could not support a great museum or a great library and still carry out the promotion of science in the wider sense, which was his ideal aim. He wished for a national museum and a national library, but only at national expense. He approved of the far-reaching explorations and collections which the genius of Professor Baird initiated and by untiring labors promoted, but he did not wish the enormous mass of material thus brought together to be a charge upon the slender funds of the Institution. His policy was to distribute to other institutions of learning, museums, and colleges, as soon as worked up, everything except a typical series of the specimens [not *type specimens,* but a correctly labeled set], thus at once promoting research at other points and economizing space and the expenses of preservation. Arrangements were made with naturalists all over the country by which material in their special lines of research was shipped to them as soon as received, and remained indefinitely, until reported upon [in other words, they were paid no salary but the retained specimens were held to compensate for the time spent] . . . .

Meanwhile Baird's ambitions and endeavors were leading toward the establishment of a national museum in fact, if not in name. Multitudinous expeditions were set on foot. . . . From each and all of these a stream of the most precious material for study flowed toward the Smithsonian Institution. . . . A bevy of students, poor in purse, but rich in enthusiasm, in energy and devotion, found shelter there. . . . How difficult in such a case to hold the balance true! To preserve for study what was needed and yet not to exceed the limits imposed by circumstances. To be loyal and true in spirit, as well as in letter, to the policy of the chief, and yet to hold securely for the future that which the future would need. Yet this task, so perplexing and so difficult, was successfully performed by Baird.[2]

All this is no reflection on one of the most loved of American biologists. Acquisition of material was for Spencer F. Baird only the first step, since the more important thing, the "purposed end of all accumulation," was the diffusion of knowledge. One of his outstanding characteristics, moreover, was his absolute indifference as to who should have the credit, so long as the work was done. It was not the men of science whom he feared, but the human nature so abundantly manifest in the political heat of Washington.

With the control of his specimens satisfactorily adjusted between himself and the Washington authorities, Marsh entered upon his work as Vertebrate Paleontologist for the Survey. The connection thus established had at least two important results, one of which was certainly not foreseen. In the first place, the greatly increased funds at his disposal made it possible for him to bring together a wealth of material that was at the time unequaled, and that formed a permanent enrichment of the science of Vertebrate Paleontology. In the second place, the very bulk of these collections, and the time spent in directing their acquisition, preparation, and study, so overburdened him that he was unable to bring to fruition, personally, the many extensive monographs that he had planned, and this work had to be left to others.

During his ten years of active service on the Geological Survey, Marsh had at least fifty-four persons on his staff, some serving for a month or more during a field season, others employed for a year or, in one instance, for as long as nine years. Thirty-seven of them collected fossils in the Rocky Mountain region, nine were preparators, who freed the bones from the rock matrix and assembled them, and eight were either assistants in Paleontology, illustrators, or clerical helpers. For this service, for field and freight bills, and for laboratory material, the Survey paid nearly $150,000. Of this amount, $39,480 went to Marsh and was put by him back into the work. His

2. *Ann. Rept., U. S. Nat. Mus.,* for 1897, Pt. II (1901), pp. 25–27.

staff was paid about $103,250, freight charges took $5,500, and laboratory supplies $1,500.[3] These figures do not include the cost of lithographic plates or woodcuts, or of printing three memoirs by Marsh that appeared between 1885 and 1896.

The idea of monographing various groups represented among the fossils coming in so abundantly from the Rocky Mountain country was in Marsh's mind already in the seventies. His plan then was: (1) to make as large collections as the boneyards of the West would yield and his purse could pay for; (2) to publish brief preliminary papers descriptive of this material as fast as it could be developed out of the rock by his preparators; (3) to illustrate the material by wash drawings reproduced on stone, ready for printing by the lithographic method then in vogue and so satisfactory to an artistic eye, but very costly; and finally (4) to describe the fossils in detail in the monographic manner. This plan was exemplified by the striking volume on birds with teeth, which the King Survey published in 1880, and of which we shall hear more later.

When Marsh became Vertebrate Paleontologist of the Federal Survey, his earlier plan widened out greatly, as may be seen from the following letter sent him by Director Powell on May 23, 1885:

Prof. O. C. Marsh,
New Haven, Conn.,

Dear Sir:

I have the honor to acknowledge receipt of a memorandum from yourself setting forth your plan for the publication of nine volumes of vertebrate paleontology, as follows:

Monographs:

Vol. I. Odontornithes (Toothed Birds), 34 Plates and 40 woodcuts. 1880. [Already published.]

Vol. II. Dinocerata (Terrible Horn), 56 Plates and 200 woodcuts. 1884. [Author's edition published in 1885, Survey edition in 1886.]

Vol. III. Sauropoda (Lizard Feet), 90 Plates.

3. Compiled from data prepared by the United States Geological Survey after Marsh's death, to facilitate the separation of the material belonging to the Survey from that of Professor Marsh. The senior author saw this manuscript at the time the separation was being made and he was again allowed access to it in 1936.

Vol. IV. Stegosauria (Plated Lizard), 65 Plates.
Vol. V. Brontotheridae (Thunder Beast), 60 Plates.
Vol. VI. Ornithopoda (Bird Feet), 60 Plates.
Vol. VII. Theropoda (Beast Feet), 60 Plates.
Vol. VIII. Pteranodontia, 50 Plates.
Vol. IX. Mosasauria, 80 Plates.

The comprehensive plan which you present covers a very interesting and important field of paleontology, and is hereby approved.

I am, with respect,
Yours, etc.,
[Signed] J. W. POWELL
Director.

On April 23, 1887, Powell approved, in addition, Monograph X on Jurassic mammals, and on February 7, 1893, Monograph XI on Ceratopsidae.

With his plan of action thus crystallized and approved, the decade from 1882 to 1892 turned out to be the busiest one of Marsh's life. Direction of the many collectors required much correspondence, and in several years their work was inspected in the field. When he was at the Museum, he made the rounds of the preparators almost every day, often retarding their work by telling them to go so far in unearthing the bones from the rocks and no farther until he saw them again. Most of his time, however, was occupied in directing his assistants in Paleontology, who were carrying out definite lines of research under his guidance; in consultation with the artist who was making drawings of the bones; and in laying out plates for the lithographer and wood blocks for the engraver. In the course of these ten years, drawings were made for more than 300 plates (including those for the Dinocerata volume), and at least 246 of these were lithographed. Among the plates thus assembled were the following:

Brontothere monograph	60
Sauropod monograph	90
Stegosaur monograph	63
Ceratopsia monograph	19
Theropoda monograph	14
	246

Marsh died before any one of Monographs III–XI was completed, and, in fact, no finished manuscript for them was found. In the ten years that he was connected with the Survey, his published output numbered about 40 papers, aside from the memoir on the Dinocerata. For the previous decade, the number had been more than 100, exclusive of the monograph on the toothed birds. Subsequent to 1892, when his active connection with the Survey ceased, that organization published his important memoir on the North American dinosaurs (1896) and his long paper on the vertebrate fossils of the Denver Basin (1896).

Some idea of the magnitude of the task that Marsh laid out for himself may be gained by looking at the subsequent history of the monographs he had planned, and for which he had gathered the material. In 1900, the year after Marsh's death, Director Walcott of the United States Geological Survey turned over to Professor Henry F. Osborn, who succeeded Marsh as Vertebrate Paleontologist of that organization, all of Marsh's work that belonged to the Survey, consisting of about two hundred carefully prepared lithographic plates, many drawings and wood engravings, but no manuscript whatever.[4] In an attempt to carry out Marsh's plan, Osborn invited F. A. Lucas to write the monograph on the Stegosauria (Vol. IV of Marsh's outline). This project did not materialize and in 1906 the task was turned over to C. W. Gilmore, who restricted himself to the Marsh Collection in the National Museum, and published his results in 1914 ("Osteology of the armored Dinosauria in the United States National Museum," *Bull.* 89, U. S. Nat. Mus., 136 pages, 36 plates). Gilmore described more Marsh material in 1920 in his "Osteology of the carnivorous Dinosauria" (*Bull.* 110, U. S. Nat. Mus., 159 pages, 36 plates), and in this work published 14 of the plates made for Professor Marsh's Volume VII.

No general monograph on the Theropoda (VII) is being written nor on the Ornithopoda (VI), but of at least one ornithopod family, the Trachodontidae, the knowledge has increased to such an extent that a study of it by Professor Richard S. Lull and Nelda M. Wright has produced a manuscript

4. H. F. Osborn, in J. B. Hatcher, O. C. Marsh, and R. S. Lull, "The Ceratopsia," *Mon.* 49, U. S. Geol. Surv. (1907), p. xiii.

of at least 500 pages, which is nearly ready for publication.

The Ceratopsia monograph (XI) was given into the hands of J. B. Hatcher, who had collected nearly all the material. He died in 1904, in the midst of his studies. The work was brought to publication by Professor Lull and appeared in 1907 as Survey Monograph 49 (300 pages, 51 plates, 19 of them the original ones of Marsh). It was followed in 1933 by Lull's "A revision of the Ceratopsia or horned dinosaurs," (*Mem. Peabody Mus. Nat. Hist.*, Vol. III, Pt. 3, 175 pages, 17 plates).

Osborn himself undertook to monograph the Sauropoda (III) and the Brontotheridae (V). The sauropod monograph still remains unpublished, although Osborn reported it to be "well advanced" in 1930. The brontothere volume finally appeared in 1929 in two large and handsome quartos bearing the title, "The titanotheres of ancient Wyoming, Dakota, and Nebraska" (*Mon.* 55, U. S. Geol. Surv., 953 pages, 236 plates).

George G. Simpson took up the projected monograph on Jurassic and Cretaceous mammals (X) and published in 1929 an important volume entitled "American Mesozoic Mammalia" (*Mem. Peabody Mus. Nat. Hist.*, Vol. III, Pt. 1, 171 pages, 32 plates).

The Marsh pterodactyl material (VIII) was monographed in 1910 by George F. Eaton under the title, "Osteology of *Pteranodon*" (*Mem. Conn. Acad. Arts Sciences*, II, 38 pages, 31 plates).

In the summer of 1931, the Federal Survey, through Professor Osborn, distributed sets of the 200-odd plates belonging to the 3 first monographs listed in Director Powell's letter, sending them to 71 institutions and paleontologists in America and to 70 in foreign countries, and keeping 350 sets in reserve.

Marsh's connection with the Survey in an active capacity ceased in July, 1892, for reasons dealt with in a later chapter. He was then made Honorary Paleontologist in charge of Vertebrate Paleontology, without salary, in the hope that he would be able to complete some of the work already in hand. When Powell resigned from the directorship of the Survey in 1894, he was succeeded, to Marsh's delight, by Charles D. Walcott, who had for several years been in charge of the Division of Paleontology. To Walcott, therefore, fell the task of steering his way through the maze created by the presence of so much

Government material in New Haven, in charge of a man who was no longer connected with the Survey except in an honorary capacity. That he carried the matter through so smoothly is one more tribute to his administrative ability.

During the later years of Marsh's field work for the Survey, there had been much talk, chiefly from Cope, about Marsh's intention to retain for himself, and eventually for Yale University, a considerable part of the vertebrate fossils collected for the Government. These charges appeared in print as a part of Cope's attack on Marsh in the New York *Herald* of January 12, 1890. In refutation, the *Herald* of the succeeding day quoted Professor Osborn, Cope's best friend, as saying: "It is not true that Yale is gobbling [!] up these treasures. It is not true that the government specimens are not strictly labelled, for they are. I have myself been there and seen them." Early in 1891, Walcott made a visit to New Haven, Cambridge, and Ithaca to inspect the Government collections in the hands of scientists outside of Washington, and his letter to Marsh after his return to Washington is quoted in part, because of its bearing on this same matter:

April 2, 1891.

I made a short verbal report to the Director regarding the collections under your charge at New Haven, and he appeared to be very much pleased with it. Personally, I was delighted to see such elegant material, and to find that you had such a thorough and complete system for recording, labeling and taking care in every way of the specimens that have come to your charge from the field.

The question of Marsh's choice of type specimens, as between his own or Government material, was also one that was frequently aired, Walcott writing him on March 2, 1892:

There seems to be an impression that the types have been selected from your private collections rather than from the material belonging to the government, and material belonging to the government that was used as types has been transferred by some system of exchange to your collections.

I think you had best make up your report upon the types as soon as you conveniently can do so, as the agitation is liable to be kept up until something authoritative is available on the subject.

Marsh made some response to these charges in his printed report, quoted later, but the following pages give further evidence on this matter of "types" and their evaluation in the years when most of Marsh's collections were being made and described. In this connection, the senior author wishes to cite a few facts concerning type specimens in the National Museum which came to his personal knowledge when he was a member of its staff. Previous to 1896, there had been no catalogues of type specimens in the Geological Department of the Museum, and the making of such began after a circular letter had been issued by Director Goode on December 17, 1895, asking for a statement "showing the number of species, represented by types, in each department." In 1896, while Schuchert was at work on a catalogue of the Paleozoic types in his charge, T. W. Stanton came into his office to introduce Honorary Curator C. A. White, and the conversation turned to type specimens. White said that early in his career in the National Museum he had carefully labeled and marked, but had not listed, all the old types that he could recognize in the collections, but that he seemed to be the only one there who was interested in the subject at the time. As stated earlier in this chapter, it was Baird's great wish to build up the collections into national scope, and toward this end he was willing that naturalists should divide the material collected, keeping about half of it in consideration of the time they put on its collecting and study. It appears that nothing was said about type specimens, and these were often kept by the authors who described the types.

In 1898, Marsh made public announcement of the gift of his collections to Yale University. Walcott sent a letter of congratulation to New Haven, and added that the announcement, which received wide publicity, had naturally brought him inquiries as to the status of the Government collections at New Haven. (One of these was from W. H. Ballou, Cope's "ghost writer" of 1890, later editor of the New York *Dispatch.)* Walcott suggested that Marsh write him a letter, "stating how, in event of your death, the government collections could be readily distinguished and taken in charge by some one connected with the Survey." The two then had a conference over this matter in New York. Returning home, Marsh prepared an elaborate statement and sent a copy to Walcott. The latter, however, was away from his office at the time, and when he returned he found not only the typed report, but page proof, and a printed copy as well. He telegraphed Marsh at once not to distribute the pamphlet or have it published in the *American Journal of Science;* and then, by letter, offered serious objections to the report as it stood, inasmuch as it had been drawn up as an official document, rather than as the "personal statement" that he had expected it to be.

On the pages immediately following are excerpts from the report of February 10, 1898, which Director Walcott told Marsh to suppress, and from the later report of May 27, 1898, which replaced it. Marsh's printed bibliographies state that there was a second edition of the first report, issued on March 5, but this has not been seen.

THE VERTEBRATE PALEONTOLOGY OF THE U. S. GEOLOGICAL SURVEY AND NATIONAL MUSEUM

BY O. C. MARSH,

Paleontologist of the Survey, and Honorary Curator of the Museum.

New Haven, Conn., February 10, 1898.
Hon. Charles D. Walcott,

Director U. S. Geological Survey.

SIR:—Your letter of January 22, congratulating both Yale University and myself on the recent gift of my scientific collections to that institution, was duly received and also promptly acknowledged.

In this letter, you likewise referred to some recent inquiries regarding the Government collections of fossils obtained by me in the West, and now in my custody. This affords me the opportunity for which I have long been waiting, to give an account of my connection with the U. S. Geological Survey, as well as with the National Museum, and thus settle once for all several points which apparently have been misunderstood by persons not familiar with the subject.

A clear understanding of this matter can be best obtained, perhaps, from a resumé of my connections with these two organizations —the National Museum and Geological Survey—from the beginning down to the present time. I shall make this review as brief as possible under all the circumstances, reserving a more complete statement for another occasion.

INTRODUCTION.

. . . .

It is due to myself to state that during the first fourteen years of my western work (1868–1882), all my explorations were carried on entirely at my own expense, and all collections made were, of course, my own. These extensive collections of vertebrate fossils I have recently presented to Yale University, and with them others previously obtained and relating mainly to different branches of science.

HISTORICAL STATEMENT.

(1) The late Prof. Baird, of the Smithsonian Institution, when in New Haven in 1871, examining the collections I had recently made in the Rocky Mountains, said to me that one small drawer before him contained "fossils of more scientific value than all previous expeditions had brought back from the West." In this drawer were various new mammals, birds, and reptiles, in fine preservation, discovered in the Eocene near Fort Bridger, Wyoming, and collected by a careful systematic method first introduced by me. Prof. Baird then urged me to reserve some of my rare duplicate fossils for the Smithsonian Museum. This request he repeated on various other occasions, each time more urgently.

(2) In 1880, in Washington, Prof. Baird, then Secretary of the Smithsonian, again spoke earnestly to me of the fact that the National Museum still had almost nothing in the way of vertebrate fossils from the West, while during the previous ten years I had secured there extensive collections already widely known on account of containing so many extinct forms new to science. These collections, Prof. Baird said, were already larger than any one university could use, while the national collection at Washington remained of little account. He therefore again strongly urged me to aid the Government in securing in the West remains of extinct vertebrates for the National Museum. In one conversation lasting several hours, he brought forward many arguments to induce me to undertake this work. One argument was that the Government would furnish all the money needed for explorations, and would

bear the entire expense of publishing the results, while the whole work of collecting and describing the new material would be under my charge. That I should also have a series of the specimens thus secured, was another of Prof. Baird's propositions, an agreement he made with other scientific branches of the Government, and still in force.

These offers I at first declined, mainly on the ground that I had for twenty years carried on explorations with success, entirely at my own expense. This, I feared, might make it difficult for me to work under Government officials, and perhaps under directions that my own judgment might not approve.

(3) Another objection of much weight with me related to type specimens. I had always regarded these of much greater importance than did most American naturalists, and had [since 1876] carefully preserved together my own numerous types in fire-proof buildings. . . .

The Smithsonian and the National Museum were then not safe repositories, neither being fire-proof, and thus were especially liable to injury or destruction, as one disastrous fire in the Smithsonian had already proved. Prof. Baird endeavored to remove this objection in regard to type specimens, also, but without success. The new law of 1879, relating to Government collections, required that all specimens, "when no longer needed for investigations in progress, shall be deposited in the National Museum," a provision I myself had placed in the law.

(4) Subsequently, the proposal made to me to aid the Government was more favorably presented by both the Director of the Geological Survey and Prof. Baird, and the position of Paleontologist on the Survey was accepted by me, July 1st, 1882. My duties as stated in the official appointment were mainly to collect vertebrate fossils, and describe those of scientific interest. These fossils were first to be sent to New Haven, because their investigation required direct comparison with typical specimens, American and foreign, in the Yale Museum, which contained by far the largest collection in this country. Moreover, there was then, as now, no room available in the Smithsonian or in the National Museum itself at all adapted to the preservation and preparation of extensive collections of vertebrate fossils during their investigation and description. . . .

THE NATIONAL MUSEUM.

(5) In 1886, Prof. Baird asked me to accept the position of Honorary Curator of Vertebrate Paleontology in the National Museum, and thus have charge of that department, including the specimens placed there by me after my investigations and descriptions were completed. This position I accepted. . . .

(6) My first plan was to have large collections of vertebrate fossils placed on exhibition as soon as possible, and this duty clearly devolved upon the present U. S. Geological Survey, as all the other Government expeditions and surveys, from Lewis and Clark at the beginning of the century down to the present time, had only left in the National Museum, as a record, one small case of vertebrate fossils, however extensive the collections made may have been. To begin the work I had thus planned for the National Museum, I sent 72 large boxes of Pliocene fossils to Washington, in 1886 . . . and they were finally stored in the Armory, February 8, 1887.

An important collection of 4 boxes of vertebrate fossils, secured from the Pliocene of Florida in 1890, by my assistant on the Geological Survey, I sent, with the approval of the Director, to Dr. J. Leidy of Philadelphia, for examination, and these specimens have since been deposited in the National Museum.

In further pursuance of the plan I had laid out for the National Museum, a large wall case was specially prepared for vertebrate fossils. It was about 60 feet long, and 9 feet high, covering one side of the hall assigned to paleontology. To fill this case I sent in July, 1891, a large and very valuable collection of vertebrate fossils, in 33 boxes (weight 6,960 lbs.). These specimens were all ready for exhibition, and were placed in the large case built for them . . .

In April, 1896, I sent another important collection of vertebrate fossils, in 43 large boxes (weight 4,380 lbs.), to Washington, to be deposited in the National Museum. . . .

All the remaining specimens belonging to the Government, and now under investigation as material for the monographs and memoirs in preparation, will likewise be sent to Washington, and deposited in the National Museum, as soon as the investigations concerning them are completed.

COLLECTIONS AT NEW HAVEN.

(7) In the mean time, all the specimens, including types, belonging to the Government, and now in my custody, are carefully labelled and permanently marked, so that no difficulty will be found in identifying each and every one. Accurate records have also been kept, and copies filed in Washington, of all collections made with Government funds, under my direction, during my connection with the Geological Survey and the National Museum. . . .

Meanwhile allow me to remind you that my method of distinguishing the Government collections here from all others was carefully planned from the first. Subsequently it met the full approval of the Director of the Survey (Major Powell), when he examined it in detail, and later still was endorsed by two high officials of the Survey (one of these being yourself), who, on separate occasions, at Major Powell's request, made a careful inspection of my system of recording and preserving these specimens. All this is doubtless on record in your office, and should furnish sufficient answer to ordinary inquiries.

The remaining scientific collections in my custody, belonging to the Government, as well as those I have already sent to Washington, were all collected between July 1st, 1882, and July 1st, 1892. . . .

EXPENDITURES FOR THE GOVERNMENT.

(8) During these ten years of my direct connection with the Geological Survey, the Government funds available for collection were often insufficient for the successful prosecution of the work over the extensive field explored. I was therefore obliged to do much myself, and my own expenditures were frequently in excess of those of the Survey for the same purpose. To the collections thus obtained, the Government can have no claim, although the scientific results of the work, often important, have always been at the service of the Survey. . . .

During the past five years, I have received no salary whatever from the Survey, and my services to it have been entirely gratuitous. This is true, also, of the position of Honorary Curator of Vertebrate Paleontology in the National Museum. . . .

I may also state here that none of the types in my monograph on

Odontornithes are included in the above series, as all were obtained by me and described several years before I had any official connection with the Survey. This is true also of the type specimens in my monograph on the Dinocerata, as these, likewise, were all collected and mainly described before I became Paleontologist on the Survey. For the preparation of the former volume, including several years' work and several thousand dollars of my own money, I received no compensation. . . .

Very respectfully,

O. C. MARSH,
Paleontologist.

VERTEBRATE FOSSILS COLLECTED FOR THE U. S. GEOLOGICAL SURVEY, 1882–1892.

BY O. C. MARSH, PALEONTOLOGIST.

New Haven, Conn., May 27, 1898.

Hon. C. D. Walcott,
Director, U. S. Geological Survey.

DEAR SIR:—I shall send to Washington in a few days the fourth large instalment of the collections of vertebrate fossils made in the West, under my direction as paleontologist of the Survey. The collection I now send is very extensive,* and will, I think, form the largest single addition made to the geological department of the National Museum. These specimens, with those already sent, and others I am preparing to forward later to the National Museum, will make one of the largest collections of vertebrate fossils ever brought together, and all were secured by me during the ten years (1882–1892) that I had charge of the Division of Vertebrate Paleontology of the Survey.

This collection was all made under my special direction, and no small part of it under my personal supervision, at many different localities between the Missouri River and the Pacific coast. The assistants, carefully trained by myself, who aided me in the work, and personally collected the greater part of the specimens, were very numerous, at least forty in number, and the record of their

---

* One hundred boxes, weighing over thirteen tons. These fossils with those previously sent filled two hundred and fifty-five boxes, making a total weight of more than twenty tons.

services has been carefully preserved, as well as the localities in which they worked. . . .

I would respectfully suggest that the series of collections I have thus secured for the Government, when deposited in the National Museum, should be specifically known as "The Marsh Collection of Fossil Vertebrates." . . .

In this connection allow me to make clear one point in regard to my western work that seems to be misunderstood both in Washington and elsewhere. My explorations in the West from 1868 to 1882 (14 years) were conducted entirely at my own expense, and at a cost of about $200,000. As I was first in the field in many regions, my collections were thus very extensive, and from many localities and horizons, and my first two monographs were based on this material.

When I became Paleontologist of the U. S. Geological Survey in 1882, my principal object in collecting was to secure additional material for new monographs and memoirs. Hence, my field work was mainly in localities and horizons that promised the best returns for the special purpose in view. This resulted in large collections from a much more limited field than in my previous work, while many horizons explored by me before were not again visited, and thus many genera already known were not collected.

The monographs being my main object, I endeavored to secure from every available source all important material for examination and description, as every author should, for in no other way, as you well know, can a complete monograph be written. This material has been prepared first of all for the artists who made the drawings for the proposed publications, and specimens of special scientific interest were given the preference. Thus it often happened that only a skull or foot, or even a single tooth or bone, was cut out of rock at first, and the remainder left for some future time. The necessity for such work is obvious, although no systematic record of it could be kept. Sometimes a series of single specimens was prepared for comparison with each other, and again a skeleton was worked out, as the particular investigation made desirable at the time. When some special object was in view, an entire collection has been prepared both for the artist and for exhibition, as, for example, the large series of vertebrate fossils sent to the National Museum in 1891, to be exhibited to the International Geological Congress of that year. . . .

The series of twelve (12) skulls of the gigantic *Ceratopsia* now sent, are only in part worked out of the matrix, although considerable work has been done on nearly all of them, and this is true of most of the other Laramie fossils in the present collection. . . .

Very respectfully,

O. C. MARSH.

On April 20, 1899, a month after Marsh's death, Director Walcott asked Dr. F. A. Lucas of the National Museum to proceed to New Haven to pack for transmission to Washington "the collection of vertebrate fossils in the Peabody Museum belonging to the Government, which were formerly in charge of Prof. O. C. Marsh." Before this date, Walcott had written to Yale to ask that marks be placed on all specimens from which illustrations had been made for the four monographs being prepared under the direction of Professor Marsh, so that they might be readily unpacked upon their arrival in Washington and made accessible for study in connection with the preparation of the text for the monographs.

A few days after Lucas' arrival in New Haven, he notified Head Curator George P. Merrill of the National Museum that the packing would occupy two men for six months. To do this work he was given the help of Preparators Scollick of Washington and Gibb of the Yale staff. The packing was begun in the middle of May and was completed before the close of October.

Lucas was sent to New Haven equipped with a complete copy of the Federal payroll showing the sums of money paid each individual on Marsh's staff, and his months of service. He also had a record of all the specimens sent the National Museum by Marsh in his lifetime. The remaining collections at New Haven had been numbered by each lot as received, and the Peabody Museum accession books show these entries accompanied by a statement as to when the lot was received, of how many boxes or packages it consisted, by whom it was collected, and whether the material was the property of the Survey or of the Peabody Museum. Each box or package originally contained a card giving the locality record, the collector's name, and the date of collection; and these cards accompanied the specimens when the boxes were unpacked. In addition, Marsh kept every letter sent him, and there were hundreds of these from the collectors, making their reports or asking for their wages or acknowledging receipt of checks.

When Professor Beecher, Marsh's successor and the senior author's intimate friend, called on the latter in Washington late in April, 1899, to ask for advice as to the best methods of separating the two collections which had been kept as one, it was agreed that the most satisfactory, and, in fact, the only plan would be to make all the records accessible to each side, and then decide the ownership of each lot as the drawers of material were gone through. The record books had been kept from the beginning by T. A. Bostwick, and Beecher made him available to Lucas for the interpretation of the records and for hunting up letters from the collectors when any doubt arose as to ownership. In the few instances where doubt still remained, the lots were turned over to the Survey. All this material was finally transferred by the Survey to the National Museum as the final custodian, and in this way the desires of Spencer F. Baird were at long last fulfilled.

When the final shipment had gone forward from New Haven to Washington, Director Walcott made the following report to Secretary Langley of the Smithsonian Institution, under date of December 8, 1899, his letter appearing in *Science* for January 5, 1900:

I have the honor to state that all the vertebrate collections of the late Professor O. C. Marsh, belonging to the Government, have been shipped from New Haven, Conn., and are now transferred to the custody of the U. S. National Museum. . . . There were 1,200 trays (20–26 inches) of specimens, 200 unopened boxes as received from the field, 30 blocks and 90 prepared specimens. To ship this material required 592 boxes, forming five [freight] car loads, having an aggregate weight of 160,000 pounds [80 tons]. To this there should be added two [four] car loads containing 211 [255] boxes received from Professor Marsh on deposit in [1886], 1891, [1896], and 1898.

The actual number of specimens represented in this collection cannot be stated. They range in size from minute teeth of fossil mammals to individual specimens weighing from 500 to 2,000 pounds each. . . .

The transfer of these great collections to Washington without the loss of any material, either through imperfect recording or through misunderstanding as to the ownership of specimens, reflects the greatest credit in the business-like methods and the integrity of Professor Marsh.

Among the specimens transferred were the types of at least fifty-three species (this count is of 1907). These were:

Turtle
Glyptops ornatus

Crocodile
Rhytidodon rostratus

Snake
Coniophis precedens

Dinosaurs, 21
Allosaurus medius
Camptosaurus nanus
Ceratops alticornis
  "   montanus
Ceratosaurus nasicornis
Claosaurus annectens
Coelurus gracilis
Diracodon laticeps
Hadrosaurus paucidens
Labrosaurus ferox
Morosaurus agilis
Ornithomimus sedens
Pleurocoelus altus
  "   nanus
Priconodon crassus
Stegosaurus stenops
  "   sulcatus
Triceratops calicornis
  "   elatus
  "   galeus
  "   obtusus

Jurassic Mammals, 8
Ctenacodon potens
Dryolestes vorax
Enneodon affinis
  "   crassus
Laodon venustus
Menacodon rarus
Paurodon valens
Stylacodon gracilis

Cretaceous Mammals, 12
Allacodon fortis
  "   pumilus
  "   rarus
Batodon tenuis
Cimolodon agilis
Cimolomys gracilis
Oracodon anceps
  "   conulus
Pediomys elegans
Stagodon validus
Telacodon laevis
  "   praestans

Cenozoic Mammals, 9
Aceratherium acutum
Allops crassicornis
  "   serrotinus
Asthenodon segnis
Brontops dispar
  "   validus
Menops varians
Titanops curtus
  "   medius

Dr. Lucas was reluctant to give an estimate of the money value of these collections, but he finally set it at "upwards of $150,000." His estimate of the value of the fossil remains sent to Washington by Marsh prior to his death was $42,875, making the total but little under $200,000.

CHAPTER XII

MARSH AND HIS LABORATORY
ASSISTANTS

"Advancement—improvement in condition—is the order of things in
a society of equals."

LINCOLN.

THE group of assistants who worked with Marsh in his laboratories at various times included men who were later to become leaders in their own branches of science, and for this reason they must be considered in any discussion of his work. This becomes a somewhat difficult task, however, in view of the fact that it was from this very coterie of men that Cope derived much support in his public attack on his New Haven rival. The senior author knew at least eight of these assistants, and more than once felt the impact of their bitterness toward Marsh. Nevertheless, it is believed that nothing would be gained at this late date by an attempt at detailed refutation of the charges that appeared over their signatures that memorable but depressing Sunday morning in January, 1890; rather has it seemed better to make the discussion a more general one, based on personal knowledge and on letters and other documents in the Yale archives. And if, out of all this, a clearer, and perhaps a juster, picture of Marsh's relationships with his assistants emerges, the chapter will have achieved its purpose.

Marsh states in two of his publications that of paid assistants of one kind or another he had at New Haven between 1873 and 1898 "perhaps fifty" in all. At this late date, but twenty-three of these helpers can be traced, and the present chapter proposes to tell a little about some of them who gave more or less efficient service, and for a longer term than one year.

The first permanent appointment on Marsh's staff went to the man who was to serve him longest. By 1872, the collections had begun to accumulate so fast that someone was needed to unpack and catalogue them, and find a place to store them.

For this task, Marsh engaged a lad just out of grammar school, Thomas Attwater Bostwick (1857–1923), and from that day until he closed the Professor's eyes one morning in March, 1899, "Thomas" was as much a part of the Marsh establishment as its four walls. He kept the Museum accession books, even before there was a Museum, and thus growing up with the collections, he came to have an immense store of detailed knowledge about them that was of much service to everyone working in the Museum. He learned, also, to keep careful and minute records of other matters, at times apparently inconsequential, but often helping later to solve knotty puzzles; the sheets of yellowish paper that Bostwick produced in answer to all questions were as familiar to workers in the Museum as were the odd slips of paper in Henry Gruener's pocket to users of the Yale Library! An expert packer, it was he who went to Philadelphia in 1877 and brought back those dinosaur bones that Lakes had sent to Cope, and a pity it is that his story of the transaction was not kept. When Professor Marsh was gone, Bostwick's intimate knowledge of the collections proved of great value to those left with the task of separating the Government material from that belonging to Yale.

Another New Haven boy of fifteen, Richard Ward Westbrook (1864–1934), was added to the staff in 1879 for general work. He studied shorthand when Marsh's need for secretarial help became insistent, and served in that capacity until 1891. He was not content to stay in secretarial work, however, but turned to medicine and was graduated from the Yale Medical School in 1891. He was a successful practitioner of medicine and surgery in Brooklyn, New York, until his retirement.

The writers spent a fruitful day with Dr. Westbrook in October, 1931, at his summer home in New Canaan, Connecticut, and are greatly indebted to him for a long talk about Marsh, his methods of work, and his relations with his staff. Dr. Westbrook admitted that he probably knew Marsh's "intimate, every-day side as well as anyone during my years of association with him," and added, "Perhaps I appreciated his good points more than his other intimates, but I was too close to him to admire him."

Westbrook's secretarial work was gradually taken over by Miss Lucy Peck Bush, who joined Marsh's staff in 1883 and remained with the Museum until 1908. Although not a stenographer, she was of great help to Marsh along editorial and clerical lines. His stenographic work was handled for part of one year by Miss Mary M. Mayer, who later entered the service of Professor Russell H. Chittenden and remained with him for many years.

As Marsh's publications grew in number, he was faced with the problem of finding skilled illustrators. Fortunately for him, New Haven has always been somewhat of a center for printing and lithography. His earliest figures, those of

Fig. 16. "Pterodactyl, after Marsh," a wood engraving by W. F. Hopson.

Eosaurus, appearing in 1862, were very fine engravings on copper made by A. H. Richie. By 1868-69, he was following the fashion of the day and using hand-printed lithographs, made by L. Shierholz and printed by Punderson and Crisand, the firm which later produced the thirty-four superb plates for the memoir on toothed birds, at a cost of $8,000. Emil Crisand, becoming sole owner of the business in 1881, furnished for the Government the many plates for the various other monographs projected by Marsh, at a cost of some $60,000.

The woodcuts in Marsh's papers yielded nothing in excellence to the lithographs, and small wonder, since they were largely the work of William F. Hopson (1849–1935), later to become one of the best-known American bookplate designers and engravers. Hopson had made many sketches for Professor Dana, Professor Verrill, and other Yale scientists. He did engraving for Marsh from 1875 until the latter's death, and his payments from the Survey totaled about $10,000.

The talented artist who drew most of the figures that Hopson engraved and Crisand lithographed was Frederick Berger, formerly one of Crisand's employees. He was at the Museum from 1875 until 1892, and at times thereafter until 1898.

PLATE XIX

THE PEABODY MUSEUM STAFF ON THE STEPS OF THE OLD "BONE HOUSE" IN 1885
UPPER ROW, LEFT TO RIGHT: RICE (JANITOR), HERMANN, HATCHER, HARGER, BAUR, WILLIS-
TON. FRONT ROW: GIBB, BERGER, SHIERHOLZ (ENGRAVER), BOSTWICK

PLATE XX

W. F. HOPSON, ENGRAVER OF MARSH'S WOODCUTS
AND LATER A FAMOUS MAKER OF BOOKPLATES

HUGH GIBB AT HIS WORKBENCH IN THE OLD MUSEUM, ABOUT
1911. (RIGHT) WITH A RIB OF *BRONTOSAURUS* 1930

As the flood of fossils from the West poured into the Museum, it soon became apparent that help was imperative to clean the bones out of the rock, to harden them, and then to restore them by fitting the pieces together to make a whole. The first man trained by Marsh for this work of preparing fossil bones was a German by the name of Adam Hermann. Hermann, a brass turner in the Sargent hardware-manufacturing company, had turned to taxidermy as a supplementary source of income, and it was specimens of his work displayed in a store window that attracted Marsh's attention. He was further recommended as a workman by Henry B. Sargent, who had been a member of the first Yale expedition. He entered Marsh's service in October, 1876, and under the latter's guidance learned to be an excellent and ingenious preparator, although not always entirely loyal to his employer. When the work became more than Hermann could handle alone, he brought into the Museum, in 1882, his young Scotch brother-in-law, Hugh Gibb (1860-1932), then foreman in a weaving mill in New Britain, Connecticut. When Hermann left the Yale Museum ten years later to join the much larger group working at the American Museum of Natural History in New York, Gibb was well equipped to take his place. And for fifty years this sterling Scotsman, trained to Old World pride in his work, gave his best to the Museum, wherein still remain, as striking monuments to his skill and industry, such mounts as the Otisville mastodon, *Brontops, Claosaurus, Stegosaurus, Morosaurus, Archelon,* and, last of all, the giant *Brontosaurus.* In addition, thousands of bones and hundreds of skulls were worked out of their enclosing rocks by him and made ready for study by paleontologists. The extraordinary beauty of Gibb's character brought to his corner of the workshop associates and students and professors alike, and his unswerving devotion to Professor Marsh while he was alive and to his memory long after he was dead should serve as a partial counter to the winds of bitter criticism that have so often howled about his chief. It can not be truthfully denied that he also was at times subjected to unjust treatment, but he seemed always to see beyond these hurts to the quality of the man inflicting them. He, too, was a witness to Marsh's ability to pick men.

One of Marsh's favorite methods of spreading knowledge about his strange fossil beasts was through plaster replicas of the more interesting of the restored bones or skeletons. His first employee along these lines was a German Swiss, Tobias A. Kappeler by name, who began to work for him on odd jobs as early as November, 1874, but later devoted his time to Marsh almost wholly until his term of service ended in 1885. During these years Marsh paid him about $7,500. Kappeler's plaster casts included such well-known replicas as those of the entire skeleton of the Bavarian flying reptile, *Rhamphorhynchus*, and of various skeletal elements of the great dinosaur, *Atlantosaurus immanis*, the Cretaceous toothed bird, *Hesperornis*, and the horned mammals, *Dinoceras* and *Tinoceras*.

From the restoration of individual bones and their reproduction by plaster casts, the next step is to give lifelike restoration to the complete animal. In the 'seventies, however, Marsh was not ready to go that far. When the centenary of the Declaration of Independence was to be celebrated by the International Exposition at Philadelphia, the Smithsonian Institution was asked if it would not be possible to place on exhibition restorations of ancient monsters as they looked in the flesh. Secretary Baird wrote Marsh for his opinion on this matter, and their exchange of letters follows:

National Museum: Smithsonian Institution,
Washington, Nov. 22, 1875.

Dear Prof. Marsh:

We have had a great pressure brought to bear upon us to expend a portion of our Centennial appropriation in employing Waterhouse Hawkins [an English sculptor] to make some restorations of prehistoric animals for the Philadelphia exhibition, the backers being LeConte, Cope, Guyot, and other gentlemen. Prof. Henry is inclined to accede to the proposition, which, however, I do not favor, very much, for two reasons. First, that the money is needed for other more serviceable purposes; second, that I have no confidence in Hawkins' or any other person's ability, with the materials at command, to make these restorations. It is as much as we can do to rely upon the bones we have to restore those that are missing from the skeleton; and how far we can judge of the dermal peculiarities, in addition, is to me a puzzle. I wish you would give me your views on this subject. If you say you think it would be a good thing, and that you think Hawkins can secure the solution of the problem, we will at any rate do something in the matter.

Yours truly,
[Signed] SPENCER F. BAIRD.

Yale College Museum,
New Haven, Conn.,
Dec. 20, 1875.

Dear Professor Baird,

I was absent in New York when your letter in regard to Restorations for the Centennial came, or I should have been more prompt in my reply.

I do not believe it possible at present to make restorations of any of the more important extinct animals of this country that will be of real value to science, or the public. In the few cases where the materials exist for a restoration of the skeleton alone, these materials have not yet been worked out with sufficient care to make such a restoration perfectly satisfactory, and to go beyond this would in my judgment almost certainly end in serious mistakes. Where the skeleton, etc., is only partially known, the danger of error is of course much greater, and I think it would be very unwise to attempt restoration, as error in a case of this kind is very difficult to eradicate from the public mind, e.g., the old restoration of Labyrinthodon (with a frog-like body) still continues to appear in popular scientific books, although it has for years been known that that is the only Batrachian that has *not* been found among the Labyrinthodonts.

A few years hence we shall certainly have the material for some good restorations of our wonderful extinct animals, but the time is not yet.

[From an unsigned copy.]

Despite the cold water poured by Marsh on the project, Hawkins did make a plaster restoration of Cope's dinosaur *Hadrosaurus* for the Philadelphia Exposition, and later on it was set up in the open air in front of the National Museum in Washington. Here it slowly melted away and it was destroyed a few years before the senior author joined the staff of the Museum in 1893.

In the middle 'eighties, when Marsh had completed his monograph on the fossil mammals known as Dinocerata, he felt that the species *Dinoceras mirabile* was well enough known to justify the exhibition of a mounted skeleton of it in the Museum. Not, however, one made up of the original bones! At that time, no paleontologist would have committed the sacrilege of showing the bones themselves mounted in a life-like attitude, or even of modeling the missing parts in plaster. No! The bones must be kept apart forever in drawers, or laid

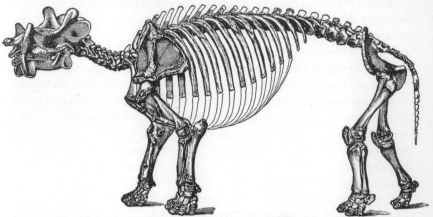

Fig. 17. The mammal *Dinoceras,* as restored by Marsh. This is the restoration from which many replicas were made by J. H. Emerton.

away on padded shelves, so that the paleontologist alone might handle them and inspect every joint in the most minute detail. To meet this convention, and yet be able to show the restored animal, Marsh engaged another modeler, J. H. Emerton, to make several replicas of the skeleton as mounted by his preparators, after which the bones were disassembled. Emerton worked at this task between January, 1885, and August, 1888. Molds of every bone were made, either directly from undistorted originals or from clay models. In these molds were laid several thicknesses of glue-soaked strips of blotting paper. These were patted down or squeezed into place and then reinforced with papier-mâché, purchased at Washington and consisting, strangely enough, of ground-up greenbacks redeemed by the United States Treasury. Truly, millions of greenback promises must have gone into these fossil replicas! Emerton's work is now one of the lost arts, but a description of it may be found in the *Proceedings* of the Boston Society of Natural History, Vol. XXIII (1888), pages 342–343. The entire paper model of the *Dinoceras* skeleton weighed less than 40 pounds, but the making of it and its duplicates cost Marsh about $2,240. The modern method of mounting the actual bones in a restored skeleton for public exhibition was introduced by Henry F. Osborn, as told in another chapter.

From the technical and clerical assistants of Professor Marsh we may now turn to the better-known group of scientific men who aided him in his laboratory studies. The first of these seems to have been George Bird Grinnell (1849–1938). As stated earlier, Grinnell was a member of the Yale Expedition of 1870 and the friendship with Marsh thus begun lasted throughout the latter's life. In 1872, Grinnell, returning to the West, went on a buffalo hunt with the Pawnees under Major North, and from that time on he was a student of the Indians, later being made a member of the Blackfoot tribe. During much of 1871–72 he was engaged in the preparation of osteological material, which he sold to Marsh. The next year he was appointed on the regular staff of the Museum as Assistant in Paleontology, and he was in charge of the growing Osteological Collection for six years. In 1874, Marsh sent him out to join the first Custer expedition into the Black Hills, as naturalist, and thus he was with the party that brought back news of the gold in that region. The following year, with the younger Dana, he accompanied the Ludlow Expedition to the Yellowstone Park, and here again Marsh helped to finance his travels. The observations of Grinnell and Dana were published in five papers between 1875 and 1877. During these years Grinnell was working toward a doctorate in the Yale Graduate School, which he received in 1880, his dissertation being on the "Osteology of *Geococcyx californicus.*"

Grinnell was an exceedingly helpful and loyal assistant to Marsh and no discord between them has ever been mentioned. In the monograph on birds with teeth, he is thanked by Marsh "for much valuable assistance, especially while the volume was in press," and he wrote for the *American Journal of Science* a long and detailed review of the book. Although the custom of giving "honor names" to fossils was so little followed by Marsh that only 21 of his almost 500 species bear such, one of those 21 was *Crocodilus grinnelli*. (Incidentally, Marsh's classically formed names were a happy contrast to the outlandish ones often proposed by Cope, among his particularly felicitous choices being *Hesperornis regalis*, the "regal western bird"; *Brontosaurus gigas*, the "great thunder saurian"; and *Eohippus validus*, the "true dawn horse.")

After leaving Marsh late in 1880, Grinnell had a long and notable career as ethnologist, explorer, author, and editor. His lifelong interest in the American Indian found expression in many books preserving the lore of the Cheyenne, Blackfoot, and Pawnee tribes; his thirty-five-year editorship of the magazine *Forest and Stream* made his name familiar to all lovers of the out of doors; and his work for the preservation of Yellowstone and Glacier National Parks brought him the title of "Father of American Conservation."

Some years after Marsh's death, Grinnell wrote, for the volume entitled *Leading American Men of Science*, one of the two most appreciative sketches extant of his former chief in the Peabody Museum.

The first permanent Assistant in Paleontology in the Peabody Museum was Oscar Harger (1843–87), and a very valuable one he proved to be. Harger was born on January 12, 1843, at Oxford, Connecticut, of Huguenot ancestry. Through his own almost unaided efforts he found money enough to prepare himself for Yale College at the Connecticut Literary Institute at Suffield, and he was graduated from Yale with honors in 1868, his expenses at college having been met chiefly by making mathematical calculations for insurance companies and for Professor Newton. After graduation he abandoned the mathematical career open to him and began the study of Zoology with Professor Verrill in the Sheffield Scientific School, and was by him recommended to Marsh. Marsh made it possible for him to become a member of the Yale Expeditions of 1871 and 1873 by paying his expenses ($950), and he served as a sort of quartermaster on the second of these trips. From

July to September, 1872, he was aboard the Coast Survey steamer, *Bache*, dredging marine life with Professors Verrill and S. I. Smith. He entered Marsh's service in the fall of that year, at $35 a month, and his salary was increased until he was getting $1,500 a year in 1883.

Undersized, and never well because of a hypertrophied heart, Harger was a born student—in the words of Yale's President Dwight, a "kindly and gentle spirit." In contrast to Marsh, who, although he subscribed liberally to scientific journals and purchased many scientific books, is said never to have been a voluminous reader, Harger read widely, and especially in those subjects in which Marsh was most interested. According to Westbrook, Marsh placed much reliance upon Harger's judgment in Paleontology, and often tried out manuscripts on him, regarding him as a valuable balance wheel. The relations between the two did not remain pleasant, however, Harger becoming unhappy because he was not allowed to set forth his knowledge of vertebrate fossils in publications of his own or jointly with Marsh. To this Marsh never consented, although he was willing that Harger should publish on invertebrates. Harger talked over his grievance with his associates in the laboratory, and at least two of the professors in the Museum interceded for him with Marsh, but to no avail. This was perhaps unfortunate, for in the opinion of Professor Smith, Harger had "a truly philosophical grasp of the bearing of the facts on evolution and classification; and only the few who knew his attainments can appreciate how much palaeontological science would have been advanced had he been able to publish his observations and conclusions." [1] This latter surmise might have been true had Marsh been minded to make Harger co-author with himself, but at least two of Harger's associates in the laboratory told the senior author that, without Marsh's support, the younger man would not have succeeded markedly in Vertebrate Paleontology, because he lacked certain necessary qualities.

The preface to the Marsh memoir called *Odontornithes* (1880) and that to the Dinocerata monograph (1885) contain a brief acknowledgment of Harger's important aid. After the latter's death, Marsh stated that Harger had collected some

1. S. I. Smith, "Oscar Harger," apparently a privately printed sketch.

of the specimens of toothed birds himself, and that he made
"a special synopsis of all the forms described, and took full
notes of all the vertebrae, on which the later descriptions were
essentially based"; also, that he was "ever faithful and sympathetic, and his rare scholarship and good judgment rendered
his assistance of great value." [2]

Harger's papers include one on living North American
myriapods, two on living isopods, and one on a Coal Measures
spider from Mazon Creek, Illinois.

The next young man to come to Marsh's laboratories was
Samuel Wendell Williston, who had started his work in Paleontology as a member of one of Marsh's collecting parties in
Kansas, as told in an earlier chapter. In February, 1876, on
Professor Mudge's recommendation, he came to New Haven
and spent some weeks learning Marsh's collecting methods and
studying the osteology of birds, in order that he might be
better able to find bones of the Kansas Cretaceous birds on
which Marsh was then at work. He spent the summer of 1876
in the field, and the winter again in New Haven. The field
season of 1877, however, he found a tiring one, since he was in
the West at least ten months. Moreover, it had never been his
intention to be a collector only. Commenting in his unpublished
autobiography on his invitation to come to New Haven, he
said:

I had lived practically all my life remote from scientific men, and
authors were almost unknown. I had always been a bookworm of
the most accentuated type, and had grown to reverence, almost to
worship, the writers of books and especially of scientific books.
. . . Such men as Huxley, Darwin, Dana, Gray, and Marsh were
my ideals of all that was great and good. I thought them impec-
cable and almost infallible. My greatest ambition was to follow in
their footsteps—to write a book myself and to make discoveries." [3]

In pursuance of this ambition, Williston had been studying
fish skeletons in his own time, although under Marsh's direction; but when he requested permission to do research on
Cretaceous fishes, Marsh refused it, on the ground that such

2. "Reply to Cope," New York *Herald,* January 19, 1890.
3. Quoted by R. S. Lull, "Biographical memoir of Samuel Wendell Williston, 1852–1918," *Mem. Nat. Acad. Sci.,* XVII (1924), 117.

work would distract his attention from his regular duties. This setback, and others of a similar nature, showed Williston that if he were to do original research it would have to be in some field other than Vertebrate Paleontology, and he therefore turned to the living world and began to study the Diptera (flies). His first contract with Marsh, signed March 28, 1876, to work in the field or at the Museum for three years at $40 a month, was replaced on July 1, 1879, by an agreement to stay with Marsh for another three years "for the sum of $2500," but gave him the privilege of continuing at the Yale Medical School, for nine months, studies already begun in Iowa. He received the M.D. degree in June, 1880, and was appointed Assistant in Osteology in Yale College. A third contract, signed July 1, 1882, was as "assistant in the Yale Museum, or the Geological Survey [as Marsh may decide] for five years from date . . . for the sum of $1500 per annum." This agreement was terminated by mutual consent on July 1, 1885. In the meantime, Williston had continued his studies on the Diptera and in June of 1885 he received the Ph.D. from Yale, his dissertation being "A synopsis of the North American Syrphidae."

In the Museum laboratory, Williston helped to prepare the dinosaur bones for illustration and description. He also made notes and took measurements, and, according to the preface of the Dinocerata volume, he acted as amanuensis and aided in the preparation of the bibliography. His discontent with Marsh's illiberal attitude toward research on the part of his assistants was evidently aggravated by the irregularity with which his salary was reaching him, since he complained of this to the Director of the Survey on October 15, 1884, only to be confronted by Marsh with his letter, sent back to the latter by Powell. He was one of the four assistants who told Cope what was going on in the Museum and a statement by him was included among those published in 1890.

While with Marsh, Williston published but two brief papers on fossil vertebrates, but he wrote five short ones on living vertebrates, one on Indian figures in western Kansas, and at least twenty-two short papers and four long ones on living insects, chiefly flies, of which he eventually became the fore-most American authority. After leaving Marsh, he had a somewhat varied career. For five years, he practiced medicine and taught Anatomy in New Haven, as well as acting as city health officer. In 1890, the University of Kansas gave him an opportunity to return to his first love in science by offering him a professorship in Geology, which he held until 1902, when he was called to the University of Chicago as professor of Paleontology. His later work on fossil vertebrates was mainly with the Reptilia, on which he published some eighty contributions, establishing his position as one of the leading students of this class.

Still another student who worked for Marsh while doing postgraduate work was Erwin H. Barbour of the class of 1882, Yale College. His dissertation for the doctorate granted him in 1887 was on "The osteology of the Heloderma." He contributed to the general chorus of disparagement of Marsh in 1890 with his "Notes on the paleontological laboratory of the United States Geological Survey under Marsh." [4] He was professor of Geology at Grinnell College for two years, and held a similar position in the University of Nebraska from 1891 until his retirement in 1938.

In 1882–83, when Federal money was becoming available, Marsh began to look around for still other scientific assistants, and recalling the helpful Privatdozenten whom he had seen at work in the German laboratories, he appealed to Professor Karl A. von Zittel of Munich, a guest in his home in the fall of 1883, to help him find such. Zittel, enthusiastic over Marsh's hospitality and his collections, felt sure that he knew of several promising young men. Not long after his return to Munich, he wrote Marsh that one of his own students, Max Schlosser, was "pleased to go to America," and that another budding paleontologist, George Baur, would probably join him. When these two young Germans reached the Museum in the spring of 1884, they found a third, Otto Meyer, already on the ground.

Meyer, who had been in America for some time, worked on Cenozoic invertebrates for most of his first year with Marsh and then studied mammal jaws from the Morrison formation. Unable to get on with Marsh, however, he resigned in August, 1886, and went into business. It was Westbrook's opinion that Meyer gave Marsh little real help in the laboratory.

4. *Amer. Nat.*, XXIV, 388–400.

PLATE XXI

PART OF THE PEABODY MUSEUM STAFF IN 1888 FROM A PHOTOGRAPH TAKEN IN
THE LABORATORY (ROOM 10)

STANDING (LEFT TO RIGHT): BARBOUR, HERMANN. SITTING: BERGER, CRISAND. THE BIG
SKULL WHICH BERGER IS DRAWING IS PROBABLY THAT OF MARSH'S *TITANOPS ELATUS*
(=*BRONTOTHERIUM GIGAS*)

PLATE XXII

GEORGE BAUR
ABOUT THE TIME HE
JOINED MARSH'S STAFF

GEORGE R. WIELAND
WHO WAS WITH MARSH
IN THE 'NINETIES

GEORGE BIRD GRINNELL
FROM THE PHOTOGRAPH
IN HIS CLASSBOOK

OSCAR HARGER

FOUR OF MARSH'S SCIENTIFIC ASSISTANTS

Max Schlosser (1854–1932), although recommended by Zittel as an able, conscientious, dependable, and industrious worker, stayed in New Haven even less time than Meyer, returning to the Alte Akademie in Munich early in 1885. In contrast to Meyer, however, he remained an ardent student of fossil mammals throughout his life, and became their leading interpreter in Germany. He also worked on fishes and invertebrates, and was especially well informed on cave faunas. There is an excellent, but brief, memorial of him by Professor Broili.[5]

Gibb and Westbrook remembered Schlosser as a very difficult man to live with, suspicious, exceedingly nervous, outspoken, and excitable. One day while walking with Baur past the old Treasury Building he was run into by some students just dismissed from the building. He at once challenged the lot of them, and raising his cane, threatened to whip them all. Baur, however, got him away unharmed. Schlosser did not like American ways, and Westbrook agreed that he never fitted himself into the Marsh laboratory. His return to Germany was due in part to difficulties with Marsh, and in part to illness.

George Baur (1859–98), the third young German to work in Marsh's laboratory, and the most gifted of them all, came from a family that had been noted for university professors. Born at Weiswasser, Bohemia, he finished the *Gymnasium* at Stuttgart in 1877, and in the following autumn entered the university at Munich. In 1880 he studied at Leipzig and the next year was again at Munich, where he took up Paleontology with Zittel, and, after defending his dissertation, "Der Tarsus der Vögel und Dinosaurier," was given a doctorate in 1882. Of his ability in Anatomy, Embryology, and especially in Microscopy, Zittel had spoken in the highest terms.

Baur became Assistant in Paleontology at Yale on April 1, 1884. In the six years that he was with Marsh, he published no fewer than 64 short papers and 11 long ones, totaling about 430 pages. These contributions, treating of the embryology and morphogeny of living and fossil vertebrates, show the brilliance of Baur's mentality, his marked productivity, and his great store of information. Moreover, they would seem to put forever at rest the often repeated assertion that Marsh

5. F. Broili, "Max Schlosser," *Centralb. f. Min.* (1933), pp. 69–78.

would not allow any of his assistants to do research on fossil vertebrates. In the eight years after leaving New Haven, Baur published some 68 additional papers, with about the same number of pages, mainly along the same general lines, but including 2 remarkable articles on the flora and fauna of the Galapagos Islands, in which he demonstrates that these islands are not oceanic in type but are subsiding volcanic peaks standing on a lost continent.

From February to July, 1887, Marsh sent Baur on an extended trip to Europe, to search out, study, and illustrate the notable fossil Reptilia in the museums and among the dealers and collectors. During part of this trip he was accompanied by another of Marsh's assistants, Charles E. Beecher. Baur's letters to Marsh during this period show a very friendly attitude; he was being received kindly everywhere and he was learning much. Ten days after his return to New Haven he sent to the printer corrected proof for his longest memoir, *Beiträge zur Morphologie des Carpus and Tarsus, Teil I, Batrachier*, which appeared in 1888. In the introduction to this memoir, he says that the second part will treat of the Sauropsida and the third of the mammals; these never appeared.

In studying the relations between Marsh and Baur, one is immediately struck by the latter's continuous shortage of money. It was Marsh's custom to start his assistants at $50 a month, but Baur, after the trial months, was given $250 a quarter-year. This was increased to $1,600 a year in 1885 and to $1,800 in 1888. By the end of the first year he was in debt to Marsh to the sum of $500, largely as a result of his marriage, three months after his arrival, to a young woman of whom his family disapproved. In addition to increasing Baur's salary, Marsh bought his private collection of vertebrate embryos, microslides, and instruments, for $300; and on February 2, 1887, paid him $400 "in advance for scientific expenses in preparation of work on osteology of reptiles"; the receipt is endorsed "advance on mutual work," and a slip attached to it says, "advances on book to be mutually prepared." A contract in triplicate for the above-mentioned joint work by Marsh and Baur, to be published by Fischer of Jena, is in the Marsh archives. This book was to bear the title,

Grundzüge der vergleichenden Osteologie der Reptilien, was
to have about 480 pages and 365 zinc plates, and to appear
in the same format as Wiedersheim's *Lehrbuch der vergleichenden Anatomie.* The contract was never fulfilled, and no such
book was ever written by Baur.

It would seem, from this evidence, that Marsh recognized
Baur's great ability, and that he went much further to keep
him satisfied than he had ever done with any of his other
assistants. In spite of this, Baur's feeling toward him grew
increasingly bitter. That Baur was brilliant there is no denying, but hand in hand with this brilliance went the lack of
balance that so frequently accompanies it. Baur had, moreover, the sense of superiority that belongs to his class in
Germany (although he came from South Germany, his looks
suggest the Prussian), and it was not long before he began to
feel that Marsh's mental equipment and knowledge were much
inferior to his own, particularly in Embryology, and his talk
of these and other shortcomings helped to poison the minds of
an already restive staff. This was the belief of both Gibb and
Westbrook. This feeling of Baur's was further aggravated by
his desire to become the holder of a professorship at Yale,
and he tried to have Marsh take steps to have a chair established
for Anatomy and Embryology of the Vertebrates. This would
have been a desirable thing to do, from the scientific point of
view, but it must be acknowledged that in 1884 Yale had no
such ambition.

A further indication that Baur's mind was set on teaching,
as was natural with his ancestry and training, is to be found
in the following letter:

> *Harvard University,*
> *Cambridge, Mass.,*
> *21 Apr. 1888.*

Dear Professor Marsh:

I have offered Dr. Geo. Baur an instructorship here with a smaller
salary than that which he now receives from the Survey. Teaching
seems to have some attraction for him.

In conversation with him I learned for the first time that you
"imported" him. I supposed him to be an officer of Yale, until he

told me how he was paid. The chance of his accepting our modest invitation is probably small; but I want to tell you myself how we came to ask him. His subjects happen to fit into a hole in our scheme of zoölogical courses. We lack a man for vertebrates. If he decides to stay where he is, perhaps you can tell me of some good man in the same line. With many apologies for incommoding you, I am

Very truly yours,
[Signed] CHARLES W. ELIOT.

Inquiries have failed to reveal any copy extant of Marsh's answer to this letter, and the only light we have on the matter comes from Dr. Thomas H. Barbour of Harvard, who writes that the files of the Museum of Comparative Zoology, of which he is director, have a letter from Baur in which he stated, under date of April 30, 1888: "Professor Marsh does not like that I leave him, I therefore decided to stay here for the next time." The addressee of the letter is not directly apparent, but Dr. Barbour thinks it was probably Alexander Agassiz.

The last note from Baur in the Marsh files is dated February 13, 1889. In it he agrees to pay Marsh $40 a month "until my indebtedness is paid in full," said indebtedness in that year being $470.

Baur and Marsh — one young, brilliant, dogmatic; the other past middle age, slower to reach conclusions, equally dogmatic, hard to convince. Probably harmony between such decisive personalities was too much to expect. That they could not agree was really a tragedy, for had they been able to work harmoniously together, they might have attained greater results than were achieved by either separately, and science would have been the gainer.

After resigning from Marsh's staff in January, 1890, Baur went to Clark University as lecturer. In 1892, he received appointment as assistant professor of Comparative Osteology and Paleontology in the newly founded University of Chicago, and three years later was promoted to an associate professorship. His health began to break down in the fall of 1897, and in December the University gave him an extension of leave to go to Germany, but his disease (general paresis, to which a brother also had succumbed) made constant headway. It was soon found necessary to transfer him to an asylum, and he died there on June 25, 1898.[6]

In the attempt to find the basic reasons underlying the discontent among Marsh's assistants in the 'eighties, and its growth into the active dislike that led them to make printed charges against him in 1890, the authors have spent many hours of speculation and discussion.

What must an administrator do to keep his staff contented and efficient? One must say that at least four things are of prime importance: 1, adequate wages, regularly paid; 2, recognition of the value of work performed; 3, sufficient work to keep hands and minds occupied; 4, no interference from outsiders. The first three of these were within Marsh's power to give, and it must be admitted that not all of them were forthcoming.

On the score of adequate wages, he might perhaps more readily be absolved. He was a hard bargainer, it is true, but it does not appear that the wages he paid were much if any below the scale of the day, which was certainly not high, even for University professors. However, whatever wage he paid was bound to seem niggardly, coming from a man of such obvious wealth. In irregularity of payment, on the other hand, he was a decided sinner. It will be remembered that his methods of managing his finances were under criticism as long ago as his Andover days. He kept meticulous records, yes, but they were for his own information; what he did with his money was no one's business but his own. When wages or similar matters were in dispute, he never failed to produce contracts or signed receipts. Apparently, even when the payroll of his staff was being met by the Federal Survey, the money did not reach them regularly, being sent from Washington only as he turned in vouchers for it to Chief Clerk McChesney. Never having been dependent upon a salary himself, he seems to have had no vision of how all-important it is, especially when one's income is small, to have it come to hand on a given date. That he was generous with his men in the matter of loans and gifts is well known, but their wages often had to wait until he had time

6. For an excellent memorial of Baur, see W. M. Wheeler, "George Baur's life and writings," *Amer. Nat.,* XXXIII (1899), 15–30; another sketch (unsigned) appeared in *Nature* for August 11, 1898, p. 350.

to check up his accounts or do other things that he considered more important. It seems very probable that this factor was the initial cause of discontent among his staff.

The question of recognition for work done would not have been so important, had not his scientific assistants been of so high a calibre. That he did acknowledge their help has been shown, but that he failed to give them credit for independent work is equally true. This would be especially galling to men like Harger and Baur, who felt their superiority to Marsh in some respects. However, the question of *meum* and *tuum*, as applied to scientific work done by assistants and published by their chiefs, was not confined to Marsh's laboratory, nor to Marsh's time.

Marsh's method of work was to assign to each assistant a certain series of fossil bones, either while they were still in the hands of the preparators or after they had been cleaned and restored. He then gave instructions as to what he wanted done, which usually was to have the nearest affinities of these animals sought for, either in the literature, in his own fossil collections, or in his large amount of osteological material. In due time he would sit down with each man, asking questions, discussing conclusions arrived at, and all the while making notes in regard to what he heard and what he saw in the assembled material. With so large a staff, this method seems to have been a natural one to pursue, but its inherent difficulty lay in his disregard of the fact that at least one of his assistants was his equal in Paleontology, and that several of them were as ambitious as he to publish research. The dissatisfaction arising therefrom was aggravated by his habit of keeping his own conclusions strictly to himself in these conferences, especially when he differed with his staff; he rarely exposed his final conclusions until they appeared in print.[7]

That his assistants were not intended to have joint author-

7. This curious taciturnity was of long standing. One of the students on the 1873 Expedition (H. W. Farnam) remarked in a letter home: "We expect to move camp to-morrow or next day. . . . The Professor has not yet committed himself on the subject, so that it is still as much a matter of conjecture as the weather or any other uncertain occurrence. However, the Professor never commits himself on any subject and why should he on the time of breaking camp until the tents are down and the waggons loaded?" (quoted through the courtesy of Mrs. Farnam).

ship with him should have been clear to all of them when they were engaged, since, of the several written contracts that still exist, only one, that with Baur, makes any provision to the contrary. It should also have been evident to them from the beginning that he alone was to publish on the fossil vertebrates in the Museum, and that if any of them was to do research work for himself, it could be only on material other than that in which Marsh was interested.

The charge that much of the research published by Marsh was actually the work of his assistants has been rather widely made. It would seem to be contradicted by the fact that, previous to the fall of 1872, when he had no assistants of any kind, he published 51 notes and papers totaling 210 printed pages. Westbrook, indeed, was certain that Marsh wrote or dictated all of his published work, and he received but little help in his writing from any assistant but Harger. Testimony to the same effect comes from Sir Arthur Smith Woodward of England, whose recollections, sent to the authors in 1937 and quoted in part elsewhere, contain the following paragraph:

Marsh was often accused of publishing under his own name research which was actually done by his skilled paid assistants. I knew personally all these assistants except Oscar Harger, and I think there was some unreasonableness on both sides. Marsh, however, was a remarkably keen observer, and he was quick to see the inferences which might be drawn from the facts before him. He was also one of the foremost systematists of his time, and contributed greatly to the classification of reptiles, birds, and mammals. It was natural that he should be impatient of writing out detailed descriptions and compiling tables of measurements, when he could obtain competent help in this routine work. It was perhaps sometimes difficult to avoid taking advantage of the additional observations which his assistants made in the course of the tasks he had assigned to them. Nevertheless, I am convinced that in all essentials Marsh's fundamental contributions to vertebrate palaeontology were his own and stimulated by his boundless enthusiasm for our science.

Even with these two causes for dissatisfaction—irregular payment of wages and insufficient recognition of scientific work—the unrest among Marsh's staff might not have become so deep-set if their work had been well enough organized to

leave no idle time for discussion. This, however, was not the
case. Marsh's insistence on personal supervision of every aspect
of the work, even to the cleaning of the fossils out of the rock,
left the staff with many unoccupied hours in which to discuss
the shortcomings of their employer; and these shortcomings
were a favorite topic, from preparators' workshop in the basement to scientific laboratories above stairs.

It has been said that Marsh was not a hard worker, and that
he was easily diverted by the immediate affairs around him.
These criticisms, although more or less justified in his later
years, were not true previous to his moving into his Prospect
Street home in 1881. In the 'seventies, according to Westbrook,
his most striking characteristic was his complete absorption in
his work; he had no deep interests other than fossils. The drive
and determination of his earlier years, however, spent themselves as his wealth increased and his contacts widened, and
especially as his leadership in the National Academy and the
Geological Survey brought him added administrative duties.
Through this lack of intense concentration he lost much time,
and both Westbrook and Gibb agree that he became a marked
procrastinator. Nevertheless, the oft-repeated assertion that
he was lazy is surely not true; rather, he frittered away much
time in relatively unimportant matters. The real cause of his
inadequate productivity after 1882 was that he had become
overwhelmed and confused by the very mass of his fossil riches,
and by the effort required to direct his superabundant staff
in the laboratory and in the field. At times, his assistants were
left for a day or more with nothing to do except talk over
their grievances, while Marsh lingered in New York at the
University Club or the Century Club, where he undeniably liked
to "spread himself." It must be remembered however, that the
contact with men prominent in business, in politics, and in
science, whom he met at these clubs, was a source of strength
to him in his position in the National Academy and in the
Survey. In the 'nineties, the quest that led him there even
more frequently was for some wealthy person who would complete the Peabody Museum as it was originally designed.

Westbrook's feeling that it was a great pity that Marsh
could not have made better use of all the talent he had assembled
in the Museum is certainly justified, in view of the fact that

between 1883 and 1887 the New Haven staff numbered eighteen persons.

Whether or not Marsh might have worked out some sort of salvation with his assistants, had it not been for the fourth factor—outside interference—is uncertain. Even one dissatisfied employee, if he be outspoken enough, can infect a whole group; what, then, might be expected of a staff that included five such excitable and positive persons as Hermann, Baur, Williston, Barbour, and Schlosser? However, he was never to have the chance. It is well known that Baur, for example, was getting comfort from others outside of New Haven in his disputes with Marsh. Cope might have been attracted to Baur by the similarity of their scientific fields, and by their like philosophic trend of thought; but it is not to be assumed that their conversation, once they did meet, was confined to Vertebrate Paleontology in the abstract. Such disaffection as was already in the minds of the men mentioned above was exactly the sort of culture to grow the seed that Cope was only too anxious to sow, be his motive what you will. Possibly it is unjust to assume that the initiative came from Philadelphia. As to that, we can only judge from Cope's own letters and from unwritten but prolific Copeana.

On October 27, 1885, when a Congressional investigation of the Geological Survey was afoot, Cope wrote Osborn:

The 4 men at Yale are anxious to publish in both Europe and America their statement. . . . There is however one difficulty. Dr. Baur . . . who furnishes a good deal of the backbone, is in Marsh's debt some $650 and he can do nothing till that is paid as he is a married man. I want to find someone to lend him the money or part of it, because if it is paid out of his wages, he cannot pay it till next April, which will be too late for the paper to be of any service in the investigation. . . . I have taken upon me to try & raise $200 of this amount. . . . Now Dr. Baur will probably ask you whether you can lend him this amt. or part of it.[8]

On November 28, 1885, continuing the subject further, Cope said:

8. H. F. Osborn, *Cope: Master Naturalist* (1931), pp. 380–381. Princeton University Press.

I agree with you about the form of publication [of the statement by the assistants at New Haven]. It should, if possible, be published in Science, but failing that separately. I have told the boys that I should have no connection with it in any way, both for effect & because I have done my share in that quarter. . . . It is a business I do not like, but it is absolutely necessary, or our Government aid to Science will be forever ruined, & the reputation of the country compromised.[9]

On July 27, 1886, Cope wrote his wife: "I want to stop over a day in New Haven and see Dr. Baur." [10] On August 6, 1886, he wrote Osborn: "I spent a day at New Haven, recently, with Baur and Williston." [11] During the National Academy meeting at New Haven in November, 1888, Cope boarded with Baur.

However the alliance between Cope and Marsh's assistants came about, the result was the mass attack upon Marsh under Cope's leadership in January, 1890. The pity of it is that the long pent-up bitterness which found release in this ill-judged newspaper polemic was so unnecessary. Practically all Marsh's assistants had successful careers in Paleontology or Geology, despite his refusal to allow most of them to start independent work while on his payroll. And who shall say that the abundant fossil material with which they worked at Yale, and the training they received therefrom, was any handicap to them in later years? As for the two major opponents in whose quarrel they were but pawns, the field of exploration and research was wide enough to fulfill the ambitions of both; and had they lived a generation apart, the story of the early days of Vertebrate Paleontology in America might have been quite different. Not that the science did not profit, undoubtedly, by the competition between these two men, at least so far as the making of extensive collections was concerned; but had they chosen to divide the field, and each till his particular portion, the harvest would have been unattended by the resentment that had such far-reaching consequences.

9. Osborn, *op. cit.,* pp. 381–382, with more to the same effect on p. 388.
10. *Ibid.,* p. 374.
11. *Ibid.,* p. 384.

CHAPTER XIII
SUNSET YEARS

IT IS given to some men to descend the slope of life in peace and serenity. This was not to be the fate of Professor Marsh, and it may be that he would not have had it so. The 'seventies were for him years of new and striking discoveries on the western plains. With the 'eighties, he came into full power, with ample funds to supplement his material and prepare it for publication in great monographs, with position secure at Washington, with his enemies for the time in the background, and only the troubles among his immediate staff to annoy him. But as he rounded the turn into the 'nineties, Fortune began to smile upon him less and less.

The new decade had scarcely started when Cope, smarting under a series of unsuccessful attempts to regain his lost ground at Washington, and believing himself greatly wronged by Marsh, laid his case before the public. That some of the mud thrown at Marsh stuck fast, in spite of his refutation of Cope's charges, there is no denying. But that the "spattering," to use Bromley's phrase, extended likewise to the author of the charges is equally true. That the entire affair did no credit to either party, and certainly no good to science, may once more be reiterated. Here we are concerned with it merely as one of the things that clouded Marsh's later years, even though he was able, strictly speaking, to repel the attack.

The echoes from this bitter public quarrel had only begun to die away when Marsh's plans were under fire from another quarter—Congress. As in the Red Cloud affair, his was only a small part in a drama of much wider scope. His appointment as Vertebrate Paleontologist of the United States Geological Survey had been made by Director Powell in 1882, and the alliance between them had held great advantages for both. In return for generous funds to spend on fossils, Marsh had much to offer in the way of political support from his affiliates in science and from his Yale friends, and so tightly did the

Powell-Marsh coalition hold that for years Congressmen, Cope, and others beat upon it in vain.

Within Congress, Powell had the constant support of the powerful Senate Appropriations Committee, headed by William B. Allison of Iowa, one of the few "western" senators who were looked upon with favor by such financially minded easterners as Platt, Aldrich, and Spooner. The Survey had been established, curiously enough, not so much by Congress as by the Appropriations Committee; it was, as one protesting senator put it, "nakedly the creature of an appropriations bill—it has no other father or mother." This "inadvertence," so styled, made it possible for the director to expend his funds as he chose, submitting no itemized budget to Congressional scrutiny and no detailed annual reports that could be similarly "audited."

Powell, it has been said, was not a "practical politician," insofar, that is, as the use of the Survey for economic purposes was concerned. He might be intensely "practical" in getting money to spend, but when it came to spending it, he was actuated primarily by his vision of what might be accomplished by the reclamation of arid lands. This vision had come to him in the 'sixties and 'seventies as he rode across hundreds of miles of the Great West, and he had set it before the Forty-second Congress in 1878 in his "Report on the lands of the arid regions of the United States," [1] a milestone in the conservation movement. He had seen that the public lands available for new settlers were rapidly becoming exhausted, and that the only way to replenish the supply was to provide stores of water that would reclaim the desert areas. Even then he foresaw that this was too vast a project to be undertaken by any agency other than the Government itself. He saw, too, that the main difficulties would not be engineering ones, great as these were, but the protection of the projects from becoming the spoils of those who would rush to speculate in lands and water rights. As a geologist, he felt that the only proper preparation for such a far-reaching plan would be a detailed survey of the states in need of reclamation projects, and the making of topographic and geologic maps that would show the classification of the various types of lands, the best areas

1. *House Executive Document* 73, 195 pp.

to be impounded, suitable sites for dams and reservoirs, and so on. To further this idea he had asked for—and received— from Congress in 1882 authority "to complete a geologic map of the United States."

It became apparent to Congress before long, however, that, from its point of view, this grant had been a mistake, and attempts were made to retrieve it as the congressmen could make no headway in finding out how Powell proposed to spend his increasing appropriations. A Congressional committee was appointed in 1885–86 to investigate several of the Federal scientific bureaus, including the Geological Survey; Powell told this committee that he could complete the geologic map in twenty years at a cost of $18,000,000, but one of his critics remarked that at the rate he was progressing it would take one hundred years and cost over $100,000,000. The western congressmen, especially, under pressure from home to get action for irrigation, were becoming out-and-out opponents of Powell. Nevertheless, in 1888 the Geological Survey was given an appropriation of $250,000, and authorized to segregate lands capable of irrigation and lay out suitable plans for reservoirs. Still no definite results were forthcoming to appease the clamor for quick action from a public that was in no mood to appreciate the careful groundwork that Powell was laying. Clarence Dutton, one of Powell's geological staff, told his Yale classmates at a reunion that Powell's insistence on using funds, appropriated for "irrigation," to carry on topographic surveys would prove his ruination, and he was a true prophet.

What had been a general pressure for reclamation of arid lands was swelled to an outcry by the drought year of 1890, but no breach was made in Powell's defenses until the Fifty-second Congress met for its first session in 1892. At this time, in addition to the drought, the country was feeling the adverse effects of the Sherman Silver Purchase Act; and the financial "recession" that confronted President Cleveland almost immediately he took office in 1893 was already in the making. As a consequence, Congress was in a mood to scrutinize expenditures more carefully than was its wont when money was easy. And surely—in the minds of the western congressmen at least—there could be no better place to start economizing than in the Geological Survey. But how? As one senator complained:

"When we talk individually with each other we say to each other 'There is something wrong about this survey,' and everybody says 'Yes, that is so, but you must not touch the paleontology, or you must not touch the geology, or you must not touch the geography.' " [2]

It seems curious to count among the factors that led to Professor Marsh's removal from the Survey payroll the doggedness of an Alabama lawyer and the obsession of a Harvard professor, but a search of the pages of the *Congressional Record* certainly leaves that impression. When the question of appropriations for the Geological Survey came before the House of Representatives in May, 1892, as a part of the Sundry Civil Bill, a proposal to cut out the entire allotment for Paleontology was at once advanced by Hilary A. Herbert of Alabama. Herbert had been a member of a Congressional committee appointed in 1885–86 to investigate the Survey, and was one of two members to bring in an unfavorable minority report— an isolated position in which, it is said, he was considerably surprised to find himself, and which apparently was the result of a sudden change of mind on the part of all but one of his colleagues on the committee. In any event, he insisted on spreading the minority report on the pages of the *Record*, reporting that he had been greatly influenced by a long conversation with Professor Alexander Agassiz of Harvard—not a paleontologist, incidentally—who told him that Paleontology

is just one of the things which private individuals and learned societies can do just as well as the government. They will do it cheaper. There are always in the different universities plenty of people who will be thankful to do such work for the honor of doing it, and who will manage to get the gist of their results published by scientific societies to which they belong.[3]

As an example of this sort of coöperation, Agassiz had cited the publication by the Agassiz Museum of the reports on the material collected by the *Blake* and by the Coast Survey vessels: fourteen quarto volumes to date, issued at a cost of

2. The story as outlined here is taken from the *Congressional Record,* Vol. XXIII, Pt. 5, pp. 4389–4396, 5885–5893; Pt. 6, pp. 6151–6160.

3. *Op. cit.,* pp. 4390, 4393.

$30,000, one quarter to one sixth of what he was sure these books would have cost the Government. These were the years, it should be said, when Agassiz was almost a lone crusader against what he called "political scientists"; i.e., the domination of Washington in scientific affairs.

The minority report of 1885 shows the basis for Agassiz' contention, and also for Powell's strength. Citing the names of 69 men outside of Washington who were on the Survey payroll, from 21 states or territories, it summarized them as including 7 state geologists and 24 professors of Geology or allied sciences.

Asked in 1892 if he were attacking Marsh personally, or as head of the Survey Division of Paleontology, Herbert denied any personal bias, but he nevertheless went on to a dramatic move which, unimportant in itself, undoubtedly had some part in the final result. He held up a copy of Marsh's monograph on toothed birds (*Odontornithes*)—a sumptuous volume, with morocco binding, gilt edges, wide margins, specially tinted paper, and a wealth of illustrations—and pointed to it as an excellent example of the way in which large amounts of Government money were being wasted on the description of such worthless objects as "birds with teeth"![4] He stated, further, that not only had this book been published by the Government at great cost, but that it had been republished in the *Third Annual Report* of the Geological Survey, thus duplicating the expense.

Returning to the subject the next day, Mr. Herbert admitted that he had had a letter from Marsh in 1886, in which the latter pointed out that this memoir had been published before he became a member of the United States Geological Survey (it was Volume VII of the King Survey), that the cost of the illustrations had been borne by himself, and that what appeared in the *Annual Report* was merely a 40-page abstract, using the same figures. Herbert nevertheless continued to hold the memoir up to ridicule, and succeeded to the extent of making "birds with teeth" a catchword that appeared in the speech of every congressman who had anything to say about the

4. Marsh's comment on this to another Congressman was: "There is more money wasted every year in the United States searching for coal in places where a paleontologist would know at a glance none could be found than would pay for all the works ever published in paleontology."

paleontological appropriations, pro or con. His amendment
to stop all work in Paleontology after July 1, 1892, was carried, 90 votes to 60.

When the Sundry Civil Bill came up for discussion in the
Senate in July, the Appropriations Committee moved to add
an amendment to strike out the House proviso that all paleontological work should be stopped, and to add another inserting
the paleontological salaries omitted by the lower chamber.
This opened the way for a further attack on Paleontology, in
the course of which such western senators as Vest of Missouri,
Wolcott of Colorado,[5] and Stewart of Nevada [6] rose to astonishing heights of oratory in their polemics against the Survey and
against Paleontology in particular. In spite of Representative
Herbert's admission that he had received Marsh's letter pointing out the injustice of citing *Odontornithes* as an example of
Survey extravagance, the monograph was again held up to
ridicule as an "elegant book" that had cost from $3,000 to
$4,000 a volume. Senator Platt of Connecticut, defending
Marsh, said that he saw no reason why Paleontology should be
crippled because the senators did not like Powell. Whereupon
Senator Wolcott, revealing the real core of senatorial irrita-
tion, remarked that this was the only way the Senate could get
at the Survey appropriations. "This Geological Survey," he
said, "comes to this body in some way, the Lord only knows how,

5. E. O. Wolcott, Yale ex-'70, for many years leader of the Republican party
in Colorado, a free silverite, and a dependable "regular" in party matters.
6. William M. Stewart, Yale ex-'52, specialist in mining law, who received
fees of $500,000 for his successful defense of the interests of the original claim-
ants to the Comstock Lode; "possessed of unlimited confidence, colossal self-
assertion, unflagging energy, and indomitable perseverance, he was a striking
product of the mining frontier" (*Dictionary of American Biography*).
One of the curious souvenirs in the Marsh archives is a letter from Senator Stewart to President Dwight of Yale, dated June 21, 1892, wherein he
said, replying to the latter's request that he use his influence to retain the
item for Paleontology in the Sundry Civil Bill, "I shall do all I can to
secure the appropriation, but it is very difficult at this session of Congress
to obtain needful appropriations to carry on the Government. The Demo-
cratic party seems determined to make a record for the fall election without regard to the merits of any particular appropriation. They are striking
in the dark for the purpose of reducing the aggregate amount, without
regard to the effect upon the business of the country, or matters of educational or scientific importance." He adds that he expects to be in New
Haven on the twenty-eighth to attend the reunion of his class, unless prevented by press of Congressional duties.

and we hear nothing about it until the appropriations bill comes in providing about a million dollars every year to be expended by this survey. . . . There is nothing important, I think, connected with these two paleontologists but here is a chance to cut Survey appropriations."

Another curious feature of this debate was Senator Allison's admission that he had received a letter from Professor Osborn, charging that Marsh was spending too much time and money on Vertebrate Paleontology. In the absence of this letter, it is impossible to comment on it directly. A copy of it had been sent to Marsh by Powell, who had received it from Allison, and Marsh wrote Powell about it on June 16, 1892, prefacing his remarks by the statement, "As you already know, the whole matter is with him a personal one." The next paragraph is a curious one, for which the present writers will attempt no explanation; it reads:

Professor Osborn begins by giving his own estimate of the relative importance to geology of invertebrate and vertebrate paleontology, virtually disparaging the latter, which he regards as "less practical and of a more purely scientific character."

In spite of these onslaughts, the Survey supporters in the Senate won this preliminary skirmish, the salary amendment passing by a vote of 31 to 21, the proviso cutting off Paleontology being struck out by a vote of 29 to 18, and the $30,000 allocated to Paleontology receiving 27 votes to 21.

When the bill calling for a general Survey appropriation of $561,400 came before the Senate on July 14, the western senators renewed their attacks. Wolcott's amendment to have the Survey appropriation cut to $400,000 was lost, 24 to 28, but to Senator Carey of Wyoming[7] fell the honor of proposing the amendment that finally toppled Powell—and with him, Marsh—from the positions so long thought impregnable. His proposal, cutting the Survey appropriations to about $335,000, and specifying two geologists at $4,000, one at $3,000, one at $2,700, and two paleontologists at $2,000 each, was sustained 26 to 23; in other words, by a shift of five votes, gained, accord-

7. J. M. Carey, first United States Attorney to Wyoming Territory, and the state's first senator. Author of the Carey Act of 1894, which authorized the Secretary of the Interior to patent lands to states having desert areas, provided they could cause such lands to be reclaimed and irrigated.

ing to the New York *Times* of July 15, from eastern and southern senators, "for personal reasons."

During the course of these debates over the appropriations bill, Marsh was kept fully aware of the danger that threatened. The letters from his various Washington correspondents, and the few of his that remain, indicate that he was somewhat at a loss to understand the attacks on his work. Representative Herbert, he felt, had been waiting for revenge since 1886; however, he states that when he had written the congressman at that time refuting the charge about the alleged costly reprinting of *Odontornithes,* he had received a letter from the latter acknowledging the correction. When Herbert repeated the charge in 1892, Marsh again refuted it, only to have it reappear in the Senate from Senator Stewart. Just why Herbert and Stewart picked *Odontornithes* for attack is not clear, unless because of its expensive appearance. And at that, the King Survey edition had not possessed all the de luxe characteristics that were present in the special edition that Marsh had had printed for private distribution—but it is safe to say that the copy which Representative Herbert held up to show his colleagues was one of the latter! The reappearance of the memoir in shortened form in the *Annual Report* of the Survey had ample precedent, since the preceding report had carried similar abstracts of three of the Survey's monographs, Dutton's on the Grand Canyon, Gilbert's on Lake Bonneville, and Becker's on the Comstock Lode; the last of these memoirs had an obviously economic bearing, but hardly the other two. The hostility of the western senators Marsh could not explain, since he had considered Wolcott and Carey, at least, friendly to him; he intimated, however, that he had finally learned the cause of Wolcott's shift of opinion. In the attempt to stem the tide he had written to such of the congressmen as he felt might help, and he went to Washington himself the latter part of June. As indicated above, however, neither his efforts nor those of Powell, who was at the time handicapped by severe pain from his amputated arm, were of any avail; and on July 20 Marsh received a telegram from Powell which read: "Appropriation cut off. Please send your resignation at once." This was followed on August 5 by a letter from Powell appointing him Honorary Paleontologist of the Survey and expressing the hope that he would supervise the preparation of monographs already under way, to which Marsh assented.

Shortly afterward Marsh received a letter from Charles D. Walcott, who had been placed in charge of the entire Division of Paleontology in 1891, stating that the balance left for Paleontology was so small that only five paleontologists in Washington could be carried; "these, with one assistant and a laborer, comprise what is left of the Paleontologic branch, in which there were twenty-eight persons during the last fiscal year." Walcott's next letter, dated October 12, 1892, is abstracted rather fully below, as throwing some light on the state of affairs in Washington:

Mr. Hague told me a day or two ago that you had received a letter from the Secretary of the Interior notifying you that you had been dropped from the U. S. Geological Survey force. This was the first intimation I had of such action, as I had supposed that you were legislated out by the action of Congress. Have made inquiries and learn that when the Director was consulting with Mr. Gilbert regarding the proposed changes in the geological force, it was decided that Pumpelly, Emmons, Becker, and Marsh should be dropped, and the Chief Clerk was so notified. But for hearing through Emmons and Becker of the action in relation to the geologists I knew nothing of any formal request having been sent to the Secretary, or that it was necessary in your case.

In regard to Henry S. Williams, Alpheus Hyatt, and William M. Fontaine, I looked after their re-appointment, at a nominal per diem, so as to retain their official connection with the Survey. This came about from the fact that they reported directly to me and I had their matters in charge.

I do not think that the Director intended that the letter of dismissal should be sent to you as it was, as I cannot conceive, after all the support that he has given to your work, that he would intentionally place you in such a position. When he was here he was sick and unfit to think of, or transact, business which necessitated recalling matters, or planning for the future.

When he went away he left a great many matters unattended to, and Mr. McGee has been obliged to write his annual report for the past fiscal year. I expect that he will return here the latter part of this month or early in November, when I will speak to him at once about your matter.

He requested me to make up the estimates for the next fiscal year, and I put in an item which read in this way: "For paleontological researches relating to *vertebrate* fossils and for continuing the preparation of the reports thereon, five thousand dollars." When he came to consider the estimates he decided it was best to incorporate this sum in the general amount, and *not* make a distinct statement; and as thus corrected the estimates were sent in.

The plan of estimates for the Survey, as a whole, if adopted by Congress and carried into effect will reorganize the Survey on a new basis, which, I think, will be satisfactory to Congress and the people of the country. . . .

Personally, I wish to see your work completed and published under your charge; and I hope that, in connection with field operations in the West, Hatcher may be enabled to continue investigations that will bear on geologic and paleontologic problems. . . . I do not think that the Major intended to slight you or your work. At all events, I will learn from him upon his return *how* it occurred.

[Signed] CHARLES D. WALCOTT.

Marsh's world may well have seemed to be crashing about his ears that July morning in 1892. Not only was it a severe blow to his pride to be thus summarily dismissed from the commanding position he had held for a decade, but the quite unexpected removal of $4,000 from his annual income coincided with a "low" in his other finances. One of his biographers said that Marsh planned his scientific work as if he expected to live forever. It might equally well be said of him that he spent his money as if he expected the source of it to be eternal. He had long been receiving the major part of his income from the two funds set up by George Peabody, the so-called Boston Trust, established before the latter's death, and the Peabody Trust established by his will. In each of two peak years (1872 and 1877) these two funds turned over to Marsh more than $50,000. The Boston Trust continued to yield him about $3,000 a year until just before his death; but the other, larger fund, after a payment of $37,598 in 1888, representing a partial distribution of the principal, paid him less than $1,000 more during his lifetime. The Peabody will had provided that the trust which it set up for his heirs should be kept open until all the nephews and nieces were deceased. However, a letter to Marsh from his cousin, Singleton Peabody, on February 25, 1891, reminded him that the distribution asked for by certain of the heirs in 1888 had been as "final" as possible under the circumstances; and stated that he saw little if anything more coming from the fund, unless the Broad Top property, which had been a "veritable heritage of woe" for twenty years, should be sold. "*Ex lapide non sanguis*," he added, "and the 'estate' is now like a squeezed orange."

Like many another man in those years of the early 'nineties, therefore, Marsh faced a great cut in income, and his letters to relatives and friends during this period show how exceedingly difficult he found it. He could no longer maintain his beautiful home, and mortgaged it to the University for $30,000, and for the first time his name was put on the University salary list. Recognizing that he had no more money for extensive collecting, he stopped Hatcher's search for Ceratopsia material and set him, instead, to the much less expensive task of studying in the field the distribution of the Ceratops beds; and from this time on he acquired material only through an occasional purchase or from short field trips.

The notable Yale assemblage of the ancient plants known as cycads represents the last flare-up of Marsh's collecting energy. It is probable that his first interest in these was stratigraphic rather than biologic, and was connected with his desire to prove that the Potomac formation and other beds along the eastern coast were Jurassic in age and not Cretaceous, as held by other Federal geologists. The subject of cycads had received new impetus in 1893 and 1894 from collections made in Maryland and in the Black Hills, both of which were discussed by Lester F. Ward of the United States National Museum. The cycads from the Black Hills localities, collected for the most part by Professor T. H. Macbride of the State University of Iowa, were considered to be Lower Cretaceous in age, but, inasmuch as none had been found in place (i.e., actually imbedded in rock formations), this point could not be regarded as established. The European cycads, on the other hand, with which Marsh was familiar, were of Jurassic time. With these things in mind, he began in 1895 to press H. F. Wells, a collector who had been sending him mammals from South Dakota, to get specimens of cycads, and especially to hunt for such in place. None was forthcoming, however, until March of 1897, when Wells sent in Cycad No. 1 of the Yale Collection from the Black Hills.[8] By October, Marsh was telegraphing for more cycads, and by the end of the next year he had $1,500 worth, no inconsiderable part of this amount being required for the freight bills on these exceedingly heavy specimens. The last lot to be purchased had been intended for the United States National Museum, but at the final moment that institution had refused to pay the amount asked by Wells, and Marsh took the whole shipment, totaling nearly 15,000 pounds. Most of these Black Hills cycads were described by Ward, but in the meantime Marsh had found, in the person of George R. Wieland, an enthusiast who was eager to carry on further intensive study of the cycads, with a view to determining their evolutionary significance. Marsh did not live to see this work carried out, but the memorable volume that appeared seven years after his death bore the title he had suggested for it—"American fossil cycads"—and it is due largely to his foresight in collecting the material, and to his encouragement of Wieland, that we now know so well the plants which paralleled the dinosaurs in the Mesozoic world, and which are recognized to include primitive flowering types. As Wieland himself said, up to the time Marsh began to collect cycads, all that was known about them was something of the trunk structure and considerably more about the nearly mature stages in the seed-bearing fruit in two species. That so much is now known is "quite solely due to the habit of Professor Marsh . . . to collect 'all'. . . . Had these fossil plants been scattered in various small collections and studied separately it might have been many years before all the facts they teach could have been correctly correlated." [9]

8. In 1867, when Marsh was in Baltimore, he had been presented by Philip Tyson with two cycads from the Iron Ore beds of Maryland, and the Museum also had a portion of an Isle of Portland specimen, presumably given to it by Gideon A. Mantell, but nothing had ever been done with these.

9. G. R. Wieland, "The Yale Collection of Fossil Cycads," *Yale Sci. Mo.*, Vol. VI, No. 6 (March, 1900), pp. 211–221.

In these years of the later 'nineties, Marsh's great ambition came to be the completion of a new wing of the Museum to house his wonderful material, and his constant importunities to this end made him unwelcome in many quarters. He also determined, belatedly, to finish some of his long-projected monographs, and in this he was more successful, producing in 1896 two of his most important contributions, "The dinosaurs of North America," perhaps his greatest work, and "Vertebrate fossils [of the Denver Basin]."

In April, 1895, he retired from his twelve-year presidency of the National Academy, and that summer he was in Europe, attending the British Association meeting at Ipswich and the International Congress of Zoology at Leyden. He was again abroad in 1897, for the International Geological Congress in Russia, whence he wrote the following amusing letter to Professor Brush:

Moscow, le 10° Sept. 1897.

Dear Brush.

The Congress is over as a whole, and many of the geologists left yesterday in various directions. Most of them on the three great excursions. . . . The last public session was in St. Petersburg but the ceremonies were continued here, winding up with a grand banquet. I have had enough of it all, and feel much as the small boy does the day after the 4th of July. I shall therefore leave tomorrow (via Warsaw) for Vienna direct, and hope there to do some work on the fossils my good friend Suess is to show me. A few days in Munich and Paris, and I shall sail on the St. Paul from Southampton on the 25th and hope to be home by Oct. 2d.

There were about 600 members of the Congress at St. Petersburg, among them many of your friends. Geikie, Hughes, and Bauermann from England, Gaudry, Barrois, Margerie and Bertrand from France, Zittel, Haeckel, von Richthofen and many others from Germany, and no end other nationalities from the South.

The Russians, of course, were most numerous, but the Americans (so called) were not far behind. From James Hall (86) who took in the Ural excursion and everything else, Banquets, Balls etc., without injury, to one small boy (80 years younger at least) and various forlorn damsels of forbidding aspect and uncertain age, America was amply if not wisely represented. You will soon get the particulars of it all, but I will not risk spoiling the story by trying to condense it here. Some of it will not soon be forgotten.

Emmons was my companion du voyage, but has just left for Mt. Ararat. I wanted to go, hoping to find a bone or two from Noah's menagerie, but I have some that Noah never saw, awaiting me at New Haven, and I must hurry back.

With kind remembrances to your family and my other New Haven friends,

> Yours sincerely,
> [Signed] O. C. MARSH.[10]

The end of 1897 brought Marsh one of the greatest honors of his life, the Cuvier Prize given every three years by the French Academy for "the most remarkable work either on the Animal Kingdom or on Geology," and awarded heretofore only to Louis Agassiz and Joseph Leidy in this country. Albert Gaudry, as secretary for the prize commission, described to the Academy his visit to "Mr. Marsh's Museum of Paleontology," and added fulsome praise of Marsh's work, calling him a true successor to the great savant for whom the prize was named.[11] This recognition must have been doubly sweet, coming as it did in the midst of so many difficulties. His prior honors had included the first Bigsby Medal awarded by the Geological Society of London, in 1877, the honorary degree of doctor of philosophy from the University of Heidelberg, and that of doctor of laws from Harvard University, both given him in 1886.

At the beginning of 1898, Marsh put into effect what had long been in his mind, the gift of his collections to Yale University. The description of the collections in the deed of gift, the conditions under which the gift was made, and the letter of transfer are given below:[12]

(1) *The Collection of Vertebrate Fossils.* This is the most important and valuable of all, as it is very extensive, contains a very large

10. Quoted by kind permission of Mrs. Louis V. Pirsson.
11. *Compt. Rend., Acad. Sci. Paris,* CXXVI (Jan. 10, 1898), 126–129.
12. O. C. Marsh, "Presentation of scientific collections to Yale University," *Science* (new ser.), VII (January 21, 1898), 77–79.

number of type specimens, many of them unique, and is widely known from the descriptions already published. In extinct Mammals, Birds and Reptiles, of North America, this series stands preëminent.

This collection was pronounced by Huxley, who examined it with care in 1876, to be surpassed by no other in the world. Darwin, in 1878, expressed a strong desire to visit America for the sole purpose of seeing this collection. Since then it has been more than doubled in size and value, and still holds first rank. The bulk of this collection has been secured in my western explorations, which have extended over a period of nearly thirty years, during which I have crossed the Rocky Mountains twenty-seven times.

(2) *The Collection of Fossil Footprints.* These specimens are mainly from the Connecticut Valley, and thus have a special local interest. They also form one of the most extensive and complete collections of the kind in this country, if not the most valuable of all.

(3) *The Collection of Invertebrate Fossils.* This includes a large number of interesting specimens from many formations and localities, both in this country and in Europe. Some of these fossils I collected myself, but the greater number were secured by purchase. Among the series of specimens especially valuable may be mentioned several thousand from the famous Mazon Creek locality in Illinois; a very extensive collection of Crinoids from Crawfordsville, in Indiana; the largest collection of nearly entire Trilobites yet discovered, and one of the rarest series of Silurian Sponges known, including important type specimens.

(4) *The Collection of Recent Osteology.* This is believed to be the most complete collection in this country for purposes of study. I have made special efforts for many years to secure the skeletons of rare existing vertebrates from every part of the world, particularly of Mammals, Birds and Reptiles. The collection is rich in Anthropoid Apes, the Gorillas being represented by no less than thirteen individuals, and the other genera by rare characteristic specimens.

(5) *The Collection of American Archæology and Ethnology.* This collection is the best in the country in several branches of the science, being particularly rich in Central American antiquities, several thousand specimens in number and many of them unique. Some of these I obtained myself in Central America, and among

the others is the famous de Zeltner collection, rich in gold ornaments, which I secured by purchase. The specimens from Mexico
are also of great interest, and the series is a representative one.
It includes the well-known Skilton collection.

(6) *The Collection of Minerals.* This is a limited collection,
but contains many valuable specimens, among them probably the
most interesting series known of Nova Scotian Zeolites. . . .

Professor Marsh's letter accompanying his deed of gift is
essentially as follows:

To the President and Fellows of Yale University.

GENTLEMEN: It is thirty years and more since Mr. George Peabody
established at Yale, by a gift of one hundred and fifty thousand
dollars, the Museum that now bears his name. This was in 1866,
the year I began my work as Professor of Paleontology, and I
secured this gift mainly with a view of building up a Department
of Paleontology that should be a school of original research as
well as one of instruction. The collections of natural history which
I had thus brought together were subsequently deposited in the
Peabody Museum, and from that time I have endeavored in every
way to increase these collections, so that at present they are
in many respects the most extensive and valuable in this country.

It has always been part of my plan that these scientific collections should eventually become the property of Yale University,
and from the first I provided in my will for such a disposition of
them. As it now seems probable that I may not be able to carry
out my original intentions in regard to a Department of Paleontology at Yale, I have decided to present these collections to the
University, subject only to certain conditions that appear necessary for their permanent care and preservation. The deed of
gift, which I herewith enclose, bears the date of January 1st, 1898.

. . . .

On learning of the acceptance of this gift on the part of the
Corporation of Yale University, with the conditions stated in
the accompanying deed, I will make the formal transfer to them
of all the collections above named.

Very respectfully,

O. C. MARSH.

Yale University, January 1, 1898.

The conditions on which Professor Marsh gives his invaluable collections to Yale University, for the benefit of all departments of the University, are few in number, the more important being the following:

(1) The scientific collections I now give to Yale University shall be kept in the present Peabody Museum building or in additions thereto equally safe from fire.

(2) During my life, these collections shall remain, as now, under my supervision and control, available for my own investigation and description, or for the work of others designated by me.

(3) At my decease, and forever after, these collections shall be under the charge of the Trustees of the Peabody Museum and their successors, and in the special custody of Curators recommended by them and appointed by the Corporation of Yale University.

(4) The type specimens and others of special importance in these collections shall not be removed from the Museum building. Less valuable specimens, however, especially duplicates, may be so removed by vote of the Trustees of the Museum.

From a scientific point of view, the value of the collections now presented to Yale is beyond price, each one containing many specimens that can never be duplicated, and already of historical interest in the annals of science.

Among the prominent features of one of these collections, that of extinct vertebrates, may be mentioned (1) the series of fossils illustrating the genealogy of the horse, as made out by Professor Marsh, and accepted by Huxley, who used it as the basis of his New York lectures; (2) the Birds with teeth, nearly two hundred individuals, described in Professor Marsh's well-known monograph 'Odontornithes;' (3) the gigantic Dinoccrata, several hundred in number, Eocene mammals described in his monograph on this group; (4) the Brontotheridæ, huge Miocene mammals, some two hundred in number; (5) Pterodactyles, or flying dragons, over six hundred in number; (6) the Mosasaurs, or Cretaceous sea-serpents, represented by more than fifteen hundred individuals; (7) a large number of Dinosaurian reptiles, some of gigantic size. Besides there are various other groups of Mammals, Birds and Reptiles, most of them including unique specimens.

The resolutions of the Corporation of Yale University, accepting Professor Marsh's gift, and showing their appreciation of his services to the University, are given below:

Yale University, January 13, 1898.

The President and Fellows having received a deed of gift from Professor Othniel C. Marsh, presenting to the University his very valuable collections now in the Peabody Museum, which represent the labor of many years on his part and also the expenditure of a large amount from his personal fortune, desire, as they accept the gift, to communicate to him and to place on record an expression of their grateful acknowledgment of his generosity.

In this grateful acknowledgment they are confident that all the graduates and friends of Yale will unite, when they learn of this most recent manifestation of his long-continued interest in the University, even as they already fully appreciate the unselfish devotion of his time, his talents and his energies, for more than thirty years, to the scientific researches which have given him such personal distinction and have brought such renown to the institution.

TIMOTHY DWIGHT,
President.

The summer of 1898 found Marsh once more in Europe, replying for the American delegation at the opening of the International Congress of Zoology at Cambridge, taking an active part in a symposium on the origin of mammals, and then going to Bristol in September for the sessions of the British Association. Richard Lydekker, writing of this visit later, said it was apparent to all that Marsh was far from well, and he had, indeed, been ill during that year with arterial trouble so that he was no longer able to walk readily, as he had done all his life.

The last of February, 1899, he made a trip to Washington —not a pleasant one, doubtless, as Walcott was pressing him to close up his Survey connections and send material on to Washington—and he stopped off in New York on the way back to attend a dinner for Carl Schurz, long one of his friends. Returning to New Haven next morning, he walked from the railway station to the New Haven House through heavy rain, and Bostwick and Westbrook, summoned thither, found him wet through and chilly. His illness really started from that time, although he insisted on coming to work at the Museum each day, driving around to the back door in a cab and having the men take him up to his office in the freight elevator. One day Gibb found him about as usual when he went up at noon to make his tea, but at three-thirty Bostwick came rushing down to the basement with the word, "The Professor's sick." Gibb went upstairs immediately and Marsh stretched out his hand toward him, saying, "Gibb, I'm sick," but at the same time put a finger to his lips so that Gibb should tell no one else. Gibb took him down in the elevator and helped him into a cab. Asked if someone should not go home with him, he shook his head, lay back on the seat, and dropped his hands beside him. Gibb got into the cab and begged to be allowed to go along. Marsh again said "No," then, shaking Gibb's hand, said "Goodbye, Gibb," and was driven off. He never left his home again, and in less than a week (March 18) he was dead of pneumonia. After services in Battell Chapel, with a memorable eulogy by Professor George P. Fisher of the Yale Divinity School, he was buried in the Yale plot in Grove Street cemetery.

His death was the occasion for widespread comment by the press, and few were the newspapers that did not carry some account of his colorful career or some one of the countless "tall stories" that had grown up around his name. Perhaps the fullest account was that by Ray Stannard Baker which, although originally intended for *McClure's Magazine*, appeared as a syndicated article in many papers in May, 1899. One smiles a little to think how all this fanfare would have delighted the subject of it!

The Marsh will, drawn January 14, 1898, left to the Peabody Museum, as a fund to be used in publishing the results of his western explorations, the sum of $30,000 that he was permitted to bequeath under the Peabody will. To the National Academy of Sciences he left $10,000 to be used in promoting research in the natural sciences; because of necessary delay in paying this bequest, his executors increased the sum by an equal amount. His home was given to the University for a botanical garden, or, if not so used, to be sold at the end of three years and the proceeds turned into a fund for scientific research. The residuary estate went to Yale.

Although Marsh was survived by at least one half brother and half sister, his will made no family bequests. His nephew, Robert H. Waters, son of his older sister Mary, made an unsuccessful attempt to break the will on the following curious grounds:

That Yale University induced Prof. Marsh to give his time, labor and money to the university without salary or compensation, and thereby impoverished him for many years. That Prof. Marsh, on account of his hard and nerve-shattering work for the university, labored under the delusion that there was no hereafter, and that immortality could be obtained by human agencies. That Yale, taking advantage of this delusion, encouraged him in it, and induced him to give all of his collections, his personal effects and his remaining property to the university, under the promise that such gifts would gain for him immortality.

At the time the action was brought, the statement was made that, in the first decade of his life at Yale, Marsh had announced to his closest friends his determination to leave all he had to the University when his work there should be done. Had he died ten years earlier, with a similar will, his bequests would have been as munificent as he had hoped. However, the last decade of his life had strained his resources badly, and his total cash assets when he died were represented by the sum of $186 on deposit at the bank. Had it not been for skilful management on the part of his executors, Professor Brush and, more especially, Treasurer William W. Farnam of Yale, the University might not have profited much from his will. His home, for example, although located in a highly desirable neighborhood, was in itself of a type difficult to use and hardly likely to appeal to anyone else as a dwelling. Moreover, the University already held a mortgage of $30,000 upon it, probably half its actual value, and the law ruled that this sum must be paid back from the estate. The furnishings of the house, and the orchid collection, when sold at auction in March, 1900, in New York City, brought $18,694. The grounds surrounding the Prospect Street home now form the

Marsh Botanical Garden, and the house itself, called Marsh Hall, is used for research in plant life and growth.

Fortunately for the University, but, ironically, far too late for Professor Marsh, the Peabody investments righted themselves in the years following his death, and his estate benefited thereby to the amount of some $59,000. By this means, the indebtedness to the University was finally cleared up in 1926, and Yale received some $10,000 as residuary legatee.

As has been stated, Marsh received no salary from Yale University until the year 1895. It may be said, therefore, that he served Yale without salary for twenty-nine years. He did almost no teaching, it is true, and his professorial contributions to the University were, rather, along the line of prestige gained from his high standing among scientific men the world over, the result of his great collections and the research he published upon them—intangibles which have no market value.

His collections, presented to Yale in 1898, are, again, difficult to evaluate in terms of money, but a conservative estimate would probably name a figure above a million dollars.

The New York *Evening Post*, writing of Marsh's will, said that he had treated Yale University "much as an only and deserving child," a feeling that is echoed by the words placed upon his tombstone by Professor Brush:

"To Yale he gave his collections, his services, and his estate."

CHAPTER XIV

MARSH THE MAN

IN personal appearance, Marsh followed a type that was—and still is—quite definitely marked in his father's family. He stood perhaps 5 feet 10 inches in his shoes, although at least two contemporary accounts describe him as a little below medium height for a man; he was stockily built, broad-shouldered, and held himself with an erectness that seemed to give him added inches. In early life he probably weighed about 160 pounds and in later years some 15 pounds more. In middle age his nose, mouth, and chin were average in character, his face round, his complexion fair and of a healthy color. His early portraits show the rather full lower lip so clearly seen in the portrait of his grandfather, John Marsh. His hair and eyebrows were sandy in tone, his beard tending toward red. He had widely spaced blue eyes, which often twinkled humorously, and, although his eyesight was somewhat defective, he wore glasses only when reading or writing and none of his many portraits show him with such. His forehead was high, and a scantiness of front hair caused it to appear even unduly so; with middle life he became slightly bald. As a youth he wore a flowing mustache but all his later portraits show a well-dressed full beard. Minor physical peculiarities that impressed themselves upon the memory of even the casual acquaintance were the blinking of his searching blue eyes, and the seeming impatience shown in his nervous, half-articulated "What, What's that?" When he was on horseback, this nervous habit translated itself into a constant succession of commands directed at the horse, leading the Indians to give him the rather unflattering nickname of "Heap Whoa Man."

His early life as a farmer's son had developed for Marsh a strong frame and a robust body. Nowhere does he dwell on the hardships of life or on the dangers and fatigue of field work in his pioneer days in the Rocky Mountain region, and he was never seriously ill at any time in his life. In the 'nineties, the worries, financial and professional, that piled upon him took their toll of his strength, as his photographs of that time plainly show. The last two years before his death he developed arterial trouble, which curtailed the use of one leg somewhat, and this was a great cross to him, as he had always been an active walker. Nevertheless, his death from pneumonia, after but a few days' illness, came as a great surprise even to close friends and to members of his own family.

As for Marsh's character, the salient traits in it should have emerged from the foregoing chapters, insofar, at least, as they were reflected in his actions. It may be interesting, however, to recapitulate some of them, and to speculate as to their source. The earliest one to appear, and undeniably the most persistent, was an inborn love of Nature. The normal life of all country boys takes them into the fields and woods, and many of them learn to observe the ways of flowers and birds and insects. Still others, like young Othniel, start to make collections of these things. But the great majority of these youthful collections are forgotten as the wider interests of school life take up the boy's attention. This did not occur in Marsh's case. From the time he started to collect minerals under Colonel Jewett's stimulation, his collection grew steadily, and it was so much in the forefront of his attention that everyone who knew him was aware of it. It was not enough for him to see a mineral; he must have it, if possible. The trait of acquisitiveness was therefore also strong in him from the very beginning and may have been inherited.

Along with the wish to acquire went a determination that paid little attention to obstacles, unless to regard them as something to be joyously surmounted. When his cousin, George Harmon Peabody, wrote to congratulate him over the outcome of the Red Cloud controversy, he said: "You have shown the stubborn nature of the Peabodys when they know they are right," possibly with reference to the motto on the family coat of arms: *Murus aureus conscientia sana*—"a clear conscience is a wall of brass." It was this trait—call it determination or stubbornness or what you will—that, as soon as he had earned sufficient money, took him back to Danvers, away from the farm environment at Lockport that he so disliked. It is not in evidence, curiously, in his Danvers diary of 1851, which shows him in a year of indecision. His first year at

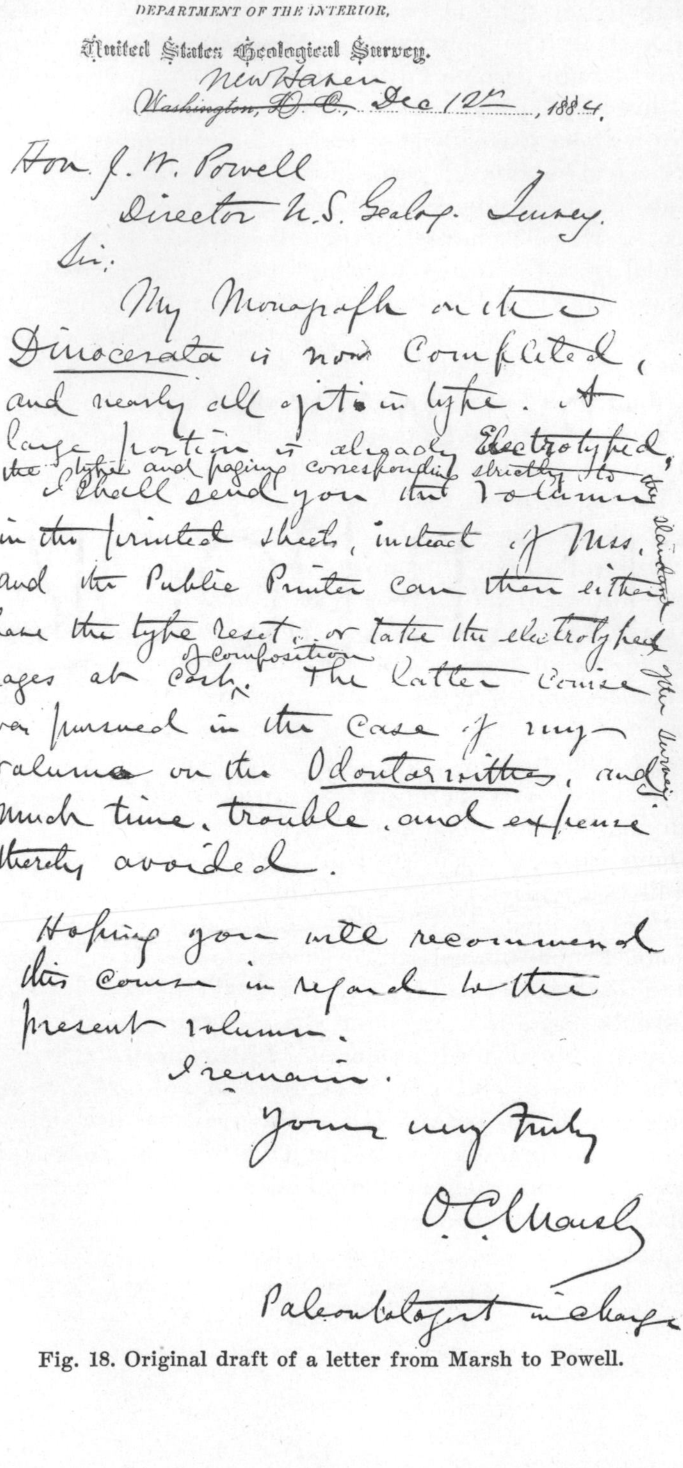
DEPARTMENT OF THE INTERIOR,

United States Geological Survey.

~~Washington, D. C.~~ New Haven, Dec 12th, 1884.

Hon J. W. Powell

Director U.S. Geolog. Survey.

Sir:

My Monograph on the Dinocerata is now completed, and nearly all of it in type. A large portion is already electrotyped, the type and paging corresponding strictly to the standard of the Survey. I shall send you the volume in the printed sheets, instead of Mss. and the Public Printer can then either have the type reset, or take the electrotyped pages at cost of composition. The latter course was pursued in the case of my volume on the Odontornithes, and much time, trouble, and expense thereby avoided.

Hoping you will recommend this course in regard to the present volume.

I remain.

Yours very truly

O. C. Marsh

Paleontologist in charge.

Fig. 18. Original draft of a letter from Marsh to Powell.

Andover seems to have passed in somewhat the same desultory fashion. But in the summer of 1852 his ambition was awakened and he turned decisively into the path that he was to travel for the rest of his life. As to what led to this resolve, he gives no hint. It seems likely that he was influenced by some friend or relative who recognized that he had better than average ability. This may have been his Aunt Judith, his mother's sister; it may have been his Aunt Mary Marsh. It was apparently one of these two, probably the former, who presented his case to George Peabody, although the tradition in still a third branch of the family is that this move was made by his stepmother, Mary Latten.

The next trait to show conspicuously in young Marsh was coolheadedness and caution. He never advanced upon a terrain until he had looked it over thoroughly, and thus he never fell short of ammunition and never left flank or rear unguarded. This appears already at Andover in the way in which he gained the election to the presidency of the Philomathean Society, and those who set themselves against him in later life, on more serious matters, learned it to their cost. Osborn's comment on the contrast in methods in the Marsh-Cope newspaper controversy in 1890 stresses this fact; he said:

Whereas Cope attacked after a truly Celtic fashion, hitting out blindly right and left with little or no precaution for guarding the rear, Marsh's reply was thoroughly of a cold-blooded Teutonic, or Nordic, type, very dignified and, under the cover of wounded feelings reluctantly breaking the silence of years, as if this reply had been forced upon him.[1]

It was this accumulation of evidence over long periods that made it possible for Marsh to reply to Cope's attack in such great detail only a week after it appeared, and the same was true of his letter to President Grant in 1875 regarding the Indian abuses.

The ability to arrange affairs to his own advantage was aided, in the early days at least, by a friendly manner, a love of company, and a fund of good nature that attracted people to him.

1. Osborn, *Cope: Master Naturalist* (1931), p. 405. Princeton University Press.

With a strong will, a cool head, and an attractive personality, Marsh might be said to have been marked for success. To what measure he would have achieved it, or along what line, if he had been left to his own resources, one can only conjecture. Instead, he found himself rather suddenly included in that magic circle of young men and women who had the good fortune to be nephews and nieces of the wealthy bachelor banker, George Peabody, and who had every reason to expect that they would fall heir to a considerable portion of his money. When Mr. Peabody talked this matter over with Marsh in the latter's freshman year, he said: "If I make you rich, you will never do anything." However, this unusual cynicism from the kindly philanthropist was beside the mark so far as Othniel Marsh was concerned, since, of the fourteen nephews and nieces, he was the only one to achieve national (not to say international) prominence. This was in part due to intellectual powers of high order, backed by a disciplined will that kept him hard at work to attain his ambition, but possibly even more to the fact that he was able to follow the one occupation that he would have chosen above all others—natural science. Here was not only a field that he had loved since boyhood, but one that was coming rapidly into prominence on both sides of the ocean. The Peabody money set him free to cultivate it, to the great benefit of science.

The effect of the power that money gives was, unfortunately, less happy so far as Marsh himself was concerned. His wealth freed him from the necessity of adjusting himself to other personalities in the course of his professional life, once he was established in his unsalaried professorship, and his bachelor state released him from it in his leisure hours. He thus became a law unto himself. Self-reliance he had, Beecher says, "to an extraordinary degree, and it naturally led to a self-centering of his life and ambitions." Although access to him was easy, the marked self-confidence that comes with wealth and position was at once apparent. It was but natural that he should be proud of his ancestry, especially of his relationship to George Peabody, who had made his career possible; and he was very proud indeed of his unique professorship at Yale and of his standing among the leaders of science. As obstacles once formidable were overcome with comparative ease, each successive advance tended to make him tighten his grip on the field of research that he had marked for his own, and to try to keep others out of it. Hence his questioning of the dates of some of Cope's papers, which might throw certain of his own scientific names into the discard, and hence his attempt to keep Cope out of the Bridger Basin from which his own fine collections had been made in 1870 and 1871. Hence also his refusal to allow his assistants to publish independent work on his material. As Beecher again says, "Having practically created the modern science of Vertebrate Paleontology in America, he resented every encroachment upon the particular type of research in which he was engaged."

Certain unfortunate experiences both in the field and in the Museum, arising out of his quarrel with Cope, tended to intensify a marked suspiciousness, which he may always have had in his nature, since one is inclined to read it between the lines of some of Caleb Marsh's letters as well. This finally led him to extraordinary lengths to protect his fossil treasures from what he regarded as prying eyes. In fact, the tendency grew to such proportions that it overshadowed some of his admirable qualities; anyone meeting him for the first time—and especially anyone asking for information about fossils—instantly felt the caution of the man, which did not disappear until he had made sure that he knew the whys and wherefores of the meeting. In these days when friendly coöperation is one of the greatest assets science has, this seems like an indefensible attitude, but we must remember that Marsh's professional training was received on the continent of Europe, where rivalries were acute in science as well as in other pursuits, and at a time when interchange of ideas and material was far less easy than it is today.

The unwillingness to talk about his own affairs, which has been so often spoken of in these pages, was the logical product of Marsh's suspicious nature and his lack of domestic ties. Out of it came, as Beecher remarks, "an absence of the complete exchange of confidence which normally exists between intimate friends. Even where perfect confidence existed, he seldom revealed more about any particular matter than seemed to him necessary or than the circumstances really demanded." However, this taciturnity with regard to his own business was not accompanied by any desire for seclusion, and he had a certain ease in meeting people whom he had no cause to suspect of desiring to poach on his particular preserves.

A trait that did far more damage to Marsh's chosen science than any of the foregoing was his habit of procrastination, also of long standing. This was not due to laziness, because, for most of his life, he was a hard worker. But he always undertook far more things than he had time for, and as his mass of material increased and as he became more and more involved in Washington affairs, the habit of procrastination grew and grew. It led him into conflict with the geologists of the Federal Survey, who were at times forced to wait months for his reports on fossil vertebrates on which to base their stratigraphic conclusions; and it eventually resulted in the greatest tragedy of all, his failure to leave finished manuscript for any of the comprehensive monographs that he had planned. As a consequence, many of the groups he had studied so long, and about which he knew so much, had to be restudied by others without the benefit of his great store of knowledge. Beecher put the matter admirably when he said: "He planned his life-work on the basis that immortality is here and not in the hereafter. It seemed difficult for him to realize the limitations of human existence and worldly accomplishment."

With friends and acquaintances of whom he had no cause to be suspicious, Marsh doubtless seemed quite a different person. Beecher records that "the sunny side of his nature was nearly always uppermost," and Huxley that he was "a wonderfully good fellow, full of fun and stories." His manner with the ladies seems to have been too formal and, in later years, too pompous to make him a favorite, but among his friends in the New York clubs he was regarded as a raconteur of parts, and certainly he had a wide field of experiences to draw upon; as Ray Stannard Baker says, "Upon the first provocation he told you a story,—and a very good one, too," —a judgment confirmed by more than one of these pages.

On one occasion, a discussion was started in one of these clubs as to the possibility of distinguishing different articles of food that were being served. One of the party produced a small bone and offered to bet a dinner for the whole crowd if any one of them, or anyone else, could tell from that bone alone whether it belonged to fish, flesh, or fowl. George St. John Sheffield, one of Marsh's friends, accepted the bet and sent the bone to New Haven, requesting an answer by telegraph. Professor Marsh's prompt reply was: "Left shin bone of a big bullfrog. Double your bet and let me in."

In the 'seventies, Marsh was one of fourteen of the *beaux esprits* of the country who formed themselves into a club known as the Round Table, which dined once a month at Delmonico's. One wonders if it was a member of this club who addressed to Marsh the following poem, which was widely quoted at the time, and which has been attributed to Clarence King or to the California naturalist, R. E. C. Stearns:

Catastrophism

TO PROFESSOR O. C. MARSH

By a Non-Uniformitarian

Break, break, break
At thy cold gray stones, O. C.!
And I would that my tongue could utter
The thoughts that arise in me.

O well for the five-toed horse!
That his bones are at rest in the clay:
O well for the ungulate brute!
That he roams o'er the prairie to-day.

Thy rocks bear their record of life,
Evolved from Time's earliest dawn;
But O for the view of a vanished form!
And the link that is missing and gone!

Break, break, break
At thy fossils and stones, O. C.!
But the gentle charm of Uniform Law
Can never quite satisfy me.

San Francisco, November, 1877.

Another trait that developed naturally from those discussed above was Marsh's love of the limelight. He learned the value of publicity early, and he used it with skill and, it must be admitted, to good purpose, since it brought to him news of many a treasure for the Museum. Smith Woodward's comments reflect this:

Like other great men, Marsh had his failings; and close association with him soon revealed both his unrestrained jealousy and his love of popular adulation. His early rivalry with Cope and his late rivalry with Osborn were never-ending subjects of conversation. Flattering newspaper notices pleased him, and I remember he was delighted when the English journal *Punch* published a little picture of him discoursing on the newly discovered skull of *Triceratops* to the British Association at Leeds in 1890. This picture was drawn by E. T. Reed, who could not find a portrait of the Professor and so represented him in back view in accordance with a description which I supplied. [See Figure 10.]

Marsh's craving for popular applause was never more marked than on one Sunday in the summer of 1898, when I took him to Tring to see the Hon. Walter Rothschild's great zoological museum. Mr. Rothschild met us and showed us the collection, and then we were invited by his parents, Lord and Lady Rothschild, to join their luncheon party at Tring Park. The party consisted chiefly of aristocrats interested in politics and country sports, and none of them appeared to have heard either of Professor Marsh or of his discoveries. We were treated merely as the erratic friends of the erratic son, and I shall always remember the disappointed expression of Marsh as we left on our return to London. Still, he had seen another phase of life, and he was duly impressed with the solid gold dessert service which was used at the end of the repast.

This last sentence points to Marsh's almost naïve love of fine living. He liked extremely well to be with the rich and the great, and he often was, as his correspondence amply shows. That the farm boy from Lockport should have been "duly impressed" by the Rothschild display was natural enough, even though he had doubtless seen more than one gold dessert service before he reached the age of sixty-seven. One of the notes found with his memorabilia is to the effect that in 1885 he was invited by the Queen to lunch at Balmoral, along with several other scientific men, although the Queen did not know when the invitation was given that he was the nephew of her favorite, George Peabody.

Marsh took such delight in exposing errors, fakes, and humbugs, that he might be said to have been a sort of Jack the Giant Killer. He began this as early as 1862, when he corrected no less a savant than Louis Agassiz in regard to a certain feature in *Eosaurus*. Six years later, on his first trip to the West, certain so-called "human" remains, found nearly 70 feet below the surface in western Nebraska, were shown by him to belong to three-toed horses and associated extinct animals; and huge footprints supposed to have been left by giants in ancient Nevada turned out, under his searching examination in 1883, to be those of a well-known species of fossil ground sloth.

The richest exposure in which he figured was beyond question that of the Cardiff Giant, in 1869. This giant was "a gypsum man, ten and a half feet long, nude, virile and unabashed," which had been dug up in the dark of an October night in Onondaga County, New York, and was being widely shown at fifty cents a head. State Geologist James Hall, inspecting it undisturbed for a full quarter of an hour, publicly stated it to be "the most remarkable object yet brought to light in this country and although perhaps not dating back to the Stone age . . . nevertheless deserving the attention of archeologists." The "discoverers" of the giant were getting rich when Professor Marsh, suspicious of this prodigy from his native state, inspected the giant at Syracuse and made sure that it was indeed composed of gypsum. He then wrote a letter to a friend of his, the Honorable John F. Seymour of Utica, pointing out that, since gypsum is soluble in water, the statue could never have retained, after burial, the high polish that it showed; and stating that it was, as he had suspected, "of very recent origin, and a most decided humbug." This letter was published in the Buffalo *Courier* on November 25 and at once widely copied by other newspapers throughout the country, thus exploding what was called by John M. Clarke the most uproarious hoax ever "launched upon the credulity of a humbug-loving people."

The actual story of how the giant was carved in Chicago out of a block of Iowa gypsum, shipped to Cardiff, hauled by night to its burying place, and "resuscitated with full attention to all necessary details," was finally run down by W. A. McKinney (Yale 1861) of Binghamton.[2]

For a thoughtful picture of Professor Marsh as he appeared to his Yale colleagues, and one that brings out the good qualities in his nature, which may seem to have been somewhat neglected in the present discussion, we may turn to President Timothy Dwight, who was, it seems likely, the last person to see him alive, aside from his medical attendants and his immediate household. This kindly philosopher wrote, in his *Memories of Yale Life and Men:*

In his personality, Professor Marsh was, as we may say, a man quite by himself. He was intelligent, with a manly intelligence, and a careful student, patient in his researches. But at the same time, as a collector and discoverer, he had the irrepressible zeal which is characteristic of an enthusiast. Every new thing in his own sphere of investigation which revealed itself—everything which had in it the promise of a revelation—gave him fresh happiness and stirred him to fresh activity. He would press forward with all energy, and any needed outlay of effort or means, to secure what it might have to give him. When he had made it his own, and found it of true value, he hastened with joyful ardor to relate his good fortune to his friends, as if he had possessed himself of a hidden treasure.

His manner of speaking rendered what he told more impressive. It was a part of the man, which united itself with his inward satisfaction and the intensity of his feeling, and thus brought the listener, for the time being, into sympathy with his delight.

In conversation with friends or intelligent visitors—especially when his visitors were prominent men in scientific lines—his mind was often awakened to its highest activity and interest. He

2. For the full history of the Cardiff Giant, see John M. Clarke, *Life of James Hall* (1921), pp. 438–443; W. A. McKinney, "The History of the Cardiff Giant Hoax," *New Englander* (October, 1875), pp. 1–12. The New York *Sun* for April 9, 1899, retold the tale, and added amusing details about the controversy over the giant between Marsh and the Rev. Alexander McWhorter. Marsh's notes show that he had intended to use the Cardiff Giant as the subject of one of the chapters of his popular book. The tale would have lost nothing by his telling!

showed himself, at such times, to be full of information, gained alike through his own researches and as the result of his intercourse with scholars in different parts of the world. He had travelled extensively and, wherever he went, had formed the acquaintance of those whom it was most desirable to know. He thus had abundance of anecdote, as well as of learning, and could make use of whatever he possessed for the entertainment or instruction of his guests. No undue prominence, however, was assumed for himself in such friendly interviews; he was as ready to listen, as to speak, and was ever with open mind towards new knowledge, from whomsoever it might come.

In his attitude and in his manner of expressing himself, a certain formality was characteristic of him. Especially was this manifest in cases where he sought an interview with others on matters of business, or on subjects of interest with respect to his own particular work. The slight and somewhat peculiar hesitation in his utterance rendered this formality more conspicuous. I was always struck with this singularity of manner when he called upon me. . . . Whatever the object might be, the manner of the man was the same. It was as if we had been two ministers of state having little acquaintance with each other, who had met for the settlement of some great question of public concern. All was serious with a dignified solemnity, and measured with a diplomatic deliberateness. . . . Such idiosyncrasies made the man the more interesting. They certainly gave him an individuality which distinguished him from others. . . .

In his inmost thinking the deepest life of his manhood—my belief is that he always lived apart from those about him. He thought after his own manner, and in an independent way, and I doubt whether even his most intimate friends penetrated the recesses, or really in any measure understood him in that central region of the soul where it turns toward the unseen things. I question, indeed, whether he had intimate friends, in the fullness of intimacy which is known by men whose inner life opens itself with greater readiness. . . . There was a solitariness of this character in Professor Marsh's life, notwithstanding the abundant outwardness in its activities and its intercourse with other men, which, as I observed or thought of him, was very suggestive to me. . . . For himself, I think, this characteristic of his nature lessened in some degree the happiness of his life, and gave him sometimes the feeling that he was a lonely man;—a feeling respecting him which those of his friends who visited his house—so rich in its interior and so beautiful in its location—after his final departure from it, must have found arising in themselves.[3]

3. Timothy Dwight, *Memories of Yale Life and Men* (1903), pp. 410–413. Dodd, Mead & Company.

CHAPTER XV
MARSH'S HOME

IN the early days of his professorship, Marsh lived in an apartment of three rooms at 9 College Street, where Professor Farnam, calling on him, found the floor "littered up knee deep with all kinds of printed matter"; here, also, he had parts of his vertebrate collection, cleaning, restoring, and describing it. In 1878 he moved to 144 Prospect Street. His meals he took at various boarding houses until the autumn of that year, when he began to eat at Moseley's New Haven House, a Yale rendezvous, and continued to do so until the close of 1882 and intermittently thereafter as long as he lived.

When the construction of the Peabody Museum was in progress, Marsh began to think of a home of his own, and on July 1, 1876, he notified the executors of his uncle's estate that he wished to use the $30,000 set aside for such a purpose for each of Mr. Peabody's heirs. With this money he bought land further north on the crest of Prospect Street, opposite the home of his friends, Mr. and Mrs. William W. Farnam. Other parcels of land added later gave him a plot of about 7 acres, with a frontage of 500 feet on Prospect and Mansfield Streets, 600 feet on the north adjacent to the home of Mr. E. H. English, and 700 feet along Hillside Place (formerly Munson Street). The lot was well wooded and sloped quite sharply to the west. A prettier site for a home could hardly have been selected, since Prospect Street runs along the top of a ridge of red Triassic sandstone, with excellent views, on either side, of the much higher trap ridges ending in the palisaded cliffs of East and West Rocks.

The building of a home on this land was begun in the summer of 1876 but was not completed until late in 1878, and the interior was not finished until 1881. From Marsh's bank account, it seems probable that the house cost him around $30,000, and almost as much went into its furnishings. In later years a greenhouse was added, and in the late 'eighties this housed a collection of more than 1,300 rare orchids, for which he paid about $3,600.

The grounds around the house were conspicuously beautiful, and small wonder, since the landscape architect who laid them out was none other than Donald G. Mitchell ("Ik Marvel"), who had been a friend of Marsh since his college days. As the Marsh Botanical Garden, they still remain one of the beauty spots of New Haven.

The home that Marsh built for himself was a three-story brownstone house with eighteen rooms and a tower. Its most striking room was the high octagonal reception hall which he called his "Wigwam"; he relates that when Red Cloud came into it, he looked up as if in search of the hole where the smoke went out. This hall had a bewildering amount of art objects: paintings, Japanese and Chinese cloisonné and bronzes and *kakemonos*. To the left of the entrance was a very large round oak table of special design covered with western memorabilia, from which Marsh loved to pick up the peace pipe that he and Red Cloud had smoked in 1874, the Mormon Bible that Brigham Young had given him, or some other interesting souvenir, and talk about it to his guests. Ernest Howe, who remembered the Professor "not as a scientist or partizan, but as a rather pompous but kindly old gentleman who had hunted buffalo in the dim past," says that in the 'nineties, during Sundays of the winter term, it was Marsh's custom to entertain small groups of students at his home, where

After a luncheon planned to satisfy even the appetites of Yale undergraduates we were taken to the "Wigwam," a sort of trophy room filled with mementos and treasures from all over the world. Here a scalp or a pair of buckskin leggings, or a frontiersman's pistol would recall some incident of the west and Yale seniors became small boys again, listening to tales of Indian savagery, or of hairbreadth escapes from stampeding buffalo.

All the rooms in the house showed the same astonishing abundance of bric-a-brac that characterized the one already mentioned, and a hint as to why it took Marsh so long to furnish the house might be found in a story about the oriental rugs that he had in such profusion. Such rugs were something of a

PLATE XXIII

MARSH'S HOME AT 360 PROSPECT STREET FROM THE SOUTH-
EAST; WEST ROCK RIDGE IN THE DISTANCE

THE LARGE OCTAGONAL ENTRANCE HALL
WHICH MARSH CALLED "THE WIGWAM"

PLATE XXIV

PART OF A MUCH LARGER GROUP PHOTOGRAPH TAKEN AT THE PICNIC GIVEN FOR THE INTERNATIONAL CONGRESS OF ZOOLOGY DURING ITS CAMBRIDGE MEETING IN 1898

1. J. COSSAR EWART; 4. H. F. OSBORN; 5. H. G. SEELEY; 6. R. TRIMEN; 7. P. L. SCLATER; 8. H. WOODWARD; 9. O. C. MARSH; 10. A. MILNE-EDWARDS; 11. ALEX. HILL (VICE-CHANCELLOR); 12. ANTON DOHRN; 14. W. BATESON; 16. E. W. MACBRIDE; 17. H. H. BRINDLEY; 18. D. MACALISTER; 19. S. J. HICKSON

novelty in those days, according to Professor Farnam, who continues:

An itinerant Armenian rug dealer came to New Haven with a fine assortment, and Marsh picked out the best of the collection, and asked the Armenian to send the rugs up to his house on approval. He then went to New York, educated himself on the subject of rugs, and on returning home selected those that he desired to keep.

One of Marsh's own favorite stories had to do with the acquisition of certain of his curios. Coming up from New York, he recognized P. T. Barnum on the train, and entered into a conversation with him. Barnum told him of a number of objects which had been picked up in Mexico for his museum, but which his agent in New York, not realizing their value, had offered for sale before they could be put on exhibition.

"And were they sold?" asked Professor Marsh.

"Yes; some little cuss up in New Haven bought them," replied Barnum.

"I thought so," said Marsh, smiling and handing out his card. "I was the little cuss."

One other bit of information about Marsh's domestic arrangements, likewise contributed by Professor Farnam, deserves telling. It was customary in the early days of the telephone to provide each instrument with a ground wire, so that when a thunderstorm approached, a plug could be put in to connect with this wire and lessen the risk from lightning. Marsh kept his telephone thus plugged all the time when it was not in use by him, because, as he said, he had had it put in for his own convenience and not for that of others, an oddity which Professor Farnam attributed to his "never having been obliged to consult the wishes and convenience of other people in his domestic arrangements as he would have had to do had he been married."

This fine home of Marsh's entertained many distinguished visitors in his lifetime. Two years after its opening, in 1883, it provided the setting for two notable functions, one a reception for Red Cloud, and the other a brilliant public reception for the National Academy of Sciences, meeting for the first time under Marsh's presidency. From Europe it welcomed Lord Aberdeen, Karl Diener, Karl von Zittel, W. Boyd Dawkins,

Albert Gaudry, Marie Pavlow, T. McKenny Hughes, A. A.
Hubrecht, Alfred Russel Wallace, Fridtjof Nansen, and E. B.
Poulton; its American visitors included Alexander Graham
Bell, John Hay, and Edward Everett Hale.

Fig. 19. Thomas Nast's reply to an invitation to attend a reception given to the National Academy of Sciences at Marsh's home
in 1883.

It must be apparent from what has been said that Marsh's
house was but another manifestation of his collecting instinct.
It was, in fact, merely another museum—certainly no home
that a woman could have lived in happily. Indeed, the most
conspicuous lack in the establishment was a chatelaine.

Why did Marsh remain a bachelor? It seems strange that so
fine a matrimonial prospect should have been allowed to escape,
and there are many indications of willingness on the part of

various ladies to share his life. If romance really touched him, however, we have no hint of it. "Disappointments," yes. When he first came to New Haven, he found its wider social world less receptive than that of Andover. This may have been modified, of course, after George Peabody visited Yale in 1857 with his pretty niece Julia! At any rate, more than one of the sentiments inscribed in his classbook speak of his gallantry toward the opposite sex, and his special friend among these classmates, W. E. Park, wrote in 1899 that he had been a "prominent figure" and a "great favorite" at the parties and entertainments given by New Haven citizens during their senior year.

As a student at Andover, and in his early years at Yale, he was much under the influence of his Aunt Judith Peabody Russell. Shortly after he came to Yale, he formed the acquaintance of another mature woman whose personality made a deep impression upon him. This was Elizabeth Cogswell Dixon, wife of United States Senator James Dixon of Hartford. His meeting with her was brought about by the senator's sister, who had married Marsh's uncle, the Reverend Ezekiel Marsh, and had been left a widow by his death in 1844. Within a short time Marsh was in lively correspondence with both ladies, and the two series of letters furnish an amusing parallel, since from Mrs. Dixon's there is no intimation that his regard for her family is other than general, whereas from those of his Aunt Eliza it is early apparent that his attention is in reality directed toward "Clemmie," one of the daughters! It was Mrs. Marsh who kept him in touch with the activities of the family and advised him as to the best course to pursue in his courtship.

The letters of Mrs. Dixon suggest that if the daughter possessed but half the mother's charm, it is not strange that Marsh's choice fell upon her. The Washington home presided over by Senator Dixon's wife and daughters after his election in 1857 was a center for "elegant hospitality," and he and his family moved in the highest circles of society, diplomatic, Congressional, and military. They entertained much also at their home in Hartford, where Marsh was a frequent guest. In New Haven, their special friends were the Mitchells of "Edgewood." Mrs. Dixon's letters to Marsh—there were fifty-six of them from 1858 to 1867—reveal a woman of wit and grace, devoted to her husband and children, never lacking the *mot juste* with which to acknowledge a gift—and Marsh made many to her and her girls—or to decline an invitation, of which there were likewise many. By the end of 1859 her letters were beginning, "Mr. Marsh, My dear Nephew," and ending, "Affectionately your Aunt," and their tone of sincerity and affection continues throughout the correspondence.

It is hardly to be doubted that the friendship of so cultured a woman should have been beyond price to a young man of Marsh's ambition, and it must have been a sore disappointment to him that he did not become her son-in-law. Just why he did not, does not appear from the letters that we have. Aunt Eliza had warned him, however, that the Dixon girls' feeling for him was respect rather than affection, and it is probable that the greater age and learning of Marsh (he was, we must remember, already in his thirties) would tend to this result. (Incidentally, this lack of response to Marsh's good qualities seems to have been shared by the young ladies of New Haven, who, if stories from various sources are to be credited, were wont to giggle among themselves about "Oh see" Marsh.) Aunt Eliza, hinting that she discerns a "growing interest . . . which may indicate that you have not fully realized how much you have staked in the thing," nevertheless adds, drily, "I am glad you are one, whose preferences can be controlled in this line and that you have other engrossing objects of pursuit and therefore your happiness is not at the mercy or caprice of *any lady.*"

Marsh went abroad in 1862, somewhat dubious over what effect his absence might have on his matrimonial hopes. The lady was still unwed, however, on his return in 1865, and under date of December, 1866, while his Uncle George was in this country, we have one of the rare copies of letters written by Marsh himself, setting forth his desire to "secure" Clemmie for his own and asking his uncle's approval. There seems little likelihood that Mr. Peabody would not have approved, since the Dixon family met all the requirements that he had set up for the helpmeets of his heirs, and, moreover, he had made their acquaintance during his stay in Washington, Mrs. Dixon and the favored daughter being in his rooms at the Willard Hotel when President Johnson called on him to express the nation's thanks for a gift recently made. Neither is it likely that Senator or Mrs. Dixon would have raised objections, in view of their long friendship with Marsh. Hence we must conclude that, although all other elements to a successful match were present, the one thing needful was lacking on the young woman's part. Doubtless her association with the dashing young officers at Washington had not tended to change her feeling of "respect" for the learned young man who had been spending these years acquiring still more learning in Europe.

The second young lady on whom we know Marsh to have set his—heart seems hardly the word; perhaps we should say, set his mind—was the daughter of a Baltimore railroad magnate. The affair was broken off, it is said, because of the lady's displeasure at a too marked display of devotion on the Professor's part. Marsh often expressed regret at his loss, saying to Hatcher on one occasion that although his house was finished and its furnishings in place, it needed a "garret [t]" to make it complete.

In the 'seventies, acting as guardian for his youngest half sister Mary (born 1852), of whom he was very fond, he sent her to Miss Porter's school in Farmington, Connecticut, and afterward had her with him in New Haven, where she is still remembered as a very charming person. It is possible that he thought of her as a hostess for the new home going up on Prospect Street, but fate had other plans for "Mollie," who married Samuel E. Williamson of Cleveland in 1878, and died three years afterward, following the birth of twin daughters.

An English home in which Marsh was always welcome was that of his special friend, Henry Woodward, with its gracious hostess and its many daughters, but he was apparently immune to English feminine charm. As his prestige grew, his social circle widened, until he was a guest in exclusive homes in New Haven, in Newport, in New York, in Philadelphia, and in Washington, not to mention many abroad. But, moving with ease—if not with grace—in all these circles, he remained the wealthy bachelor, probably consoling himself more and more, as the years went by, with the thought that his great uncle also never married. It would be undeniable that George Peabody set his stamp upon his nephew in ways other than financial. The glimpses of the life the banker led in his London apartments or in his Scottish castle, the readiness with which introductions from him opened carefully guarded doors in Europe, the knowledge of his great donations and the opportunity to guide some of these—all would have their effect upon any young man. And that he had not only example but precept to consider can be judged from the fact that, in his college years, he was warned by his Aunt Judith that while he and the other nephews and nieces might in due time expect to inherit Mr. Peabody's money, they were in danger of being cut out of his will if they married contrary to the rules he had laid down.

Marsh's celibacy of course exposed him to the usual amount of joking from his friends. At one of his class reunions the orator of the day remarked on how strange it was that, with all the bones Marsh had collected, he had never found himself a rib. An even more celebrated remark, however, was that of Professor Brush, who said that he supposed Marsh was a bachelor because he would never be content with anything less than a "collection" of wives!

SCIENTIFIC WORK

CHAPTER XVI

MARSH AS A STRATIGRAPHER

WHEN Marsh was receiving his training in Geology in the late 'fifties and early 'sixties, the stratigraphy of the marine formations was as yet very much generalized, and of the fresh-water deposits there was hardly any known chronology at all. The time had not yet arrived when lake and river deposits could be clearly distinguished from those of the seas. Besides, there was little information that was reliable about the genetic and chronologic sequence of the plants and the animals found fossil in continental strata. These things must be kept in mind when we consider Marsh's publications in stratigraphy.

Lake Basins versus Flood Plains

In the early 'seventies, when Marsh began his researches on the Cenozoic deposits of the Great Plains east of the Rocky Mountains, it was the general belief that these strata had accumulated in vast lake basins. The first edition of Dana's *Manual of Geology* (1862) held that these formations were of lacustrine and brackish-water origin, laid down in bodies of water that had been of long endurance and had covered great areas. These erroneous ideas about lake and estuarine basins did not begin to break down until the last decade of the nineteenth century. It is not strange, therefore, that Marsh's paper of 1875 on "Ancient lake-basins of the Rocky Mountain region" tells of the "existence of several large fresh-water lakes . . . now well established, mainly through the researches of explorers whom the striking scenery of the 'Bad Lands,' or the extinct animals entombed in them, have attracted thither." [1]

The oldest of these lake basins, and the only one now accepted as such in part, is the *Green River Lake Basin*. It was visited by Marsh in 1868, but first explored in 1870, when, as he says, he

1. 1875A, p. 49. References throughout the chapters on Marsh's scientific work are to the Bibliography at the end of the book.

traced its deposits for several hundred miles, and from the rich vertebrate fauna fully determined its Eocene age [this correlation was published as early as March, 1871]. These same beds have since been pronounced Miocene by Prof. Hayden and others, but the 150 species of extinct vertebrates now known from them prove them Eocene as conclusively as any single formation has yet been determined in this country. A comparison of almost any group of these fossils with the corresponding one from the Paris basin will afford sufficient evidence on this point. . . . The Tertiary deposits in the Green River Basin are [as he correctly states] all of fresh-water origin . . . 6,000 feet [thick] at least.[2]

Describing a second of these lake basins, the *Uintah*, he wrote:

South of the Uintah Mountains, a second and larger lake existed in the Eocene. It was 2,000 feet or more lower than the northern lake, and received part of its waters from that source. It had the Rocky Mountains for its eastern border, the Wasatch on the west, and extended from the Uintahs far to the southward, doubtless quite to the present territory of New Mexico. This basin was first explored, and its Eocene age established, in [late September and early October of] 1870, by the writer, who finding it distinct from the Green River basin on the north, named it the Uintah basin [in March, 1871]. . . .

The fauna entombed in both these Eocene lakes is essentially the same, and indicates a tropical climate. This is seen especially in the great number of Tapiroid mammals, monkeys, crocodiles, lizards and serpents. Remains of *Dinocerata*, the largest of Eocene mammals, have as yet been found only in the northern basin.[3]

South of the Black Hills of South Dakota, in badlands which Hayden did much to bring to light, there was a third ancient basin which Marsh considered to be Hayden's *White River Lake*. This lake, he writes,

was comparatively shallow, appears to have extended south from the Black Hills to near where the Republican River now is. . . . The best exposures of these Miocene [Oligocene] beds are seen near the White River. . . .

2. *Ibid.*
3. *Ibid.*, p. 50.

The fauna . . . indicates a climate much less tropical than that of the Eocene lakes, as is seen in the absence of monkeys and scarcity of reptilian life. The *Brontotheridae* . . . are peculiar to the lower strata of this basin.[4]

In this paper of 1875, Marsh also names the *John Day Lake Basin*, discovered by the Reverend Thomas Condon, then State Geologist of Oregon, and explored by Marsh in 1871 and again in 1873. The thickness of the inclined strata in this basin is not less than 5,000 feet. The upper beds alone, he says, correspond to the deposits in the White River Basin; the lower beds also are clearly Miocene [Oligocene], as shown by their vertebrates.

The *Niobrara Lake Basin* of Marsh was formed over the White River Lake Basin but extended

much farther east, and stretching south nearly to the Gulf of Mexico . . . its deposits attained a thickness of nearly or quite 1,500 feet. This [Pliocene] lake basin may with great propriety be called the Niobrara basin. . . . The fauna of this lake-basin indicates a warm temperate climate. The more common animals are a mastodon, rhinoceroses, camels and horses, the latter being especially abundant.[5]

As has been said, it was the fashion during the 'seventies and 'eighties of the previous century for geologists to interpret the fresh-water deposits of the Rocky Mountains and the High Plains as those of great inland lakes. The fact that most of these basins were hundreds of miles across while two or more were 1,000 miles long did not cause these conclusions to be questioned, even though Superior, one of the largest of present fresh-water lakes, has a length of only 250 miles. It is true that the deposits of the Green River Lake Basin of Eocene time bear internal evidence both in the sediments themselves and in their entombed fossils of being laid down in part in a body of very shallow standing water, and the surrounding rock structure gives abundant support to the idea of a lake between mountains. But in most of the other "lake basins" there is no supporting topographic evidence, and this is especially true for those of Oligocene, Miocene, and Pliocene times.

4. *Ibid.,* p. 51.
5. *Ibid.,* p. 52.

Nor did the geologists ask themselves how long these lakes
endured. They were content to believe that each one lasted the
length of an epoch; today we point out that these epochs each
endured some tens of millions of years. We even find Marsh,
in his vice-presidential address of 1877, stating the "remarkable
fact" that fishes and crocodiles were almost entirely absent in
the Oligocene lake basin, and explaining their absence by the
assumption that the waters were too alkaline for their existence.

Those were the days of "marine geology," when more than
nine tenths of all the stratified rocks were explained as the
deposits of seas, and when the leading textbooks had almost
nothing to say of "dry-land geology"; i.e., the stratigraphy of
river, wind, and desert or semidesert deposition. The senior
author well remembers the day in 1892 when Hatcher described
to him the rock environment of the Miocene *Protoceras* skull
that he had secured, ending his description by saying that the
sandstones in which it occurred were locally replete with fossil
wood and that the beds wound irregularly through the country
like a river—facts which made him skeptical of the theory of
lake deposits. In other words, the day had arrived when the
detail of the bedded sediments and their entombed life was
being observed and described. N. H. Darton was among the
first to ask how these western "lakes" could have deposited the
many coarse and thick conglomerates he had seen. His statement, read by W. M. Davis, stimulated the latter to search
through the literature relating to these great western "lakes."
He had seen none of these continental deposits in the field, but
at one of the meetings of the Geological Society of America
he rose to say that these "lake" deposits appeared to him to be
actually the work of streams, aggrading their deposits on plains
to the east of the Rockies, under a semiarid climate. His admission that he had not seen the strata themselves, however,
set some of the geologists in the audience against him. But the
seed was planted, and it soon bore fruit, first in paleontologists
like Hatcher and W. D. Matthew, and later, more strongly,
in the sedimentationist Joseph Barrell. Today all these "Tertiary lake-basins," with the exception of Green River Lake,
have been "transformed" into basins of continental deposits
wherein rivers lost their load of sediments in intermont areas

or on the plains in front of the mountains, as their waters evaporated under a semiarid climate.

Vertebrate Life Zones

As a natural result of his long geologic and biologic training, Professor Marsh, from the beginning of his field work, was careful to note the general superposition of the strata from which he was collecting vertebrate fossils; but, curiously, in none of his publications do we find that he ever actually measured or described in detail a stratigraphic sequence. He was satisfied with noting that his fossils came from the lower, the middle, or the upper part of a formation or even a series of beds. It was his ambition mainly to work out the biologic sequence—the course that evolution had taken among the extinct vertebrates—and to name the "beds" after the most characteristic animal in them, as, for instance, the Atlantosaurus beds, the Miohippus beds, etc.

In his description of new species of fossil vertebrates, Marsh —most unfortunately—rarely gave exact information as to their geologic level and detailed geographic position, his usual citation being "Upper Eocene of Wyoming," "Coryphodon beds, or lowest Eocene of Wyoming," "Pliocene of Idaho," "Ceratops beds or the Laramie of Wyoming," "Atlantosaurus beds of the upper Jurassic in Colorado," and so on. For this lack of detail he was severely censured by his colleagues, and the statement was often made verbally that his reason for making these citations so vague was because he did not want other collectors to go to his localities. In his monograph on birds with teeth—a final publication—he is more specific than usual, and says that these remarkable Kansas birds occur "in the Middle Cretaceous [which] corresponds to the strata named by the writer the 'Pteranodon beds.'" The Pteranodon beds, he adds, "are included in sub-division number three [=Niobrara] in Meek and Hayden's section."

In 1898, citing the horses as illustrating his method of chronology, he says:

Near the base of the Eocene the genus *Eohippus* is found, representing the oldest known member of the horse tribe. Higher up in the Eocene *Orohippus* occurs, and still higher comes *Epihippus*, near the top of the Eocene. Again through the Miocene more genera of horses, *Mesohippus*, *Miohippus*, and others, follow in succession, and the line still continues in the Pliocene, when the modern genus *Equus* makes its appearance. Throughout this entire series, definite horizons may be marked by the genera, and even by the species of these equine mammals, as there is change from one stage to the other, both in the teeth and feet, so that every experienced paleontologist can distinguish even fragments of these remains, and thus identify the zones in which they occur.[6]

Marsh's belief in the value of vertebrate fossils as time indicators, as compared to other fossils and especially as compared to plants, probably had its basis in a precept of Professor Goeppert, one of his teachers at Berlin, who taught his students "to doubt the value of fossil plants as indices of the past history of the world." [7] Consequently, in a number of his articles, beginning with 1870 and culminating in his paper of 1898 entitled "Comparative value of different kinds of fossils in determining geological age," he was outspoken in his view that fossil plants were of least value in this respect. It is well known that previous to the early 'seventies the paleobotanists were often decidedly wrong in their time correlations, and the senior writer well remembers Marsh telling him in 1892 that the paleobotanical clock was always "one hour fast," meaning that plants frequently seem to indicate an age younger by an entire period of geologic time than that shown by the animals. On this point Marsh wrote:

The evidence of detached fossil leaves and other fragments of foliage that may have been carried hundreds of miles by wind and stream, or swept down to sea-level from the lofty mountains where they grew, should have but little weight in determining the age of the special strata in which they are imbedded, and failure to recognize this fact has led to many erroneous opinions in regard to geological time.[8]

Here, of course, Marsh goes entirely too far, since it is only wood that may be transported these long distances, whereas

6. 1898K, p. 486.
7. 1896F, p. 440.
8. 1898G, p. 114.

the well-preserved leaves of the "Dakota sandstone" or the "Laramie formation," or those of the Cenozoic, surely have not as a rule been transported more than a few miles from where they grew. He then goes on to say:

There are, however, fossil plants that are more reliable witnesses as to the period in which they lived. Those found on the spot where they grew, with their most characteristic part preserved, may furnish important evidence as to their own nature and geological age. Characteristic examples are found among the plants of the Coal Measures, in the Cycads of Mesozoic strata, and in the fossil forests of Tertiary and more recent deposits.[9]

This prejudice of Marsh's against the evidence of fossil plants led him in later years into grave error, as will appear in the discussion of the eastern Jurassic. It is of course an established fact today that Paleobotany is a dependable helpmate in chronology, beginning with the Lower Devonian where land plants for the first time occur in some abundance.

In his paper of 1891, "Geological horizons as determined by vertebrate fossils," Marsh uses (correctly) the degree of evolution attained by the fossils to work out the superposition of the principal horizons which he had personally investigated in the West; and then, taking, in each, the largest and most dominant vertebrate form which characterized it, he used its generic name for the zone. In the same way, some of the principal horizons of the East were named, and the whole brought together in a section to illustrate the succession of vertebrate life in America. Such a chart, with the geological column on the left and the vertebrate succession on the right, was presented by him for the first time in the Nashville address of 1877, and was several times republished with emendations.

The names of characteristic fossils thus given to various horizons, he says,

were not intended to replace those already supplied, but merely to supplement them, and by new evidence, to clear up those in doubt. The same principle had long before been found to work admirably in Europe, where certain characteristic invertebrate

9. *Ibid.*, p. 114.

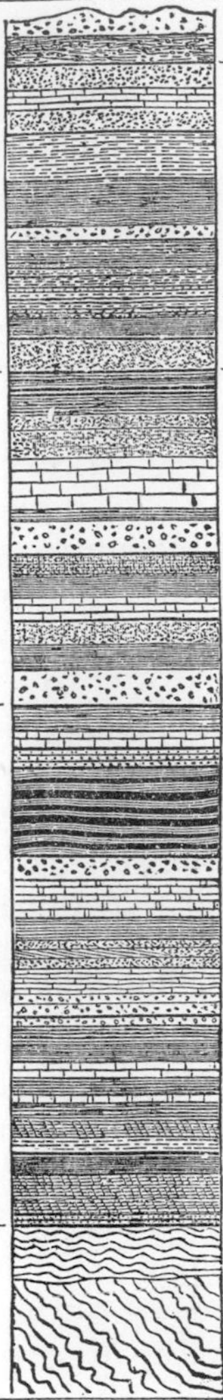

Cenozoic.	Recent. Quaternary.			Tapir, Peccary, Bison. *Bos, Equus, Tapirus, Dicotyles, Megatherium, Mylodon.*
Cenozoic.	Tertiary.	Pliocene.	Equus Beds. Pliohippus Beds.	*Equus, Tapirus, Elephas.* *Pliohippus, Tapiravus, Mastodon, Procamelus. Aceratherium, Bos, Morotherium, Platygonus.*
Cenozoic.	Tertiary.	Miocene.	Miohippus Beds. Oreodon Beds. Brontotherium Beds	*Miohippus, Diceratherium, Thinohyus, Protoceras.* *Oreodon, Eporeodon, Hyænodon, Moropus, Ictops. Hyracodon, Agriochœrus, Colodon, Leptochœrus.* *Brontotherium, Brontops, Allops, Titanops, Titanotherium, Mesohippus, Ancodus, Entelodon.*
Cenozoic.	Tertiary.	Eocene.	Diplacodon Beds. Dinoceras Beds. Heliobatis Beds. Coryphodon Beds.	*Diplacodon, Epihippus, Amynodon, Eomeryx.* *Dinoceras, Tinoceras, Uintatherium, Palæosyops, Orohippus, Hyrachyus, Colonoceras, Homacodon.* *Heliobatis, Amia, Lepidosteus, Asineops, Clupea.* *Coryphodon, Eohippus, Eohyus, Hyracops, Parahyus.* Lemurs, Ungulates, Tillodonts, Rodents, Serpents.
Mesozoic.	Cretaceous.		Ceratops Beds of Laramie Series.	*Ceratops, Triceratops, Claosaurus, Ornithomimus,* Mammals, *Cimolomys, Dipriodon, Selenacodon, Nanomyops, Stagodon.* Birds, *Cimolopteryx.*
Mesozoic.	Cretaceous.		Fox Hills Group.	
Mesozoic.	Cretaceous.		Colorado Series, or Pteranodon Beds.	Birds with Teeth, *Hesperornis, Ichthyornis, Apatornis.* Mosasaurs, *Edestosaurus, Lestosaurus, Tylosaurus.* Pterodactyls, *Pteranodon.* Plesiosaurs, Turtles.
Mesozoic.	Cretaceous.		Dakota Group.	
Mesozoic.	Jurassic.		Atlantosaurus Beds. Baptanodon Beds. Hallopus Beds.	Dinosaurs, *Brontosaurus, Morosaurus. Diplodocus, Stegosaurus, Camptosaurus, Ceratosaurus.* Mammals, *Dryolestes, Stylacodon, Tinodon, Ctenacodon.*
Mesozoic.	Triassic.		Otozoum, or Conn. River, Beds.	First Mammals, *Dromatherium.* First Dinosaurs, *Anchisaurus, Ammosaurus, Bathygnathus, Clepsysaurus.* Many footprints. Crocodiles, *Belodon.* Fishes, *Catopterus, Ischypterus, Ptycholepis.*
Paleozoic.	Permian.		Nothodon Beds.	Reptiles, *Nothodon, Eryops, Sphenacodon.*
Paleozoic.	Carboniferous		Coal Measures, or Eosaurus Beds.	First Reptiles (?) *Eosaurus.* Amphibians, *Baphetes, Dendrerpeton, Hylonomus, Pelion.* Footprints, *Anthracopus, Allopus, Baropus, Dromopus, Hylopus, Limnopus, Nasopus.*
Paleozoic.	Carboniferous		Subcarboniferous, or Sauropus Beds.	First known Amphibians (Labyrinthodonts). Footprints, *Sauropus, Thenaropus.*
Paleozoic.	Devonian.		Dinichthys Beds. Lower Devonian.	*Dinichthys, Acanthodes, Bothriolepis, Chirolepis, Cladodus, Dipterus, Titanichthys.*
Paleozoic.	Silurian.		Upper Silurian. Lower Silurian.	First known Fishes.
Paleozoic.	Cambrian.		Primordial.	No Vertebrates known.
	Archæan.		Huronian. Laurentian.	No Vertebrates known.

Fig. 20. Diagram, made by Marsh, to show the chief geological horizons for vertebrate fossils in America.

fossils, especially Ammonites, had served to mark definitely various subdivisions of a single formation.[10]

His method, in other words, rested on the principle of biologic zoning.

In pursuance of this method of naming the successive life zones after their most characteristic vertebrate, Marsh had by 1896 named 17 life zones above the Paleozoic, as follows:[11] Triassic 1 (Otozoum*), Jurassic 3 (Hallopus,* Baptanodon, Atlantosaurus), Cretaceous 3 (Pleurocœlus, Pteranodon, Ceratops), Eocene 4 (Coryphodon, Heliobatis,* Dinoceras, Diplacodon*), Oligocene 3 (Brontotherium, Oreodon, Miohippus), Pliocene 2 (Pliohippus, Equus*), and Pleistocene 1 (Bos*). About ten of these life-zone terms are still useful for the Rocky Mountain region.

The marine *Baptanodon beds* (=Sundance formation in part), of late Jurassic time, were first proved to be Jurassic in age by F. B. Meek in 1859. When Professor Marsh began his work on American fossil vertebrates, he was surprised to find no ichthyosaurs or plesiosaurs in the Jurassic, since these marine animals were very common in deposits of the same age in western Europe. In January, 1879, however, he announced the discovery of an ichthyosaurian in the marine Upper Jurassic of Wyoming, naming it *Sauranodon natans*. By February of the next year he had eight specimens of this form, with three skulls, but, he adds, there were "still no indications of teeth, so that we may consider these reptiles as entirely edentulous." [12] *Sauranodon*, he notes, had six complete digits, a character "not before observed in any air-breathing vertebrate." In June, 1880, he found the name *Sauranodon* preoccupied and replaced it with *Baptanodon*,[13] his term of 1879—Sauranodon beds—likewise giving way to Baptanodon beds.

The "Baptanodon beds" lie immediately below the Morrison formation with its wonderful array of late Jurassic dinosaurs.

10. 1891F, p. 336.
11. Names marked with an asterisk have lost their zonal value, and will not be referred to in later pages.
12. 1880B, p. 170. Gilmore showed in 1905–6 that these animals had a full complement of teeth, very much like those in *Ichthyosaurus*.
13. 1880E, p. 491.

The stratigraphic sequence of the Upper Jurassic in the Freeze Out Hills, Wyoming, as determined for Marsh by W. H. Reed, is as follows:

"Dakota sandstone"
[Probable break]
Barren clays, 30 feet
Atlantosaurus beds, 55 feet
White sandstone with small cycads and bones
Sandstones and shales with *Laosaurus*, 66 feet
Marine Baptanodon beds or Sundance formation, 35 feet

{ Fresh-water strata—Morrison formation

The *Atlantosaurus beds* of late Jurassic time (=Morrison formation) were named by Marsh in 1877 in a footnote, as follows:

Since this address [Nashville] was delivered, I have determined the beds containing gigantic Dinosaurs, on the flanks of the Rocky Mountains, to be upper Jurassic, and called them Atlantosaurus Beds.[14]

In the following year came this important addition:

On the flanks of the Rocky Mountains, a narrow belt of strata can be traced for several hundred miles, marked always by the bones of gigantic Dinosaurs. Its position is above the characteristic red Triassic beds and immediately below the hard sandstone of the Dakota group.[15]

This definition was a natural one to make in 1878, but later it was seen that between the Atlantosaurus beds and the red Triassic lie the marine Baptanodon beds, while in places, the Jurassic horizon is overlaid by sandstones much like the Dakota formation but yielding different dinosaurs and large cycads which are now known to indicate a time well up in the Lower Cretaceous series. Marsh goes on to say that Hayden, Cope, and others (he himself was one of them) had regarded the Atlantosaurus horizon as Cretaceous but that the abundant vertebrate remains now known from it "prove its Jurassic age beyond a reasonable doubt." [16]

14. 1877F, p. 10.
15. 1878G, p. 411.
16. *Ibid.*, p. 411.

This correlation of Marsh's was doubted because (1) the Atlantosaurus beds south of the Black Hills are followed by sandstones that have been found to be of late Lower Cretaceous age, (2) these sandstones appear to go unbroken into the "Dakota," and (3) western Kansas has yet other sandstones (Washita=Cenomanian) rich in dicotyledons which are very much like those of the Upper Cretaceous; and conflicting opinions naturally arose which were not reconciled until the present century.

Most of the European dinosaurs are found in the Wealden of England, a formation which, like the Atlantosaurus beds (=Morrison), has been the subject of controversy. Marsh commented on the age of this formation on September 14, 1895, at the Ipswich meeting of the British Association, as follows:

The Cretaceous age of these deposits appears to be taken for granted here, but the evidence as it now stands seems to me to point rather to the upper Jurassic as their true position. If I should find the vertebrate fossils now known from your Wealden in the Rocky Mountains, where I have collected many corresponding forms, I should certainly call them Jurassic, and have good reason for so doing.[17]

Simpson, discussing the age of the Wealden, said in 1926:

Professor Marsh, whose first-hand knowledge of Morrison and Wealden dinosaurs has not been equaled by any other writer, and to whose opinion, therefore, very great weight should be attached even after the passing of thirty years, stoutly maintained the equivalence of the Morrison and Wealden . . . [a view that] is quite incontrovertible now as then.[18]

In the case of the *Pleurocœlus beds* of the eastern Lower Cretaceous (=Potomac formation in part), Marsh was on the wrong side of the controversy, insisting that they also were Jurassic. It was in connection with these strata of the Atlantic Coastal Plain, in fact, that he came most sharply into contact with his colleagues of the United States Geological Survey. He was led into error by his lack of regard for the evidence of

17. 1895F, p. 412.
18. George G. Simpson, "The age of the Morrison formation," *Amer. Jour. Sci.* (5), XXII, 205.

fossil plants, already mentioned, and by his reliance on certain dicta regarding the color of rocks that he had absorbed from Professor Roemer (as he himself told the senior author). However, the opinion of geologists in general, and those of the Federal Survey in particular, was opposed to this idea and held that the eastern beds with dinosaurs were not contemporaneous with the Atlantosaurus horizon of the West, but were, rather, Cretaceous in age. The controversy over this question of correlation was both protracted and acute, beginning with Marsh's paper of 1888 on the dinosaurs of the Potomac [19] and lasting into 1897. In December, 1896, he presented one of the longest papers he had ever published in a single issue of the *American Journal of Science*, showing that he had not yielded his point in any degree.[20] It was one of the greatest battles of his career, and one of the few in which he was not successful.

The inherent trouble with this Jurassic-Lower Cretaceous controversy was the fact that, although the remains of dinosaurs were abundant enough, nowhere in America could the freshwater beds containing them be tied into a standardized marine sequence dated by the more reliable invertebrate fossils. The solution came only when the dinosaur beds of what was formerly German East Africa were found interbedded with marine strata holding late Jurassic ammonites and trigonias and passing unbroken into marine Lower Cretaceous deposits.[21]

The *Pteranodon beds* of the Upper Cretaceous were characterized by the pterosaurs, or flying lizards, regarded by Marsh as amongst the most interesting reptiles of Mesozoic time; their remains are known in America almost entirely from the soft marine chalk deposits (Niobrara formation) along the Solomon, Saline, and Smoky Hill Rivers of western Kansas. Other characteristic vertebrates of these beds were the Mosasauria, rulers of the Cretaceous seas of Kansas, the genus *Mosasaurus* being typical also of the Upper Cretaceous of Europe.

19. 1888A.
20. 1896F.
21. See Charles Schuchert, "The Upper Jurassic age of the Tendaguru dinosaur beds," *Amer. Jour. Sci.* (5), XXVII (1934), 463–466. Also, "Age of the American Morrison and East African Tendaguru formations," *Bull. Geol. Soc. America,* XXIX (1918), 245–280.

An interesting observation on beds of approximately equivalent age to those of Kansas was made by Marsh when he was in the Fort Bridger region with the Expedition of 1870. He saw a coal bed near Brush Creek which interested him greatly, because at this time the age of these lignites was in dispute, their plants much resembling those of the Miocene. He soon found that the coal was overlaid by marine strata with *Ostrea congesta* Conrad and "a new and very interesting crinoid, allied apparently to the *Marsupites* of the English Chalk." [22] This crinoid was later named *Uintacrinus* by Meek, and in more recent years it has been found in great numbers in the yellow chalk (Niobrara formation) of western Kansas.

In the shales directly below the coal bed, Marsh went on to say, "cycloidal fish scales and coprolites were abundant; and, lower down, remains of Turtles of Cretaceous types, and teeth of a Dinosaurian reptile, resembling those of *Megalosaurus*, were also discovered." [23] This evidence satisfied him, and correctly so, that the age of the coal beds was Cretaceous and not Cenozoic (Miocene) as maintained by Lesquereux and the Hayden Survey.

The *Ceratops beds* of the latest Cretaceous (=Lance formation) were given that name by Marsh in 1889.[24] Previous to 1888, no one knew much of the ceratopsian dinosaurs or their geologic environment, but by August, 1891, Marsh was able to state that the "most remarkable of the new horizons recently determined are the Ceratops beds in the Laramie series, at the top of the Cretaceous." [25] These fresh-water strata with brackish interbeds are typically exposed in Niobrara (formerly Converse) County, Wyoming. They are underlaid conformably by the Fox Hills marine formation and overlaid disconformably by the Fort Union fresh-water series of the Paleocene epoch. The gigantic horned dinosaurs named Ceratopsidae by Marsh are especially abundant in these beds, and "determine the horizon with accuracy."

Another stratigraphic question on which Marsh took a firm stand was that of a *break between the Mesozoic and the*

22. 1871B, p. 195.
23. *Ibid.,* p. 195.
24. 1889G, p. 501.
25. 1891F, p. 338.

Cenozoic. It was his opinion that there was a long hiatus at this level in the geologic column that was unrecorded in the fresh-water strata. In his address of 1877, he said: "If line there be, separating our Cretaceous from the Tertiary, [it] must at present be drawn where the Dinosaurs and other Mesozoic vertebrates disappear, and are replaced by the mammals, henceforth the dominant type." [26] This uncertainty of 1877 regarding the boundary line began to change toward certainty when Hatcher in the 'eighties found dinosaurs and mammals in the Ceratops beds of Converse County. Even so, as late as 1892 Marsh continued to hold that the break between Mesozoic and Cenozoic was a long one. He says:

The geological lesson now taught by these mammalian relics and their associated vertebrate fossils is no less important [than the anatomical knowledge he had previously been discussing], but hardly what was expected. These remains are not transitional between Mesozoic and Tertiary forms, but their affinities are with the former beyond a doubt; thus indicating a great faunal break between the . . . Coryphodon beds, or lower Wahsatch (Puerco) . . . and the Ceratops beds of the Laramie. Each of these faunas is now known by many species of vertebrate fossils represented by hundreds of specimens, and the more the two are compared the stronger becomes the contrast between them. . . . The faunal break as now known between the Laramie and the lower Wahsatch is far more profound than would be the case if the entire Jurassic and the Cretaceous below the Laramie were wanting.[27]

Present knowledge indicates surely that no such long time interval is indicated by the faunal change between the Laramie (Lance) and the Wasatch. This break is now considered to be filled by the Fort Union or Paleocene series, about 1,000 feet thick.[28] According to Simpson:

There is, geologically speaking, no considerable time interval in the Late Cretaceous and Paleocene unrepresented by sediments in the North American West. It is also clear, on stratigraphic grounds alone that the Lance and Puerco were very close to one

26. 1877F, p. 19.
27. 1892B, pp. 250–251.
28. See Glenn L. Jepsen, "Stratigraphy and paleontology of north-eastern Park County, Wyoming," *Proc. Amer. Philos. Soc.*, CIX (1930), 463–528.

another in time. This is strongly supported by the mammalian evidence as now interpreted.[29]

Marsh's work in the Green River Basin and elsewhere in that region led him to establish *four faunal divisions for the Eocene*. He explored this basin for the first time in September, 1870, and in 1885 he reported that the Eocene deposits are at least two miles in vertical thickness. The lowest division, he says,

resting unconformably on the Cretaceous, has been termed the Vermilion Creek, or Wasatch, group. It contains a well-marked mammalian fauna, the largest and most characteristic genus of which is the ungulate *Coryphodon*, and hence the writer has called these deposits the Coryphodon beds. The Middle Eocene strata, which have been termed the Green River and Bridger series, have been designated by the writer the Dinoceras beds, as the gigantic animals of this order are only found here. It is, however, better to separate the [older] Green River series, under the term "Heliobatis beds," and this is done in the present article. The name "Dinoceras beds" will then apply to the [younger] Bridger series alone. The uppermost Eocene, or the Uinta group, is especially well characterized by large mammals of the genus *Diplacodon*, and hence termed by the writer Diplacodon beds.[30]

Since Marsh's day, the additions to our knowledge of the Eocene have been great in detail, and the Fort Union series, replete with dicotyledons (in which Marsh saw no stratigraphic value), is now yielding the transition mammals which he predicted would be found.

With regard to *faunal divisions of the Miocene*, as defined by Marsh, it must be remembered that most of his "Miocene" was the "Older Miocene," which later came to be called Oligocene. Under his definition, the "Miocene" lake basins

contain three faunas, nearly or quite distinct. The lowest Miocene [Oligocene], which is found east of the Rocky Mountains, alone contains the peculiar mammals known as the *Brontotheridae*,

29. George G. Simpson, "American Mesozoic Mammalia," *Mem. Peabody Mus. Nat. Hist.*, Vol. III, Pt. I (1929), p. 156.
30. 1885E, p. 252.

and these deposits have been called by the writer the Brontotherium beds.[31]

The strata next above the Brontotherium beds, which represent the middle Oligocene, are of the Brule formation, which has as its characteristic fossils the genus *Oreodon;* Marsh called them the Oreodon beds. The upper "Miocene" (=upper Oligocene, or John Day formation) of Oregon, which is of great thickness, Marsh designated the Miohippus beds, after one of its most important fossils. In Marsh's time, little was known of the American mammals of the Pliocene, although these are now among the best established of the Cenozoic era.

Land Bridges

Marsh's study of mammal migrations had made him a firm believer in the theory of land bridges. As early as 1877, he stated that the line of mammal migration was from western America across the Alaska-Siberia bridge to China, India, Greece, Germany, and France, "indicating thus, as I believe, the path by which many of our ancient mammals helped to people the so-called Old World." [32] Recently Scott has stated that in the Eocene and Oligocene "eastern Asia and western North America were parts of the same geological province, and the Gobi faunas are more akin to America than to Europe." [33]

Regarding the Alaska-Siberia land bridge, Marsh had this to say:

If, now, we bear in mind that an elevation of only 180 feet would close Behring's Straits, and give a road thirty miles wide from America to Asia, we can easily see how this [Miocene or Pliocene] migration might have taken place. That such a Tertiary bridge did exist, we have much independent testimony, and the known facts all point to extensive migrations of animals over it.[34]

Of mammal types originating in North America and then peopling other continents he notes "the horse, rhinoceros, and tapir, all the existing odd-toed Ungulates, and, besides these,

31. *Ibid.,* p. 254.
32. 1877F, p. 27.
33. W. B. Scott, "Vertebrate paleontology since 1888," *Bull. Geol. Soc. America,* L (1939), 382.
34. 1877F, pp. 37–38.

the camel, pig, and deer. All these, I believe, and many others, went to Asia from our Northwest coast." He also says there is little doubt that the rodents are "a New World type" and probably had their origin in North America. The carnivores (such as *Machærodus*) of the North American Oligocene and Pliocene apparently followed the ungulates across Asia to Europe. "With this genus went *Hyænodon,* and some typical wolves and cats, but the bears probably came the other way with the antelopes." [35]

As for the Panama land bridge between the Americas, Marsh held that it was not in existence until Pliocene time. Across it into South America, he believed, spread the northern horse, tapir, mastodon, elephant, llama, deer, peccary, and other mammals. His conclusion that the edentates spread in the same direction was erroneous, but he appears to have been correct in thinking that these mammals originated in North America much earlier (Osborn and Matthew have proved their presence in the Eocene), although they died out here before Pliocene time.

35. *Ibid.,* p. 39.

CHAPTER XVII

MARSH'S WORK IN VERTEBRATE PALEONTOLOGY. I. THE ASTOUNDING DINOSAURS

A T the time when Marsh began his western collecting remains of dinosaurs were very rare indeed, and knowledge of them, in this country at least, was very limited. The first two editions of Dana's *Manual of Geology*, published in 1862 and 1869, devoted three short paragraphs to the dinosaurs and gave pictures of two teeth. A comparable British book, Lyell's *Elements of Geology*, had no mention of the word dinosaur in the edition of 1871, contenting itself with a short description of certain huge Jurassic reptiles known as *Megalosaurus* and *Iguanodon:* in fact, little was known of these forms outside of the English rocks of Wealden age.

Cope, summing up what was known of dinosaurs in America in 1869–70,[1] listed or discussed 18 "species" in 13 "genera." Only 3 genera were known to any extent, 5 being represented by teeth only, 1 by a jaw, and 2 by vertebrae. The best-known American genera were *Trachodon* and *Lælaps* from the Upper Cretaceous of New Jersey, and the Triassic *Megadactylus* from the Connecticut Valley. The Jurassic, the only period known to have had dinosaurs in Europe, had so far yielded none on this side of the water.

The large size of some of these animals was recognized, Cope submitting a table of lengths which attributed 28 feet to *Iguanodon* and to *Trachodon*, thought to be its American representative; 35? feet to *Ornithotarsus*, based solely on fragments of a tibia, which was thought to indicate a hind limb at least 13 feet long; and 30 feet to the European *Megalosaurus*, although Cope felt that this last estimate was "exaggerated."

Cope's synopsis of Cretaceous vertebrates made in 1875 [2]

1. E. D. Cope, "Synopsis of the Extinct Batrachia, Reptilia, and Aves of North America," *Trans. Amer. Philos. Soc.*, XIV, 86–122.

2. E. D. Cope, "The Vertebrata of the Cretaceous Formations of the West," *U. S. Geol. Surv. Territories*, II, 246–249.

shows that the dinosaurs were beginning to come into prominence. Nevertheless, the scattered results, although interesting individually, gave no hint of dinosaurian abundance; this was supplied by Cope himself in 1876, when he made a dangerous expedition into the Upper Cretaceous formations of the Judith River badlands of Montana, and from the collection there made described no fewer than 21 dinosaur "species" (each represented only by teeth, however), and a skeleton of what was later determined to be a ceratopsian dinosaur, *Monoclonius crassus.* Sternberg, in his vivid account of this expedition on which he was Cope's assistant, says: "We came upon localities literally filled with the scattered bones and teeth of dinosaurs";[3] this being so, why the expedition brought back the teeth only is somewhat incomprehensible. In any event, Cope's report made it clear that dinosaurs had been present in the West in considerable abundance in Cretaceous time, although his material gave little hint of their skeletal structure or of their spectacular size.

Just why the dinosaurs of the West had escaped detection for so long is still more of a mystery when we read Williston's comments on this subject made in 1878. He says:

The [Jurassic] beds containing them had been thoroughly studied by geologists of experience, under the surveys of Hayden and King, and their position and extent carefully described and mapped out. . . . In several of the localities, thus mapped out, I have observed acres, literally strewn with fragments of bone, many of them extremely characteristic, and so large and conspicuous as to have taxed the strength of a strong man to lift them! Three of the localities known to me are in the immediate vicinity, if not upon the actual town-sites, of thriving villages. . . . The abundance and wide extent of their remains is almost incredible.[4]

The possibility of the Great Plains as a major source for dinosaur remains may have suggested itself to Marsh on his first transcontinental trip in 1868, as told elsewhere. In 1871, while on the second of the Yale western expeditions, he found the greater part of a 15-foot dinosaur in the marine Upper Cretaceous strata of western Kansas; describing the animal in

3. C. H. Sternberg, *Life of a Fossil Hunter* (1931), p. 77.
4. S. W. Williston, "American Jurassic dinosaurs," *Trans. Kansas Acad. Sci.,* VI (1878), 43.

April, 1872, he referred it to Leidy's genus *Hadrosaurus*, already known from the New Jersey marls, and gave it the specific name *agilis*. It was not until 1877, however, that he entered actively into a search for dinosaur remains. Once he had started, there were two periods in his career when the dinosaurs of the Plains were on the march to New Haven in carload lots. The first of these migrations was of late Jurassic forms, beginning in 1877 and lasting until 1886; the other, of late Cretaceous dinosaurs, began in 1888 and continued until 1892.

The finding of the many "bone yards" in Wyoming and Colorado finally led to the employment by Marsh of dozens of collectors, and between 1877 and 1886 he and the United States Geological Survey together spent upward of $10,000 a year in this work. In the course of these ten years at least 480 large boxes of dinosaur bones came from Como, Wyoming, alone, which was then the most famous locality in all the Rocky Mountain region. In addition, Marsh received about 270 boxes from Cañon City, Colorado, and 230 from Morrison in the same state. All in all, the late Jurassic formations—Marsh's Atlantosaurus beds—yielded him not less than 1,115 boxes, large and small, of dinosaur remains. Out of this Jurassic material he described 21 new genera and 41 new species, truly the richest harvest of dinosaurs ever garnered by a single paleontologist. Among them were the largest members of the order, *Brontosaurus* and *Diplodocus*, and also some of the most bizarre, *Stegosaurus* and *Ceratosaurus*.

As reiterated earlier, this flood of dinosaur material was so great and so costly, and its cleaning, study, and restoration so time-consuming, that Marsh was unable to fulfil his promise of presenting it to the world in a series of monographs. His work on the Dinosauria is recorded in 55 papers and books, issued between 1872 and 1899. Most of the results of the first 50 papers were summarized in his two quartos of 1896, "Dinosaurs of North America," and "Vertebrate fossils [of the Denver Basin]."

In these publications, Marsh named and described 76 new species (4 are synonyms), and these he classified in 35 new genera of which 28 are still in use (1 each lost to Leidy, Cope, and Johnston, and 4 to himself), in 6 new suborders (Ceratosauria and Hallopoda not now recognized), and 3 new orders

(Predentata not now used). This is surely an astonishing record for one man to make in a single subclass of reptiles in less than thirty years. Moreover, the perfection of much of the material left to posterity appears to be even of greater value than his description of these remains. All these dinosaurs are now in the United States National Museum or at Yale University.

In November, 1896, Marsh distributed author's copies of his masterly quarto on the dinosaurs of North America, with eighty-five plates and many text figures. This volume, a synopsis of what he had so far accomplished on these reptiles, is one of his three outstanding works, the other two dealing with toothed birds and with the mammals known as Dinocerata. Of the three, the dinosaur monograph is probably to be considered the greatest; it may not be based on as significant material from an evolutionary standpoint, nor is it as finished a product, as the volume on the toothed birds; nevertheless, as the foundation of dinosaur knowledge, it will long remain the most widely used of all his publications.

When the dinosaur memoir appeared, it was very favorably reviewed by the English geologist, H. B. Woodward, whose notice closed as follows:

The book is but a first installment to a much more elaborate work which the author has in contemplation to produce. We trust that health and strength may be spared to Professor Marsh to complete this large task, and we will accept the present Memoir merely "on account," for which we are indeed truly grateful, but like Oliver Twist, we are still "asking for more."[5]

As Woodward indicated, "Dinosaurs of North America" was not intended by Marsh to be a final study of these highly specialized reptiles. His plan of publication was, first, to describe the animals in preliminary form in a series of pamphlets, and then to bring this knowledge together in far greater detail in paleontological monographs that should be worthy of the rich ancient vertebrate life of North America. While he was issuing the preliminary papers, more material was being collected, so that in the end he could describe the genera and species much more accurately, illustrate them fully and artistically, and discuss their genesis, as should be done in works of monographic

5. *Geol. Mag.,* dec. IV, IV (1897), p. 44.

character. Even previous to 1881 he had planned de luxe monographs on the dinosaurs, and when his connection with the Survey seemed to make these possible, he submitted an outline that included five such monographs, for the Sauropoda (approved by the Survey in 1881), the Theropoda and Ornithopoda (approved in 1881), the Stegosauria (approved in 1885), and the Ceratopsia (approved in 1890). The fate of these monographs has been told in an earlier chapter.

Classification of the Dinosaurs

Williston has well said that it is only the paleontologist who is competent "to express opinions concerning the larger principles of classification of organisms, and especially the classifications of reptiles." On this basis, Marsh was eminently qualified to draw up and present a classification of the dinosaurs, and the one he offered in 1896, based as it was on much more complete skeletons than had before been available, was widely followed. According to Zittel, in his interesting *History of Geology and Paleontology*, 1901, Marsh inaugurated a sweeping reform in the classification of the Dinosauria. Before Marsh's time there were but few divisions recognized other than families, and these were not many in number. The astonishing material that Marsh unearthed led him to raise the Dinosauria from an order to a subclass, which embraced his three orders, the carnivorous Theropoda and the herbivorous Sauropoda and Predentata. The last-named order he separated into three suborders, Stegosauria (the plated forms), Ceratopsia (horned dinosaurs), and Ornithopoda (birdlike and duckbilled dinosaurs).

With the increase of knowledge, Marsh's classification has been modified somewhat, and the one which is given below shows the present views as adopted by Hay, 1930, with the names proposed by Marsh and the number of his species in bold-face type.

TABLE OF DINOSAURIA

(*Synonyms in parentheses. European genera not given, nor any proposed after 1899.*)

Subclass Dinosauria Owen, 1839, 1842.

Order **Theropoda**, 1879. Carnivorous dinosaurs. (Divided by

Hay into the following superfamilies: 1, Zanclodontoidae; 2, Megalosauroidae; 3, Cœluroidae.)

Family Zanclodontidae Zittel, 1882 (Plateosauridae, 1895). Triassic of Europe.

Family Megalosauridae Huxley, 1870. Jurassic and Cretaceous of Europe.

Family Anchisauridae, 1885 (Amphisauridae, 1882). Upper Triassic. Genera: Anchisaurus, 1885 (*Megadactylus* Hitchcock, 1865. Amphisaurus, 1878), 2. Ammosaurus, 1891, 1. Family present in Europe also.

Family Dryptosauridae, 1890 (Allosauridae, 1879). Jurassic and Upper Cretaceous. Genera: Dryptosaurus, 1877 (*Lælaps* Cope), 1. *Antrodemus* Leidy, 1870 (Allosaurus, 1877), 1. Creosaurus, 1878, 1. *Tyrannosaurus* Osborn, 1905, 1.

Family Labrosauridae, 1882. Upper Jurassic. Genus: Labrosaurus, 1879, 2.

Family Macelognathidae, 1884. Upper Jurassic. Genus: Macelognathus, 1884, 1.

Suborder Cœluria, 1881 (Cœluroidea Hay, 1930).

Family Cœluridae, 1881. Upper Jurassic. Genus: Cœlurus, 1879, 3. Family also in Europe.

Suborder Compsognatha Huxley, 1870.

Family Compsognathidae, 1882. Upper Jurassic of Germany.

Suborder Ceratosauria, 1895 (not recognized by Hay, 1930).

Family Ceratosauridae, 1884. Upper Jurassic. Genus: Ceratosaurus, 1884, 1.

Family Ornithomimidae, 1890. Upper Cretaceous. Genus: Ornithomimus, 1890, 5.

Suborder Hallopoda, 1881 (not recognized by Hay, 1930).

Family Hallopodidae, 1881. Upper Jurassic (upper Morrison). Genus: Hallopus, 1881, 1.

Order Sauropoda, 1878. Herbivorous dinosaurs, among them the largest members of the subclass.

Family Camarasauridae, Cope, 1877 (Morosauridae, 1882; Pleurocœlidae, 1889). Upper Jurassic. Genera: *Camarasaurus* Cope, 1877 (Morosaurus, 1878), 4. Lower Cretaceous (Potomac). *Astrodon* Johnston, 1865 (Pleurocœlus, 1888), 3.

Family **Atlantosauridae**, 1877. Upper Jurassic. Genera: Atlantosaurus, 1877 (Titanosaurus, 1877), 2. **Apatosaurus**, 1877, 2. **Brontosaurus**, 1879, 2.

Family **Diplodocidae**, 1884. Upper Jurassic. Genera: Diplodocus, 1878, 2. Barosaurus, 1890, 2. **Apatodon**, 1877, 1. *Amphicœlias* Cope, 1877.

Family Titanosauridae Lyddeker 1879. Cretaceous of India, East Africa, and Patagonia.

Family **Cardiodontidae**, 1898. Well represented in Upper Jurassic of Europe (Wealden). Includes *Cetiosaurus* Phillips.

Order Orthopoda Cope, 1866 (**Predentata**, 1894). Herbivorous dinosaurs.

  Suborder **Ornithopoda**, 1881.

Family **Camptosauridae**, 1895 (**Camptonotidae**, 1881). Upper Jurassic. Genus: **Camptosaurus**, 1885 (**Camptonotus**, 1879), 4.

Family **Laosauridae**, 1895. Upper Jurassic. Genera: Laosaurus, 1878, 3. **Dryosaurus**, 1894, 1.

Family **Hypsilophodontidae**, 1895. Upper Jurassic of England.

Family Iguanodontidae Huxley, 1869. Jurassic-Cretaceous of Europe.

Family **Trachodontidae**, 1895 (included by Hay 1930 in Hadrosauridae). Upper Cretaceous. Genus: *Trachodon* Leidy, 1856, 2.

Family Hadrosauridae Cope, 1869 (**Claosauridae**, 1895). See Trachodontidae. Upper Cretaceous. Genera: *Hadrosaurus* Leidy, 1858, 1. **Claosaurus**, 1890, 1.

Family **Nanosauridae**, 1878. Upper Jurassic (upper Morrison). Has the smallest of known dinosaurs. Genus: **Nanosaurus**, 1877, 2.

  Suborder **Ceratopsia**, 1890 (= Superfamily Ceratopsoidae Hay, 1902, 1930).

Family **Ceratopsidae**, 1888 (Agathaumidae Cope, 1889). Upper Cretaceous. Genera: **Ceratops**, 1888, 2. *Agathaumas* Cope, 1872 (*Polyonax* Cope, 1874). **Torosaurus**, 1891, 2. *Monoclonius* Cope, 1876. **Triceratops**, 1889 (**Sterrholophus**, 1891), 10. Family also present in Europe.

Suborder **Stegosauria,** 1877 (Stegosauroidae Hay, 1902, 1930).

Family **Stegosauridae,** 1880. Upper Jurassic and Upper Cretaceous. Genera: **Stegosaurus,** 1877, 6. **Diracodon,** 1881, 1. *Palæoscincus* Leidy, 1856, 1 (referred to Nodosauridae by Hay, 1930). **Priconodon,** 1888, 1 (referred to Nodosauridae by Hay, 1930). Also in Upper Jurassic of Europe.

Family Scelidosauridae Huxley, 1870. Jurassic and Cretaceous of Europe.

Family **Nodosauridae,** 1890. Upper Cretaceous. Genus: **Nodosaurus,** 1889, 1 (see Stegosauridae).

Genetic Relations of the Dinosaurs

With regard to the relationships of the dinosaurs to other reptile groups, Marsh had arrived at the conclusion that the sauropods were the "least specialized of Dinosaurs," as early as 1878, and thought that they showed "such an approach to the Mesozoic Crocodiles as to suggest a common ancestry at no very remote period." [6] In 1884, he called attention to the relationship between the dinosaurs and the Aëtosauria of the German Triassic, a group which shows strong affinities with Crocodilians.[7] Subsequent studies indicated that the "Hallopoda" were also of the first importance in estimating dinosaurian affinities. The belodonts were likewise considered to be allies of the dinosaurs, but, he adds, "Belodon has been investigated by many anatomists, who will appear to have regarded it as Crocodilian; an opinion that in the light of our present knowledge may fairly be questioned." [8]

In 1895, Marsh was not disposed to accept the view that the dinosaurs belong to two or more distinct groups, each of independent origin, his reason being that the information at hand regarding many dinosaurs was still fragmentary.[9] There is a marked tendency among recent authors, however, to abandon the term Dinosauria, because it appears to include reptiles of two phylogenetic lines, with independent origins.

6. 1878G, p. 412.
7. 1884A, p. 167.
8. 1896H, p. 232.
9. 1895J, p. 492.

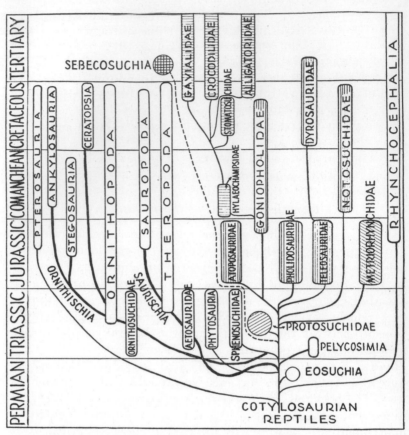

Fig. 21. Diagram, after C. C. Mook, to show the lines of descent of the crocodiles, dinosaurs, and other reptiles. Note that while these groups had a
common origin in Permian reptiles known as cotylosaurs, the winged pterosaurs were the first to branch away from the main line. Probably late in
Permian time one dinosaur stock (heavy black line), leaving the parent
stem, gave rise to the theropods and sauropods, with the Triassic aëtosaurs
as one stage in this evolution. A second dinosaur stock, which eventually
deployed into several types—ankylosaurs, stegosaurs, ornithopods, and ceratopsians—did not come directly from the main stem but was an offshoot of
the line that gave rise to the African Permian reptiles called sphenosuchians.
Marsh was right in some respects in considering the sauropods as primitive,
and in suspecting their nearness to the aëtosaurs, small reptiles which were
beginning to change from sprawling legs into those of running type.
Used through the courtesy of the American Museum of Natural History.

Restorations of Dinosaurs

Early in his work on fossil vertebrates, Marsh saw the desirability of making these strange beasts come to life in authentic skeletal restorations that would visualize their former appearance. Leidy had never made a restoration even of an entire foot of any fossil vertebrate. Cope, on the other hand, displayed to the American Philosophical Society in December, 1877, a drawing, made under his direction by Dr. John A. Ryder, to show the restored skeleton of his *Camarasaurus supremus;* this never appeared in print, however, until Osborn and Mook published it in 1921. Marsh therefore was the leader in setting such restorations before the public. His first try at these restorations —"the working hypotheses of paleontologists"—was with the toothed birds, *Ichthyornis* and *Hesperornis*, and appeared in his memoir of 1880 on that group. It was followed the next year by a restoration of the mammal *Dinoceras mirabile*. When the material coming in from Como yielded an almost complete skeleton of *Brontosaurus*, Marsh naturally thought of setting before the world a restoration of this great sauropod, and did so in 1883. *Triceratops* and *Stegosaurus* appeared in 1891, *Claosaurus* and *Ceratosaurus* in 1892, *Anchisaurus* in 1893, and *Camptosaurus* in 1894.

These restorations of Marsh's were commented on at some length by Richard Lydekker in *Nature* for July 27, 1893, five of them being illustrated.[10] The review was on the whole a friendly and favorable one, but it aroused Marsh to protest, because it used Cope's names *Hypsirophus* for *Stegosaurus*, and *Agathaumas* for *Triceratops*. He made a rather sharp reply in the same periodical for September 7.[11]

When his studies of the American dinosaurs were nearing completion in 1895, and he desired to have a better understanding of their genetic relationships, Marsh took up a review of the European forms, with the idea of bringing all the known dinosaurs under one system of classification; and toward that very desirable end he made several visits abroad. Having made a number of restorations of American dinosaurs, he felt himself competent to do the same for such European skeletons as were

10. *Nature,* CXVIII, 302–304.
11. *Ibid.,* pp. 438–439.

Fig. 22. Dinosaur restorations made under Marsh's direction. From above downward: *Anchisaurus colurus* Marsh, 1/24 natural size. *Ceratosaurus nasicornis* Marsh, 1/60 natural size. *Brontosaurus excelsus* Marsh, 1/220 natural size. *Anchisaurus* from the late Triassic of Connecticut; the other two from the late Jurassic of Colorado and Wyoming, respectively.

sufficiently complete. Accordingly, in November, 1895, he presented restorations of four European genera; namely, the carnivorous *Compsognathus* and the herbivores *Iguanodon, Hypsilophodon,* and *Scelidosaurus.*[12] Finally, in the next month, he brought the twelve dinosaur illustrations together and published them on one large sheet—a most striking array.

These restorations of Marsh's were copied far and wide, in textbooks, in encyclopedias, and in more popular publications, and thus served to familiarize the public both with the skeletal appearance of these dinosaurs and with the skill of the master who had restored them.

Life-size plastic restorations of dinosaurs had been made in Europe long before Marsh presented his diagrams, Waterhouse Hawkins having produced such in 1854 for the grounds of the Crystal Palace in London. Marsh had of course seen pictures of these, but apparently did not consider it worth his while to study the restored monsters themselves until 1895. His visit to them resulted in the following scathing comment at the Ipswich meeting of the British Association:

The Dinosaurs seem . . . to have suffered much from both their enemies and their friends. Many of them were destroyed and dismembered long ago by their natural enemies, but, more recently, their friends have done them further injustice in putting together their scattered remains, and restoring them to supposed lifelike forms. . . . So far as I can judge, there is nothing like unto them in the heavens, or on the earth, or in the waters under the earth. We now know from good evidence that both *Megalosaurus* and *Iguanodon* were bipedal, and to represent them as creeping, except in their extreme youth, would be almost as incongruous as to do this by the genus *Homo.*"[13]

These curious and grotesque affairs were still in existence in London, in recent years, but replicas of them in Central Park, New York City, were broken up and thrown into the park lagoon by order of a former mayor of the city, not because they were incorrect scientifically, but because he considered them inconsistent with the doctrines of revealed religion!

12. 1895F, pp. 409–412.
13. *Ibid.,* pp. 407–408.

THE CARNIVOROUS THEROPOD DINOSAURS

Triassic Theropoda. These, the dinosaurs which lived nearest to Marsh's home, received his attention considerably later than their more striking relatives of the Rocky Mountain area. The large Yale collection of fossil footprints from the Connecticut Valley, which includes many dinosaur tracks, was begun by him shortly after he was appointed to his professorship, but he never published any account of it; his memoir of 1896 remarks that most of these tracks were for a long time believed to be of birds, but that they were in reality the footprints of dinosaurs "which usually walked on their hind feet, yet sometimes put their fore feet to the ground. Others occasionally sat down, and left an impression which proved that they, too, were not birds." [14]

Of the actual animals that made these tracks, only one had been recognized prior to 1889.[15] This was a "saurian reptile" found at Springfield, Massachusetts, which, at the suggestion of Sir Richard Owen, had been named *Megadactylus polyzelus* by Edward Hitchcock, Jr., in 1865. Marsh, finding the name *Megadactylus* preoccupied, renamed the genus *Amphisaurus*, but this term also had been used and was replaced in 1885 by *Anchisaurus*. In 1889, Triassic rocks near Manchester, Connecticut, yielded up the skeleton of a dinosaur which Marsh named *Anchisaurus colurus*, and which he described as "perhaps the most perfect Triassic Dinosaur yet discovered, as the skull and greater portion of the skeleton were found in place, and in fine preservation." [16] The skull was 5½ inches long, and the entire animal 6 feet. To this species also belong the first dinosaur remains found in the Connecticut Valley Triassic, discovered in 1818 at East Windsor, Connecticut, which were reported in the *American Journal of Science* as "probably human," and were identified almost a century later by Professor Richard S. Lull as being *Anchisaurus colurus*. *Anchisaurus solus* (1892), the third species of the genus, found likewise

14. 1896H, p. 147.
15. A Triassic dinosaur found in Pennsylvania had been described in 1851 by Isaac Lea as *Clepsysaurus pennsylvanicus*.
16. 1891G, p. 267.

near Manchester, also preserves the skull; the animal had a length of 3 feet, being "about as large as a small fox." [17]

Of Marsh's skeletal restoration of *Anchisaurus,* based on four skeletons, Lull, in offering his own restoration with flesh modeled on one side, says that the older conception "presents but few points to which in our more exact knowledge of the dinosaurs as living beings we can take exception." [18]

The fourth Connecticut Valley theropod known from skeletal remains is *Ammosaurus major,* described by Marsh in 1889. It is represented by the posterior portion only, the block containing the rest of the skeleton having apparently been built into the abutment of a bridge. Marsh tried in vain to have the missing block located, but, as Lull says, the bridge "still has the unique distinction of being the mausoleum of a dinosaur." [19]

Jurassic Theropoda. Marsh proposed his order Theropoda in 1881, in an outline classification of the dinosaurs, and defined it briefly in January, 1882. One of his more striking papers on American Jurassic dinosaurs, "The order Theropoda," appearing in April, 1884, announced the fortunate discovery of two almost perfect specimens of this order, as well as several others in good preservation, which made it possible for him to elaborate somewhat his definition of the order and of the families referred to it. The four Jurassic genera *Allosaurus* (=*Antrodemus*), *Cœlurus, Labrosaurus,* and *Ceratosaurus,* each including species of large size, the natural enemies of the gigantic herbivorous forms, he considered to belong to as many distinct families.

Of Marsh's Jurassic theropod genera, the great carnivore *Allosaurus* is probably the best known, largely because of the fine skeleton found in 1879 at Como by F. F. Hubbell, one of Cope's collectors, and now mounted in the American Museum of Natural History in the act of devouring the carcass of a *Brontosaurus.* The type specimen of an even stranger carnivore, *Ceratosaurus nasicornis,* collected by M. P. Felch near Cañon City, Colorado, and described by Marsh in 1884, is now one of the great prizes in the exhibition series of the National Museum.

17. 1892F, p. 545.
18. R. S. Lull, "The Triassic life of the Connecticut Valley," *Bull.* 24, Connecticut Geol. Nat. Hist. Surv. (1915), p. 142.
19. Lull, *op. cit.,* p. 150.

The skeleton is almost complete and was to a considerable extent articulated when found. In life, the animal was about 22 feet in length and stood some 12 feet high. Gilmore redescribed its osteology in 1920 and presented newer restorations of the animal, Marsh's dating from 1892. The skull is very large in proportion to the skeleton, and possessed a high, trenchant horn, which must have formed a most powerful weapon for offense and defense.[20]

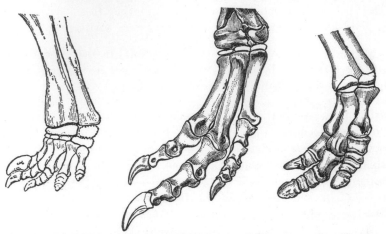

Fig. 23. Hind feet of the three chief types of dinosaurs, after Marsh. Left, an amphibious sauropod, *Morosaurus* (= *Camarasaurus*) *grandis* Marsh; middle, a carnivore, *Allosaurus* (= *Antrodemus*) *fragilis* Marsh; right, a beaked trachodont, *Claosaurus annectens* Marsh.

The genus *Cœlurus*, described in 1879 without family reference, was considered by Marsh in 1881 to represent a new suborder, Cœluria, of uncertain position. The following year he placed it under the Theropoda, where it still remains.

Another suborder, placed by Marsh under the Theropoda in 1882, was erected for the European *Compsognathus*. This genus includes what is probably the most interesting single specimen of a theropod in Europe—*Compsognathus longipes* Wagner 1861 from the Upper Jurassic lithographic limestone of Solenhofen, Germany, a diminutive dinosaur measuring about 20 inches along the backbone. The skull and nearly the

20. C. W. Gilmore, "Osteology of the carnivorous Dinosauria in the United States National Museum," *Bull.* 110, U. S. Nat. Mus. (1920), 159 pp.

entire skeleton are preserved. Of this tiny beast Marsh said in 1897:

The gem of the collection [in the Alte Akademie, Munich] is still the unique *Compsognathus*, which in several previous visits I had studied with care. A reëxamination impressed me even more with the fact, that this is one of the most perfect and interesting vertebrate fossils yet discovered, and no other example of the genus is known. It was in this unique specimen that years before [1881] I had detected the embryo, and this fossil still affords the only known evidence that Dinosaurs were viviparous.[21]

Marsh's notebook, however, shows that at the time he was studying the specimen in 1881 he was not so certain about this conclusion, for he wrote:

Inside this specimen are the bones of a small one, which was probably eaten. It appears to be of the same species. It lies between the ribs mainly, but some bones are outside. One jaw (about ¼ as long as adult) lies near the pubis and the other ramus is outside one inch from the end of the fibula. The tail is bent and broken and lies in the fore part of the abdomen. . . . This young animal would seem to be too large for a fœtus.

Nopsca, our more modern authority, also thinks the small specimen is an ingested reptile.

A third suborder which Marsh eventually placed under the Theropoda, after a period of uncertainty as to its position, was the Hallopoda. In September, 1877, he described two small dinosaurs from the Cañon City region, proposing for them the new genus *Nanosaurus* and calling the species *N. victor* and *N. agilis*. The first of these little creatures, about the size of a rabbit, puzzled him for a long time because it apparently had hind legs that were adapted for leaping. Four years later, he made *Nanosaurus victor* the genotype of his new genus *Hallopus*, and said of the new order Hallopoda, proposed at the same time, that future discoveries would probably bring to light intermediate forms between the Hallopoda and the crocodilian aëtosaurs on the one hand and the typical dinosaurs on the other. The distinctive character of the hallopods is the back-

21. 1897E, pp. 414–415.

ward extension of the calcaneum, a feature which, in connection with the greatly elongated metatarsals, suggested the generic name *Hallopus* ("leaping foot"). In another publication, Marsh remarks that the bones of *Hallopus* were birdlike and hollow, possibly pneumatic, and that all three pelvic bones aided in forming the acetabulum, as in typical dinosaurs.[22]

The pelvis of *Hallopus* suggests affinity with *Compsognathus.* Huxley, while visiting Marsh, sketched a restoration of *Compsognathus* beside the Wagner figure of that genus, and Marsh published it in his paper of 1895 dealing with the restorations of European dinosaurs.[23] The sketch represents the animal as sitting, a posture based on some of the Connecticut Valley "footprints," which Huxley, accompanied by Marsh, had examined at several localities with great interest.

Marsh was never certain of the geological horizon of *Hallopus victor* and *Nanosaurus agilis,* but he finally believed it to be Triassic, or at least lowest Morrison (Jurassic), and he gave it the name of Hallopus beds. A careful restudy of all the data in the Peabody Museum files has recently shown that these small dinosaurs apparently came from a chocolate-colored, sandy, noduliferous shale horizon, 30 feet thick, in the upper part of the Morrison formation.[24]

Cretaceous Theropoda. The late Cretaceous Ceratops beds (Lance formation) of Colorado have highly specialized, slender, ostrichlike dinosaurs which Marsh at first referred to his suborder Ornithopoda, under the Predentata. One of them, described in January, 1890, as *Ornithomimus velox,* was found in the Denver beds at Green Mountain near Denver, by George L. Cannon, Jr.; two others described at the same time were *O. tenuis* and *O. grandis.* The family proposed for the genus, Ornithomimidae, was said by Marsh to be distinguished from all other dinosaur families by the hind feet, which show three functional metatarsals, the middle one having its proximal end much diminished in size and crowded backward behind the second and fourth, as in many living birds.[25]

22. 1896I, pp. 481–482.
23. 1895F, p. 410.
24. Charles Schuchert, "The geological horizon of the dinosaurs *Hallopus* and *Nanosaurus agilis,*" *Amer. Jour. Sci.,* CXXXVII (1939), 19–26.
25. 1896H, pp. 203–204.

By May, 1892, when *Ornithomimus sedens* and *O. minutus* were described, Marsh had decided to refer the genus definitely to the order Theropoda, where it is still placed. Of *O. sedens* he had a nearly complete pelvis, various vertebrae, and other skeletal parts. The most striking feature of the pelvis he took to be the firm coössification of ilium, ischium, and pubis, as in recent birds and in *Ceratosaurus*. The sacrum had five vertebrae, also firmly coössified, as were the sacral spines. All the bones were very delicate and some of them, at least, apparently were pneumatic. The parts preserved in *O. minutus* indicate an animal about the size of the common fowl, and "may pertain to a bird." [26] As Marsh had no skulls of *Ornithomimus*, he was unaware of the important fact that these animals had no teeth.

THE SAUROPOD DINOSAURS

The Sauropoda, that group of herbivorous dinosaurs which includes the largest reptiles, and, indeed, the largest land animals the world has ever seen, were first recognized as a distinct suborder by Marsh in November, 1878, when he had remains of the four striking genera *Atlantosaurus, Morosaurus, Apatosaurus,* and *Diplodocus.* The first great sauropod to reach him was the *Titanosaurus* (renamed *Atlantosaurus*) found by Lakes and Beckwith near Morrison, Colorado, in March, 1877. Late in the same year Marsh named two other sauropods, *Apatosaurus ajax* and *A. grandis*, both associated with *Atlantosaurus* and both collected by Lakes in Colorado. The next year he described a second species of *Atlantosaurus*, *A. immanis,* which, when alive, he thought might have been "near one hundred feet in length . . . although it may have been much less." [27] By 1896, he spoke of it as being "about seventy feet or more in length and twenty in height." [28] Originally the femur of this animal was said to be over 8 feet in length, but by 1896 [29] it had shrunk to "over six feet long."

Morosaurus impar, described by Marsh in March, 1878, was found by Williston at Como. The genus, Marsh said, is allied

26. 1892E, pp. 451–452.
27. 1878C, p. 242.
28. 1896I, p. 489.
29. 1896H, p. 166.

to *Apatosaurus* but may be distinguished from the latter by the sacrum, as well as by other characters, *Apatosaurus* having three sacral vertebrae while *Morosaurus* has four. The head of *Morosaurus*, described in November of the same year,

shows in its fixed quadrates and some other features a resemblance to that in the Crocodiles. The rami of the lower jaw are not united by symphysis. The teeth are numerous. . . . The neck was elongated, and, except the atlas, all the cervical vertebrae have deep cavities in the sides of the centra, similar to those in birds of flight. . . . They are also strongly opisthocœlus. The atlas and axis are not ankylosed together, and the elements of the atlas are distinct.[30]

Morosaurus grandis, also from Como, is known from a nearly complete skeleton found together in almost perfect preservation. This animal was about 40 feet in length, but its brain "was proportionately smaller than in any known vertebrate." [31] The type specimen of *Morosaurus agilis*, found by M. P. Felch near Cañon City and described by Marsh in 1889, was redescribed by Gilmore in 1907.[32] *M. lentus*, a fourth species, described in the same year as *M. agilis*, but from Como, is about 21 feet in length as mounted in the Yale Museum; however, this is an immature individual and adults may have been twice as long.

The genus *Camarasaurus* of Cope, which includes some of the gigantic forms of the Sauropoda, was said by Marsh in 1896 to be apparently nearly allied to *Morosaurus*, and perhaps belonging to the same family.[33] The present view is that the two genera are identical and that Cope's name has precedence, but the above statement is as near as Marsh ever came to admitting identity.

Brontosaurus, one of the largest dinosaurs known, was described by Marsh in 1879 from an almost complete skeleton that was dug out by W. H. Reed in Quarry 10, eight miles east of Como, Wyoming. When found, the huge skeleton

30. 1878G, p. 412.
31. *Ibid.*, p. 414.
32. C. W. Gilmore, "The type of the Jurassic reptile *Morosaurus agilis* redescribed, with a note on *Camptosaurus*," *Proc. U. S. Nat. Mus.*, XXXII (1907), 151–165.
33. 1896I, p. 498.

lay nearly in the position in which the bones would naturally fall after death, and fortunately the entire scapular arch was in excellent preservation. The coracoids were in apposition with their respective scapulae on each side, between them lay *two* flat bones, that clearly belong to the sternum. This discovery, as interesting as it was unexpected, removes the main uncertainty about the scapular arch of Dinosaurs.[34]

Just a year later, Marsh announced that the sacrum in *Brontosaurus excelsus* is composed of five ankylosed vertebrae, whereas none of the other sauropods has more than four.[35]

Finally, in August, 1883, Marsh presented the first restoration of a sauropod dinosaur, based on the *Brontosaurus* skeleton. The head in this genus, he said, was smaller in proportion to the body than in any vertebrate hitherto known, exceeding that of *Morosaurus* in this respect. The neck, he continued,

was long, and, considering its proportions, flexible, and was the lightest portion of the vertebral column. The body was quite short, and the abdominal cavity of moderate size. The legs and feet were massive, and the bones all solid. The feet were plantigrade, and each foot-print must have been about a square yard in extent. The tail was large [about 28 feet long] and nearly all the bones solid. . . . When living, the animal must have weighed more than twenty tons. The very small head and brain, and slender neural chord, indicate a stupid, slow moving reptile. . . . In habits, *Brontosaurus* was more or less amphibious, and its food was probably aquatic plants or other succulent vegetation. The remains are usually found in localities where the animals had evidently become mired.[36]

It is now fifty years since "Bill" Reed sent to Yale the bones that constitute the much prized *Brontosaurus* in the Peabody Museum. They were collected by the pick-up-and-rake-together method and arrived at New Haven in sacks; and the wonder is that the preparators were ever able to put the pieces together. They solved the puzzle, however, and in 1902 the hind legs of

34. 1880D, p. 395.
35. 1881E, p. 417.
36. 1883A, pp. 81–82.

this mighty monster were set up in the old Museum, where they remained until the building was torn down in 1917. Ten years later, when Chief Preparator Hugh Gibb and his assistants, F. W. Darby and C. B. Allderige, started the long task of setting up the entire skeleton in the Great Hall of the new Museum, it was at once apparent that their job would be even greater than had been anticipated. The original preparation of the bones which had cost Marsh not less than $10,000, as he told the senior author in 1892, had been done with gum arabic, and this gum had crystallized, so that the bones broke apart even with the most careful handling. This meant that all the glued joints had to be reopened, the gum removed, and the bones reset with modern cements, a process that took the three preparators nearly four years. In the meantime the iron supports to hold up the 6½ ton skeleton had to be made, and this occupied two skilled ironworkers for nearly two years. It was a tense day in the annals of the Museum when, after months of preparation and hours of testing, the traveling crane picked up the huge sections of backbone and ribs and swung them into place. The finished specimen is truly a wonderful relic of the medieval period of geologic time, but its cost has mounted to about $30,000! Small museums, and especially college museums, are rarely able to install one of these grotesque beauties. The only other brontosaur to be set up on its legs is that in the American Museum of Natural History, New York City, which came from Bone-Cabin Quarry, near Medicine Bow, Wyoming; it is 66 feet 8 inches long, 15 feet high, and had an estimated live weight of 38 tons. The Yale specimen as mounted is a few inches longer and a foot higher.

Marsh objected strenuously to the mounting of his specimens for exhibition, and it is interesting to speculate what he would say if he could see his prize dinosaur. When the great brontosaur was at last mounted, in 1931, the only one of Marsh's many assistants left was Hugh Gibb, whose long career as a preparator reached its culmination in this masterpiece.

It had long been a source of grief to Marsh's successors that they were not able to place this entire skeleton of *Brontosaurus* on exhibition, because the original museum had no room long enough to contain it. Their predicament was thus described in seriocomic vein in the *Yale Alumni Weekly* for March 7, 1913:

LYRA YALENSIS
THE SOLUTION

"The lack of proper and safe equipment for the priceless American fossil collections now stored—much of it still unstudied for lack of room—in Peabody Museum, has for nearly forty years been a cause of worry and lowered scholarly efficiency."—ALUMNI WEEKLY, January 24, 1913.

Methinks I hear in chorus
Each half-mounted Brontosaurus,
Each Iguanodon, Pteranodon, and Spoon-Bill Dinosaur,
Cry against their profanation:
'O respect our age cretacian,
Give us room to live our lives out! Can't you set us up once more?'

I

Is this the famed museum where great Huxley longed to be?
(Consult his *Life and Letters,* chapter thirty-one.) Ah me!
Shall we send out expeditions to explore unknown Peru,
When the cellar of Peabody offers work enough to do?
Who can tell what there lies hidden, who is rash enough to state
What's concealed within this barrel, what is buried in that crate?
How it sets the pulses beating when we think what may be found
In the basement of Peabody, just a few feet underground.
In this room a saurian's two legs rise proudly into space:
Read its card—'Left uncompleted; for the rest there is no place.'
Think in every walk of life how many fossils meet our glance;
Is it only in Peabody that a fossil has no chance?
Have we no respect for family, have we no regard for birth?
Just consider that these creatures were the biggest things on earth.

II

The solution is quite simple. Pious founders pass them by,
But we cannot hear unmoved the pleading Dinosaur's loud cry.
Start a club; that seems too easy, yet this plan is sure to win—

Make it quite select—at once both men and money will come in.
Six months gone, the affluent treasurer will say in his report:
'Shall we build a marble mansion, Grecian temple, bombproof fort,
Tiger Inn, or Hasty Pudding?' No; one better we will see 'em
And eclipse all clubs that have been famed by founding—a Museum.
Sands of time await our foot-prints, or we pass away unknown.
Let us honour these old creatures who left foot-prints in the stone.
Give each fossil space to breathe in, mount them on their favourite
    rocks;
What's the use of having fore-legs if they're hidden in a box?
Then when all is put in order, as a Huxley would have planned,
Call a meeting of the Club, inspect the building, then—DISBAND!

Methinks I hear a chorus,
The Ajax Apatosaurus,
Each Triceratops, each Saurian, each Spoon-Bill Dinosaur,
Crying out in desperation:
'Oh respect our age Cretacian,
Give us room to live our lives out! Can't you set us up once more?'

The long-limbed sauropod *Diplodocus longus*, found by Williston near Cañon City, Colorado, was described by Marsh in November, 1878, from a few skeletal remains. It was distinguished from other genera already known, he said,

by the caudal vertebrae, which are elongated, deeply excavated below, and have double chevrons, with both anterior and posterior rami. . . . To the last character, the generic name refers. The tibia, also, is a very characteristic bone, as it is deeply grooved above to receive the fibula.[37]

In the meantime, more of the skeleton was being recovered from the dump to which it had been consigned by Williston and Felch, and the bones were being cleaned out of the rock and restored at the Museum. Returning to the genus in February, 1884, for a fuller description, Marsh reported that the skull was of moderate size, the brain very small, and possessing a very large pituitary body. The dentition was the weakest in any known dinosaur, "and strongly suggests the probability that some of the more specialized members of this great group were

37. 1878G, p. 414.

PLATE XXV

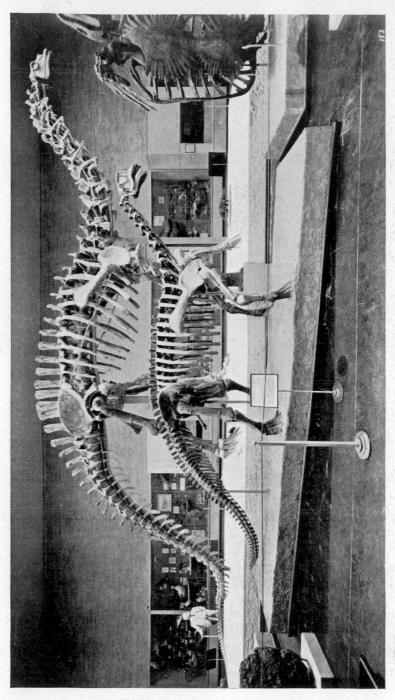

MOUNTED SKELETON OF THE GREAT SAUROPOD DINOSAUR *BRONTOSAURUS EXCELSUS* MARSH, COLLECTED IN 1881 BY W. H. REED AT COMO, WYOMING. A MUCH SMALLER COMO SAUROPOD, *MOROSAURUS LENTUS*, 21 FEET LONG, IS TO BE SEEN IN THE FOREGROUND

PEABODY MUSEUM OF NATURAL HISTORY

PLATE XXVI

CLAOSAURUS ANNECTENS MARSH, AS MOUNTED AT YALE. COLLECTED BY HATCHER AND SULLINS IN CONVERSE (NIOBARA) COUNTY, WYOMING, IN 1891, AND MOUNTED IN 1901 BY HUGH GIBB UNDER THE DIRECTION OF CHARLES E. BEECHER. THE FIRST DINOSAUR SKELETON TO BE MOUNTED IN AMERICA

edentulous. . . . The teeth are entirely confined to the front of the jaws. . . . The position of the external nares indicates an aquatic life." [38]

Marsh never had complete enough material of *Diplodocus* to describe it in any such detail as he did *Brontosaurus*. However, as a result of subsequent collecting by other museums, it has become probably the best known of all sauropods. The United States National Museum has a mounted specimen, which is said to have taken one man's labor for nine years to prepare and mount. The Carnegie Museum at Pittsburgh has two mounted skeletons, and the American Museum a partial one. The *Diplodocus longus* at Washington has 11 feet of body, 21 feet of neck, and 32–40 feet of whiplike tail, making a total length of about 70 feet between perpendiculars; it has a height of 12½ feet over the hips, and the head is posed 14½ feet above the floor. *D. carnegii* in the Pittsburgh Museum, familiar because of its widely distributed replicas, has a length along the backbone curvature of 84½ feet.

In the spring of 1889, Marsh returned once more to the Sauropoda. He now had much more material, so that in many genera both skull and skeleton were known. *Brontosaurus, Morosaurus,* and *Diplodocus* were each represented by a skull, some of them nearly complete, and characteristic portions of the skulls of other genera had been collected. In Europe, he found the sauropods also well represented, and especially so in England, but the material consisted of scattered bones, making it well-nigh impossible to determine the family characters of the forms described. No Atlantosauridae or Diplodocidae, however, appear to have lived in Europe, but all the ilia, ischia, and pubes there recovered agree in their main features with those of the Morosauridae, "so that there can be little doubt that the same general form is represented in both countries." The Cardiodontidae of Europe he considered to be allied to the Morosauridae but to be as a rule less specialized.[39]

Discussing the brain of the sauropods in his final dinosaur monograph, Marsh said that the neural canal in *Apatosaurus* and all the other genera

38. 1884A, pp. 165, 166.
39. 1889B, pp. 324–326.

is much enlarged, being especially expanded above each vertebral
centrum, thus leaving a vaulted chamber in the united neural
arches of the sacral vertebrae. . . . This enlargement of the
neural chord in the sacral region exists to some degree in reptiles
and birds now living, but does not approach that found in the
Sauropoda, or especially that in the Stegosauria, where . . . this
expansion reaches its maximum, and its functional importance
must make it a dominant factor in the movements of the reptiles
in which it is so highly developed. This great development has
been found only in extinct reptiles in which the brain was especially
diminutive, and the relation of the two nervous centers to each
other offers a most interesting problem to physiologists.[40]

THE HERBIVOROUS DINOSAURS OF MARSH'S ORDER PREDENTATA

After seventeen years of dinosaur study, Marsh concluded
in 1894 that all the herbivorous forms other than the sauropods belong in one great group, which might be regarded as
an order, the most significant feature being the predentary
bone, which no other vertebrates possess. For this group he
proposed the term Predentata, equal in rank with the Sauropoda and the Theropoda, and possibly also the Hallopoda, the
whole to constitute the subclass Dinosauria.[41] In his classification of 1896, however, he placed the Hallopoda under the
Theropoda as a suborder. The Predentata embraced his suborders Ornithopoda (1881), Stegosauria (1877), and Ceratopsia (1890). In Hay's classification of 1930 it gives way to
the order Orthopoda Cope 1866.

Ornithopods or Bird-footed Dinosaurs

All the ornithopods from the Upper Jurassic of America
were more or less birdlike, according to Marsh's memoir of
1896, and especially was this true of the small forms, in which
the tibia is longer than the femur—a strong avian character,
seen among dinosaurs only in the small birdlike herbivores and
in the carnivorous *Cœlurus*, *Compsognathus*, and Hallopoda.
The known Cretaceous forms, on the other hand, were all large

40. 1896H, pp. 166–167.
41. 1894E, p. 90.

and highly specialized, and this appears to have been true of the Old World species as well.

Upper Jurassic Ornithopods. The first of the birdlike dinosaurs to be brought to light by Marsh was *Nanosaurus agilis*, found in the upper beds of the Morrison formation near Cañon City, Colorado, and named in September, 1877. *N. agilis* was based on a single skeleton with parts of the skull; it was described later as "avian in form and in many respects the most bird-like dinosaur yet discovered. . . . When alive . . . about half the size of a domestic fowl." [42] In another place he spoke of it as follows:

In *Nanosaurus*, nearly all, if not all, the bones preserved might have pertained to a bird, and the teeth are no evidence against this idea. In the absence of feathers, an anatomist could hardly state positively whether this was a bird-like reptile or a reptilian bird.[43]

Laosaurus of Wyoming was named by Marsh in March, 1878, and redefined in November. Its species are small and were said to possess "many features now seen only in existing birds, especially in those of the ostrich family." *L. celer* (no larger than a fox) and *L. gracilis* (one of the smallest dinosaurs) "show these avian features best of all, and it would be difficult to tell many of the isolated remains from those of birds." [44] *L. consors* (1894) is a larger species, based on several specimens that together make a nearly complete skeleton; in life it measured 8 to 10 feet in length. An immature individual of it, collected by Marsh and Reed at Como in 1879, is among the mounted skeletons in the Yale Museum.

The skull of *Laosaurus* is of medium size, and the rami of the lower jaw

are edentulous in front, and apparently were not united by symphysis. . . . The fore limbs were quite small, less than half as long as the hind limbs, and evidently were not much used in locomotion.

42. 1896I, pp. 484–485.
43. 1894E, p. 88.
44. 1896H, p. 199.

. . . The pubis . . . unites with the ischium below the acetabulum, and sends backward and downward a long slender ramus, which is clearly homologous with the so-called pubic bone in birds.[45]

Comparing the pelves of the toothed bird *Hesperornis*, the ornithopod *Laosaurus*, and the sauropod *Morosaurus*, Marsh finds intimate relations between the pubic bones, saying that:

If this series be extended by adding the pelves of some existing birds (for example *Geococcyx*), and of a few other reptiles, it will become still more evident that the bone called "pubis" in a bird, is a different bone from the pubis of a crocodile.[46]

Of the pes, he says that it possesses three well-developed digits (II, III, IV). The outer one (V) is wanting, and the hallux is represented only by a remnant of the metatarsal.[47]

In December, 1879, Marsh named another ornithopod *Camptonotus dispar*, but finding the generic name preoccupied, he changed it in February, 1885, to *Camptosaurus*. In the original description he pointed out that *Camptosaurus* is most nearly allied to *Laosaurus* but that the nine cervical vertebrae are all opisthocœlous, whereas those known in the latter genus are nearly plane. The genus was fully described in July, 1894, and four species discussed (*C. dispar*, the genotype, 1879; *C. amplus*, 1879; *C. medius*, 1894; and *C. nanus*, 1894). So far as then known, he says, "these species are found in successive deposits of the same general horizon, the smallest below and the largest above." *C. amplus*, when alive, was "about thirty feet in length"; it was an ally of *Iguanodon*, of which Marsh presented a skeletal restoration in November, 1895. *C. dispar*, which he regarded as one of the most characteristic forms of the Ornithopoda, was about 20 feet long and stood 10 feet high. An excellent account of the osteology of *Camptosaurus* has been given by Gilmore, and the mounted skeletons of *C. nanus* and *C. browni* at Washington were described by him a few years later.[48] The remains used in the mounts were found

45. 1878G, p. 415.
46. *Ibid.,* pp. 415–416.
47. *Ibid.,* p. 416.
48. C. W. Gilmore, "Osteology of the Jurassic reptile, *Camptosaurus,*" *Proc. U. S. Nat. Mus.*, XXXVI (1909), 197–332; "The mounted skeletons of *Camptosaurus* in the United States National Museum," *ibid.,* XLI (1912), 687–696.

8 miles east of Como Station in the Stegosaurus quarry (Marsh's No. 13) by W. H. Reed and Fred Brown; a skeleton of *C. medius*, found by Reed in the same quarry, has recently been mounted at Yale.

Another of Marsh's ornithopods was *Dryosaurus*, based on the species described in 1878 as *Laosaurus altus*. This dinosaur was about 12 feet long, "one of the most slender and graceful members of the group," its skeletal characteristics being intermediate between *Laosaurus* and *Camptosaurus*.[49]

In Europe, the Ornithopoda are present in many genera, and of these the best known is *Iguanodon* of the Wealden of England and the Continent, represented conspicuously in Belgium by at least a score of skeletons, which Marsh studied several times at Brussels. *Hypsilophodon* Huxley 1870 is also well known. Marsh considered the Camptosauridae to be the American representatives of the Iguanodontidae, and *Laosaurus* he took to be allied to *Hypsilophodon*. Of his restoration of the latter in 1895 he says that the "mystery of the Dinosaurian pelvis," which baffled Cuvier, Mantell, and Owen, was solved mainly by Huxley and Hulke, and that the more perfect American specimens have demonstrated the correctness of nearly all their conclusions.

Upper Cretaceous Ornithopoda. This group includes the first dinosaur described by Marsh, *Hadrosaurus minor* 1870, based on a few remains found in the late Cretaceous Greensand near Barnsboro, New Jersey. The first good dinosaur he had to describe was another species which he thought to be of the same genus, *Hadrosaurus [Claosaurus] agilis* 1872, the remains of which had been collected the year before in the Niobrara formation near the Smoky Hill River in western Kansas. This western species, not more than 15 feet in length, was hardly more than a third the bulk of Leidy's *H. foulkii* from the New Jersey Greensand; it was "of more slender proportions, with the tail much elongated. . . . The sacrum . . . is composed of six confluent vertebrae." [50] It was this form that Marsh later made the genotype of his genus *Claosaurus*, the

49. 1894E, p. 86.
50. 1872E, p. 301.

teeth being "of the *Hadrosaurus* type." [51] All these dinosaurs had broad ducklike bills.

Another later Cretaceous (Lance) duckbilled species was *Claosaurus annectens* (1892), which Marsh based on an almost complete skull and skeleton found by Hatcher and Sullins in the Ceratops beds of Converse County, Wyoming. The length of the animal in life was about 30 feet, and it stood some 15 feet high. Of it Hatcher said:

This skeleton when found was in a partially erect position, the limbs extended, and every bone in its natural position except where exposed and worn away by recent weathering. . . . The whole showed that the animal in its wanderings had mired in the quicksands, and in its struggles for liberation had been engulfed by them.[52]

This superb specimen, now in the exhibition series of the Peabody Museum of Yale University, was the first dinosaur to be mounted in this country. An equally good specimen, also collected by Hatcher, is in the exhibition series of the United States National Museum. (See Plate XXVI.)

The skull and brain of *C. annectens* were discussed by Marsh in January, 1893; the teeth, he said,

are confined entirely to the maxillary and dentary bones. In each, the teeth are very numerous, and are arranged in vertical series, so that they succeed each other as the functional teeth are worn away. . . . The food was probably soft vegetation.[53]

The form described by Marsh in April, 1889, as *Hadrosaurus breviceps* is now referred to the genus *Kritosaurus*. It is from the Ceratops beds of Montana. The extraordinary magazine of teeth in this form was discussed in May, 1890; "there were at least five distinct series of teeth in place at once," he said, "but only two or three rows were in use at the same time." [54] In this same paper he described *Trachodon longiceps*, based on dentary bones.

51. 1890D, p. 423.
52. J. B. Hatcher, "The Ceratops beds of Converse Co., Wyoming," *Amer. Jour. Sci.* (3), XLV (1893), 143.
53. 1893B, p. 85.
54. 1890D, p. 423.

Stegosaurs or Armored Dinosaurs

Late in 1877, the *American Journal of Science* carried a one-page notice of "A new order of extinct Reptilia (Stegosauria) from the Jurassic of the Rocky Mountains." So out of the ordinary was the dinosaur for which the new order was founded that Marsh was uncertain for several years as to the meaning and position of parts of its curious skeleton and armature. He named it *Stegosaurus armatus*, basing the species on "the greater portion of the skeleton of a huge reptile, which proves to be one of the most remarkable animals yet discovered." [55] The bones, well preserved in a very hard sandstone, were found by Lakes and Beckwith near the place where they had secured *Atlantosaurus montanus*, that is, in the neighborhood of Morrison, Colorado.

Sending a copy of this paper to Professor Owen on December 1, 1877, Marsh accompanied it with a letter, part of which is quoted below through the courtesy of Librarian A. C. Townsend of the British Museum (Natural History):

I hope soon to have something of interest to send you . . . as my volume on the *Odontornithes* approaches completion. Just now I can only send you a Note on some very strange Reptiles, which I shall soon describe in detail. *Stegosaurus* is one of the strangest of animals. Our Jurassic proves at last to be rich beyond all anticipation in Reptiles, and I am hoping soon to find Birds and Mammals in it. I feel sure they are there, and I am bound to have them. I think we are on the eve of some most important discoveries.

The formation yielding *Stegosaurus armatus* was thought at first to be the Dakota sandstone of the Upper Cretaceous, but Marsh later came to regard it as "corresponding nearly to the Wealden of Europe . . . which may be classed as upper Jurassic." [56] He at first had the idea that the limb bones indicated aquatic life but this view was subsequently abandoned.

During the next two years (1878–79) Marsh received still more stegosaur material from Reed and Williston at Como, and in December, 1879, he described this as *Stegosaurus ungulatus*, adding, in the following March, that the Stegosauria prove to

55. 1877G, p. 513.
56. *Ibid.*, p. 513.

be one of the most specialized of the known dinosaurs, differing widely from the other groups. The skull, so far as known,

was remarkably small. In its main features it agreed more nearly with that of the genus *Hatteria*, from New Zealand, than with any other living reptile. . . . As a whole, this brain was lacertilian rather than avian. . . . [The size of] the brain was only 1/100 that of the Alligator, if the weight of the entire animal is brought into the comparison. . . . *Stegosaurus* had thus the smallest brain of any known land vertebrate.[57]

The beaked heads of the stegosaurs were comparatively small, about 17 inches in length, with a brain about 5 inches long and weighing about 2½ ounces. In living elephants, the brain averages 8 pounds, or more than fifty times that in the dinosaur.

Quarry 13 at Como, from which the most remarkable stegosaur material has come, was worked by Reed from 1879 until 1888, when the bone-bearing layer was exhausted.

Discussing the dentition of the stegosaurs in 1880, Marsh said that the single row of functional teeth in the type genus was rapidly replaced as it wore out by a series of successional teeth lodged in a large cavity which extends through the whole dental portion of the maxillary. The teeth in use were "loosely implanted in separate sockets."

The most remarkable thing about *Stegosaurus*, however, was the series of ossifications forming its offensive and defensive armor. These "consist of numerous spines, some of great size and power, and many bony plates, of various sizes and shapes. . . . Some of these plates are a meter, or more than three feet, in diameter."[58]

The sacrum of *Stegosaurus*, described in a later paper, shows

a very large chamber . . . formed by an enlargement of the spinal canal. This chamber was ovate in form, and strongly resembled the brain case in the skull, although very much larger, being at least ten [twenty in *S. ungulatus*] times the size of the cavity which contained the brain. . . . In this respect it is entirely without a parallel. . . . The physiological effects of

57. 1880C, pp. 254–255.
58. *Ibid.*, p. 258.

a posterior nervous center, so many times larger than the brain itself is a suggestive subject. . . . It is evident, however, that in an animal so endowed, the posterior-part was dominant.[59]

An interesting item jotted down in Marsh's notebook while he was in the Berlin Museum in 1881 reads as follows:

Heliophobius (a rodent from Mozambique) has pterygoid muscles *in the brain cavity* (see Peters Mem. p. 141). No other case is known. In rodents with *large* suborbital foramen, muscles and nerves both. When this is small it contains only nerves. Hence pelvic cavity in *Stegosaurus* may have contained *muscles*, as well

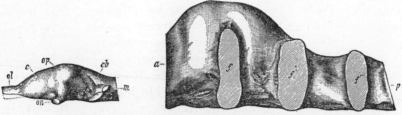

Fig. 24. Side views of the brain cast of *Stegosaurus ungulatus* Marsh (left), and of a cast of the neural cavity ("hind brain"). Both 1/4 natural size. After Marsh.

as cord. The large openings in the side suggest this. Roughnesses inside might show attachments and a comparison of the other pelves (*Camptonotus*, etc.) might show what muscles were most likely to be inserted in cavity.

That this "hind brain" was indeed a "suggestive subject" was realized by a latter-day poet, who wrote of it thus, in a manner that Marsh would surely have appreciated:

> Behold the mighty Dinosaur,
> Famous in prehistoric lore
> Not only for his weight and length
> But for his intellectual strength.
> You will observe by these remains
> The creature had two set of brains,
> One in his head (the usual place),
> The other at his spinal base.

59. 1881A, pp. 167–168.

Thus he could reason a priori
As well as a posteriori.
No problem bothered him a bit,
He made both head and tail of it.
So wise he was ; so wise and solemn,
Each thought filled just a spinal column.
If one brain found the pressure strong,
It passed a few ideas along.
If something slipped his forward mind
'Twas rescued by the one behind.
And if in error he was caught,
He had a saving afterthought.
As he thought twice before he spoke,
He had no judgement to revoke.
For he could think without congestion
Upon both sides of every question.
O! Gaze upon this model beast,
Defunct ten thousand years, at least.

                                                          B. L. T.

Diracodon laticeps, described by Marsh in May, 1881, was
at first thought to be related to *Laosaurus,* but later on he
placed it with the Stegosauria. It also is from the Upper
Jurassic of Wyoming.

Stegosaurus stenops, a smaller species than those of Como
—but at that, more than 15 feet long and about 8 feet tall
to the top of the dermal plate just back of the hip—was
found by M. P. Felch in the Marsh Quarry near Cañon City,
Colorado, in 1887, and was described by Marsh in November
of that year. Of it he had a skull and a nearly complete skeleton,
with most of the dermal armor in place, the bones lying almost
in the position in which the animal died. He was now able to
report that:

The various species, and perhaps the sexes, differed more or less
in the form, size, and number, of portions of their dermal covering.
This was especially true of the spines, which are quite characteristic in some members of the group, if not in all. . . . The upper
portion of the neck, back of the skull, was protected by plates,
arranged in pairs on either side. These plates increased in size
farther back, and thus the trunk was shielded from injury. From

the pelvic region backward, a series of huge plates stood upright along the median line, gradually diminishing in size to about the middle of the tail. . . . The offensive weapons of this group were a series of huge spines arranged in pairs along the top of the distal portion of the tail, which was elongate and flexible, thus giving effective service to the spines, as in the genus *Myliobatis*. In *Stegosaurus ungulatus*, there were four pairs of these spines.[60]

Stegosaurus sulcatus, also described in 1887, had only one pair of tail spines. Marsh was now satisfied that the Stegosauria were closely allied to the Ornithopoda, "with a com-

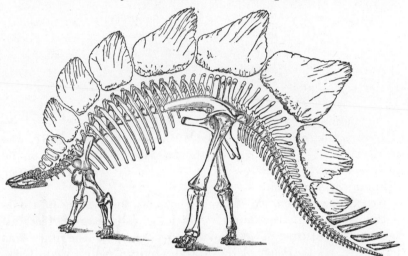

Fig. 25. Restoration of *Stegosaurus ungulatus* Marsh, about 1/60 natural size. After Marsh.

mon ancestry," although they differ from the latter in a large number of characters.[61]

By August, 1891, Marsh had more than twenty individuals belonging to the Stegosauria, and he was therefore able to offer a restoration of the skeleton of *Stegosaurus ungulatus*. Of this restoration he says:

The dermal armor is the most striking feature, but the skeleton is almost as remarkable, and its high specialization was evidently

60. 1887C, p. 415.
61. *Ibid.*, p. 417.

acquired gradually as the armor itself was developed. . . . In life, the animal was protected by a powerful dermal armor, which served both for defense and offense. The throat was covered by a thick skin in which were embedded a large number of rounded ossicles. . . . The series of vertical plates which extended above the neck, along the back, and over two-thirds of the tail, is a most remarkable feature, which could not have been anticipated, and would hardly have been credited had not the plates themselves been found in position. . . .

The four pairs of massive spines characteristic [of *S. ungulatus*], which were situated above the lower third of the tail, are apparently the only part of this peculiar armor used for offense. In addition . . . there was a pair of small plates just behind the skull, which served to protect this part of the neck. There were also . . . four flat spines, which were probably in place below the tail, but as their position is somewhat in doubt, they are not represented in the restoration.[62]

The mounted composite skeleton of *S. ungulatus* at Yale, 19½ feet long and almost 12 feet high, abundantly bears out the statement that the stegosaurs were undoubtedly the strangest of all dinosaurs.

The stegosaurs that were collected by Marsh's men for the United States Geological Survey are now among the treasures of the National Museum at Washington. Between 1906 and 1913, several preparators were constantly at work preparing the bones for further study and exhibition, and they were fully described by Gilmore in 1914, with reproductions of ten of Marsh's unpublished plates.[63]

Stegosaurus stenops, mounted at Washington, is the only specimen, according to Gilmore, that gives positive evidence as to the arrangement of the dermal armor. F. A. Lucas was the first to point out, in 1901, that the probable arrangement of the dorsal plates was in two rows, and he later suggested that the plates were alternating. He also reduced the spines on the tail from six to four. Marsh arranged the plates in a

62. 1891E, pp. 180–181.
63. C. W. Gilmore, "Osteology of the armored Dinosauria in the United States National Museum, with special reference to the genus *Stegosaurus*," *Bull.* 89, U. S. Nat. Mus. (1914), 136 pp.

PLATE XXVII

STEGOSAURUS

PTERODACTYLS AND A
SAUROPOD

DIPLODOCUS

RESTORATIONS OF DINOSAURS AND FLYING REPTILES
PAINTED IN WATER COLOR BY ARTHUR LAKES

PLATE XXVIII

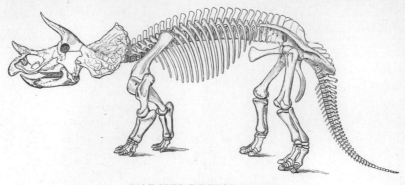

MARSH'S RESTORATION

MOUNTED SKELETON IN THE UNITED STATES NATIONAL
MUSEUM, FROM THE MARSH COLLECTION. NOTE ESPECIALLY
CHANGE IN POSTURE OF FRONT LEGS

Photograph from C. W. Gilmore

THE HORNED DINOSAUR *TRICERATOPS* MARSH

single row, and Lull in 1910 in two paired rows. However, Gilmore finally demonstrated:

(1) That the armor of the neck, back, and tail was formed by two rows of erect plates, the elements of one row alternating with those of the other. (2) That the total number of plates in the two rows was not less than 20 and not more than 22. (3) That the position of the largest plate of the series appears to be above the base of the tail and not over the pelvis. (4) That the usual number of dermal spines on the tail is four, arranged in two pairs.[64]

The restoration of *Stegosaurus* painted by Arthur Lakes (Plate XXVII), which is used on the jacket of this book, shows the plates arranged in pairs, reflecting the view current at the time it was made.

The tail of *Stegosaurus*, Gilmore thinks, must have been "a heavy, stiff appendage, incapable of more than cumbersome lateral movements and wholly unsuited for use on an active enemy."

The only Cretaceous stegosaurian so far found in America was described by Marsh in August, 1889, as *Nodosaurus textilis;* it is from the Upper Cretaceous (Niobrara) of Wyoming. The skull is not known, but various portions of the skeleton were secured. Here, again, the dermal armor is a characteristic feature, and appears to have exceeded in completeness that in any of the other American forms. This armor Marsh said,

covered the sides closely, and was supported by the ribs, which were especially strengthened to maintain it. In the present specimen, portions of it were found in position. It was regularly arranged in a series of rounded knobs in rows, and these protuberances have suggested the generic name. . . . The fore limbs are specially massive and powerful, and are much like those of the Jurassic *Stegosaurus*. . . . The animal when alive was about thirty feet in length.[65]

Of the English stegosaurians, *Omosaurus* Owen (1875) is from the Upper Jurassic (Kimmeridge), and *Scelidosaurus* Owen (1859) belonged to the same period. Of the latter Marsh made a restoration in 1895, regarding it as of moderate size, as

64. Gilmore, *op. cit.,* p. 99.
65. 1889E, p. 175.

related to *Stegosaurus*, and as the latter's predecessor in a
lower geological horizon.[66] His restoration was based essentially
upon the original description and figures of Owen, supple-

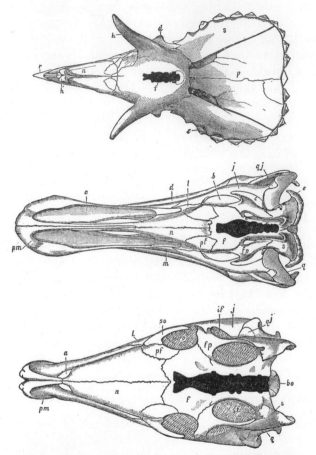

Fig. 26. Dinosaurian skulls, to show size of brain (black).
From above downward, *Triceratops flabellatus* Marsh,
1/25 natural size; *Claosaurus annectens* Marsh, 1/12
natural size; *Camptosaurus medius* Marsh, 1/5 natural
size. After Marsh.

mented by his own notes and sketches made while he was examining the type specimen in the British Museum. An earlier
restoration had been made by Woodward in 1890.

66. 1895J, pl. X.

Ceratopsia or Horned Dinosaurs

The discovery of the last group of dinosaurs to be brought to light by Professor Marsh was due in part to the fact that the United States Geological Survey was urging him to help Whitman Cross fix the age of the Denver formation. As told in an earlier chapter, Cross sent to Marsh in 1887 a pair of large horn cores that had been found near Denver, in the hope that these might cast light on the problem. Marsh promptly announced that they belonged to a fossil bison, which he named *Bison alticornis*, and that their age was probably Pliocene. This did not agree at all with Cross's idea of the stratigraphy of the region, but no solution of the puzzle came until, through Hatcher's work, the horn cores were seen to belong to a dinosaur of a new type, and of late Cretaceous age. In subsequent years Marsh naturally had to put up with much banter from his friends about these errors, as well as sarcasm from his critics. However, as he later said, the horn cores

were pronounced by some of the best osteologists in this country to be mammal, with which [they] agree in every anatomical character then apparent. . . . Seriously no anatomist however wide his experience, could have identified many portions of the skull of these remarkable saurians, and it was not until the genius of my able assistant, J. B. Hatcher, discovered the entire skulls of several species that the mysterious fragments, so long unknown, fell into their appropriate positions and one of the most remarkable creations of the past assumed its place in the records of science.[67]

Hatcher's comment on the matter was to the same effect:

Nor is Professor Marsh's error to be wondered at, but on the other hand it is quite excusable, since at that time nothing was known regarding the structure of the skulls of these strange dinosaurs, and in size, surface markings, and form these horn cores more nearly resembled those of certain extinct bisons than of any other known animals. . . .

The supposed ischia of *Polyonax mortuarius*, described and figured by Cope, were seen to be portions of the supraorbital horn cores, while the element considered by the same author as an episternal of *Monoclonius crassus* proved to be a parietal. The

67. 1890B, p. 13.

horn cores described by Marsh as pertaining to a bison proved to belong to a dinosaur, and the supposed dermal plates mentioned by him in his description of the type of *Ceratops montanus* became the squamosals of that animal. . . . [these are] striking examples of the many pitfalls that beset the path of the [vertebrate] paleontologist when attempting to describe from insufficient or fragmentary material new genera and species.[68]

Hatcher's marvelous work in collecting these great skulls, spoken of more at length elsewhere, netted Marsh a new suborder (Ceratopsia), a new family (Ceratopsidae), four new genera (*Ceratops*, 1888; *Triceratops*, 1889; *Sterrholophus*, 1891; *Torosaurus*, 1891), and fourteen new species. These remarkable discoveries, moreover, confirmed in Marsh's mind his previous conclusion that the subclass Dinosauria, before its extinction,

developed into many highly specialized forms, of which suggestions, at least, were seen in those from lower horizons. The large number and variety of these specialized forms could hardly have been anticipated, and they make prominent the probability that the Reptilian age reached its culminations near the close of the Cretaceous.[69]

The first ceratopsian dinosaur described by Marsh as such was *Ceratops montanus*, found in 1888 by Hatcher in the Cretaceous of the Judith River region of Montana, the name ("horned face") referring to the pair of large horns represented by massive horn cores on the upper part of the head. For it he erected the family Ceratopsidae, and remarked, temperately, that "with its horned head and peculiar dermal armor, it must have presented in life a very strange appearance."[70]

By April, 1889, he had another species, *Ceratops horridus*, and in connection with it he said:

The strange reptile described by the writer as *Ceratops montanus* proves to have been only a subordinate member of the family.

68. J. B. Hatcher, O. C. Marsh, and R. S. Lull, "The Ceratopsia," *Mon.* 49, U. S. Geol. Surv. (1907), pp. 6, 8.
69. 1892E, p. 449.
70. 1888D, p. 478.

Other remains received more recently indicate forms much larger, and more grotesque in appearance. They also afford considerable information in regard to the structure of these animals. . . . The skull as a whole must have had at least fifty times the weight of the skull of the largest *Sauropoda* known.[71]

Ceratops horridus was based on the skull found by E. B. Wilson in Converse County, Wyoming, the horn cores of which had led Hatcher to the discovery of the Ceratops fauna. Marsh at first thought that it had only two horns, like *Ceratops montanus*, but a later paper, written probably after the skull had undergone further preparation, reported that in addition to the pair of massive horn cores on top of the head, there was a third one, on the nose, whence the new name, *Triceratops*. The face of the skull, and the anterior part of the jaw, Marsh wrote, form

a projecting beak, like that of a tortoise. Over all, there was, evidently, a huge horny covering, like the beak of a bird. . . . There is a huge occipital crest, extending backward and outward. In the present specimen, this is bent downward at the sides, like the back part of a helmet, thus affording, in life, strong protection to the neck. . . . The skull appears to have been at least two meters in length, aside from the horny beak.[72]

Triceratops flabellatus, described in the same paper, was even larger than *T. horridus*, and of it Hatcher sent Marsh the skull, the jaws, and a good deal of the skeleton. A striking peculiarity of the skull in this form was the occipital crest, which Marsh described as extending "upward and backward, like an open fan. Its margin was armed with a row of horny spikes, supported by separate ossifications, some of which were found in position." The skull was 6 feet long by 4 feet wide, and the horn cores were about 3 feet in height, dimensions that "far surpass any of the *Dinosauria* hitherto known, and indicate to some extent the wonderful development these reptiles attained before their extinction at the close of the Cretaceous." [73]

71. 1889C, pp. 334–335.
72. 1889E, pp. 173–174.
73. *Ibid.*

The most perfect ceratopsian skull found up to that time was described by Marsh in January, 1890, as belonging to *Triceratops serratus*. This species, with a skull nearly 6 feet in length, was characterized by a series of bony projections on the median line of the parietal crest. Another fine skull, found near Denver by Mr. Cannon, became the type of *T. prorsus*.

"Additional characters of the Ceratopsidae" formed the title of a paper published in May, 1890, with three plates of illustrations. Herein Marsh decides that the group is distinct enough to warrant being made a suborder, Ceratopsia. Of other features he said:

The brain of *Triceratops* appears to have been smaller in proportion to the entire skull, than in any known vertebrate. . . . The teeth of *Triceratops* and its near allies are very remarkable in having two distinct roots. This is true of both the upper and lower series. . . . The teeth form a single series only in each jaw.[74]

During the field season of 1889, Marsh was in the West to see the stratigraphy of the Ceratopsia localities, reporting later that the formation consists of

fresh-water or brackish deposits, which form a part of the so-called Laramie, but are below the uppermost beds referred to that group. In some places, at least, they rest upon marine beds which contain invertebrate fossils characteristic of the Fox Hills deposits.[75]

Furthering this stratigraphic discussion, in February, 1893, Hatcher published a paper called "The Ceratops beds of Converse County, Wyoming," in which he stated that these beds are made up of alternations of sandstone, shale, and lignites, having an estimated thickness of 3,000 feet. The lower 400 feet is unfossiliferous. The Laramie dinosaurs, he said,

are, in degree of development and point of numbers both as to individuals, and genera and species represented, probably un-

74. 1890D, p. 419.
75. 1889G, p. 501.

surpassed in any previous similar division of the Mesozoic; while as regards degree of specialization, they are superior to all previous forms.[76]

The effect that this excess development of the head armor must have had upon the individual animal, and eventually on the Ceratopsia as a group, was noted by Marsh as follows:

The peculiar armature of the skull has a parallel in the genus *Phrynosoma*, among the lizards, and *Meiolania*, among the turtles, and it is of special interest to find it also represented in the Dinosaurs, just before their extinction. Such a high specialization of the skull . . . profoundly affected the rest of the skeleton . . . gradually overbalanced the body, and must have led to its destruction. As the head increased in size to bear its armor, the neck first of all, then the fore limbs, and later the whole skeleton, was especially modified to support it.[77]

A summary paper on the ceratopsians, entitled "The gigantic Ceratopsidae, or horned dinosaurians of North America," appeared in February, 1891, with 10 plates. This was a presentation in greater detail of a talk that Marsh had given the year before at the Leeds meeting of the British Association.

In April, 1891, Marsh presented a skeletal restoration of *Triceratops*—an animal that may have weighed 10 tons in the flesh—based in the main on two individuals, one of which was *T. prorsus.* The forefeet show 5 well-developed ungulate digits, and the massive fore limbs, "proportionally the largest in any known dinosaur, correspond to the head, and indicate slow locomotion on all four feet." [78] He thought the size in life would be about 25 feet in length and 10 feet in height. Gilmore's reconstruction of the animal in 1919 was somewhat different. The mounted skeleton of *Triceratops prorsus* in the National Museum has a length of nearly 20 feet and a height at the hips of 8 feet 2 inches. The skull is 6 feet long. Beside this animal stands the smallest American horned dinosaur yet

76. J. B. Hatcher, "The Ceratops beds of Converse County, Wyoming," *Amer. Jour. Sci.* (3), XLV (1893), 142.

77. 1889G, p. 506.

78. 1891C, p. 340.

mounted—*Brachyceratops*—with a length of 6 feet 9 inches and a height of 2 feet 4 inches at the hips.[79] (See Plate XXVIII.)

Three other ceratopsians were described by Marsh in September, 1891: *Triceratops elatus, Torosaurus gladius,* and *T. latus.* The skull of the genus *Torosaurus* was described and illustrated the following January; the unusual feature of this head was that "the extreme lightness and great expanse of the posterior crest . . . make it probable that it was encased in the integuments of the head, and that no part of it was free." [80] The last paper on new ceratopsians was in print in July, 1898, presenting the skulls of *Triceratops calicornis* and *T. obtusus.*

In the monographic revision of the Ceratopsia begun by Hatcher and finished by Lull in 1907, the latter arranged the dinosaurs of this group in two phyletic lines. One series begins in *Monoclonius* Cope of the Judith River formation, includes *Centrosaurus* Lambe, *Agathaumas* Cope, *Diceratops* Lull, and *Sterrholophus* Marsh, and ends in *Triceratops* Marsh. The other phyletic line begins in *Ceratops* Marsh and culminates in *Torosaurus* Marsh.[81]

79. See C. W. Gilmore, "The mounted skeleton of *Triceratops prorsus,*" *Proc. U. S. Nat. Mus.,* XXIX (1905), 433–435; *"Brachyceratops,* a ceratopsian dinosaur from the Two Medicine formation of Montana," *Prof. Paper* 103, U. S. Geol. Surv. (1917), 45 pp.

80. 1892A, p. 82.

81. J. B. Hatcher, O. C. Marsh, and R. S. Lull, *op. cit.,* pp. 167–174.

CHAPTER XVIII

MARSH'S WORK IN VERTEBRATE PALE-ONTOLOGY. II. PTERANODONS, MOSA-SAURS, AND BIRDS WITH TEETH

THE dinosaurs described in the preceding chapter were beyond any doubt the most striking reptiles in the medieval world of Geology, but there were at least three other groups that deserve attention, both because of their intrinsic interest and because of the part that Marsh played in bringing them to light. All were of Cretaceous age, and all were found by him in western Kansas.

PTERANODONS, GIANT DRAGONS OF THE AIR

Pterodactyls were flying reptiles of Mesozoic times, and the last of these were the giant pteranodons of the Cretaceous, called by Raymond "one of the greatest freaks of all time." Representatives of the group were first discovered in 1784, in the Jurassic lithographic limestone about Solenhofen, Bavaria, but they were not at all understood until the great French anatomist, Cuvier, correctly described them in 1801.

As a student in Germany in 1865, Marsh visited the extensive limestone quarries in northern Bavaria, which had long been notable not only for the very finest stone used in lithographic work, but even more for the remarkable fossil remains preserved in this stone. These wonderful specimens included the toothed bird *Archæopteryx*, the carnivorous dinosaur *Compsognathus*, pterodactyls of various kinds, and a host of fishes, crustaceans, and other invertebrates, among them jellyfishes, those most delicate of animals, with the entire umbrella preserved. At Eichstätt he examined one small pterodactyl in particular, and noted that certain of the limestone layers holding it were mud-cracked. Returning to Berlin, he spoke of his observations before the Geological Society of Germany, and showed a photograph of the 8-inch pterodactyl that he had seen during the summer. This skeleton, he said, was one of the best preserved, all the bones being present in their natural position. In some of its parts it was close to *Pterodactylus longirostris* Cuvier, but in others differed from it, leading him to conclude that it might be a new species; he did not name it, however, nor could he then afford to buy so valuable a specimen. As for the well-developed mud cracks, he inferred from them that the part of the sea bottom on which the sediments making the lithographic stone had been deposited had been exposed to the air for some time. This was a far-reaching observation, since these areas of lithographic limestone are now interpreted as the consolidated muds of lagoons lying within the reefs of former atolls, where they would be exposed for days if not for weeks to drying out by the air.

The first pterodactyl that Marsh actually collected was found in 1870 in western Kansas, and it was the first indication that flying reptiles had been present in this country. He got more bones of this dragon in June, 1871, and they confirmed his impression as to its large size. The story of the discovery has been told in an earlier chapter.

At first, Marsh regarded the Kansas pterodactyls as belonging to the European genus *Pterodactylus*. The first species to be named was *P. oweni* (1871), so called in honor of the eminent English anatomist and osteologist; unfortunately this name had already been used and so Marsh had to rechristen his species *P. occidentalis*. Early in 1872, he was ready to say that these peculiar reptiles, so long considered to be wanting in North America, were apparently well represented here during the later Cretaceous; also that the largest wing so far found had a length of at least 8½ feet, and that the full spread of the animal when flying was 18 to 20 feet.

In the midst of these successes, Marsh's attention was again drawn to Europe early in 1873 by news of the finding of an entire specimen of a long-tailed pterodactyl near Eichstätt. He decided promptly that he must have it for comparison with his Kansas material. The specimen was the property of Martin Krauss and there was great rivalry as to which museum should get so fine a treasure. Marsh cabled his friend, Professor H. B. Geinitz, director of the Natural History Museum in Dresden: "Buy Eichstätt pterodactyl for Yale College." The quiet German professor, somewhat bewildered at this precipi-

tate way of doing things, and knowing that the price of the
fossil was more than twice that asked for any previous pterodactyl—in fact, more than his annual salary—wrote Marsh on
the twenty-seventh of February that Krauss had been offered
1,000 florins for the specimen, but would not sell it without
other Solenhofen material (including dragonflies, crustaceans,
and fishes) ; a Mr. Büke of Bern was after the prize, and
likewise Professor Louis Agassiz of Harvard; moreover, Professor Zittel was very anxious that it stay in Germany. However,
Marsh's cable seemed to leave Geinitz no alternative, and he
purchased the pterodactyl and the associated specimens early
in March, at Krauss's price of 1,250 thalers gold, which then
meant about $1,062.83 in greenbacks. A draft for this amount

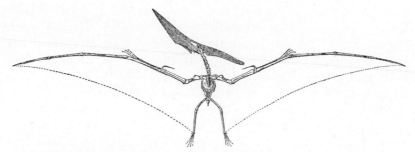

Fig. 27. Skeletal restoration of *Pteranodon* Marsh. After Eaton, 1910.

was sent Geinitz on March 28, and the pterodactyl was on its
way to Yale before the other museums had received answers to
their cautious requests for photographs, etc. Marsh was indeed
happy! The specimen arrived late in May, but it was nine
years before the rest of the scientific world learned anything
about it. Rumors as to the price paid by Marsh have ranged
as high as $5,000, but the bank memorandum in the Peabody
Museum archives sets it at a little over one fifth that amount.

As all previously known pterodactyls were provided with
teeth it must have surprised Marsh greatly to learn that his
Kansan forms had none at all! In view of the fact that in this
respect and in others they differed so widely from the pterodactyls of the Old World, he proposed a new order for the
American types this same year, calling them Pteranodontia,
and naming the family Pteranodontidae, from the typical genus

Pteranodon. The nearly perfect skull and jaws of *P. longiceps*, he said, were more like those of birds than of any known reptiles; and the head of *P. ingens* was no less than 4 feet long. The tail was slender and short and the posterior limbs, although small, were well developed. Later in the same year he described the new genus *Nyctosaurus*, with *Pteranodon gracilis* as genotype; the difference between the genera lies in the scapular arch, the coracoid in *Nyctosaurus* not being coössified with the scapula.

Summing up his knowledge of the group in the Nashville address, Marsh said:

Nothing is really known to-day of the earlier genealogy of the *Pterosauria;* but our American forms, without teeth, are clearly the last stage in their development before this peculiar group became extinct. The oldest European form, *Dimorphodon,* from the Lower Lias, had the entire jaws armed with teeth, and was provided with a long tail. The later genus, *Pterodactylus,* retained the teeth, but had essentially lost the tail; while *Rhamphorhynchus* had retained the elongated tail, but had lost the teeth from the fore-part of both jaws. In the genus *Pteranodon,* from the American Cretaceous, the teeth are entirely absent, and the tail is a mere rudiment. In the gradual loss of the teeth and tail, these reptiles followed the same path as birds, and might thus seem to approach them, as many have supposed. . . . They are an aberrant type of reptiles, totally off the line through which the birds were developed.[1]

The structure of the pterodactyl "arm" or wing had long been in dispute, doubtless because of the smallness of the European species, but the Kansas Cretaceous material enabled Marsh to give the osteology correctly in 1882. There were five digits in the hand, and the first one "undoubtedly supported a membrane in front of the arm. The second, third, and fourth are small, and armed with claws. The large wing finger is the fifth, corresponding to the little finger of the human hand." [2]

Two years later he was able to state that the skull of *Pteranodon* differs from that of the other known pterosaurs in these particulars:

1. 1877F, p. 17.
2. 1882C, p. 255.

(1) The absence of teeth; (2) the absence of anterior nasal apertures distinct from the antorbital openings; (3) the presence of the elongated occipital crest; (4) the whole jaws were apparently covered with a horny sheath, as in recent birds.[3]

In 1882, Marsh described his European pterodactyl for the first time, regarding it as a new species of Von Meyer's genus *Rhamphorhynchus*, which he named *R. phyllurus*. The bones of this remarkably preserved specimen are nearly all in position, and those of both wings show very perfect impressions of volant membranes still attached to them. These wing membranes, each about a foot across, were thin and delicately striate; they were similar to the wings of modern bats but devoid of all hair. The greater portion of the long tail was free, and without volant attachments, but the distal end, including the last 16 short vertebrae, supported a vertical membrane which had spines to keep it in an upright position. This fluke evidently was used as a rudder in flight. Marsh's reason for not describing the *Rhamphorhynchus* sooner was, he says, *"l'embarras des richesses* nearer home." [4]

A life-size lithograph of the pterodactyl, in color, accompanied this paper of 1882, and a small reproduction of it was used by H. G. Seeley, the English specialist on these dragons, as the frontispiece to his very interesting book, *Dragons of the Air* (1901). Marsh also offered in his paper a restoration of *Rhamphorhynchus*, one-seventh natural size. (See Plate XXIX.)

Between 1865 and May, 1884, Marsh published 11 notes and longer papers on pterodactyls, and these by no means exhausted the osteological information contained in his wonderful array of specimens, which he used to say had reached the number of 600; however, of these, less than 10 are skeletons that can be said to be more or less complete, the great majority being single bones of limbs and chiefly of the great wings. The Yale Collection was obtained during the years 1874 to 1877 by Williston, Mudge, Brous, Guild, Cooper, and Marsh himself. In the decade beginning with 1871, he described and named the suborder Pterosauria (1876), 3 new genera (one a synonym),

3. 1884D, p. 426.
4. 1882C, p. 256.

and 8 new species (one preoccupied) from his Kansas Cretaceous material.

After 1876, so many extraordinary fossils crowded in upon Marsh that he was never able to write a detailed account of his pterodactyls. This was well done later on, however, by Williston, in 11 papers published between 1891 and 1911, and by George F. Eaton[5] in his monograph, "Osteology of *Pteranodon*," which is illustrated by 31 handsome quarto plates, 2 of which present restorations. From this last memoir we learn that the spread of wings in the usual run of pteranodons was between 11 and 16 feet, but that the largest, *P. ingens*, shows a breadth of 22 feet 3 inches, and single large bones indicate a probable maximum of 26 feet 9 inches. The bones are a marvel of lightness, Williston estimating that the entire animal when alive did not weigh more than 30 pounds. This combination of great wing expanse and extreme lightness of body was of great interest to Samuel P. Langley of the Smithsonian Institution in his pioneer aviation studies, and it was at his request that a reconstruction of *Pteranodon* was made for him by F. A. Lucas of the National Museum staff.

MOSASAURS, THE GREAT CRETACEOUS "SEA SERPENTS"

In Europe, where their remains have been known for centuries, especially in the building-stone quarries of southern Holland, Marsh became familiar with Cretaceous marine lizards which had been named mosasaurs by Conybeare in 1822; and shortly after his return he began to search for them in rocks of similar age in New Jersey, where they had been known since 1834. Both he and Cope were describing mosasaurs from the Atlantic coast states in 1868 to 1870, Marsh naming 7 species (one of them *Mosasaurus copeanus*) and Cope 10. Up to this time, however, Marsh's material had consisted only of single bones and parts of skulls. The finding of extraordinarily complete mosasaurian skeletons in Kansas in the succeeding years, along with remains of birds with teeth and flying dragons without teeth, was one of the remarkable events of Marsh's life, and the way he was led to the discovery is of considerable interest.

5. George F. Eaton, "Osteology of *Pteranodon*," *Mem. Conn. Acad. Arts Sci.* (1910), II, 38 pp.

From his notebook of 1870, it appears that Marsh had been given information about the Kansas field by Dr. George M. Sternberg, a surgeon at one of the western Army posts. Dr. Sternberg, a brother of the Charles H. Sternberg who later became a well-known collector of fossil vertebrates, told Marsh of finding bones in 1868 in the Cretaceous of western Kansas, between Fort Wallace and Monument Station, along the old immigrant wagon road; and he was certain that a fine lot of fossils could be secured in three weeks' time about Monument Station, in the small ravines running into the Smoky Hill River. The valleys of the Republican, Solomon, and Saline Rivers north of the Smoky, Marsh noted, "are probably equally rich, but have never been explored. Chalk Bluff Creek, opposite Monument Station, is also a rich locality, and probably it would pay well to explore this stream from its mouth to source." Dr. Sternberg also recommended October, November, and December as a good time for this exploration, as there would then be no Indians in the region.

In accordance with this advice, Marsh postponed his visit to Kansas in 1870 until after his party had started back from California. Outfitting at Fort Wallace, with Ed Lane as guide and hunter, they started for Sheridan on November 22 and the next day went on to the north fork of the Smoky Hill River. Four miles below Sheridan on the west side of the creek a good locality was found, yielding the mosasaurs *Clidastes* and *Liodon*, and several large fishes. More mosasaurians were collected on November 24, and on the four following days reconnoitering on the east side of the north fork brought to light several skeletons of *Liodon* and the greater part of an enaliosaurian. Each day until December 6 more bones were seen, in fact, more than could be taken up. Collecting had to cease on that date because of the cold weather.

With the mosasaurs, as with the pterosaurs, Marsh had so much other and more fascinating material that he never became deeply interested in describing them, although, as a result of the intensive collecting of Mudge and Williston in the years following 1870, his collection had come to include, in the latter's phrase, "literally thousands of specimens," some of them so complete that there is scarcely anything concerning them that is not known. He did, however, publish 8 brief papers relating to the mosasaurs—as against 25 by Cope—proposing 7 new genera (2 lost to himself and 2 to Cope) and 18 new species (1 lost to Cope).

Marsh's first paper on these marine reptiles of the Kansas Cretaceous appeared in June, 1871, with descriptions of the new genus *Edestosaurus* (2 new species) and 2 new forms of Cope's genus *Clidastes*. These specimens, he says, "are of great interest," particularly because they establish a fact not hitherto known with certainty; i.e., that 3 of the Kansas genera had posterior limbs. However, it finally turned out that *Edestosaurus* is the same as *Clidastes*.

A further discovery, announced in April, 1872, was that the entire body of the mosasaurians was protected by osseous dermal plates, this covering being present in *Edestosaurus*, *Liodon*, *Holcodus*, and *Clidastes*. The scutes, being apparently different in each species, he believed to afford an important means of identification. In later years Williston was to show that this armature is present on all parts of the body and that the pattern differs in each species.

June of 1872 brought Marsh's most important paper on the mosasaurs, entitled "On the structure of the skull and limbs in mosasauroid reptiles," with four plates of lithographed illustrations. Here he described the new genera *Lestosaurus* (which proved to be the same as *Platecarpus* Cope 1869), with 4 new species, and *Rhinosaurus*, with 1 new species and 3 previously named by Cope. Cope, noting that the latter generic name was preoccupied, quickly replaced it by *Rhamphosaurus;* this name, too, was found to have been long in use, and Marsh returned the compliment by again changing the name, this time to *Tylosaurus*. The newly discovered stapes of the skull, he said, lies "in the groove on the postero-inferior face of the suspensorium." The cylindrical columella of the skull, heretofore believed to be absent in these reptiles, he now found "adhering to the basisphenoid." The anterior limbs were expanded paddles, as shown in his illustration, and the posterior paddles were usually smaller than the anterior ones.

In his Nashville address, Marsh said that these great marine lizards of the American Cretaceous seas ruled supreme, as their numbers, size, and carnivorous habits, enabled them to easily vanquish all rivals. . . . On one occasion, as I rode through a valley washed out of this old ocean-bed, I saw no less than seven different skeletons of these monsters in sight at once.[6]

This abundance of mosasaurs in the Kansas late Cretaceous contrasts strangely with their comparative rarity in New Jersey and in Europe, as Marsh commented in his final paper on the group in 1880. This paper discusses the sternum in *Edestosaurus*, figures the entire skeleton of the fore and hind paddles, illustrates the hyoid bones, describes the transverse bone of the skull and the pterygoids, and concludes that these new characters "are all Lacertilian, rather than Ophidian. The important characters of the Mosasauroids now known indicate that they form a suborder of the *Lacertilia*, which should be called *Mosasauria*." [7]

After considering Marsh's work on the Mosasauria, we may agree with his earlier biographer, Charles E. Beecher, that among his contributions to reptilian knowledge it is of great importance; and that his 8 papers on these marine reptiles set forth the most essential characters of the group, as well as establishing the fact that these rulers of the Cretaceous seas grew to lengths of 30 and exceptionally of 40 feet, with skulls as long as 5 feet, and with backbones made up of more than 100 vertebrae.

Williston later became the leading authority on the mosasaurs, having made a notable collection of their remains, and his series of papers on them is probably his most important contribution to Vertebrate Paleontology.

BIRDS WITH TEETH

At the outset of his fruitful career in Paleontology, Professor Marsh was well aware that the remains of birds are among the rarest of fossils, and he was constantly on the hunt for them. The first single bones he secured came from deposits in New Jersey that were considered at the time to be of Cretaceous age but have recently been placed in the Eocene. These he

6. 1877F, p. 11.
7. 1880A, p. 87.

described in 1870 as three new genera and five new species of aquatic birds, all of which he regarded as representatives of families now living.[8]

In December of that same year, in the course of the first of his western explorations with student parties, Marsh found a bird tibia in the Niobrara chalk of western Kansas, and it whetted his appetite for better material. Every member of the next year's party was primed to look for fossil birds as it worked over the Smoky Hill region of that state, and on November 29 Marsh wrote Professor Dana that among their trophies for the season—and one that he himself had found— was the headless skeleton of a great bird. Parts of four other individuals had been found by his students and, on his return, he said, "I shall describe this unique fossil under the name *Hesperornis regalis*," a promise that he made good in the *American Journal of Science* in January of the following year.

Professor Benjamin F. Mudge had also been collecting in the Smoky Hill country in 1872, and Marsh, aware of this, wrote Mudge on September 2 inquiring about the results of the summer's work. Mudge, well disposed toward Marsh from a long acquaintance, "practically presented" the latter with a box of fossils, regarding which Marsh wrote him on September 25 that "the hollow bones are part of a bird, and the two jaws belong to a small saurian. The latter is peculiar, and I wish I had some of the vertebrae for comparison with other Kansas species." Under this belief, the specimens were described by Marsh as pertaining to different animals; the avian bones were named *Ichthyornis dispar* in October, 1872, and the "saurian" bones received the appellation *Colonosaurus mudgei* the following month.[9] Not until further preparation of the specimens had revealed a skull and additional portions of both jaws did it become apparent that all the bones belonged to one animal, a *bird with teeth*. This remarkable discovery was announced in February, 1873, in a preliminary paper in which the author modestly remarks that "the fortunate discovery of these interesting fossils . . . does much to break down the old dis-

8. 1870A, pp. 206–212.

9. The exact locality from which these bones came, as recorded in Marsh's notebook, was "on Bow Creek or middle fork of Solomon river, one mile from south bank, or about 50 miles north of Fort Hays."

tinction between Birds and Reptiles, which the *Archæopteryx* has so materially diminished." [10]

Williston later spoke of these fossils as "by far the most important specimens of these early years [of Marsh's career], if not the most important of those succeeding"; Osborn in 1931 remarked that they constituted "the most important single palæontological discovery of his life"; and Scott commented in 1939 that "nothing so startling has been brought to light since."

In his more extended description of *Hesperornis regalis* in May, 1872, Marsh considered it to be related to the Great Northern Diver *(Gavia immer)*, a reference that was later completely abandoned as a result of the discovery by T. H. Russell (of the 1872 Expedition) of a nearly perfect skeleton of the same bird, including parts of the head and teeth—"an ample reward for the hardships and danger we incurred." When the bones had been cleaned of all the adhering chalk, they were seen to represent a diving bird, 6 feet long, and larger than any other known aquatic form, fossil or living. The maxillary bones were massive, and had throughout their length a deep inferior groove, thickly set with sharp, pointed teeth.

Writing Sir Richard Owen on November 19, 1875, about his work on these remarkable birds, Marsh said:

Dear Professor Owen.

I sent you a few days since a paper on my Birds with Teeth which I trust you received. I was very sorry that I could not have sent you figures of these rare fossils long before. . . .

Both *Ichthyornis* and *Hesperornis* I have now studied with some care, and I hope soon to figure and describe them fully. One specimen of the latter genus, I worked on over a month with my own hands, cutting it out of the rock, to prepare it for the artist. This I was obliged to do as I had no assistant whom I could trust to do it. I have now two artists at work, and hope before many months to publish my Memoir on the *Odontornithes*, which will be illustrated by about 25 quarto plates.

I wish very much you could come here and see my fossil treasures from the Rocky Mountain region. I have at least 15 Birds from

10. 1873E, p. 162.

the Cretaceous, and not less than 50 from the Tertiary. My Eocene Mammals, especially the *Dinocerata, Tillodontia,* and *Bronto-theridae,* are almost as wonderful as the Birds with teeth, and I have now many hundred specimens of them. . . .

Very truly yours,

[Signed] O. C. MARSH.[11]

These astonishing discoveries were brought into even greater prominence in 1880, when Marsh produced his first monograph, a *magnum opus* entitled *Odontornithes: A monograph on extinct birds of North America,* which, according to Woodward of England, "as a scientific publication . . . surpasses any which have already appeared devoted to paleontology." [12] This book, a sumptuous royal quarto with 201 pages, 40 woodcuts, and 34 lithographic plates (costing $8,000), was published as Volume VII of the reports of the United States Geological Exploration of the Fortieth Parallel, under Clarence King, and as Memoir 1 of the Peabody Museum at Yale. It was printed by Tuttle, Morehouse and Taylor in New Haven, on special, tinted paper; the plates were drawn by Berger and lithographed by Crisand, and the woodcuts were mainly the work of Hopson. There was an author's edition of 250 copies for which Marsh paid $720.14, and which he began to distribute on July 17, 1880.

This first memoir of Marsh's was widely distributed by him, not only to scientific workers but to many of his friends as well, particularly to those who were in the public eye, and the letters he received concerning it brought him rich reward. Thomas Nast's pictorial comment appears on the opposite page, and we may quote another master of humor, who said:

Beverly Farms, Mass., July 19, 1882.

My dear Sir:

I feel very much obliged to you for the copy of your admirable Monograph. When I heard that you had found birds with teeth in their jaws I was as much surprised—startled, I might almost say—as the midwife who first looked into the mouth of the baby Richard Third. The fact is of profound interest in many points

11. Quoted through the courtesy of Librarian A. C. Townsend of the British Museum (Natural History).

12. *Geol. Mag.,* dec. II, VII (1880), 522.

of view, not the least of which is that it hints at our coming upon "the missing link" some day when we are not looking for it, perhaps. I often envy you Champollions of Nature's hieroglyphics, and when I think of all that a single generation may teach I could

EZEKIEL, XXXVII

".. WAS FULL OF BONES ...
THERE WERE VERY MANY .... AND
LO, THEY WERE VERY DRY."

RESTORATION
OF
(ICHTHYORNIS)
DISPAR.

Fig. 28. Thomas Nast's acknowledgment of a copy of Marsh's memoir on toothed birds.

wish to reverse the order of the figures which tell me that I am myself a fossil.

Thanking you most cordially for your polite attention in sending me this beautiful volume with its wonderful revelations, I am dear sir

With great respect,

Yours truly,
[Signed] O. W. HOLMES.

Some years later, the mail brought still another letter to be cherished, from Professor W. S. Forbes of Jefferson Medical College, Philadelphia, which read in part:

October 24, 1887.

In a charming visit I made to Sir Richard Owen, in July . . . he took your book from a table in his room and said "This is the best contribution to Natural History since Cuvier." On my saying "We all feel proud of it," the dear old "Nestor" added "Well, I say it with emphasis."

When Marsh published this volume, he had in his possession about all the material extant—bones of some 125 individuals— and he certainly had all the worthwhile remains. In 1898, Williston estimated that about 175 individual bird finds had been made in the Niobrara chalk of western Kansas, their collectors being Marsh, Mudge, T. H. Russell, Guild, Cooper, Brous, Williston himself, and his brother F. H. Williston.

Marsh opened his great monograph auspiciously with the promise that it was "the first of a series of Monographs designed to make known to science the Extinct Vertebrate Life of North America." The number of new species of fossil vertebrates collected by himself and others for the Yale Museum since 1868 he estimated to be about 1,000, of which "at least one-half remain to be investigated."

The text of *Odontornithes* is a most detailed description, bone by bone, of nearly entire skeletons of five species of toothed birds: *Hesperornis regalis, H. crassipes, Ichthyornis dispar, I. victor,* and *Apatornis celer.* These descriptions were based upon about 50 different individuals of *Hesperornis* and 77 of *Ichthyornis*—a testimonial to the care and patience with which Marsh's collectors combed the Kansas chalk for this rare material. "Never before," wrote Sir Archibald Geikie in his review of the memoir, "has it been possible, we believe, to reconstruct so perfectly so ancient an organism." The plates, which included a full-size restoration of *Ichthyornis* and one of *Hesperornis* half-size, were, he said, marvels of reproduction, "combined [with] an artistic finish which had made each plate a kind of finished picture." [13] In defense of these elaborate

13. Archibald Geikie, "The toothed birds of Kansas," *Nature* (September 16, 1880), pp. 457–458.

plates, Marsh said later that his aim had been "to do full justice to the ample material . . . and where possible, to make the illustrations tell the main story to anatomists. . . . The text of such a Memoir may soon lose its interest, and belong to the past, but good figures are of permanent value." [14]

Aside from the above monograph, Marsh published 15 pamphlets and notes on fossil birds between 1870 and 1880, to which he added but 8 short articles during the next twenty years. In these 23 publications he described 1 new subclass (Odontornithes), 2 new orders, 16 new genera (2 are synonyms: *Colonosaurus = Ichthyornis,* and *Lestornis = Hesperornis*), and 43 species (3 are synonyms, 1 of which was lost to Cope). Of these species, 1 occurs in the Jurassic, 15 in the Cretaceous (12 in the Niobrara, 1 in the Claggett, 2 in the Lance), and 24 in the Cenozoic.

Marsh emphasized the fact that the most striking difference between the Kansas Cretaceous birds and living ones was the presence of "true teeth," with their distinctive characters as well marked as those of any reptile. Of these teeth he said, further:

The teeth of *Hesperornis* may be regarded as a character inherited from a reptilian ancestry. Their strong resemblance to the teeth of reptiles, in form, structure, and succession, is evidence of this, and their method of implantation in a common alveolar groove (Holcodont), conforms strictly to what we have in one well known group of reptiles, exemplified by *Ichthyosaurus.* This method of insertion in the jaw is a primitive dental character, quite different from what we should naturally expect as an accompaniment of the modern style of vertebra, and is a much lower grade than the implantation of the teeth in distinct sockets (Thecodont), a feature characteristic, as we shall see, of another group of Odontornithes, of which *Ichthyornis* is the type. These teeth indicate unmistakably that *Hesperornis* was carnivorous in habit, and doubtless was descended from a long line of rapacious ancestors.[15]

After studying the brain cavities in his marvelous specimens of toothed birds, Marsh remarked that the brain of the late Cretaceous bird, *Hesperornis,* was quite small and more rep-

14. 1885A, p. xvii.
15. 1880F, pp. 112–113.

tilian in type than in any adult bird so far examined by him. In comparison, the brain of the living loon is about three times as large. Approximately the same proportion was found to hold true in a comparison of the much smaller Cretaceous bird, *Ichthyornis*, with the living tern *Sterna*.[16] These facts he regarded as especially important, "since they tend directly to show that the essential principles of brain growth, established by the writer in extinct mammals, apply also to birds." [17]

The posterior limbs of the great diving bird, Marsh pointed out,

present an admirable example of adaptive structure. The means of locomotion were confined entirely to these extremities, and the life of *Hesperornis* was probably more completely aquatic than that of any known bird. It may be fairly questioned whether it could even be said to walk on land, although some movement was of course a necessity. Considering the posterior limb as a whole, it will be found a nearly perfect piece of machinery for propulsion through the water. Provision was made for a very powerful backward stroke.[18]

In connection with this "backward stroke," it should be said that all Marsh's restorations were made on a large drawing board, where each bone in outline, cut out of paper, was moved about until the proper relation was ascertained. This method, however, allows of motion in but one plane, and as all living water birds thrust the legs backward in swimming, it was only natural that Marsh should ascribe the same motion to *Hesperornis*. The senior writer well remembers when Preparator Scollick of the National Museum came to Curator Lucas one day in 1903 and said that he was in difficulty with the mount of *Hesperornis*—the first to be attempted in a lifelike attitude—because he could not make the legs strike backward, and that he was forced to conclude they must have moved sidewise and backward. After looking at the temporary mount, Lucas said: "You are correct, Scollick, this bird never struck out backward in the same way that modern birds do." Confirming this in his paper of 1903, Lucas said that, in

16. *Ibid.*, p. 8.
17. *Ibid.*, p. 10.
18. *Ibid.*, p. 87.

swimming, the legs of *H. regalis* must have stood out almost at right angles to the body, in a manner suggestive of a pair of oars; and that, like oars, they may have been moved together and not alternately.[19] As a result of this discovery, the well-known restoration of *Hesperornis* in swimming attitude was made by the artist Gleason under Lucas' supervision.

Commenting on the small wings of *Hesperornis*, Marsh said:

The rudimentary wings, viewed in the light of modern science [1880], clearly indicate that *Hesperornis* was in this respect a degraded type. The Struthious characters which we have noticed in various parts of the skeleton might be regarded, not as evidence of close relationship, but rather as general reptilian characters, common to the two groups through inheritance from a remote reptilian ancestry. According to this view, the wings may have been gradually lost by disuse, after the aquatic life was assumed. In proportion as the wings diminished, the legs and feet increased in size, for their work increased. This change would be strictly in accordance with the law of compensation, and the well known economy of nature.[20]

The tail of *Hesperornis*, according to Marsh,

was clearly of great service in its aquatic life. In the number of vertebrae and length, it exceeds nearly all known birds, and it is unique in its widely expanded transverse processes and in its depressed, horizontal, ploughshare bone. This broad horizontal tail reminds one of that of the beaver, and was undoubtedly of great assistance in steering, and in diving. Whether it was, like the beaver's tail, destitute of feathers, or like the tail of *Plotus* was furnished with long stiff *rectrices*, so as to act as a rudder, cannot at present be determined with certainty, although the latter view seems more probable. That *Hesperornis* was provided with feathers of some kind, we can hardly doubt.[21]

Ichthyornis was a small bird with a disproportionately large head, powerful wings, and small legs and feet. It differed widely

19. F. A. Lucas, "Notes on the osteology and relationship of the fossil birds of the genera *Hesperornis, Hargeria, Baptornis,* and *Diatryma*," *Proc. U. S. Nat. Mus.*, XXVI, 95.

20. 1880F, p. 113.

21. *Ibid.*, p. 116.

therefore in form and habit from the contemporary *Hesperornis*. Its biconcave vertebrae, moreover, separate it widely from all other birds, recent or extinct, and point back unmistakably "to a very lowly ancestry, even below the reptiles." [22] In fact, jaws, teeth, base of skull, and brain in these birds were all reptilian in character.

The bones of *Ichthyornis* were more or less pneumatic, and this fact, together with their small size, was perhaps the main reason, Marsh thought, why so few good ones had been discovered. *Apatornis*, a probable near ally, was another small bird, scarcely larger than a pigeon, but suggestive of the tern in its powerful wings and small legs and feet, and doubtless of similar habits.

The teeth of *Ichthyornis* were implanted in distinct sockets, thus differing widely from those of *Hesperornis*, which lay in a common groove. Moreover, the method of tooth replacement was not lateral, as in *Hesperornis* and the mosasaurs, but vertical, as in the crocodiles and dinosaurs—an important and highly interesting fact.

The wings in *Ichthyornis* and *Apatornis* clearly indicate strong power of flight, again differing widely from the same parts in *Hesperornis*. The tail is notable mainly for being "of the modern ornithic type." The legs and feet are comparatively small and agree with the corresponding parts in modern carinate birds.

The skeleton of *Ichthyornis*, therefore, can be interpreted only, Marsh said, "by supposing that certain parts have become highly specialized in the direction of recent birds, while others have been derived, with but little change, from a reptilian, or even a more lowly, ancestry." [23]

In the skull, reptilian features are seen in the teeth, in the diminutive brain, in the single-headed quadrate, and in the union of the lower jaws in front, by ligament only.

The vertebrae, Marsh believed, hold the key to the origin of one remarkable character in recent birds. In all living birds and in the other known fossil forms the vertebrae have a peculiar saddle-shaped articulation of the centra, but in *Ichthyornis* and *Apatornis* the vertebrae are biconcave. This

22. *Ibid.*, p. 119.
23. *Ibid.*, p. 178.

latter form is seen in a few recent reptiles, in many extinct ones, and in the amphibians, but it is especially characteristic of fishes and was undoubtedly inherited from them by the higher groups. A clue to the origin of these saddle-shaped centra is seen in one of the cup-shaped vertebrae of *Ichthyornis*. In this third cervical vertebra, Marsh observed,

we catch nature in the act, as it were, of forming a new type; by modifying one form of vertebrae into another. . . . In the anterior articulation of this vertebra . . . the surface looks downward and forward, being inclined at an angle of nearly 60° with the axis of the centrum. In vertical section, it is moderately convex, while transversely it is strongly concave; thus presenting a near approach to the saddle-like articulation. None of the other known vertebrae of *Ichthyornis* possess this character.

This highly specialized feature occurs at the first bend of the neck, and greatly facilitates motion in a vertical plane. If, now, we consider for a moment that the dominant motion in the neck of a modern bird is in a vertical plane, we see at once that anything that tends to facilitate this motion would be an advantage, and that the motion itself would tend directly to produce this modification. With biconcave vertebrae, the flexure in any direction is dependent on the elasticity of the fibrous tissue that connects them, as the edges of the cups do not slide over each other. An increasing movement in the neck of *Ichthyornis* in a vertical plane would tend to deflect the upper and lower margins of the circular cup, and to produce a vertical constriction, and at the same time to leave the lateral margins projecting; and this is precisely what we have in the third vertebra of this genus.[24]

The classification and development of the various forms of vertebrae were finally summed up by Marsh as follows:

(1) *Biconcave vertebrae* (Fishes and Amphibians); the primitive type; a weak articulation, admitting free, but limited motion. From this form, have been directly derived the other varieties, namely:

(2) *Plane vertebrae* (Mammals) affording a stronger joint, with motion still restricted.

(3) *Cup-and-ball vertebrae* (Reptiles); a strong and flexible

24. *Ibid.,* p. 181.

joint, well fitted for general motion, and evidently produced by it. The vertebrae are procœlian when lateral motion is dominant (Serpents); opisthocœlian with varied motion (Dinosaur cervicals).

(4) *Saddle vertebrae* (Birds); the highest type; a very strong and free articulation, especially adapted to motion in a vertical plane, and mainly due originally to its predominance.[25]

Striving to recreate the habits of the living creature, as he frequently did, Marsh said:

In considering the mode of life, and habits of *Ichthyornis*, many important suggestions may be derived from its structure, as well as from the localities where the remains are found. The sharp cutting teeth of *Ichthyornis* prove, beyond a doubt, that it was carnivorous; its great powers of flight, long jaws, and its recurved teeth suggest, moreover, that it captured its prey alive. Its food was probably fishes, as their remains are found in great abundance mingled with those of *Ichthyornis*. These fossils occur in the bed of the old Cretaceous ocean in which *Hesperornis* swam. . . . That *Ichthyornis* was provided with feathers is proved beyond question by the tubercles for the attachment of quills on the forearm.[26]

The fossil toothed birds known to science include three famous genera. *Hesperornis* and *Ichthyornis* are two of these; the third, longer known and from an older geologic period, is *Archæopteryx*. This unique Jurassic type has been found only in Europe, but it was closely studied by Marsh and must therefore receive some discussion here.

Archæopteryx, the oldest-known bird, represented by three specimens found in the Upper Jurassic lithographic limestone of northern Bavaria, is probably one of the world's most celebrated fossils. The first part to be recovered, in 1860, was the impression of a feather, and on it Von Meyer established the name. In the following year, a complete skeleton, apparently with no head attached, was secured at Pappenheim, three-and-a-half hours' walking distance from the Eichstätt locality that was to yield the second skeleton, with the head preserved. The first skeleton is now one of the great treasures of the British Museum (Natural History) in London, and the

25. *Ibid.*, p. 183.
26. *Ibid.*

second is in the Natural History Museum of the University of Berlin. The Berlin specimen, found on the Blumenberg near Eichstätt, in the quarry of a Mr. Dürr, was bought by the well-known preparator of Solenhofen fossils, E. Häberlein. The find was soon heralded in the scientific journals of Germany, where it was seen by Spencer F. Baird, who at once imparted the information to Marsh, taking occasion also to poke fun at his friend:

> *Smithsonian Institution,*
> *Washington, D. C.,*
> *June 8, 1877.*

Dear Prof. Marsh.

Are you aware—probably it is an old story to you—that Ernest Haeberlein, of Pappenheim near Solenhofen, has discovered his second *Archæopteryx*, said to be more perfect than the first, as having the head?

The German journals express the hope that this may not be brought away from that country. Now is your chance for a cable dispatch, to send the specimen regardless of cost!

> Yours truly,
> [Signed] SPENCER F. BAIRD.

On receipt of Baird's letter, Marsh promptly sent a cable to Professor Geinitz, following it by the letter quoted below:

> *Yale College Museum,*
> *New Haven, Conn.,*
> *June 10th, 1877.*

Dear Professor Geinitz,

I sent you a cable message yesterday in regard to the new *Archæopteryx*, which I learn Haeberlein of Pappenheim has for sale. I hope you can get the specimen for me, as I am now at work on "*Birds with teeth*," and I should like to study *Archæopteryx* before I publish my large Memoir now nearly ready, for the press.

If the price asked for this specimen is *very high*, please get the refusal of it, and telegraph me the amount before finally completing the purchase. If there is time to write, please also inform me how perfect the fossil is. . . .

> Very truly your friend,
> [Signed] O. C. MARSH.

Geinitz' reply on June 20 stated that, according to information received from Zittel, the bird, when found, lay in a slab of the lithographic limestone 10 millimeters thick, with the head showing on one side and the skeleton on the other; the tail, with feathers preserved, was in a third piece. Under these circumstances, Zittel doubted if the bird could be fully revealed; he had, nevertheless, offered 1,000 marks for it, but his offer had been refused. Häberlein in the meantime had carefully cemented the thin slab and the tail piece to the thicker piece from which they had parted, and had then very skilfully worked away the thinner slab, so as eventually to reveal almost the entire skeleton. In the cleaning process, naturally, some parts had been lost and others so rounded by the tooling as to destroy their finer detail.

As to the price, Geinitz protested that it was "usurious" and added that Zittel strongly advised against anyone's yielding to such outrageous terms as Häberlein was asking. It became known, however, that Marsh was again in the market, and feeling ran high in the Vaterland that this treasure must not be lost, as had been Marsh's *Rhamphorhynchus* and the British-owned *Archæopteryx*, whose purchase price is said to have provided a dowry for a professor's daughter. To keep the specimen at home, one of Prussia's great industrialists, Dr. Werner Siemens, bought the rare fossil in 1880 for a reputed 20,000 marks and resold it at cost to the University of Berlin. It was fully described in 1884 by Dames.[27]

In the summer of 1881, Marsh went to Europe for the purpose of studying all the reptiles which promised to throw light on the early forms of birds, and especially *Archæopteryx* and *Compsognathus*. On August 10, his notebook records that he spent three hours over the Berlin *Archæopteryx*, about which he made pages of notes. Later he examined the London specimen, and commented in his notebook that it has "five teeth in sight, two or three displaced, hence set in groove (2), one tooth small." He next went to York to attend the fiftieth-anniversary meeting of the British Association. Sir Edward Poulton, reminiscing about this meeting in a presidential

27. W. Dames, "Ueber Archæopteryx," *Palæont. Abhandl.*, Bd. 2, Heft 3, pp. 119–196.

address at the Nottingham meeting of 1937, had this to say of Marsh and the *Archæopteryx:*

Prof. O. C. Marsh had come over from Yale, his main object being to buy for his University Museum the second and more perfect fossil of the wonderful ancestral bird *Archæopteryx.* . . . Marsh soon realized, as he told me, that the second was not for sale on any terms. "We let the other go and I believe they would kill me if this were sold," was the reply given to him by the authority in Munich. He was, however, able to study the fossil, and his description and drawings of the teeth, in the Geological Section, followed the only attack on evolution itself, as distinct from its causes, which I have ever witnessed at any of our meetings. It was the exhibition by H. G. Seeley of his reconstruction of *Archæopteryx* from this fossil, which aroused the fury of the palæontologist, old Dr. Thomas Wright of Cheltenham; "*Archæopteryx* hasn't got a head, how can it possibly have teeth?" he growled, knowing nothing of the latest find or of the fact that a detached head and scattered teeth had been detected on the slab in which the older specimen was embedded.[28] In spite of Prof. Newton's positive statement and the form of the teeth, drawn by Prof. Marsh at the request of the chairman, Dr. Wright, quite unconvinced, continued muttering "*Archæopteryx* is a very good bird," its virtue in his opinion entirely uncontaminated by any taint of reptilian affinity.

Prof. Marsh also read a paper in the Zoological Section on his own wonderful discoveries of toothed birds from the rocks of the western United States. Richard Owen, president of the Section, was in the chair, and, with the memory of old and embittered controversies in his mind, the author told me that he had felt rather anxious in bringing his communication forward. But in that friendly atmosphere there was no reason for alarm. Owen welcomed the paper warmly and in confirmation told us, in the most charming manner, of the traces of teeth found in an embryo parrot.[29]

28. The writers, surprised at the above reference to a "detached head" in what has long been considered to be a headless specimen, wrote to Mr. A. Tindell Hopwood of the British Museum for an explanation, and were told by him in a letter dated November 25, 1938, that the British *Archæopteryx* indeed has "an endocranial cast, a few fragments of [head] bone, and the remains of one side of the upper jaw with teeth."

29. *Nature* (September 4, 1937), p. 396.

When the first skeleton of *Archæopteryx* was found, it was considered to be a reptile by Wagner, who had described the splendid specimen of *Compsognathus*. According to Marsh, however, "the best authorities . . . now agree with Owen that *Archæopteryx* is a bird, and that *Compsognathus*, as Gegenbaur and Huxley have shown, is a Dinosaurian reptile." The former genus, he held, represents "certainly the most reptilian of birds." Presenting his conclusions about *Archæopteryx* before the British Association, he summed up its principal characters thus:

The presence of true teeth, in position, in the skull. These are similar in both crown and root to those of *Hesperornis*.

Biconcave vertebrae, resembling those of *Ichthyornis*, but without the large lateral foramina.

A scapular arch strongly resembling that in modern birds.

A well-ossified, broad sternum.

Pelvic bones separate, as in young birds and in all known dinosaurs.

Distal end of fibula in front of tibia, as in dinosaurs (*Iguanodon*).

Three digits only in the manus, all with claws. Three free metacarpals, as in young birds of today. "The bones of the reptile are indeed there, but they have already received the stamp of the bird."

Metatarsals separate, or imperfectly united.

Brain, although comparatively small, like that of a bird and not like that of a dinosaur.

The nearest approach to birds now known, he goes on to say:

would seem to be in the very small Dinosaurs from the American Jurassic. In some of these, the separate bones of the skeleton cannot be distinguished with certainty from those of Jurassic birds, if the skull is wanting, and even in this part the resemblance is striking. Some of these diminutive Dinosaurs were perhaps arboreal in habit, and the difference between them and the birds that lived with them may have been at first mainly one of feathers.[30]

In 1880, Marsh regarded the Odontornithes, or birds with teeth, as a subclass, which he divided into three orders. (1) Odontocolcae, for the *Hesperornis* type; (2) Odontotormae,

30. 1881H, p. 340.

for the *Ichthyornis* type (in modern classification these are of the order Carinatae); and (3) Saururae of Haeckel, for *Archæopteryx*. Comparing *Hesperornis* and *Ichthyornis*, as the types of their respective orders, the Odontocolcae and Odontotormae, he noted that the contrast in their principal characters is as striking as it is unexpected, viz.:

Hesperornis had teeth implanted in a continuous groove, a low, generalized character; with, however, the strongly differentiated saddle-shaped vertebrae. *Ichthyornis*, on the other hand, had the primitive biconcave vertebrae, and yet the highly specialized feature of teeth in distinct sockets. Better examples than these could hardly be found to illustrate one fact brought out by modern science, that an animal may attain great development in one set of characters, and at the same time retain other low features of the ancestral type. This is a fundamental principle of evolution. . . .

That the three oldest known birds should differ so widely from each other points unmistakably to a great antiquity for the class . . . but the reptilian characters they possess are convergent toward a more generalized type. No Triassic birds are known. . . . They will doubtless be found, however, and if we may judge from Jurassic Mammals and Reptiles, the next classes above and below Birds, the avian forms of that period would still be birds, although with even stronger reptilian features. For the primal forms of the bird-type, we must evidently look to the Palæozoic; and in the rich land fauna from American Permian we may yet hope to find the remains of both Birds and Mammals.[31]

This hope has not yet been realized.

Marsh next looked into the characters that should occur in the generalized form that must have given rise to the birds, and concluded that this animal was more reptile than bird.

Such a form [he says] would be on the road toward the Birds, rather than on the ancestral line of either Dinosaurs or Pterodactyles, as feathers were not a character of these groups. With this exception, all the [nine] characters named belong to the generalized Sauropsid, from which both birds and the known Dinosaurs may well have descended. An essential character in this ancestral type would be a free quadrate bone, since this is a universal feature

31. 1880F, pp. 185, 187–188.

in Birds, and only partially retained in the Dinosaurs now known.

The Birds would appear to have branched off by a single stem, which gradually lost its reptilian characters as it assumed the ornithic type, and in the existing Ratitae we have the survivors of this direct line. The lineal descendants of this primal stock doubtless early attained the power of flight. The volant birds doubtless separated early from the main avian stem, probably in the Triassic, since, in the formation above, we have *Archæopteryx*, with imperfect powers of flight.

This power of flight probably originated among the small arboreal forms of reptilian birds. How this may have commenced, we have an indication in the flight of *Galeopithecus*, the flying squirrels (*Pteromys*), the flying lizard (*Draco*), and in the flying tree-frog (*Rhacophorus*). In the early arboreal birds, which jumped from branch to branch, even rudimentary feathers on the fore limbs would be an advantage, as they would tend to lengthen a downward leap, or break the force of a fall. As the feathers increased, the body would become warmer, and the blood more active. With still more feathers, would come increased power of flight, as we see in young birds of today. A greater activity would result in a more perfect circulation. A true bird would doubtless require warm blood, but would not necessarily be hot-blooded, like the birds now living.

The short wings and clumsy tail of *Archæopteryx* were quite sufficient for short flights from tree to tree, and if the body were essentially naked, as now supposed, we have in this Jurassic form an interesting stage in the development of birds before full plumage was attained. Whether *Archæopteryx* was on the true Carinate line cannot at present be determined, and this is also true of *Ichthyornis;* but the biconcave vertebrae of the latter evidently suggest that this form was an early offshoot. . . .

These three ancient birds, so widely different from each other, and from all modern birds, prove beyond question the marvelous diversity of the avian type in Mesozoic time.[32]

Lucas, discussing this matter of the origin of birds twenty years later, in Zittel's *Handbook of Paleontology* (1902), held that birds are descended without question from reptiles. Although the affinities between the two classes are so intimate,

32. *Ibid.,* pp. 188–189.

however, he objected to Huxley's merging them under the common designation of Sauropsida. Writing of *Hesperornis* the following year, he said:

The struthious birds are heavy, short-bodied land birds, whereas *Hesperornis* was a long, lithe, proportionately slender-bodied diver. . . . In skull and shoulder girdle *Hesperornis* presents an interesting combination of characters, on the one hand showing generalized features and on the other close resemblances to modern birds. Thus we have in the Cretaceous a bird with a palatal structure quite unlike that of any struthious bird and with a vestigial wing which yet preserves many features found in the limbs of birds possessed of the power of flight. Add to this that no struthious bird is, as yet known, from North America, and we have an argument for those who believe that if birds did not have a diphyletic origin they at least divided into two very distinct branches early in their career. . . .

That *Hesperornis* should stand in the direct line of ascent of the grebes is, of course, quite out of the question, as it would imply the derivation of a modern bird of flight from a degenerate, flightless form. That the two may have had a common ancestor is an entirely different proposition, but if such be the case we must go far back in time to seek for this hypothetical form.[33]

Alexander P. Wetmore, in his *Systematic Classification for the Birds of the World, Revised and Amended* (1934), agrees with Marsh's views as to the systematic relations between the Mesozoic birds and the more recent ones. He refers the Jurassic reptilian birds to the subclass Archæornithes (ancestral birds), while placing the Cretaceous toothed birds in the subclass Neornithes (true birds), the superorder Odontognathae (New World toothed birds), and the orders Hesperornithiformes *(Hesperornis* and *Hargeria)* and Ichthyornithiformes *(Ichthyornis)*. Although this places them near the ostriches (superorder Palæognathae or struthious birds) among recent birds, they are not considered closely allied to that group, as was Marsh's contention.

33. F. A. Lucas, "Notes on the osteology and relationship of the fossil birds of the genera *Hesperornis, Hargeria, Baptornis,* and *Diatryma," Proc. U. S. Nat. Mus.,* XXVI (1903), 548–552.

On Marsh's work in general on the toothed birds, Dr. Wetmore's comment to the writers was:

Marsh's discovery of the toothed birds in the fossil deposits of Kansas though made at so early a day still ranks as one of the outstanding discoveries in palæornithology in North America. And to his original studies little that is new has been added, except to refute Marsh's belief that these Cretaceous species were closely allied to the living ostriches. In point of fact the toothed birds seem set apart by themselves from all living forms.

In view of the very definite specialization of *Hesperornis* and its allies for an aquatic existence, and of *Ichthyornis* for life in the air it seems strange that no cursorial type has yet been discovered in Cretaceous deposits, though birds of this kind are found well developed in the Tertiary.

CHAPTER XIX

MARSH'S WORK IN VERTEBRATE PALE-
ONTOLOGY. III. MAMMALS

MAMMALS IN GENERAL

MARSH originally intended to devote most of his time to the study of fossil mammals, and on his return from Germany the first bones he unearthed were those of *Homo*, found in the burial mounds of Ohio (1866). In the next year he published a brief note on the discovery of a mastodon at Cohoes, New York, which is now one of the mounted treasures of the State Museum at Albany. Thereafter for a long time his attention was diverted from mammals to bird and reptile remains, as a result of the wonderful material found in the Cretaceous strata of western Kansas. In the meantime, however, through the early Yale expeditions to the West, he had acquired enough mammal remains to understand the Eocene and Oligocene forms, the first to come into his hands. By 1877, he had an astonishing knowledge of American fossil mammals, which enabled him, in his memorable vice-presidential address at Nashville before the American Association for the Advancement of Science, to give a remarkable summary of the chronogenesis of the various mammalian lines. From 1877 onward, his wealth of dinosaur remains, with their revelation of the extraordinary evolution in this group, kept him so much occupied that his projected monograph on the Mesozoic mammals failed to materialize, although the handsome one on the Dinocerata appeared in 1885.

Principles of Mammalian Classification

In the classification of mammals, experience has shown that the most reliable characters are the teeth and feet, but also that no scheme is satisfactory unless consideration is given to the evolution of the entire animal in time and space. The teeth of mammals, Marsh said in 1877, were gradually modified with other parts of the structure. The primitive form of tooth was clearly a cone, and all others are derived from this. . . . In the higher mammals, the incisors and canines retain the conical shape, and the premolars have only in part been transformed. The latter gradually change to the more complicated molar pattern, and hence are not reduced molars, but transition forms from the cone to more complex types. Most of the early Tertiary mammals had forty-four teeth, and in the oldest forms the premolars were all unlike the molars, while the crowns were short, covered with enamel, and without cement. Each stage of progress in the differentiation of the animal was, as a rule, marked by a change in the teeth; . . . Hence, it is often easy to decide from a fragment of a jaw, to what horizon of the Tertiary it belongs. The fossil horses of this period, for example, gained a grinding-tooth for each toe they lost. . . .

The foot of the primitive mammal was, doubtless, plantigrade, and certainly five-toed. . . . This generalized foot became modified by a gradual loss of the outer toes, and increase in size of the central ones, the reduction proceeding according to systematic methods, differing in each group. Corresponding changes took place in the limb-bones. One result was a great increase in speed, as the power was applied so as to act only in the plane of motion. The best effect of this specialization is seen to-day in the horse and antelope, each representing a distinct group of Ungulates, with five-toed ancestors.[1]

Origin of Mammals

In addition to his taxonomic work on the mammals, to be discussed presently, Marsh was much interested in the problem of their origin. At the time of his Nashville address he knew of but few Mesozoic mammals, and those chiefly European; and the two "mammal" jaws then recorded from the Triassic of North Carolina have since proved to be reptilian. One of the latter, *Dromatherium*, he regarded as probably belonging to a marsupial, and he thought that this was the stock that gave rise to the placental or higher mammals.

In contrast to the dearth of Mesozoic knowledge, he says,

In the lowest Tertiary beds of this country a rich mammalian fauna suddenly makes its appearance, and, from that time through

1. 1877F, p. 42.

the age of mammals to the present, America has been constantly occupied by this type of life in the greatest diversity of form.[2]

At the International Congress of Zoology held at Cambridge University in August, 1898, Marsh was one of the speakers in a symposium which discussed the origin of mammals. His opinion then was that this class of animals contains such diverse groups that it may fairly be regarded as an open question whether they all have a common origin.

Seeking the origin of mammals in the reptiles, Marsh considered the mammal-like teeth in the latter group as of comparatively small importance, inasmuch as the same general forms of teeth are to be found, not merely in the reptiles supposed to be nearest to the mammals, but also in other widely different groups. In such crocodiles as the extinct *Notosuchus* of Patagonia, for example, all three kinds of teeth are well distinguished. The dinosaur *Triceratops* has teeth with two roots, a supposed mammalian character, and the fish *Anarrhichas* also has three kinds of teeth. It is more than probable, therefore, he concludes, that the peculiar resemblance between the teeth of mammals and those in the lower vertebrates is merely one of parallel development.[3]

Modern research has shown that the ancestors of the mammals were in all probability the early Triassic cynodont reptiles of Africa, a group that was not well known in Marsh's time. From the cynodonts, the mammal line is now thought to have passed through the ictidosaurs of late Triassic time, which, according to Scott, in almost all points of skeletal structure might be regarded as mammals.[4]

Brain Growth in Mammals

Studies of the brain of extinct vertebrates and the evidence thus revealed as to the increase of intelligence in geologic time were among Marsh's most telling researches. From 1870 on, whenever he had sufficient material it was his rule to have his preparators cut apart the rear end of fossil skulls and clean out all the rock filling the brain cavity. Into this cavity was

2. *Ibid.*, p. 18.
3. 1898J, p. 407.
4. W. B. Scott, *A History of Land Mammals in the Western Hemisphere* (2d ed., 1937), p. 80.

then poured warm gelatine, which, because of its marked pliability when cold, could be easily pulled out without tearing off any of the projecting parts. From this gelatine cast a more permanent mold would be made, which permitted the taking of other replicas. By 1874, he had brain casts of many Cenozoic mammals, enough to enable him to make a first attempt at a generalization regarding brain growth in geologic time. On the evening of June 17, he presented his conclusions before the Connecticut Academy of Arts and Sciences in New Haven. The Eocene mammals, he said,

all appear to have had small brains, and in some of them the brain cavity was hardly more capacious than in the higher reptiles. The largest Eocene mammals are the *Dinocerata*, which were but little inferior to the elephant in bulk. In *Dinoceras* . . . the brain cavity is not more than one-eighth the average size of that in existing Rhinoceroses. In the other genera of this order, *Tinoceras* Marsh and *Uintatherium* Leidy, the smallness of the brain was quite as remarkable. The gigantic mammals of the American Miocene [Oligocene] are the *Brontotheridae*, which equalled the Dinocerata in size. In *Brontotherium* Marsh . . . the brain cavity is . . . about the size of the brain in the Indian *Rhinoceros*. In the Pliocene strata of the West, a species of *Mastodon* is the largest mammal, and although but little superior in absolute size to *Brontotherium*, it had a very much larger brain, but not equal to that of existing Proboscidians. The Tapiroid ungulates of the Eocene had small brain cavities, much smaller than their allies, the Miocene *Rhinocerotidae*. The Pliocene representatives of the latter group had well developed brains, but proportionally smaller than living species. A similar progression in brain capacity seems to be well marked in the equine mammals, especially from the Eocene *Orohippus*, through *Miohippus* and *Anchitherium* of the Miocene [Oligocene], *Pliohippus* and *Hipparion* of the Pliocene, to the recent *Equus*.[5]

In 1876, Marsh briefly recapitulated his knowledge as follows:

First, all Tertiary mammals had small brains; *second*, there was a gradual increase in the size of the brain during this period; *third*,

5. 1874F, pp. 66–67.

this increase was mainly confined to the cerebral hemispheres, or higher portion of the brain; *fourth*, in some groups, the convolutions of the brain have gradually become more complicated; *fifth*, in some, the cerebellum and olfactory lobes have even diminished in size. There is some evidence that the same general law of brain-growth holds good for Birds and Reptiles from the Cretaceous to the present time.[6]

These statements he repeated in his Nashville address the following year, adding:

In the long struggle for existence during Tertiary time, the big brains won, then as now; and the increasing power thus gained rendered useless many structures inherited from primitive ancestors, but no longer adapted to new conditions.[7]

In his monograph on the Dinocerata, Marsh formulated an "outline of a general law of brain growth," which included the five points stated in 1876, and made the following addenda:

1. The brain of a mammal belonging to a vigorous race, fitted for a long survival, is larger than the average brain of that period in the same group.

2. The brain of a mammal of a declining race is smaller than the average of its cotemporaries of the same group.[8]

Geikie's comment on Marsh's contributions to our knowledge of brain growth was as follows:

Although observations had been made by previous investigators, on the size of the brain in Tertiary mammals, Prof. Marsh was the first to institute any systematic inquiry into the laws which governed and the causes which acted upon, brain-growth in these ancient animals.[9]

Summary of Marsh's Work on Mammals

Marsh treated of fossil mammals in 85 different publications, and his most productive years for their elucidation were the

6. 1876G, p. 61.
7. 1877F, p. 41.
8. 1885A, p. 59.
9. A. Geikie, "Yale College and American palaeontology," *Nature* (December 4, 1879), p. 103.

    * Brontotheres. 13 genera (5), 21 species (5).

    Tapirs. 2 genera, 3 species.

    Rhinoceroses. 5 genera, 14 species.

  Suborder Ancylopoda.

    Chalicotheres. 1 genus, 3 species.

Order Artiodactyla.

    Oreodonts, swine-like animals, camels, deer, antelopes, etc. 20 genera (4), 49 species (1).

MESOZOIC MAMMALS

Mesozoic mammals are among the greatest rarities as fossils, but they have nevertheless been found in all the continents except Australia and Antarctica, and they are everywhere so much of the same general type as to indicate that the faunas of which they were a part were world-wide in distribution. The animals which these scarce remains represent are considered by present-day authorities to have been of very small size, ratlike or shrewlike in appearance, with a more or less sprawling gait.

From the phylogenetic standpoint, Simpson, the leading student of these early types, says,

The known specimens of Mesozoic mammals are among the most precious and important remains of extinct life which have yet been discovered. They are the sole direct evidence of the fundamental first two-thirds of the evolution of the Class Mammalia. . . . The magnificent Marsh Collection in the Peabody Museum of Yale University [is] the largest collection of Mesozoic mammals in the world.[10]

Jurassic Mammals

The first Mesozoic mammal jaw was found in England in 1764, but it was not recognized as such for many years. Two other jaws, found in the Middle Jurassic Stonesfield slate about 1812, by an amateur naturalist, William J. Broderip, and shown by him to Professor Buckland of Oxford, were pronounced mammalian by the great Cuvier during a visit to that venerable institution in 1818; but even with this assurance, Buckland hesitated to announce the discovery until 1824. Oc-

10. G. G. Simpson, "American Mesozoic Mammalia," *Mem. Peabody Mus. Nat. Hist.,* Vol. III, Pt. 1 (1929), pp. 1, vii.

curring as they did so far below any other known mammalian remains, these tiny specimens brought on a controversy which raged for some fifteen years on both sides of the Channel, and which subsided only when Richard Owen established their mam-

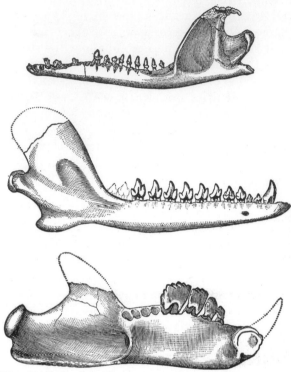

Fig. 29. Late Jurassic mammal jaws from Wyoming. Top, *Stylacodon* (= *Amblotherium*) *gracilis* Marsh, x 3. Middle, *Diplocynodon* (= *Docodon*) *victor* Marsh, x 2. Bottom, *Ctenacodon serratus* Marsh, x 3. After Marsh.

malian character conclusively, and named them *Amphitherium* (later *Amphilestes*) *broderipi*.

Marsh, from his European studies, was fully aware of the desirability of obtaining more of these early mammals, and, from a letter to Professor Owen quoted in Chapter XVII, we have seen that he felt sure such were present in the American Jurassic and that he was "bound" to have them. He kept urging his collectors to be on the watch for small fossils, and his insistence bore fruit early in 1878, when one of the best of these men, William H. Reed, excavating for dinosaurs at Como Bluffs, Wyoming, found a small broken jaw with a single tooth, which Marsh hailed with delight as belonging to one of the much-desired Jurassic mammals. He shortly visited the locality himself and found still another specimen. The jaw found by Reed he named *Dryolestes priscus* in June of that year, and stated that it represented a marsupial about the size of a weasel and allied to the existing opossums. The next year he named the specimen of his own finding *Stylacodon gracilis,* reporting that its nearest affinities are clearly with Owen's genus *Stylodon;* Simpson, however, in his reworking of the material, referred it to Owen's genus *Amblotherium.*

Marsh regarded this first-found material as merely a prophecy of riches to come and continued to impress upon his men the desirability of finding more of these tiny bones. Their constant watch was rewarded the following year by the discovery of the now-famous Quarry 9 at Como. In the course of the few years that it was worked under the direction of Reed (and particularly by his assistant, E. Kennedy, who devoted an entire year to it exclusively), Quarry 9 yielded some 250 separate specimens of jaws or teeth of mammals. A few additional specimens came from other places along Como Bluffs, and 3 from Cañon City, Colorado. "The cost involved in getting these tiny fossils," Marsh remarked, "makes their value greater than their weight in gold"; and no other mine of golden Jurassic mammals has been discovered since.

The remains of Jurassic mammals, he wrote in a later paper, are usually well preserved,

but owing to the peculiar conditions under which they were entombed, no two bones of the skeleton are as a rule found together. This fact, taken in connection with the very diminutive size of the animals themselves, and especially with the present brittle nature of the teeth and jaws, has rendered their investigation a work of great difficulty. . . . Again, these minute, delicate fossils are often embedded in a matrix from which they cannot be removed without great danger of injury or destruction. Hence, the jaws and teeth in many cases must be examined and described from the single side exposed. If the opposite side of a similar jaw should be shown in another specimen, the two may easily be regarded as distinct. This may also be the case where upper and lower jaws are found separately. Hence, a large amount of material becomes necessary for even a proximate correlation of the closely related forms.[11]

One of Marsh's two longer articles on mammals appeared in September, 1880, and in it he described five new species and one new genus, with the comment that the general resemblance of the American forms to those from the English Purbeckian was very evident. He was now convinced that these mammals could not be satisfactorily placed in any of the orders then established, and adds:

This appears to be equally true of the European forms which the writer has had the opportunity of examining. With a few possible exceptions, the Mesozoic mammals best preserved are manifestly low generalized forms, without any distinctive Marsupial characters. Not a few of them show features that point more directly to Insectivores, and present evidence, based on specimens alone, would transfer them to the latter group, if they are to be retained in any modern order. This, however, has not yet been systematically attempted, and the known facts are against it. . . . With the exception of a very few aberrant forms, the known Mesozoic mammals may be placed in a single order, which may appropriately be named *Pantotheria*. . . . The generalized members of this order were doubtless the forms from which the modern specialized Insectivores and Marsupials, at least, were derived.[12]

The "aberrant forms" mentioned above were placed by Marsh in his new order Allotheria; they included his genus *Ctenacodon, Plagiaulax,* and a few others.

Marsh's most important article on the Jurassic mammals appeared in April, 1887, with descriptions of 8 new species and 5 new genera, which he referred to 7 families, also discussed. All the known Mesozoic mammals seemingly fed upon other animals, he concluded, and they may have lived mainly upon insects "with such accessory diet as modern Insectivores affect." [13]

11. 1887A, pp. 327–329.
12. 1880G, pp. 238–239.
13. 1887A, p. 344.

Of the genetic lines of the Mammalia, he had this to say:

The modern Placental mammals were evidently not derived from Marsupials, as is generally supposed. Each group has apparently come down to the present time, by separate lines, from primitive, oviparous, forms, of which, the living Monotremes may be the more direct but specialized representatives. Among the diversified members of Placental mammals, the Insectivores are probably the nearest to the early type, and hence they show many features seen in the Jurassic and Triassic mammals of the order *Pantotheria*. . . . So far as at present known, the two great groups of Placental and Non-Placental mammals appear to be distinct in the oldest known forms, and this makes it clear that, for the primitive generalized forms (*Hypotheria*), from which both were derived, we must look back to the Paleozoic.[14]

Carrying out Marsh's original intention, all the Mesozoic mammal material that he accumulated has been elaborately monographed by George G. Simpson, who finds 44 Jurassic species in 23 genera.[15] However, even our present knowledge of these early mammals, garnered over more than a century of endeavor by many paleontologists, represents, according to Simpson, but "lights in the vast darkness of the Age of Reptiles—and very dim lights most of them are."

Simpson's conclusion is that the mammals have arisen out of the reptilian Cynodontia, apparently along at least six independent phyletic lines: (1) Multituberculata of Cope, (2) Triconodonta of Zittel, (3) Symmetrodonta of Simpson, and (4) Pantotheria of Marsh, the last giving rise to (5) Marsupialia of Baird, and (6) Placentalia of Haeckel. The origin of (7) Monotremata of Haeckel remains wholly unknown.

Marsh's term Allotheria, proposed for an order but later reduced to subordinal rank, Simpson proposes to use for a subclass.

The term Multituberculata was proposed by Cope in 1884 for a suborder, but according to Simpson "the credit for the first clear statement uniting Multituberculates into a unit is

14. *Ibid.*, p. 346.
15. G. G. Simpson, *A Catalogue of the Mesozoic Mammalia in the Geological Department of the British Museum* (1928); "American Mesozoic Mammalia," *Mem. Peabody Mus. Nat. Hist.* (1929), Vol. III, Pt. 1.

. . . due to Marsh." The multituberculates were the most characteristic and cosmopolitan mammals of Mesozoic time, and are known as fossils from the very late Triassic (Rhætic) into the Paleocene of the Cenozoic era. They probably originated in the earlier Triassic but are best known from Paleocene rocks, where skulls and parts of the skeleton are present, although rare. The Multituberculata were the longest-lived order by far of the Mammalia, but they probably gave rise to no other order.

Marsh's name Pantotheria is retained by Simpson for an order, even though a number of the criteria that the former set up for it are today open to exception. Marsh, in his original definition of the order in 1880, thought that it probably gave rise to the insectivores and the marsupials. By 1887, he omitted the marsupials from this line of descent, concluding that the allotheres represented the Mesozoic marsupials, and the pantotheres, the Mesozoic placentals. Simpson comments that Marsh's earlier views now seem nearer the truth than the later ones, "which, patently, were influenced by contemporaries whose first-hand acquaintance with the evidence was not equal to his own." He regards the pantotheres as the "only potentially successful and fruitful" order of the Jurassic, "destined to give rise to most or all recent mammals (save monotremes)." [16]

Late Cretaceous Mammals

It is interesting to note that as early as 1877 Marsh had in mind two fields in which he believed the most important future discoveries in Vertebrate Paleontology would lie. One of these was the large primates, among which might be found the missing link between ape and man. For this desideratum we must look, he thought, to Africa, and in this field America therefore held no inducement for ambitious explorers. The other field, equally important if less attractive, was the Cretaceous mammals, "which must have left their remains somewhere in this continent." No authentic Cretaceous mammals appear to have been found, however, until 1882, when two teeth and a fragmentary humerus were discovered by J. L. Wortman in the "Laramie formation" of South Dakota and described by Cope

16. G. G. Simpson (1928), p. 178.

as *Meniscoëssus conquistus*. Another seven years elapsed before remains of Cretaceous mammals were found in any quantity, but when the secret of their burial places had once been learned by the indefatigable Hatcher, teeth, fragmentary jaws, and even skeletal parts began to pour into Marsh's eager hands. In July, 1889, he had a paper in print describing 12 genera and 18 species, and 2 succeeding parts of this paper brought the total to 19 genera and 39 species, classified in 6 new families.

Marsh was in haste to set these tiny Cretaceous mammalian teeth before the paleontologic world, but at the same time he realized the insecurity of his new genera and species. On this point he says:

It is a matter of much less importance if such discoveries should prove that two or more specimens described as distinct really pertained to one animal. The advance of the science throughout the world has not been retarded by such preliminary reference, but has often been greatly promoted by making known promptly single facts of importance, leaving their full significance to be determined by later discoveries, made under more favorable circumstances.[17]

Discussing this matter of Cretaceous genera and species based on such isolated material, Simpson says that the teeth in the majority of cases unfortunately cannot be associated into natural genera, nor can the few jaw fragments solve many of the detailed taxonomic problems. In many instances, not even the characters of two consecutive teeth of a single genus can be determined. In the attempt at classification of this very fragmentary material, Marsh employed an analytical and artificial method, applying names not necessarily to distinct animals but to different types of teeth. This method, Simpson says, eventually broke down because the number of tooth types became so great that he had to attempt synthesis in some cases; that is, refer different types of teeth to one genus or to one species on the grounds that they possibly were different parts of the same type of dentition. Osborn, on the other hand, dealing with this subject in a series of papers appearing in 1887–88 and 1891–92, attempted a synthetic revision; i.e., gave names only to

17. 1892B, p. 250.

whole jaws, thus in many cases reconstituting the dentitions, of which scattered parts had been given different names by Marsh. This method, Simpson comments, "while simpler and giving more enduring results, also had its shortcomings." The condition of affairs is not much changed today and therefore, in Simpson's opinion, "a revision, in the strict sense, is impossible." He finally follows the Osborn method of using generic names

for agglomerations of different forms which can be separated, in various parts of the dentition, from other similar agglomerations but which must be much more comprehensive than the genera of any other fauna . . . with such exceptions as are forced by proper respect for the rules of nomenclature. Many of Marsh's generic names and perhaps the majority of his specific names are thus neither recognized as valid and used nor definitely reduced to synonymy. They are simply *included* in other genera or species which are used in a very broad sense.[18]

CENOZOIC PLACENTAL MAMMALS[19]

The higher or placental mammals of Cenozoic time are divided into clawed and hoofed forms, called Unguiculata and Ungulata, respectively. The clawed mammals will be presented first.

Clawed Mammals (Cohort Unguiculata)

INSECTIVORES

The order Insectivora includes the most primitive of placental mammals and is ancestral to all the higher types. The oldest-known representative of it comes from the middle part of the Upper Cretaceous in the Gobi Desert of Mongolia. A few occur in the Lance formation of Wyoming, of the same geologic period, and since early Cenozoic (Paleocene) time the

18. G. G. Simpson (1929), p. 99.
19. In the preparation of this portion of the book, Professor W. B. Scott's *History of the Land Mammals in the Western Hemisphere,* appearing in a second edition in 1937, has been of invaluable assistance. As elsewhere in the book, the taxonomy in the following pages has been for the most part based on O. P. Hay's very helpful *Bibliography and Catalogue of the Fossil Vertebrata of North America,* 1902, and 1929–1930.

group has been relatively abundant, Hay's catalogue of 1930 listing 61 genera with 128 species. Most of the 12 genera and 18 species named by Marsh date from 1872; 6 genera and 3 species are now known to be synonyms. Four of the forms he regarded, erroneously, as bats.

TILLODONTS

The animals of the order Tillodontia, named by Marsh in 1875, were archaic placentals of early Eocene time, the size of a black bear and with much the appearance of gigantic rodents; because of their size, however, it is unlikely that they were rodents. Marsh proposed one new genus, *Tillotherium* (1873) and four new species (one he referred to *Anchippodus* but it is now placed in *Trogosus*). He also referred to this order his genera *Stylinodon* and *Dryptodon*, but they are now placed in Cope's order Tæniodonta.

The Nashville address speaks of the tillodonts as

perhaps the most remarkable mammals yet found in America. . . . These animals seem to combine the characters of several different groups, viz., the Carnivores, Ungulates, and Rodents. . . . The skull [in *Tillotherium*] resembles that of the bears; the molar teeth are of the ungulate type, while the large incisors are very similar to those of Rodents. The skeleton resembles that of the Carnivores. . . . The feet are plantigrade, and each had five digits, all with long, pointed claws.[20]

Returning to the order in 1897, he says that a comparison of these animals with the least specialized edentates brings to light many curious likenesses in skull, teeth, skeleton, and feet. "These suggest relationships, at least, and possibly we may yet find here the key to the Edentate genealogy." [21]

TÆNIODONTS

Of the archaic placentals belonging to this order, Hay's catalogue of 1930 lists two families with 8 genera and 12 species, all found in the Paleocene and older Eocene. Of these, *Dryptodon crassus* (1876) and *Stylinodon mirus* (1874) were

20. 1877F, p. 32.
21. 1897A, p. 144.

described by Marsh. The specimens of the latter species were, he thought, somewhat similar to the South American Quaternary genus *Toxodon* Owen, but he nevertheless believed that they might represent an animal more closely allied to the edentates. In 1882 he had better material, and when Wortman's striking paper on edentates appeared in 1896, it stimulated Marsh to publish on "The Stylinodontia, a suborder of the Eocene edentates." Wortman agreed with Marsh's opinion of 1877; that is, that this great group of peculiar mammals originated in North America and then migrated to other parts of the world. This is not, however, the view of present-day students of fossil edentates, who hold that the ancestral form was a migrant, possibly from Asia, arriving in North America at about middle Paleocene time, and that the stock spread thence across the newly made Pliocene land bridge to South America. See the remarks on the order Edentata, *infra*.

EDENTATES

It is curious that on this great group of primitive and bizarre animals Marsh should have published so little. In 1874, he described the new genus *Morotherium* with two new species, and in 1877 he regarded the edentates as "evidently an American type," which attained great development and size on this continent. He did not believe that the edentates died out in North America after Eocene time, but rather that they continued to live on into the Pleistocene. Nor did he believe in a marked migration from South America via the Isthmus of Panama near the close of the Cenozoic, holding, rather, that the migration was from north to south; and that the edentates, finding a congenial home in South America, flourished greatly there for a time and are still represented by small members of the group.

In August, 1883, publishing on "human" footprints found in the sandstone quarry in the prison yard near Carson, Nevada, he showed that the tracks occur in 6 series, each with alternate left and right impressions, and are nearly all in the same horizon. The stride was from $2\frac{1}{2}$ to more than 3 feet in extent, the individual footprints 18 to 20 inches in length and some 8 inches wide. He thought that these impressions were probably the tracks of a large sloth, "either *Mylodon* or *Moro-*

therium." The horizon is "near the junction of the Pliocene and Quaternary." After seeing photographs and casts of the tracks, he was confirmed in his opinion that they had been made by large edentates.[22]

RODENTS

Of the rodents, or gnawing mammals, which first appear in the Paleocene, Marsh described 5 new genera (2 synonyms) and 11 new species (1 synonym) between 1871 and 1878, and summarized his knowledge in 1877 thus:

The earliest known forms are, apparently, all related to the squirrels; and the most common genus is *Sciuravus*, which continued throughout the Eocene. . . . In the Dinoceras beds, the genus *Colonomys* [= *Sciuravus*] is found, and the specimens preserved point to the *Muridae* as the nearest living allies. . . . All the Eocene Rodents known are of small size, the largest being about as large as a rabbit.

In the . . . Miocene . . . of the West, Rodents abound, but all are of moderate size. The hares first appear in the Oreodon beds [*Mytonolagus* of the White River is the oldest rabbit], and continue in considerable numbers through the rest of the Tertiary and Post-Tertiary, to the present day. . . . The Squirrel family is represented by *Ischyromys*, the *Muridae* by the genus *Eumys*, and the beavers by *Palæocastor*. . . . In the Pliocene, east and west of the Rocky Mountains, Rodents continue abundant; but most of them belong to existing genera.[23]

CARNIVORES

A partial classification of American carnivores, according to Scott, who gives an excellent account of them, is as follows:

Order Carnivora, or beasts of prey.
　Suborder Creodonta, or most primitive beasts of prey.
　　Family Mesonychidae. Paleocene into upper Eocene. Includes *Dromocyon vorax* of Marsh.
　　Family Oxyænidae. Lower into upper Eocene. Of Marsh's species has *Telmatocyon riparius, Patriofelis ferox, P. lati-*

22. 1883B, p. 140.
23. 1877F, pp. 32–33.

dens, Thinocyon velox, Triacodon fallax, T. grandis, and
T. nanus.

Family Hyænodontidae. Lower Eocene to middle Oligocene.
Of Marsh's species has *Sinopa vera* and *Stypolophus agilis.*

Family Uintacyonidae (or Miacidae). Of these ancestral
carnivores, Marsh described *Miacis sylvestris, Viverravus
gracilis, V. nitidus, Vulpavus palustris,* and *Ziphacodon
rugatus.*

Family Felidae, or true cats and sabre-toothed cats.

Family Canidae, or dogs, wolves, foxes, etc. Has Marsh's
Cynodictis angustidens.

Probably the best known of Marsh's carnivore species is
the middle Eocene creodont, *Dromocyon vorax* (1876), represented by a splendidly preserved and almost complete skeleton
found near Henry's Fork, Wyoming, by J. Heisey in 1876, and
mounted by Hugh Gibb two years after Marsh's death. (See
Plate XXX.)

Between 1871 and 1876, Marsh described 11 new genera (3
synonyms) and 17 new species (1 synonym) of carnivores.
These animals "are an old type," he said in 1877, "well represented in the Eocene, and, as might be expected, these early
forms are much less specialized than the living species". In the
lower Eocene, *Limnocyon* [*Telmatocyon*] was abundant. Middle Eocene carnivores were still more numerous, and many
genera have been discovered; one of them, *Limnofelis* [*Patriofelis*] was nearly as large as a lion and, he thought, apparently
allied to the cats. Another one, of nearly the same size, was
Oreocyon [*Patriofelis*], and *Dromocyon* and *Mesonyx* were
large animals related to *Hyænodon.* In the Miocene (=Oligo-
cene) he found the carnivores to be abundant, and to approach
modern types.[24]

PRIMATES

Linnæus, father of the binomial system for the classification
of plants and animals, placed man at the head of the animal
kingdom in the order Primates, not because of his body construction, which is in many ways primitive, but on account of
his great brain. The genus *Homo,* however, belongs with the

24. 1877F, pp. 34–35.

clawed animals, and its genetic line may have originated in North America, where it appears in the Paleocene in very small forms.

In this group of mammals of such special interest to man, Marsh again scored a "first" in the matter of discovery and recognition, although otherwise his contributions were not very marked. Included among various remains collected in Bridger (Eocene) rocks by the Yale Expedition of 1871, and described in the *American Journal of Science* for August-September, 1872, were 5 new genera and 7 new species, 3 of which he regarded as "small carnivorous mammals," and 4 as probable insectivores. Shortly after this paper had been published, more material came to light, and on October 8 Marsh issued an advance notice of the "Discovery of fossil Quadrumana [Primates] in the Eocene of Wyoming," stating that the genera *Limnotherium*, *Thinolestes*, and *Telmatolestes* especially—three of those described in the paper of the preceding month —seem to represent primates that were close to the lemurs. The teeth were more numerous than in any known primates, reaching the number of 40 in some species. In closing, he adds the usual tagline: "A full description of these interesting remains, the first of the order detected in the country, will be given by the writer at an early day." This note appeared in the November number of the *American Journal*, and was followed in March, 1875, by further remarks on the character of these early primates; the brain was nearly smooth, the cerebellum large and placed mainly behind the cerebrum, the orbits were open behind, and the lachrymal foramen lay outside them. The family Limnotheridae, erected for the group, he placed in the Prosimiae.

Subsequent research has shown that a good many of Marsh's "Quadrumana" in reality belonged to other orders, but Hay's latest catalogue places among the lemuroids the Marsh species *Notharctus affinis*, *N. anceps*, *N. crassus*, *N. tyrannus*, and *Smilodectes gracilis*; while the tarsioids include his genera *Hemiacodon* (*H. gracilis*) and *Euryacodon* (*E. lepidus*) and his species *Omomys pucillus* and *O. vagus*. Of these, *Notharctus tyrannus*, found by the Expedition of 1870 in Dry Creek, Wyoming, was described by Marsh in 1871 as a pachyderm!

In 1894, when the Dutch army surgeon, Eugene Dubois, described at length the "ape-man" which he had discovered in

Java and named *Pithecanthropus erectus,* the remains were accepted at once by Marsh as a "missing link" between apes and man; and in February, 1895, he wrote a long review of Dubois' memoir, in which he said that in many respects the discovery appeared to be one of the most important since that of the Neandertal skull in 1857. Dr. Dubois, he said,

has proved to science the existence of a new prehistoric anthropoid form, not human indeed, but in size, brain power, and erect posture, much nearer man than any animal hitherto discovered, living or extinct. . . .

The man of the Neander valley remained without honor, even in his own country, for more than a quarter of a century, and was still doubted and reviled when his kinsmen, the men of Spy, came to his defense, and a new chapter was added to the early history of the human race. The ape-man of Java comes to light at a more fortunate time. . . . Nearly twenty years ago [1877], the writer of the present review placed on record his belief that such missing links existed, and should be looked for in the caves and later Tertiary of Africa. . . . The tropical regions of both Asia and Africa still offer most inviting fields to ambitious explorers.[25]

In June of the next year, he returned to a more lengthy discussion of *Pithecanthropus,* saying that Dubois had shown the remains at the Leyden meeting of the International Congress of Zoology in 1895, which he had attended; and that his communication "was in many respects the most important one of the session, and its presentation with the specimens themselves was a rare treat to the large audience present, especially to those fitted to appreciate the evidence laid before them." Before the meeting took place, the president of the Congress, Professor Virchow of Berlin, Sir William Flower, and Professor Marsh were invited by Dr. Dubois to examine the remains personally. The first sight of the fossils, Marsh says, was a surprise, since

They were evidently much older than appeared from the descriptions. All were dark in color, thoroughly petrified, and the matrix was solid rock, difficult to remove. . . . All the physical characters impressed me strongly with the idea that these various remains were

25. 1895A, pp. 145–147.

of Pliocene age, and not Post-Tertiary, as had been supposed. . . .
A later examination of accompanying vertebrate fossils placed the
Pliocene age of all beyond reasonable doubt [they are now referred
to the Pleistocene]. . . .

After a careful study of all the *Pithecanthropus* remains and of
the evidence presented as to the original discovery, the position
in which the remains were found, and the associated fossils, my
own conclusions may be briefly stated, as follows:

(1) The remains of *Pithecanthropus* at present known are of
Pliocene age, and the associated vertebrate fauna resembles that of
the Siwalik Hills of India.

(2) The various specimens of *Pithecanthropus* apparently belonged to one individual.

(3) This individual was not human, but represented a form
intermediate between man and the higher apes. . . . One thing is
certain; the discovery of *Pithecanthropus* is an event of the first
importance to the scientific world.[26]

Hoofed Mammals (Cohort Ungulata)

The hoofed mammals of the cohort Ungulata are subdi-
vided into at least 14 orders, but of these we shall present but
5; namely, (1) the Condylarthra or primitive ungulates, (2)
the Amblypoda, (3) the Proboscidea or elephants and masto-
dons, (4) the Perissodactyla, and (5) the Artiodactyla. The
first 4 of these belong to the odd-toed ungulates, and the last
one to the group with an even number of toes.

In 1877, Marsh spoke of the ungulates as being the most
abundant of the Cenozoic mammals, and likewise the most important, in view of the fact that they include such a great
variety of types, "some of which we can trace through their
various changes down to the modified forms that represent
them today." The perissodactyls he thought were evidently the
oldest since they were the prevailing forms throughout the
Eocene, and even though more or less generalized, they were
still quite distinct from the even-toed forms, even at the base
of the Eocene.[27]

The Dinocerata monograph of 1885 presents at some length

26. 1896B, pp. 477, 482.
27. 1877F, pp. 22–23.

Marsh's view of the early genealogy of the ungulate mammals. In the Mesozoic, he says, there arose a well-marked group which may be called the Protungulata, the probable ancestors of all succeeding ungulates. After a discussion of the probable characters of this type, he goes on:

From this generalized ungulate, the skeleton of which we now know almost as well apparently as if we had it before us, a direct line would appear to have continued up to the present day, and be represented by the living *Hyrax* [=*Hyracoides*]. Several divergent lines passed off probably from the same stem, and three of these have continued to the present time, the survivors being the *Proboscidea*, the *Artiodactyla*, and the *Perissodactyla*.

The Proboscidian line apparently went off from the main ungulate stem in the Cretaceous. One branch ended in the later Pliocene in *Dinotherium*; another, in *Mastodon*; while the genus *Elephas* alone survives, to represent this old group.

Another strong branch, represented by a group which may be called the *Holodactyla*, probably also led off in the Cretaceous. . . . This line evidently divided near the base of the Eocene into the great groups of Perissodactyls and Artiodactyls, each with many off-shoots, and still existing. The former are now on the decline, and have but three living representatives, the horse, the tapir, and the rhinoceros.

One off-set from the Perissodactyl line separated near the top of the Eocene, where it is represented by *Diplacodon*, and perhaps ended in the extinct *Brontotherium*, of the lower Miocene [Oligocene], although this line may have been continued somewhat later in the genus *Chalicotherium*.

From the Artiodactyl line, a peculiar group branched off in the early Eocene, and in the Miocene [Oligocene] was represented by *Oreodon* and allied genera, and by later forms in the Pliocene. . . .

Another order, also, which may be termed the *Amblydactyla*, passed off apparently from the main ungulate stem in the Cretaceous, and became extinct in the Eocene. One branch terminated in *Coryphodon* [= Coryphodontia], in the lower Eocene, and the other, represented by the *Dinocerata*, . . . came to an end in the Middle [= Upper] Eocene.[28]

28. 1885A, pp. 171–173.

These lines of descent were shown graphically in a diagram, which is here reproduced.

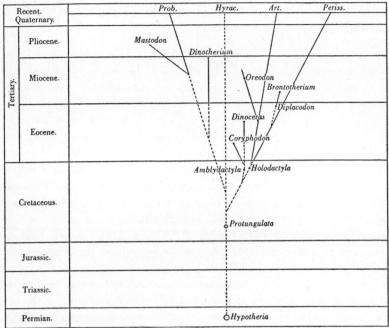

Fig. 30. One of Marsh's rare attempts at diagrammatic mammal genealogies, in this case the ungulates. From his Dinocerata monograph, 1885.

Marsh then offered the following classification:

Class Mammalia—Ungulata.
  (1) Order Hyracoidea.
  (2) Order Proboscidea.
  (3) Order Amblydactyla { Dinocerata.
                          { Coryphodontia.
  (4) Order Clinodactyla { Mesaxonia (Perissodactyla).
                          { Paraxonia (Artiodactyla).

CONDYLARTHS

The American condylarths were indistinctly ungulate, and they were common mammals throughout the Paleocene and the lower Eocene. The family Meniscotheriidae of the lower Eo-

cene has the genus *Meniscotherium* Cope, of which Marsh's
Hyracops is a synonym, his species *H. socialis* equaling Cope's
M. chamense terrærubræ. These animals were the size of a small
fox terrier. For them Marsh in 1892 proposed the order Mesodactyla, saying that the skull and teeth strongly resemble those
of the Ungulata, especially some of the early perissodactyls.
The feet, however, were digitigrade, with five well-developed
digits, apparently covered by thin nails, and were more like
those of primates than of any other group. The order, he says,
stands in somewhat the same relation to the typical ungulates
that the tillodonts do to the rodents and the chalicotheres to
the edentates; and he adds:

Very briefly defined, the *Mesodactyla* may be considered as
having the ungulate type of dentition, with the limbs and feet of
early Primates; the *Chalicotheria* as combining an ungulate dentition with the feet of Edentates, while the *Tillodontia* unite with the
rodent dentition the extremities of primitive Carnivores. These
three orders are quite distinct from each other and from the remaining Mammalia. . . .

One fact is becoming more and more evident, the near affinity of
the early Primates, Carnivores, Ungulates, and Rodents, with each
other and with the Insectivores, and more remotely with Marsupials. . . . The *Amblydactyla* of large size, the *Tillodontia* also
large, and the diminutive *Mesodactyla*, all apparently lived together in this period [Eocene], and a comparison of their special
characters points out their probable lines of descent.[29]

AMBLYPODS

Coryphodonts. Marsh's suborder Coryphodontia (Panto-
donta of Cope 1873) included amblypods that appeared in the
Paleocene and died out in the lower Eocene (Wind River).
They were the characteristic animals of early Wasatch time,
and are known also in England, France, and Mongolia.

Of the interesting and well-known genus *Coryphodon*, described first by Owen in 1846, Marsh published four accounts,
the first in 1876 and the last in 1893. In the initial one of these
he described *C. hamatus*, an animal somewhat larger than a
tapir, of which he said, further:

29. 1892D, pp. 448–449.

The brain cavity in *Coryphodon* is perhaps the most remarkable feature in the genus, and indicates that the brain itself was of a very inferior type. It was quite small, as in all Eocene mammals, but its most striking features were the small size of the hemispheres, and the large expanded cerebellum. . . . The feet are especially interesting, as they present a primitive or generalized

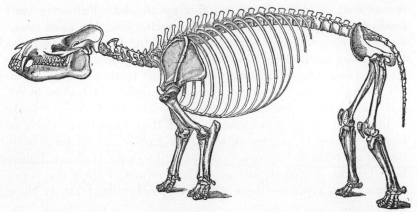

Fig. 31. Restoration of the archaic mammal, *Coryphodon hamatus* Marsh, 1/18 natural size. After Marsh.

type. The manus and pes had each five short digits. . . . The animals of this genus . . . evidently represent a distinct family which may be called Coryphodontidae.[30]

A later paper, "Principal characters of the Coryphodontidae," says that Yale has a large collection of *Coryphodon* remains from Utah, Wyoming, and New Mexico, "amply sufficient" to indicate all the more important characters of the group. Among these specimens are "portions of the same individuals described by Cope under the names *Bathmodon* and *Loxolophodon*, both of which are synonyms of *Coryphodon*. . . . The feet of *Coryphodon* . . . resemble most nearly those of *Dinoceras*." [31]

In 1893, Marsh presented a skeletal restoration of *C. hamatus*, representing an animal which, when alive, was nearly 6 feet in length and about 3 feet in height. He illustrated also

30. 1876D, pp. 426, 428.
31. 1877B, pp. 81, 83.

the detail of the various bones of the fore and hind feet of *Coryphodon, Dinoceras,* and *Elephas,* showing that they have many points in common and that their positions during life were probably nearly the same.[32]

Dinocerata. The relatively abundant short-footed amblypods for which Marsh erected the order Dinocerata (now a sub-order), and which were the subject of some of his most notable researches, lived in Wyoming during the late Paleocene and died out at the close of the Eocene epoch, being the most striking and characteristic animals of middle Eocene (Bridger) time. They are known also from Mongolia, to which they migrated from America. Some of the larger forms, standing 6 to 7 feet high at the shoulders, were elephantlike in bodily build, but they had no trunk and their curious heads were wholly unlike those of proboscideans in that they bore three pairs of horns, and, in the males at least, the upper canine teeth were drawn out into long, recurved, saberlike tusks that must have been terrible weapons, although the manner of their use is not known. It is strange to see such large saberlike teeth in these vegetarian animals.

Although Leidy was the first to describe bones of the Dinocerata, his material was very fragmentary. To Marsh, therefore, belongs, as Wortman said, "the credit of the final determination of their structure and affinities; he classified them in a separate and distinct order, Dinocerata, a name which has been very widely adopted by naturalists." [33]

In September, 1870, as Marsh and his party of students were exploring the Green River Basin, they found an extensive "bone-yard" in which mammal remains were the most abundant fossils. Among these was a partial skeleton of a large beast which Marsh the following year referred doubtfully to Leidy's genus *Titanotherium,* calling the species *T.? anceps.* He returned a number of times to this basin and to other areas, nearly as rich, in the Green River country, and brought back many more specimens of this group, which he named Dinocerata in 1873, and of which he finally had more than 200 individuals, including some 20 skulls in good condition—striking testi-

32. 1893F, p. 321.
33. J. L. Wortman, "Othniel Charles Marsh," *Science* (new ser.), IX (1899), 563.

mony to the tenacity and thoroughness so characteristic of him as a collector.

Between 1872 and 1885, Marsh issued no fewer than 34 papers treating of the Dinocerata, the series culminating in the quarto volume entitled "Dinocerata, a monograph of an extinct order of gigantic mammals," which was one of his best studies. This volume describes 3 of Marsh's own genera, *Dinoceras, Tinoceras,* and *Laoceras,* and 1 of Leidy's, *Uintatherium,* the 4 together having 23 species named by Marsh and 6 more by other authors (Cope 3, Osborn 2, Leidy 1).

It was the naming of these particular mammals that led in large part to the intense rivalry between Cope and Marsh, into which the older Leidy—a man "insensible to and unaffected by the ordinary passions of ambitions or rivalry"—was unfortunately drawn. Up to this time, the field of American Vertebrate Paleontology had been almost wholly in the hands of Leidy, who had described from the West slightly more than 100 species. Most of this material had come into his hands from the various expeditions in which Hayden had been engaged since 1853, and particularly the latter's United States Geological Survey of the Territories, with which Cope had become connected in 1870. The Yale Expedition to the West in that year, however, and its great success in securing vertebrate fossils, as reflected in Marsh's papers of 1871 describing 4 new genera and 27 new species, showed the Philadelphia group—Hayden, Leidy, and Cope—that here was a very real competitor.

Early in 1872 Cope was planning to enter the fossil fields of western Wyoming, and this move, Osborn says,

marks not only his first entry into the western fossil mammal field, but also his entry into serious competition there with Leidy and Marsh . . . Marsh disputed Cope's right to enter the Bridger field. . . . Thus began the intense rivalry in field exploration and the bitter competition for *priority of discovery and publication,* which led to an immediate break in the previously friendly relations between Cope and Marsh.[34]

Cope withdrew his operations to the Washakie Basin, which Marsh had not entered, but his determination not to be antici-

34. H. F. Osborn, *Cope: Master Naturalist* (1931), p. 177. Princeton University Press.

pated by Marsh in the naming of fossils led him to send to the secretary of the American Philosophical Society on August 17, 1872, a telegram which attempted to "define" the new genus *Loxolophodon* (inadvertently changed by the telegraph operator to *Lefalophodon*) and three of its species—a document probably unique in paleontological history. In the meantime Marsh printed in the *American Journal* for September (advance copies appearing on August 19) a definition of his new genus *Tinoceras*, and Hay in his catalogue of 1902, regarding the two genera as representing the same animal, gave the priority to *Tinoceras*. In this decision Osborn concurs in part, saying that Marsh's paper naming *Tinoceras* "preceded Cope's *Lefalophodon* telegram of August 17, 1872, in print. . . . [and] according to the laws of nomenclature the *rights of priority* in scientific names rest upon the *dates of publication*." However, it was his opinion that the names *Tinoceras* and *Lefalophodon=Loxolophodon* apply to different animals.[35]

The summer of 1872 found Leidy also collecting in the Bridger Basin of Wyoming and finding "many interesting fossils." On the twenty-fourth of July he, too, sent in from the field for publication by the Philadelphia Academy a paper (in the form of a letter to Mr. Tryon of the Academy) entitled "On some new species of fossil Mammalia from Wyoming"; a preprint of this paper was received by Marsh on August 2 and the paper itself was printed in the *Proceedings* of the Academy on September 3.[36] In this hastily written paper, Leidy named 3 new species and 2 new genera: the "pachyderm," *Uintatherium robustum*, and "a most formidable carnivore," *Uintamastix atrox*, the latter based on a saberlike canine, 9 inches long, which in the end was found to belong to the "pachyderm." Hay, attempting to straighten out the snarl, notes in his catalogue of 1902 that the name *Loxolophodon* was first employed by Cope himself in February, 1872, for *Bathmodon semicinctus*, now regarded as a species of *Coryphodon*, which is wholly unrelated to *Loxolophodon* of August, 1872. Surely, haste makes waste, and even after seventy-five years the rising generation of vertebrate paleontologists is still obliged to become familiar

35. Osborn, *op. cit.,* p. 179.
36. Also, curiously, in the *American Journal of Science* for September.

with these useless names, in which so much ugly history lies buried.

After the early 'seventies, Leidy dropped more and more out of the field of western Vertebrate Paleontology, but Cope in 1872 published 34 notes and papers on fossils from the West —a strong indication of his intention to stay there. Between 1871 and 1884, Marsh put out 34 papers on the Dinocerata and Cope at least 29, this group being the chief battlefield. Seven of Cope's papers describing new genera and species were dated 1872; Marsh doubted this dating, and set to work to find out the actual dates of issue, presenting his findings in different publications during the year 1873. As a result of this tangle of conflicting dates, the taxonomy of the Dinocerata is not yet settled and will not be until some judicially minded vertebrate paleontologist, fully conversant with the International Rules of Nomenclature, studies all the great mass of material in the various museums.

The type species of the Dinocerata, Marsh declared in July, 1881, is *Dinoceras mirabile* Marsh, and he adds that "especial pains have been taken to work out the osteology of this animal, as a key to the structure of the group." Presenting a skeletal restoration of this form, he notes as among the points of interest:

(1) The absence of a proboscis as claimed by Cope in *Eobasileus*.

(2) The "horn cores" of the skull. Examination of a large number of these, from individuals of various ages, he says,

indicates that the posterior pair, on the parietals, were sheathed with thickened integument, which may have developed into true horn, as in the Pronghorn (*Antilocapra Americana*). . . . The pair of elevations on the maxillaries are equally rugose, and bear evidence of a similar covering. The small tubercles on the nasals are usually smoother, and were probably without horn-like sheathing. The three pairs of elevations are present in both sexes, but are proportionally smaller in the females.

(3) The canine tusks, which he found to be common to both sexes but large and powerful in the males only.

With regard to the various genera he adds:

The material now available for a restoration of *Tinoceras grande* Marsh, is sufficient to show that this animal was similar in general proportions to *Dinoceras mirabile,* but of much larger size. The few specimens that can at present be referred to *Uintatherium* leave many points in its structure undecided. The type specimen of this genus is from a lower horizon than that of either *Dinoceras* or *Tinoceras;* and the evidence now at hand seems to indicate that *Uintatherium* is the oldest and most generalized form of the *Dinocerata.* One specimen in the Yale Museum from near the original locality, and agreeing, so far as the comparison can be made, with the type, has four lower premolars. This character will serve to distinguish *Uintatherium* from *Dinoceras,* to which it has various points of resemblance. *Tinoceras* is from a horizon higher than *Dinoceras,* and is much the most specialized genus of the group.[37]

A preliminary report bearing the title, "The gigantic mammals of the order Dinocerata," appeared in the *Fifth Annual Report* of the United States Geological Survey for 1885, pages 243–302. The memoir itself, with 237 pages of quarto text, 56 plates, and 200 woodcuts, appeared as Volume X in the monograph series of the Survey, under the date of 1886. An author's edition was printed privately for Marsh, on special paper with very wide margins, as in *Odontornithes.* The lithographed plates for this memoir had been delivered to the Public Printer previous to July, 1884, and cost the Survey $11,000 for an edition of 3,050 copies; the cost to Marsh for his edition of 500 copies was $1,247.50.

The question has been asked more than once: What was the actual date of publication of the Dinocerata volume? The evidence seems to be as follows: Marsh was allowed by Director Powell of the Survey to have the volume printed in New Haven by Tuttle, Morehouse and Taylor. The plates were lithographed from drawings by Berger and printed by Crisand, and the wood engravings were made by Hopson and Sherman. All the drawings had been forwarded by Marsh to the Survey on June 4, 1881, with a request for permission to have the work done as above mentioned. A letter from Marsh to Powell on December 12, 1884, says:

37. 1881G, pp. 31–32.

My Monograph on the Dinocerata is now completed, and nearly all of it in type. A large portion is already electrotyped, the type and paging corresponds strictly to the standard of the Survey. I shall send you the volume in the printed sheets, instead of MS., and the Public Printer can then either have the type reset, or take the electrotyped pages at cost of composition. The latter course was pursued in the case of my volume on the Odontornithes.

Marsh's printed letter of transmission of the volume bears the date of December 15, 1884, and the title page of the author's edition is dated "Washington, 1884." The Survey edition has 1886 as the date of publication, and on page 237 appears the following statement: "With the permission of the Director of the U. S. Geological Survey, an author's edition of 500 copies of this work was printed in February, 1885." Either verbally or by letter, Williston told Cope that this author's edition was delivered to Marsh by the New Haven printers in February, 1885, and this is correct, since the authors have before them the Tuttle, Morehouse and Taylor bill for "500 copies, Dinocerata," dated February 26, 1885. Sir Archibald Geikie acknowledged receipt of a copy in London under the date of April 8, 1885, and Harger's notes show that Marsh presented him with a copy on April 18.

In the Preface to the Dinocerata volume, Marsh says that it was his aim to make the illustrations "tell the main story. . . . What is now especially needed in Palæontology is, not long descriptions of fragmentary fossils, but accurate illustrations of characteristic type specimens."

Of the Dinocerata themselves he said:

The Dinocerata form a well-marked order in the great group of Ungulata. In some of their characters, they resemble the Artiodactyls (*Paraxonia*); in others, they are like the Perissodactyls (*Mesaxonia*); and in others still, they agree with the Proboscidians. The points of similarity, however, are in most cases general characters, which point back to an earlier, primitive, ungulate, rather than indicate a near affinity with existing forms of these groups. . . .

The Dinocerata now known may be placed in three genera; *Dinoceras, Tinoceras,* and *Uintatherium.* These may be separated by characters of the skull, vertebrae, and feet. . . . Twenty-nine species may be distinguished, mainly by the skull alone, which, at present, offers the best distinctive characters.[38]

In this monograph, Marsh goes more fully than heretofore into his "Law of brain-growth" in Cenozoic mammals. In the group under discussion, he says, the brain is "especially remarkable for its diminutive size. It was proportionally smaller than in any other known mammal, recent or fossil, and even less than in some reptiles. It was, indeed, the most reptilian brain in any known mammal." [39]

In Marsh's restorations of the male of *Dinoceras mirabile* and *Tinoceras ingens* more than 200 individuals were used, because none of the skeletons of these species was complete when found. Describing the appearance of the animal, he said:

In its stature and movements, *Dinoceras* probably resembled the elephant as much as any other existing form. Its remarkable skull, longer neck, and more bent fore limbs, gave it, however, a very different appearance from any known Proboscidian. The high protuberances on the head, the long trenchant canine tusks, and the peculiar lower jaw modified for their protection, are features seen together only in this group.

The neck was long enough to permit the head to reach the ground, and hence a proboscis was quite unnecessary. The horizontal narial opening, the long overhanging nasal bones, and the well developed turbinal bones, are likewise proof positive against the presence of such an organ. . . .

That the *Dinocerata* were very abundant for a long time during the middle Eocene is proved, conclusively, by their numerous remains in deposits of this age. . . . [The males] were certainly thrice-armed, and well fitted to protect themselves, and their weaker associates, from any of their Eocene enemies. . . .

The short robust feet of the *Dinocerata* were doubtless covered below with a thick pad, as in the elephant, since the whole under side of the foot clearly indicates such a protection.[40]

With reference to the size of the animals, he states that *Tinoceras ingens* in the flesh was about 12 feet long in body, or 16

38. 1885A, pp. 9–10, 191.
39. *Ibid.*, p. 53.
40. *Ibid.*, pp. 166–168.

feet from nose to end of tail. The height to the top of the back was about 6½ feet, the weight at least 6,000 pounds. *Dinoceras mirabile* was about one-fifth smaller. Many replicas of Marsh's restoration of the latter animal were sent out to other museums between 1885 and 1888 (see Chapter XII).

Discussing the problem raised by the extinction of these great brutes, Marsh had this to say:

In the lower Eocene, the largest land mammal was *Coryphodon*, more than the equal, in size and power, of any of the reptiles of that time. *Dinoceras* and its allies, in the middle Eocene, were much larger, and were clearly the monarchs of the region in which they lived. In the upper Eocene, *Diplacodon*, about the size of the rhinoceros, was the largest mammal, but each of these three died out in the period in which it flourished.[41]

PROBOSCIDIANS

The Proboscidea form one of the larger groups of mammals on which Marsh did almost no research. He was, however, concerned, more or less, with the collecting of two important specimens of the American mastodon.

In the autumn of 1866, a Mr. R. Safely wrote Professor Dana about the finding of a mastodon jaw imbedded in peat and driftwood in a pothole at Cohoes, New York. Marsh hastened to the place, probably thinking that he might secure the specimen, but found that it had been given to the New York State Museum. Long the pride of the Albany institution, its geological environment was elaborately described in the annual report for 1871 by James Hall and by G. K. Gilbert—the latter's introductory paper in Geology.

With the second mastodon Marsh was much more intimately connected, and the manner in which he secured it has become one of the Marsh legends, appearing in a number of different guises. Possibly the most reliable account was Wyckoff's "A chase for a mastodon," which appeared in the New York *Tribune* for May 18, 1875. Bones of the creature were first found in 1872 on the farm of Andrew Mitchell near Otisville, New York, in a little swamp which was being excavated for fertilizer. These first bones, which were ribs, were thrown on the muck

41. *Ibid.*, pp. 189–190.

heap, but when a vertebra turned up, Mr. Mitchell, inclined
to keep so curiously shaped a "root," suggested that it would
make a good spittoon. Mrs. Mitchell, however, was unimpressed
with the idea, and not until the huge pelvic arch came along,
and then the skull, did the farmer realize what a bonanza he
had. The news spread to the countryside, and thus to the newspapers, and the pilgrimage of the curious to Otisville began.
Scientists, fearful lest the valuable remains suffer from lack
of care, wrote Mitchell detailed instructions as to what should
be done with the bones, one of these advisers being Professor
Marsh and another Waterhouse Hawkins. The notoriety had
the usual effect of causing the discoverer to have visions of
millions of greenbacks, and the price of the bones began to soar.
Unfortunately for him, 1873 was a panic year, and the subsequent hard times at last narrowed the field of competitors
down to one from New Jersey (unnamed in the *Tribune* but
known to be Professor Guyot of Princeton), a local resident,
and Marsh. In the spring of 1875, Mitchell, suddenly tired of
the haggling, boxed up the bones and announced his determination to sell them at once. Marsh, although in the midst
of the Red Cloud controversy, sensed a crisis and started for
Otisville. It is at this point that the accounts differ, one stating
that Guyot and Marsh left New York on the same train,
another that Marsh was on an express that did not stop at
Otisville whereas the accommodation bearing Guyot was sched-
uled to stop there. However, all agree that after Marsh had
had a conference with the conductor of whatever train he was
on, the engineer felt sure that he had a hotbox and stopped
the train just before he got to Otisville to examine it, with the
consequence that when Professor Guyot reached the Mitchell
house, the negotiations were closed and Marsh was the owner
of the mastodon. It has been stated that the boxes of bones were
already on the station platform, addressed to Guyot, and that
Marsh persuaded Mitchell to change their destination. It is
hardly possible to refute this, after so great a lapse of time,
but it can be said that a series of friendly letters from Guyot
to Marsh, continuing for a number of years afterward, bear
no suggestion that the Princeton professor felt that he had
been tricked into losing so fine a specimen.

Marsh published a restoration of the Otisville mastodon

in 1892, and its skeleton is one of the finest in the Marsh Collections at Yale. When alive, it stood about 12 feet high and was perhaps twice that in length, including the tusks. The latter were very large, and considerably divergent; there were no inferior tusks, and no traces of their alveoli.

PERISSODACTYLS

Perissodactyls are hoofed mammals with an odd number of toes. The order is divided into two suborders: one, a highly diversified group (Chelopoda) having hoofed toes, as in the horses, brontotheres, tapirs, and rhinoceroses; the other, a

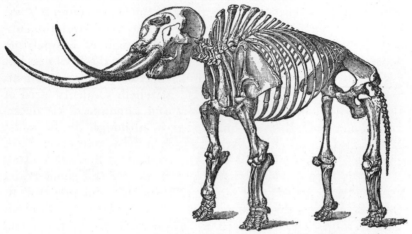

Fig. 32. Restoration by Marsh of the Yale specimen of *Mastodon americanus* Cuvier, from Otisville, N. Y. About 1/60 natural size.

small aberrant group (Ancylopoda) having clawed toes, as in the curious extinct chalicotheres. It embraces at least 10 families, 2 of horses, 1 of brontotheres, 2 of tapirs, 4 of rhinoceroses, and the chalicotheres.

Horses. Marsh's work on the fossil horses of America was among his most important pieces of research, but it has already been discussed at some length in the chapter dealing with his support of the evolutionary theory, and so needs little space in this section of the book. His initial contact with these interesting members of the ancient American faunas was made in 1868, as a result of his first trip West, when the "human" remains in the well at Antelope Station, Nebraska, were shown by him to belong to 15 species in 11 genera of fossil vertebrates of Miocene age. Among these animals were four kinds of horses, one of which, named by him *Equus* (now *Protohippus*) *parvulus*, was the smallest horse then known, about 30 inches high. The number of fossil American horses recognized at that time was 17, most of which had been named by Leidy.

Between 1868 and 1892, Marsh issued 13 papers relating to fossil horses, and in them he named 19 new species (1 a synonym) and 8 new genera (2 synonyms). His genera, arranged in the order of their description, are: *Orohippus* (1872), *Miohippus* and *Pliohippus* (1874), *Mesohippus* (1875), *Eohippus* (1876), *Epihippus* (1878), and *Helohippus* (1892, a synonym of *Orohippus*, as is *Orotherium* 1872).

His first striking paper on horses appeared early in 1874 and was entitled, "Notice of new equine mammals from the Tertiary formation." In it he describes as new the species *Orohippus major, Miohippus annectens, Anchitherium anceps, A. celer, Pliohippus pernix, P. robustus, Protohippus avus,* and *Anchippus brevidens,* the genera *Miohippus* and *Pliohippus* also being new. At this time 30 or more kinds of fossil horses had been brought to light.

In the paper of April, 1892, which he called "Recent polydactyl horses," Marsh goes into a long and detailed discussion of the feet in the different forms of horses and other mammals, and finally speculates thus as to the mammalian radicle that gave rise to the horses:

The oldest ancestor of the horse, as yet undiscovered, undoubtedly had five toes on each foot, and probably was not larger than a rabbit, perhaps much smaller. This hypothetical predecessor of the horse . . . may be called *Hippops*. A still more primitive ancestral form, and next older in the series of Ungulates, will show the more generalized characters of the group called by the writer *Holodactyla* (Dinocerata, p. 172), from which both the Perissodactyles and the Artiodactyles branched off before the equine line became distinct.

It is impossible to say from what generalized form the horse line first separated, but at present the probabilities point to a genus allied to the Eocene *Hyracotherium*, Owen (1839), as the stem.

. . . The *Helohyidae* may with some probability be now regarded as the family from which equine mammals were derived.[42]

In connection with his study of rudimentary digits in recent horses, Marsh acquired a specimen (still in the Yale Collection) which gave him one of his favorite stories. One day, while walking through a New Haven street, he met a venerable Negro driving a dilapidated horse attached to an ash cart. A peculiar protuberance on one of the horse's forelegs attracted his attention, and, on examination, he found it to be in reality a rudimentary digit. Wishing to have the specimen for his collection, he said to the old man: "George, if anything ever happens to that horse, I'll give you five dollars for that leg of his." The latter was so surprised that he could only reply, "Boss, does yo' mean dat?" "Certainly," said the Professor, and walked on.

That evening, on reaching his home on Prospect Street, the Professor was astonished to see the aged Negro waiting for him at the door, and under his arm a suspicious-looking bundle, which he offered to Marsh. Opened, the bundle proved to contain the coveted equine leg, and in reply to the Professor's look of astonishment, the old fellow, slightly embarrassed, said, "Dat ole hoss, you see, he up an' died!"

The Giant Brontotheres. On the third Yale expedition to the West, in 1872, two members of the party, H. B. Sargent and J. W. Griswold, found remains of a huge mammal to which Marsh in the following year gave the interesting name *Brontotherium gigas*, the "great thunder beast." Marsh showed this striking new type to be a true perissodactyl, and, according to Osborn who monographed the group later, "was able in a very few words to throw a flood of light upon the characters of the skeleton." These animals are often called titanotheres, but since the generic name *Titanotherium* no longer stands, it would seem that for the name of the group we should fall back upon Marsh's term brontotheres. This is also Scott's conclusion (1937). These creatures once roamed in great herds over what is now the Great Plains of eastern Colorado, Wyoming, Dakota, and Nebraska. Their brains were no larger than a man's fist in the largest of the tribe, which attained

42. 1892C, pp. 351–352.

almost the bulk of an elephant, and, as Scott says, they must have been "even more dull and stupid than the modern rhinoceros."

Although elephantine in bulk, the brontotheres were less heavily built proportionally, and stood somewhat higher. The head was saddle-shaped, with a blunt horn on either side of the nose. The first of the group were comparatively low of stature, and their "horns" were small knobs, well back of the eyes. With the passage of geologic time, the horns grew longer and the animals larger, so that the skull became a yard long and the horns a foot high and on the very end of the nose. The horns were extraordinarily varied in shape and size, and were undoubtedly used as offensive weapons.

These peculiar mammals are thought to have been immigrants to this country, presumably from Asia. They appeared early in the Eocene (Wasatch), were the largest animals in North America in the early Oligocene, and died out at the close of White River time (Chadron), covering a geologic interval of about 10,000,000 years. Recently they have been discovered in somewhat younger Oligocene strata in Mongolia, and they are found also in southeastern Europe. Their genetic evolution took place along 4 main stems, but, counting all the side branches, Osborn in 1929 indicated not less than 8 phyletic lines, with 23 genera, 8 of which were named by Marsh.

Between 1873 and 1891, Marsh published 13 papers on these animals, describing 13 new genera (4 synonyms, 1 indeterminate) with 21 new species (5 synonyms). His important article of January, 1874, "On the structure and affinities of the Brontotheridae," described *Brontotherium* with the species *B. ingens*, now held to be a synonym of *Menodus giganteus* Pomel. In his discussion of the group as a whole, he said:

Although these animals are less remarkable than the Dinocerata of the Eocene, which they seem to have replaced, they equalled them in size, and resembled them in several important features, notably in the structure of the feet, and in having the head armed with a pair of powerful horns. The general structure of the group, however, clearly indicates that they do not belong in the order *Dinocerata*, but should be placed with the Perissodactyls, in which they form a well-marked family. . . .

PLATE XXIX

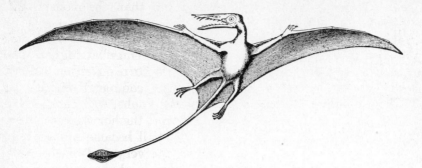

RESTORATION PUBLISHED BY MARSH IN 1882

ORIGINAL SPECIMEN, IN YALE PEABODY MUSEUM

THE BAVARIAN JURASSIC PTERODACTYL
RHAMPHORHYNCHUS PHYLLURUS MARSH

PLATE XXX

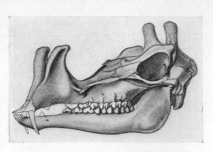

MARSH'S RESTORATION OF
THE MALE SKULL OF
PROTOCERAS CELER

RESTORATION, BY CHILDS FRICK,
OF A LATER MEMBER OF THE SAME
GROUP, *PROSYNTHETOCERAS*

MOUNTED SKELETONS IN YALE PEABODY MUSEUM

ABOVE: ARCHAIC CARNIVORE *DROMOCYON VORAX* MARSH,
ABOUT THE SIZE OF A LARGE DOG. BELOW: *BRONTOPS RO-
BUSTUS* MARSH, ABOUT AS LARGE AS A SMALL ELEPHANT.

*Frick Restoration used by permission of Mr. Frick and the American
Museum of Natural History*

Among the more marked characters of the *Brontotheridae*, which readily distinguish them from the *Rhinocerotidae*, apparently their near allies, may be mentioned the following:—There are four short and thick toes in the manus, and three in the pes. The skull supports a pair of large horn-cores, placed transversely, as in modern Artiodactyls. There are well developed canine teeth in both jaws. The molar teeth, above and below, are not of the *Rhinoceros* type, but resemble those of *Chalicotherium*.[43]

"Notice of new Tertiary mammals," published in March, 1875, has a description of *Anisacodon montanus* and *Diplacodon elatus*. Marsh now had new material from the badlands of Dakota, increasing his collection to more than 100 different individuals. He was satisfied that all brontotheres had horns, in both sexes, and that the osseous horn cores varied much in each species in size and shape, with age and probably with sex. The incisors were small and were often lost in old specimens. At this time he recognized the following brontothere genera: *Titanotherium* Lcidy (syn. *Menodus* Pomel), *Megacerops* Leidy (*Megaceratops* and *Symborodon* Cope), *Brontotherium* Marsh (*Symborodon* in part and *Miobasileus* Cope), and *Anisacodon* Marsh.

April, 1876, saw the publication of "Principal characters of the Brontotheridae," which reported that the brain cavity of *Brontotherium* was small, the cerebral hemispheres not extending at all over the cerebellum and little if any over the olfactory lobes. The hemispheres were comparatively large and much convoluted, the cerebellum small, the pituitary fossa distinctly marked. The neck was stout and of moderate length, the sacrum had four vertebrae, and the caudal vertebrae indicated a long slender tail. The nose was probably flexible, like that of the tapir, but there was evidently no true proboscis. His generic classifications were now changed somewhat, to include *Menodus* Pomel (*Titanotherium* Leidy), *Megacerops* Leidy, *Brontotherium* Marsh, and *Diconodon* Marsh (*Anisacodon*).

In October, 1887, Marsh's paper entitled, "Notice of new fossil mammals," described *Brontops robustus*, *B. dispar*, *Menops varians*, *Allops serotinus*, *Titanops elatus*, and *T.*

43. 1874B, pp. 81, 82.

curtus. The last-named genus includes the largest of the brontotheres, found in the youngest of the Brontotherium beds.

Marsh presented a restoration of *Brontops robustus* in 1889,
pointing out that it represented the largest animal of its
time. This fossil was found in 1874 by "Hank" Clifford south
of the Black Hills near Chadron, Nebraska, not far from the
White River, but not until 1896 were most of its bones finally
recovered by Hatcher, with the exception of the left hind leg.

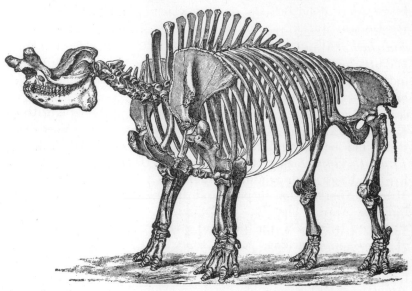

Fig. 33. Restoration of *Brontops robustus* Marsh, drawn by Berger under
Marsh's direction. Based in the main on material from South Dakota, found
by "Hank" Clifford and later collected by Hatcher, supplemented by other
bones found by Marsh himself. About 1/36 natural size. Compare Plate
XXX, bottom.

Mounted, it is one of the striking exhibits in the Yale Museum.
(See Figure 33, and Plate XXX.)

In the early 'eighties, Marsh planned a large and well-
illustrated monograph on the brontotheres, and for it made
60 lithographic plates between 1886 and 1888, at a cost of
$12,830 for an edition of 4,900. At the time of his death in
1899, however, he had not even begun to prepare the manuscript. The United States Geological Survey transferred to
Henry F. Osborn the task of writing the monograph, but he

was not able to finish it until 1919, and another ten years passed before the two handsome volumes appeared under the title, "The titanotheres of ancient Wyoming, Dakota, and Nebraska." It is pleasant to read in this, the most far-reaching work on a single group of vertebrate fossils ever published, that Marsh

made the largest and most valuable contributions to our knowledge of this family and of its evolution. He planned the monumental field work of John Bell Hatcher, by which the great collection for the United States National Museum was made [which has more than 150 skulls and jaws] and he supervised the preparation of sixty lithographic plates, which are here reproduced.[44]

In March, 1893, Hatcher discussed in detail the White River Oligocene strata composing the Brontotherium beds, which have been said to be one of the grandest of mammal-bearing horizons. The lower beds, from his account, have a thickness of 50 feet, the middle ones of 100 feet, and the upper beds of 30 feet, making a total of 180 feet. During the fifteen months of 1886–88 that Hatcher worked in these beds for Marsh, he collected or purchased nearly 200 complete skulls and many more or less complete skeletons, and scarcely a single foot of sediment within the entire vertical range of the beds is unrepresented by material. Individuals found near the bottom of the Brontotherium beds, he reports,

are little, if any, larger than the living rhinoceros. From this they gradually increase in size as we go up until at the top we find a type described by Professor Marsh as *Titanops*, rivaling the modern elephant in size.[45]

Osborn summarized Marsh's work on the brontotheres thus:

(1) He and his party explored the White River formation in Colorado and collected from it many remarkably fine specimens; (2) he demonstrated the ordinal position of the group, classifying its members as perissodactyls; (3) he recognised the fact that the titanotheres constitute a distinct family, which he named the

44. H. F. Osborn, *Mon.* 55, U. S. Geol. Surv. (1929), 953 pp., 797 figs., 236 pls. 2 vols.

45. J. B. Hatcher, "The Titanotherium Beds," *Amer. Nat.*, XXVII (1893), 214.

Brontotheridae; (4) he made the illuminating observation that his
upper Eocene genus *Diplacodon* served to connect the Oligocene
Brontotheridae with the Eocene "Limnohyidae"; (5) he published
many excellent lithographs and woodcuts, showing chiefly the
skulls and dentition of titanotheres, but including also (1889) an
excellent restoration of *Brontops robustus;* (6) he supervised the
preparation of a fine series of lithographic plates for the present
work; (7) under the auspices of the United States Geological
Survey he founded the present series of monographs on fossil vertebrates; (8) he began the preparation of the present monograph,
although he left no manuscript for it; (9) he obtained for the
National and Yale Museums their superb specimens of titanotheres,
most of which were collected by his field assistant, J. B. Hatcher,
who in turn made valuable scientific contributions to our knowledge
of these animals.

Marsh's detailed systematic work on the titanotheres was less
fortunate than his broader contributions, owing chiefly to confusion
in regard to features of the skull and jaw. . . . Cope, like Marsh,
failed to distinguish the sexes as well as the separate groups or
phyla of titanotheres.[46]

Rhinoceroses. The primitive rhinoceroses, which were abundant and varied in America in the lower and middle Eocene
but were almost gone by the end of that epoch, are divided
by Scott (1937) into four families. The two on which Marsh
worked were:

Hyrachyidae, or primitive rhinos. Included here are the Marsh
    genera *Colodon,* 1890, with *C. luxatus; Colonoceras,* 1873, with
    C. agrestis; Helaletes, 1872, with *H. boops* and *H. nanus;* and
    the species *affinis, ?bairdianus,* and *princeps* of Leidy's genus
    Hyrachyus.
Rhinocerotidae, or true rhinos. The following Marsh genera belong
    here: *Diceratherium,* 1875, with *D. annectens, D. armatum,* and
    D. oregonensis; and *Amynodon,* 1877, with *A. advenus;* and the
    species *Aphelops ? matutinus* and *Aceratherium acutum = Tel-
    eoceras fossiger* (Cope).

Helaletes, according to Marsh's Nashville address, was found
in the middle Eocene in some numbers, and was hardly larger

46. H. F. Osborn, *op. cit.,* pp. 145, 146.

than the small horses of that day. The closely allied *Hyrachyus*,
one of the most abundant forms, he considered closely related
to the lower Eocene *Lophiodon* of Europe, and strongly resembling the living tapir in teeth and skeleton, the tapir and
rhinoceros ancestry seeming to coincide to this point. *Colodon
luxatus*, a probable lineal descendant of *Helaletes*, occurs in
the Brontotherium beds of Dakota.

Of true rhinos, Marsh's *Diceratherium* of the Miocene, the
first horned rhinoceros discovered in this country, with four
species (one a synonym), had a pair of horns that were placed
transversely instead of one behind the other in the median line,
as in the rest of the family. *Aphelops* of Cope was hornless,
while *Teleoceras fossiger* (Cope), the short-legged, barrel-
bodied rhino, found in such abundance by Hatcher on his first
collecting trip to Kansas, had a very small horn on the tip
of the nose.

Of the rhinocerine phyletic lines, Marsh said in 1877:

Strangely enough, the rhinoceros line, before it becomes distinct,
separates into two branches. In the upper part of the Dinoceras
beds [= middle Eocene] we have the genus *Colonoceras*, which is
really a *Hyrachyus* with a transverse pair of very rudimentary
horn-cores on the nasal bones. In the lower Miocene [= Oligocene]
west of the Rocky Mountains this line seems to pass on through the
genus *Diceratherium*, and in the higher Miocene [= Oligocene]
this genus is well represented. Some of the species nearly equaled in
size the existing rhinoceros, which *Diceratherium* strongly resembled. . . .

Returning now to the other branch of the rhinoceros group,
which left their remains mainly east of the Rocky Mountains, we
find that all the known forms are hornless. The upper Eocene
genus, *Amynodon*, is the oldest known rhinoceros, and by far the
most generalized of the family. . . . The genus *Hyracodon* of the
Miocene [= Oligocene], which is essentially a rhinoceros . . .
[arose in] *Hyrachyus*. . . . *Hyracodon*, however, appears to be
off the true line, for it has but three toes in front. . . . In the
Pliocene are several species closely related, and of large size. Above
the Pliocene in America, no vestiges of the rhinoceros have been
found.[47]

47. 1877F, pp. 25–26.

Chalicotheres. The strange beasts that make up the sub-order Ancylopoda, clawed perissodactyls, should dispel forever the notion, first stated by Cuvier, that paleontologists can reconstruct an extinct animal from a single tooth or bone. The group had long been known in Europe, but when the first American representatives of it came into Marsh's hands, in 1873, he considered them gigantic edentates, although recognizing that the foot bones—all the material he had—were unlike those of any other American members of that group. When he described the material as *Moropus* (with three species) in 1877, he observed its affinities with the genus *Ancylotherium,* based by Gaudry in 1863 upon foot bones found in the famous Pikermi beds of Greece. He subsequently erected for the genus the new family Moropodidae.

The next step in the solution of the relationship of the animals to whom these clawed feet belonged was not made until 1887, when similar feet were found attached to a skeleton having a skull and teeth that matched those of the genus *Chalicotherium,* described from Germany in 1833 by Kaup. The new animal entity, with the teeth of an ungulate and the feet of an edentate, of course had to bear the name first proposed; i.e., *Chalicotherium;* and Cope soon suggested the ordinal name Ancylopoda, to include it and its allies. The most recent textbook on fossil mammals, that by Scott (1937), reduces the Ancylopoda to a suborder under the Perissodactyla and uses the family name Chalicotheriidae with Moropodinae as one of its subdivisions. As Holland and Peterson say, in their monograph of 1914 on the chalicotheres: "Marsh, with only a few fragments before him ventured, on what we now know to have been very insufficient grounds, to set up the family Moropodidae. . . . It was a shrewd guess, which somewhat overshot the mark." [48]

The strange creature now known to have walked on the feet that Marsh christened *Moropus* was a bundle of Cuvierian contradictions. With a skull somewhat horselike, it had the deep, short-coupled body of a camel, and feet and legs rather like those of a bear. Moreover, in spite of the great claws that were one of its striking features, its teeth show plainly that

48. W. J. Holland and O. A. Peterson, "The Osteology of the Chalicotheroidea," *Mem. Carnegie Mus.* (1913), III, 202.

it was herbivorous in diet, and the suggestion has been made that the claws were used in digging up roots, etc. Its ancestry is wholly unknown, but the animal itself has been described in great detail and many museums have complete skeletons of it, most of them from the celebrated bone quarry at Agate, Nebraska, in the Harrison stage of the lower Miocene, from which the Carnegie Museum secured much *Moropus* material. The Yale, Carnegie, and American museums each have mounted specimens, which show the animal to have been considerably larger than a horse.

Marsh commented on the distribution of the chalicotheres in his paper of 1877, saying that they have now been found in western America, China, India, Greece, Germany, and France, "indicating thus, as I believe, the path by which many of our ancient mammals helped to people the so-called Old World." [49] In America, the genus *Chalicotherium* occurs in the lower Oligocene (White River) and *Moropus* in the upper Oligocene (John Day) and middle Miocene.

ARTIODACTYLS

The order Artiodactyla embraces those mammals in which the third and fourth digits are about equally developed and the ungual phalanges are flattened on their contiguous sides, so that together they constitute a symmetrical form; in other words, they are even-toed, in contrast to the odd-toed perissodactyls. The axis, or middle line, of the whole foot lies between the third and fourth digits. The order includes such seemingly diverse types as hippopotami, swine, deer, and camels. It goes back to the beginning of the Eocene, but in the early part of its history was subordinate in importance to the perissodactyls. This relative importance was later reversed, and in the living world the artiodactyls are the most numerous of hoofed animals.

The following table, in the main after Scott (1937), gives a partial classification of the Artiodactyla, showing only the families in which Marsh describes genera or species.

Order Artiodactyla.
   Section A. Non-Ruminantia.
      Suborder I. Palæodonta. Ancient and primitive artiodactyls.

49. 1877F, p. 27.

Family 1. Leptochœridae. 1 genus (1), 2 species.

Family 2. Dichobunidae. 4 genera, 6 species.

Family 3. Entelodontidae. "Giant pigs." 2 genera, 7 species.

Suborder II. Hyodonta. Swinelike artiodactyls.

Family 4. Tagassuidae. American swine or peccaries. 1 genus (1), 10 species.

Suborder III. Ancodonta. Extinct forms.

Family 5. Anthracotheriidae. 5 genera (1), 9 species.

Genesis uncertain.

Family 6. Merycoidodontidae. 2 genera (1), 3 species.

Family 7. Agriochœridae. 2 genera (1), 2 species.

Section B. Ruminantia.

Suborder IV. Tylopoda. Camels, etc.

Family 8. Camelidae. Camels and llamas. 1 species.

Family 9. Leptomerycidae. 2 genera, 5 species.

Suborder VI. Pecora. Sheep, antelopes, etc. Marsh did very little work on this suborder.

Family 14. Bovidae. Oxen, bison, sheep, goats. 2 species (1).

Nonruminant Artiodactyls. The nonruminants, in Scott's classification, comprehend three suborders and one group of uncertain genesis. To each of the three suborders—Palæodonta, Hyodonta, and Ancodonta—and to the less well-determined oreodonts and agriochœrids, Marsh made some contribution, as summarized in the foregoing table. Most of these genera need no special mention here. Of most interest is the family Entelodontidae, or "giant pigs," within which Marsh named the following genera and species: *Ammodon* and *A. leidyanus*, 1893; *Archæotherium clavum clavum*, 1893; *A. crassum*, 1873; *Parahyus* and *P. vagus*, 1876; *P. aberrans*, 1894; *Pelonax bathrodon*, 1874, and *P. potens*, 1893.

The systematic position of this group is in doubt, according to Scott. They are usually included in the same suborder as the peccaries and swine, but the relationship may be very remote.

The family Elotheridae (included by Scott with the entelodonts), discussed by Marsh in 1894, had individuals of large size surpassed in bulk among their contemporaries only by members of the rhinoceros family and the huge brontotheres. *Elotherium* [*Archæotherium*] *crassum*, as restored by Marsh, was more than 7 feet in length and about 4 feet in height. Its remains were found in the Oligocene (Chadron) of northeast Colorado and in South Dakota. According to Marsh, its most striking features were

the large and peculiar skull, and the elongate and slender limbs and feet, characters that do not in themselves suggest the suilline affinities of the animal, which a closer study brings to light. . . . The brain itself was very diminutive. This was also true of the other known species, and was probably the main reason which led to the early extinction of the whole group.

The slender, highly specialized feet and limbs . . . indicate clearly that the animal was capable of considerable speed. . . . In each foot there are only two functional digits, corresponding to the third and fourth in man.[50]

The Palæodonta again show Marsh's tendency to study genetic lines and evolutionary principles, as indicated in still another portion of his address of 1877, in which he says:

The molar teeth . . . are very similar to those of the Eocene *Hyracotherium*, of Europe, which is supposed to be a Perissodactyle, while *Helohyus* certainly is not, but apparently a true lineal ancestor of the existing pigs. In every vigorous primitive type which was destined to survive many geological changes, there seems to have been a tendency to throw off lateral branches, which became highly specialized and soon died out, because they are unable to adapt themselves to new conditions. The narrow path of the persistent Suilline type, throughout the whole Tertiary, is strewed with the remains of such ambitious offshoots; while the typical pig, with an obstinacy never lost, has held on in spite of catastrophes and evolution, and still lives in America to-day. In the lower Eocene, we have in the genus *Parahyus* apparently one of these shortlived, specialized branches. It attained a much larger size than the true lineal forms. . . . In the . . . middle Eocene, we have still, on or near the true line, *Helohyus*, which is the last of the series known from the American Eocene.[51]

50. 1894B, p. 408.
51. 1877F, pp. 27–28.

Ruminant Artiodactyls. In one section of the ruminant artiodactyls, that of the Tylopoda or camelids, two of Marsh's genera deserve notice, if for no other reason than to emphasize his flair for the unusual and striking. Of the camels he described only one species, but that one is memorable, being the strange giraffe-camel, "exceeding in size any previously described from this country, and one in which the extremities were exceedingly elongated." [52] He referred his new species, which he called *altus,* to Leidy's genus *Procamelus,* whence it was removed by W. D. Matthew in 1901 to the more fittingly named genus *Alticamelus.*

The family Leptomerycidae, which represents an American stock of tylopod artiodactyl that lived from Oligocene into lower Pliocene time, had some of the most grotesque animals that ever roamed over North America. *Synthetoceras* Stirton, of the Texas Pliocene, as described by Scott, had two pairs of hornlike protuberances which probably were not sheathed in horn. The posterior pair were shaped like those of a cow, but the anterior pair were fused together for the most of their length and then bifurcated into two prongs that rose much higher than the posterior horns. *Syndyoceras* Barbour, of the lower Miocene, again had cowlike posterior horns, but the forward pair were united only at the base and then curved away from each other. A still older member of the series, the first to be discovered and named, was Marsh's *Protoceras* (1891), which occurs in the river channel sandstones of the upper White River beds, and which has the three species *celer, comptus,* and *nasutus.* A near ally is *Calops* Marsh (1894), with the species *consors* (1897) and *cristatus* (1894). These are decidedly smaller than *Protoceras.* (See Plate XXX.)

The story of the unearthing of the skull of *Protoceras* was a favorite one of Chief Preparator Gibb. In 1890 Hatcher purchased for Marsh, from another collector, some skulls imbedded in a very hard sandstone, with little of the bone showing. These were given to Gibb to clean out of the rock and in due time he saw emerging a head with horns such as he had never beheld before. He kept the skull out of Marsh's sight until most of it was clear of the matrix and then showed it to him. "Good Lord, what is it, Gibb?" exclaimed the startled

52. 1894H, p. 274.

Professor. "I have never seen the like of it! What *is* it?" Gibb said that he thought it was some kind of sheeplike animal. As usual, Marsh wanted the world to know at once what he had found, and he described the queer creature in January, 1891, as the female of the genus *Protoceras*. Of course, Hatcher had to go back to the locality the next year for the male. He studied the ground, found that the sandstone occurred in long, narrow, stringy lentils, and by following these soon came to see that they were the channel fillings of a former stream course (in the Brule formation of the late Oligocene), in which were imbedded much wood and remains of *Protoceras*. He got excellent male skulls and Marsh was happy.

The most striking feature of *Protoceras*, as Marsh pointed out in 1891, was the pair of horn cores, which were situated, not on the frontals but on the parietals, immediately behind the frontal suture and thus directly over the cerebral hemispheres of the brain. The name was given in allusion to the early appearance of horns in this group. The characters, he thought, suggested affinity with the giraffes, but he nevertheless placed the protocerids in a distinct family. The animals were about as large as a sheep, but of more delicate proportions.

In the matter of paired horns, he remarked:

It is an interesting fact, that while all existing mammals with horns in pairs are artiodactyles, and none of the recent perisso-dactyles are thus provided, the reverse of this was true among the early forms of these groups. The *Dinocerata* of the Eocene, a specialized order of ungulates, as well as some of the perissodac-tyles of both the Eocene and Miocene [=Oligocene], had horns in pairs, while no horned artiodactyles have hitherto been known from either the Eocene or Miocene [= Oligocene].[53]

The female skull of *Protoceras*, with its two horns, was figured by Marsh in November, 1893. The male skull had, in addition, "a pair of elevations on the frontals, and a third pair on the maxillaries. With these were elongated canine tusks."[54]

The "principal characters" of the Protoceratidae were dis-cussed in September, 1897, the resemblance of the male skull

53. 1891A, p. 81.
54. 1893G, pp. 407–408.

to that of certain of the Eocene Dinocerata being noted—"a
striking similarity in important features, between skulls pertaining to animals of two distinct orders, and from widely different geological horizons." *Protoceras* was said to have "a
long, flexible nose, if not a true proboscis," as in the living
Saiga antelope of Siberia, a point on which Scott does not
agree. The brain "was of good size, not diminutive as in the
early ungulates. It was, moreover, well convoluted for a
Miocene [Oligocene] mammal, and forms an interesting addition to our knowledge of the brain development in Tertiary
Mammalia." [55]

55. 1897C, p. 172.

LIST OF MARSH GENERA

Synonyms and homonyms in italics

INVERTEBRATES

Brachiospongia 1867
Helminthodes 1864
Ischyracanthus 1865

FOOTPRINTS

Allopus 1894
Baropus 1894
Dromopus 1894
Limnopus 1894
Nanopus 1894
Thinopus 1896

FISHES

Embalorhynchus 1870
Heliobatis 1877 = Dasyatis Rafinesque 1810

AMPHIBIANS

Eobatrachus 1887
Eosaurus 1862

REPTILES

Cotylosaurs
Nothodon 1878 = Diadectes Cope 1878
Pelycosaurs
Ophiacodon 1878
Sphenacodon 1878
Turtles
Glyptops 1890 = Compsemys Leidy 1856
Plesiosaurs
Pantosaurus 1891
Parasaurus 1891 = Pantosaurus 1891

ICHTHYOSAURS
  Baptanodon 1880 = Ophthalmosaurus Seeley 1874
  Sauranodon 1879 = Ophthalmosaurus Seeley 1874

MOSASAURS
  Baptosaurus 1870
  Edestosaurus 1871 = Clidastes Cope 1868
  Halisaurus 1869 = Baptosaurus 1870
  Holosaurus 1880
  Lestosaurus 1872 = Platecarpus Cope 1869
  Rhinosaurus 1872 = Tylosaurus 1872
  Tylosaurus 1872

LIZARDS
  Chamops 1892
  Glyptosaurus 1871
  Iguanavus 1872
  Oreosaurus 1872 = Xestops Cope 1873
  Thinosaurus 1872 = Saniwa Leidy 1870
  Tinosaurus 1872

SNAKES
  Boavus 1871
  Coniophis 1892
  Dinophis 1869 = Palæophis Owen 1840
  Lestophis 1885
  Limnophis 1871 = Lestophis 1885
  Lithophis 1871
  Titanophis 1877 = Palæophis Owen 1840

DINOSAURS
  Allosaurus 1877 = Antrodemus Leidy 1870
  Ammosaurus 1891
  Amphisaurus 1882 = Anchisaurus 1885
  Anchisaurus 1885
  Apatodon 1877
  Apatosaurus 1877
  Atlantosaurus 1877
  Barosaurus 1890
  Brontosaurus 1879
  Camptonotus 1879 = Camptosaurus 1885
  Camptosaurus 1885
  Ceratops 1888
  Ceratosaurus 1884

Claosaurus 1890
Cœlurus 1879
Creosaurus 1878
Diplodocus 1878
Diracodon 1881
Dryosaurus 1894
Dryptosaurus 1877
Hallopus 1881
Labrosaurus 1879
Laosaurus 1878
Macelognathus 1884
Morosaurus 1878 = Camarasaurus Cope 1877
Nanosaurus 1877
Nodosaurus 1889
Ornithomimus 1890
Pleurocœlus 1888 = Astrodon Johnston 1865
Priconodon 1888
Stegosaurus 1877
Sterrholophus 1891 = Triceratops 1889
Titanosaurus 1877 = Atlantosaurus 1877
Torosaurus 1891
Triceratops 1889

PTEROSAURS
Dermodactylus 1881
Nyctodactylus 1881 = Nyctosaurus 1876
Nyctosaurus 1876
Pteranodon 1876

CROCODILES
Diplosaurus 1877 = Goniopholis Owen 1842
Limnosaurus 1872
Stegomus 1896

BIRDS

Aletornis 1872
Apatornis 1873
Baptornis 1877
Barornis 1894
Cimolopteryx 1889
Colonosaurus 1872 = Ichthyornis 1872
Coniornis 1893

Graculavus 1872
Hesperornis 1872
Ichthyornis 1872
Laopteryx 1881
Laornis 1870
Lestornis 1876 = Hesperornis 1872
Palæotringa 1870
Telmatornis 1870
Uintornis 1872

MAMMALS

JURASSIC MAMMALS

Allodon 1881 = Ctenacodon 1879
Asthenodon 1887 = Dryolestes 1878
Ctenacodon 1879
Dicrocynodon 1888 = Docodon 1881
Diplocynodon 1880 = Docodon 1881
Docodon 1881
Dryolestes 1878
Enneodon 1887 = Docodon 1881
Laodon 1887 = Amblotherium Owen 1871
Menacodon 1887 = Tinodon 1879
Paurodon 1887
Priacodon 1887
Stylacodon 1879 = Amblotherium Owen 1871
Tinodon 1879

CRETACEOUS MAMMALS

Allacodon 1889 = Cimolomys 1889
Batodon 1892
Camptomus 1889
Cimolestes 1889
Cimolodon 1889 = Cimolomys 1889
Cimolomys 1889
Didelphodon 1889
Didelphops 1889 = Didelphodon 1889
Dipriodon 1889 = Meniscoëssus Cope 1882
Halodon 1889 = Meniscoëssus Cope 1882
Nanomyops 1892 = Cimolomys 1889
Nanomys 1889 = Cimolomys 1889
Oracodon 1889 = ?Meniscoëssus Cope 1882

Pediomys 1889
Platacodon 1889
Selenacodon 1889 = Meniscoëssus Cope 1882
Stagodon 1889
Telacodon 1892
Tripriodon 1889 = Meniscoëssus Cope 1882

INSECTIVORES
Anisacodon 1872 = Pantolestes Cope 1872
Apatemys 1872
Bathrodon 1872 = Microsyops Leidy 1872
Centetodon 1872
Centracodon 1872
Entomacodon 1872
Entomodon 1872
Lemuravus 1875 = Hyopsodus Leidy 1870
Mesacodon 1872 = Microsyops Leidy 1872
Nyctilestes 1872 = Nyctitherium 1872
Nyctitherium 1872
Passalacodon 1872 = Pantolestes Cope 1872
Talpavus 1872 = Nyctitherium 1872

TILLODONTS
Tillotherium 1873

TÆNIODONTS
Dryptodon 1876
Stylinodon 1874

XENARTHRA
Morotherium 1874

RODENTS
Allomys 1877
Colonomys 1872 = Sciuravus 1871
Sciuravus 1871
Taxymys 1872 = Tillomys 1872
Tillomys 1872

CARNIVORES
Dromocyon 1876
Harpalodon 1872 = Viverravus 1872 and Miacis Cope 1872
Limnocyon 1872
Limnofelis 1872 = Patriofelis Leidy 1870
Oreocyon 1872 = Patriofelis Leidy 1870
Telmatocyon 1899 = Limnocyon 1872

Thinocyon 1872
Triacodon 1871
Viverravus 1872
Vulpavus 1871
Ziphacodon 1872

PRIMATES

Euryacodon 1872
Hemiacodon 1872
Limnotherium 1871 = Notharctus Leidy 1870
Telmatolestes 1872 = Notharctus Leidy 1870
Thinolestes 1872 = Notharctus Leidy 1870

CONDYLARTHS

Eohyus 1877
Hyracops 1892 = Meniscotherium Cope 1874

AMBLYPODS

Dinoceras 1872 = Uintatherium Leidy 1872
Laoceras 1884
Tinoceras 1872 = Uintatherium Leidy 1872

SIRENIANS

Desmostylus 1888

HORSES

Eohippus 1876
Epihippus 1878
Helohippus 1892 = Orohippus 1872
Hippops 1892 (a hypothetical genus)
Mesohippus 1875
Miohippus 1874
Orohippus 1872
Orotherium 1872 = Orohippus 1872
Pliohippus 1874

BRONTOTHERES

Allops 1887
Anisacodon 1875 = Menodus Pomel 1849
Brontops 1887
Brontotherium 1873
Diconodon 1875 = Menodus Pomel 1849
Diplacodon 1875
Diploclonus 1890
Limnohyops 1890
Limnohyus 1872 = Palæosyops Leidy 1870

Menops 1887 = Menodus Pomel 1849
Teleodus 1890
Telmatherium 1872
Titanops 1887 = Brontotherium 1873

TAPIRS
Tanyops 1894
Tapiravus 1877

RHINOCEROSES
Amynodon 1877
Colodon 1890
Colonoceras 1873
Diceratherium 1875
Helaletes 1872

CHALICOTHERES
Moropus 1877

PALÆODONTS
Ammodon 1893
Antiacodon 1872
Homacodon 1872
Laopithecus 1875
Nanomeryx 1894
Parahyus 1876
Stenacodon 1872

OREODONTS
Agriomeryx 1894 = Agriochœrus Leidy 1850
Eomeryx 1877, 1894 = Protoreodon Scott-Osborn 1887
Eporeodon 1875
Hyomeryx 1894

HYODONTS
Thinohyus 1875 = Perchœrus Leidy 1869

ANCODONTS
Elomeryx 1894
Helohyus 1872
Heptacodon 1894
Octacodon 1894
Thinotherium 1872 = Helohyus 1872

PECORA
Calops 1894
Oromeryx 1877, 1894
Parameryx 1877, 1894
Protoceras 1891

BIBLIOGRAPHY OF OTHNIEL CHARLES MARSH

1831–1899

Compiled from three sources: a list of Professor Marsh's papers, prepared by Miss Lucy Peck Bush, his secretary for many years, and published privately by Professor Marsh from time to time; the bibliography appearing in Professor Charles E. Beecher's memorial; and "Bibliographies of the Officers of Yale University, covering the years 1861–1892." About three hundred titles are listed here.

1861

A. The Gold of Nova Scotia. AMER. JOUR. SCI. (2), vol. 32, pp. 395–400, November. Abstract: CANADIAN NAT., vol. 6, pp. 427–430.

1862

A. On the Saurian Vertebrae from Nova Scotia. AMER. JOUR. SCI. (2), vol. 33, p. 278, March.
B. Description of the Remains of a new Enaliosaurian (*Eosaurus acadianus*), from the Coal Formation of Nova Scotia. *Ibid.*, vol. 34, pp. 1–16, pls. i–ii, July. Abstract: CANADIAN NAT., vol. 7, pp. 205–213; QUART. JOUR. GEOL. SOC. LONDON, vol. 19, pp. 52–56, 1863.

1863

A. Catalogue of Mineral Localities in New Brunswick, Nova Scotia, and Newfoundland. AMER. JOUR. SCI. (2), vol. 35, pp. 210–218, March. Abstract: In J. D. Dana, "System of Mineralogy," 5th ed., pp. 789–791, 1868.
B. On the Science of the International Exhibition. AMER. JOUR. SCI. (2), vol. 35, pp. 256–259, March.

1864

A. Notice of a new Fossil Annelid (*Helminthodes antiquus*), from the Lithographic Slates of Solenhofen. *Ibid.*, vol. 38, p. 415, November. Abstract: ZEITS. DEUTSCH. GEOL. GESELL., vol. 16, p. 363; N. JAHRB., p. 57, 1865.

1865

A. [Ueber einen Pterodactylus von Eichstadt, alpinen Muschelkalk und *Solanocrinus costatus.*] ZEITS. DEUTSCH. GEOL. GESELL., vol. 17, p. 13.

B. [New Genus of Jurassic Annelides (*Ischyracanthus*).] *Ibid.*, vol. 17, p. 267.

C. [Double Lobe-lines of *Ceratites nodosus.*] *Ibid.*, vol. 17, pp. 267–269.

1866

A. Description of an ancient Sepulchral Mound near Newark, Ohio. AMER. JOUR. SCI. (2), vol. 42, pp. 1–11, July.

1867

A. Discovery of additional *Mastodon* Remains at Cohoes, New York. *Ibid.*, vol. 43, pp. 115–116, January.

B. A Catalogue of Official Reports upon Geological Surveys of the United States and British Provinces. *Ibid.*, vol. 43, pp. 116–121, 399–404, January. Reprint, pp. 1–14 (slightly different).

C. Notice of a new Genus of Fossil Sponges from the Lower Silurian. *Ibid.*, vol. 44, p. 88, July. Abstract: CANADIAN NAT., n.s., vol. 3, p. 301, 1868.

D. Contributions to the Mineralogy of Nova Scotia. No. 1. Ledererite identical with Gmelinite. AMER. JOUR. SCI. (2), vol. 44, pp. 362–367, November.

1868

A. On the *Palaeotrochis* of Emmons from North Carolina. *Ibid.*, vol. 45, pp. 217–219, March.

B. Observations on the Metamorphosis of *Siredon* into *Amblystoma.* AMER. JOUR. SCI. (2), vol. 46, pp. 364–374, 1 pl., November; ZOOLOGIST, London, vol. 4, pp. 1569–1580, 1869. Abstract: AMER. NAT., vol. 2, p. 493; PROC. BOSTON SOC. NAT. HIST., vol. 12, pp. 97–98, 1869.

C. Notice of a new and diminutive Species of Fossil Horse (*Equus parvulus*), from the Tertiary of Nebraska. AMER. JOUR. SCI. (2), vol. 46, pp. 374–375, November. ANN. MAG. NAT. HIST. (4), vol. 3, pp. 95–96, 1869. Abstract: N. JAHRB., p. 767, 1869.

D. On the Origin of the so-called *Lignilites*, or *Epsomites.* Abstract: PROC. AMER. ASSOC. ADV. SCI., Burlington meeting, 1867, vol. 16, pp. 135–143; CANADIAN NAT., n.s., vol. 3, p. 293.

E. On certain Effects produced upon Fossils by Weathering. Abstract: CANADIAN NAT., n.s., vol. 3, p. 305.

1869

A. Notice of some new Reptilian Remains from the Cretaceous of Brazil. AMER. JOUR. SCI. (2), vol. 47, pp. 390–392, May. ANN. MAG. NAT. HIST. (4), vol. 3, pp. 442–444. Abstract: N. JAHRB., p. 112, 1871.

B. Description of a new Species of *Protichnites* from the Potsdam Sandstone of New York. PROC. AMER. ASSOC. ADV. SCI., 1868, vol. 17, pp. 322–324; AMER. JOUR. SCI. (2), vol. 48, pp. 46–49, 1 pl., July. Abstract: N. JAHRB., p. 536, 1871.

C. Description of a new and gigantic Fossil Serpent (*Dinophis grandis*), from the Tertiary of New Jersey. AMER. JOUR. SCI. (2), vol. 48, pp. 397–400, November. Abstract: AMER. NAT., vol. 4, p. 254, 1870.

D. [The Cardiff Giant.] NEW YORK HERALD, December 1, 1869, p. 8. Reprinted from BUFFALO COURIER, November 29.

E. Notice of some new Mosasauroid Reptiles from the Greensand of New Jersey. AMER. JOUR. SCI. (2), vol. 48, pp. 392–397, November. Abstract: CANADIAN NAT., vol. 4, p. 331; AMER. NAT., vol. 4, p. 62, 1870; GEOL. MAG., vol. 7, pp. 376–377, 1870; N. JAHRB., p. 526, 1870.

F. On the Preservation of Color in Fossils from Paleozoic Formations. PROC. AMER. ASSOC. ADV. SCI., 1868, vol. 17, pp. 325–326.

G. On a remarkable Locality of Vertebrate Remains in the Tertiary of Nebraska. Abstract: CANADIAN NAT., vol. 4, pp. 322–323.

1870

A. Notice of some Fossil Birds from the Cretaceous and Tertiary Formations of the United States. AMER. JOUR. SCI. (2), vol. 49, pp. 205–217, March. Abstract: PROC. ACAD. NAT. SCI. PHILADELPHIA, vol. 22, pp. 5–6; GEOL. MAG., vol. 7, pp. 377–378; N. JAHRB., p. 512; ZEITS. GESAMMT. NATURW., vol. 5, pp. 263–264, 1872.

B. Note on the Remains of Fossil Birds. AMER. JOUR. SCI. (2), vol. 49, p. 272, March.

C. Notice of a new Species of Gavial from the Eocene of New Jersey. *Ibid.*, vol. 50, pp. 97–99, July; GEOL. MAG., vol. 7, p. 427.

D. Rocky Mountain Expedition.—Discovery of the *Mauvaises Terres* Formation in Colorado. AMER. JOUR. SCI. (2), vol. 50, p. 292, September; CANADIAN NAT., vol. 5, p. 240, 1871.

E. [New Fossil Turkey.] PROC. ACAD. NAT. SCI. PHILADELPHIA, vol. 22, p. 11, October; (with additions) AMER. JOUR. SCI. (3), vol. 4, pp. 260–261, 1872. Abstract: AMER. NAT., vol. 4, p. 317, 1871.

F. Notice of some new Tertiary and Cretaceous Fishes. PROC. AMER. ASSOC. ADV. SCI., 1869, vol. 18, pp. 227–230.

G. [New Vertebrate Fossils from New Jersey.] PROC. ACAD. NAT. SCI. PHILADELPHIA, vol. 22, pp. 2–3.

H. [New Fossil Peccary from New Jersey.] PROC. ACAD. NAT. SCI. PHILADELPHIA, vol. 22, p. 11.

1871

A. Scientific Expedition to the Rocky Mountains. AMER. JOUR. SCI. (3), vol. 1, pp. 142–143, February.

B. On the Geology of the eastern Uintah Mountains. *Ibid.*, vol. 1, pp. 191–198, March.

C. Notice of a Fossil Forest in the Tertiary of California. *Ibid.*, vol. 1, pp. 266–268, April. Abstract: N. JAHRB., pp. 892–893.

D. Description of some new Fossil Serpents from the Tertiary Deposits of Wyoming. AMER. JOUR. SCI. (3), vol. 1, pp. 322–329, May; BOLL. R. COMITATO GEOL. D'ITALIA, vol. 3, pp. 273–278, 1872. Abstract: N. JAHRB., p. 986.

E. Notice of some new Fossil Reptiles from the Cretaceous and Tertiary Formations. AMER. JOUR. SCI. (3), vol. 1, pp. 447–459, June; BOLL. R. COMITATO GEOL. D'ITALIA, vol. 3, pp. 278–283, 338–343, 1872. Abstract: N. JAHRB., p. 890; POP. SCI. REV., London, p. 436.

F. Note on a new and gigantic Species of Pterodactyle. AMER. JOUR. SCI. (3), vol. 1, p. 472, June. Abstract: N. JAHRB., p. 890.

G. Notice of some new Fossil Mammals from the Tertiary Formation. AMER. JOUR. SCI. (3), vol. 2, pp. 35–44, July; BOLL. R. COMITATO GEOL. D'ITALIA, vol. 3, pp. 343–350, 1872.

H. Notice of some new Fossil Mammals and Birds from the Tertiary Formation of the West. AMER. JOUR. SCI. (3), vol. 2, pp. 120–127, August; BOLL. R. COMITATO GEOL. D'ITALIA, vol. 3, pp. 350–353, 1872. Abstract: N. JAHRB., pp. 106–107, 1872; ZEITS. GESAMMT. NATURW., vol. 5, p. 264, 1872.

I. Note on *Lophiodon* from the Miocene of New Jersey. PROC. ACAD. NAT. SCI. PHILADELPHIA, vol. 23, pp. 9–10.

J. New Reptiles and Fishes from the Cretaceous and Tertiary Formations. *Ibid.*, pp. 103–105.

1872

A. Discovery of a remarkable Fossil Bird. AMER. JOUR. SCI. (3), vol. 3, pp. 56–57, January. Abstract: NATURE, vol. 5, p. 348, Feb. 29, 1872.

B. Yale College Expedition to the Rocky Mountains and Pacific Coast. AMER. JOUR. SCI. (3), vol. 3, p. 146, February.

C. Discovery of additional Remains of *Pterosauria*, with Descriptions of two new Species. AMER. JOUR. SCI. (3), vol. 3, pp. 241–248, April. Abstract: N. JAHRB., p. 983; NATURE, vol. 5, p. 151, June 20, 1872.

D. Discovery of the dermal Scutes of Mosasauroid Reptiles. AMER. JOUR. SCI. (3), vol. 3, pp. 290–292, April.

E. Notice of a new Species of *Hadrosaurus*. *Ibid.*, vol. 3, p. 301, April.

F. Preliminary Description of *Hesperornis regalis*, with Notices of four other new Species of Cretaceous Birds. *Ibid.*, vol. 3, pp. 360–365, May; ANN. MAG. NAT. HIST. (4), vol. 10, pp. 212–217; BOLL. R. COMITATO GEOL. D'ITALIA, vol. 3, pp. 211–217. Abstract: NATURE, vol. 6, pp. 90, 94, May 30, 1872; ZEITS. GESAMMT. NATURW., vol. 5, p. 263; POP. SCI. REV., London, pp. 316–317; N. JAHRB., p. 983.

G. Note "On two new Ornithosaurians from Kansas." AMER. JOUR. SCI. (3), vol. 3, pp. 374–375, May.

H. On the Structure of the Skull and Limbs in Mosasauroid Reptiles, with Descriptions of new Genera and Species. AMER. JOUR. SCI., (3), vol. 3, pp. 448–464, pls. x–xiii, June. Abstract: N. JAHRB., p. 983; JOUR. ZOOL., Paris, vol. 2, pp. 533–536, 1873.

I. Bowlders in Coal. AMER. NAT., vol. 6, p. 439, July.

J. Preliminary Description of new Tertiary Mammals. Pt. I. AMER. JOUR. SCI. (3), vol. 4, pp. 122–128, August. Abstract: N. JAHRB., pp. 990–991.

K. Note on *Rhinosaurus*. AMER. JOUR. SCI. (3), vol. 4, p. 147, August.

L. Preliminary Description of new Tertiary Mammals. Pts. II, III, and IV. *Ibid.*, vol. 3, pp. 202–224, September. Abstract: N. JAHRB., pp. 990–991.

M. Notice of some new Tertiary and Post-Tertiary Birds. AMER. JOUR. SCI. (3), vol. 3, pp. 256–262, October. Abstract: N. JAHRB., p. 220, 1873.

N. Preliminary Description of new Tertiary Reptiles. Pts. I and II. AMER. JOUR. SCI. (3), vol. 4, pp. 298–309, October. Abstract: N. JAHRB., p. 984.

O. Note on *Tinoceras anceps*. AMER. JOUR. SCI. (3), vol. 4, p. 322, October. Abstract: POP. SCI. REV., London, p. 94, 1873.

P. Notice of a new Species of *Tinoceras*. AMER. JOUR. SCI. (3), vol. 4, p. 323, October.

Q. Notice of some remarkable Fossil Mammals. *Ibid.*, vol. 4, pp. 343–344, October.

R. Notice of a new and remarkable Fossil Bird. *Ibid.*, vol. 4, p. 344, October; ANN. MAG. NAT. HIST. (4), vol. 11, p. 80, 1873; AMER. NAT., vol. 7, p. 50, 1873. Abstract: POP. SCI. REV., London, p. 97, 1873; ZEITS. GESAMMT. NATURW., vol. 6, p. 532.

S. Discovery of Fossil *Quadrumana* in the Eocene of Wyoming. AMER. JOUR. SCI. (3), vol. 4, pp. 405–406, November; GEOL. MAG., vol. 10, p. 33, 1873; AMER. NAT., vol. 7, pp. 179–180, 1873.

T. Note on a new Genus of Carnivores from the Tertiary of Wyoming. AMER. JOUR. SCI. (3), vol. 4, p. 406, November; GEOL. MAG., vol. 10, pp. 33–34, 1873.

U. Notice of a new Reptile from the Cretaceous. AMER. JOUR. SCI. (3), vol. 4, p. 406, November.

V. Remarks on Explorations in the Rocky Mountains, Oregon, etc. Abstract: PROC. CALIFORNIA ACAD. NAT. SCI., vol. 4, p. 200.

W. Synopsis of American Fossil Birds. In Coues's "Key to North American Birds," pp. 347–350, Salem.

1873

A. Return of the Yale College Expedition. AMER. JOUR. SCI. (3), vol. 5, pp. 71–72, January.

B. Notice of a new Species of *Ichthyornis*. *Ibid.*, vol. 5, p. 74, January. Abstract: ZEITS. GESAMMT. NATURW., vol. 6, p. 532, 1872; NATURE, vol. 7, p. 310, Feb. 20, 1873; JOUR. ZOOL., Paris, vol. 2, pp. 40–41.

C. On some of Professor Cope's recent Investigations. AMER. NAT., vol. 7, pp. 51–52, January.

D. On the gigantic Fossil Mammals of the Order *Dinocerata*. AMER. JOUR. SCI. (3), vol. 5, pp. 117–122, pls. i–ii, February; ANN. SCI. NAT. (ZOOL.), Paris, vol. 17, pp. 1–8, pl. 21; JOUR. ZOOL., Paris, vol. 2, pp. 160–168. Abstract: ZEITS. GESAMMT. NATURW., vol. 6, pp. 533–534, 1872; GEOL. MAG., vol. 10, pp. 115–116; NATURE, vol. 7, p. 366, March 13, 1873; POP. SCI. REV., London, p. 213; N. JAHRB., pp. 334–335, 1875.

E. On a new Sub-class of Fossil Birds (*Odontornithes*). AMER. JOUR. SCI. (3), vol. 5, pp. 161–162, February; AMER. NAT., vol. 7, pp. 115–117; ANN. MAG. NAT. HIST. (4), vol. 11, pp. 233–234; ANN. SCI. NAT. (ZOOL.), Paris, vol. 17, pp. 8–10. Abstract: POP. SCI. REV., London, pp. 210–211; N. JAHRB., p. 334.

F. Fossil Birds from the Cretaceous of North America. AMER. JOUR. SCI. (3), vol. 5, pp. 229–230, March.

G. Notes on the Dates of some of Prof. Cope's recent Papers. *Ibid.*, vol. 5, pp. 235–236, March; AMER. NAT., vol. 7, p. 173.

H. The Fossil Mammals of the Order *Dinocerata*. AMER. NAT., vol. 7, pp. 146–153, pls. i–ii, March.

I. Additional Observations on the *Dinocerata*. AMER. JOUR. SCI. (3), vol. 5, pp. 293–296, April. Abstract: NATURE, vol. 7, p. 491, April 24, 1873.

J. Supplementary Note on the *Dinocerata*. AMER. JOUR. SCI. (3), vol. 5, pp. 310–311, April.

K. On the Genus *Tinoceras* and its Allies. AMER. NAT., vol. 7, pp. 217–218, April.

L. Notice of new Tertiary Mammals. AMER. JOUR. SCI. (3), vol. 5, pp. 407–410, May. Abstract: NATURE, vol. 8, p. 76, May 22, 1873.

M. On the Dates of Prof. Cope's recent Publications. AMER. NAT., vol. 7, pp. 303–306, May.

N. *Tinoceras* and its Allies. *Ibid.*, vol. 7, pp. 306–308, May.

O. Reply to Professor Cope's Explanation. *Ibid.*, vol. 7, Appendix, pp. i–ix, June.

P. Notice of new Tertiary Mammals (continued). AMER. JOUR. SCI. (3), vol. 5, pp. 485–488, June.

Q. New Observations on the *Dinocerata*. *Ibid.*, vol. 6, pp. 300–301, October.

R. Discovery of new Rocky Mountain fossils. PROC. AMER. PHILOS. SOC., vol. 12, pp. 578–579; ANN. SCI. GEOL., Paris, vol. 3, pp. 99–100.

S. On the gigantic Mammals of the American Eocene. PROC. AMER. PHILOS. SOC., vol. 13, pp. 255–256.

1874

A. Return of Rocky Mountain Expedition. AMER. JOUR. SCI. (3), vol. 7, pp. 62-63, January. Abstract: NATURE, vol. 9, p. 273, Feb. 5, 1874.

B. On the Structure and Affinities of the *Brontotheridae.* AMER. JOUR. SCI. (3), vol. 7, pp. 81–86, pls. i–ii, January. AMER. NAT., vol. 8, pp. 79–85. Abstract: NATURE, vol. 9, p. 227, Jan. 22, 1874; JOUR. ZOOL., Paris, vol. 3, pp. 61–62.

C. Notice of new equine Mammals from the Tertiary Formation. AMER. JOUR. SCI. (3), vol. 7, pp. 247–258, 5 figs., March; ANN. MAG. NAT. HIST. (4), vol. 13, pp. 397–400. Abstract: NATURE, vol. 9, p. 390, March 19, 1874; ZEITS. GESAMMT. NATURW., vol. 10, pp. 463–464; JOUR. ZOOL., Paris, vol. 3, pp. 90–92.

D. Fossil Horses in America. AMER. NAT., vol. 8, pp. 288–294, figs. 73–75, May. Abstract: N. JAHRB., p. 774, 1875.

E. Notice of new Tertiary Mammals. Pt. III. AMER. JOUR. SCI. (3), vol. 7, pp. 531–534, May. Abstract: N. JAHRB., p. 774, 1875.

F. Small size of the Brain in Tertiary Mammals. AMER. JOUR. SCI. (3), vol. 8, pp. 66–67, July; AMER. NAT., vol. 8, pp. 503–504; ANN. MAG. NAT. HIST. (4), vol. 14, p. 167; JOUR. ZOOL., Paris, vol. 3, pp. 326–327. Abstract: NATURE, vol. 10, p. 273, Aug. 6, 1874; N. JAHRB., p. 772.

1875

A. Ancient Lake Basins of the Rocky Mountain Region. Pt. I. AMER. JOUR. SCI. (3), vol. 9, pp. 49–52, January. Abstract: AMER. NAT., vol. 9, p. 119; GEOL. MAG. (2), vol. 2, pp. 232–233.

B. Return of Prof. Marsh's Expedition. AMER. JOUR. SCI. (3), vol. 9, p. 62, January.

C. New Order of Eocene Mammals. *Ibid.*, vol. 9, p. 221, March; AMER. NAT., vol. 9, pp. 182–183; NATURE, vol. 11, p. 368, March 11, 1875; ANN. MAG. NAT. HIST. (4), vol. 15, p. 307; JOUR. ZOOL., Paris, vol. 4, pp. 70–71; N. JAHRB., p. 332, 1876; POP. SCI. REV., London, p. 207.

D. Notice of new Tertiary Mammals. Pt. IV. AMER. JOUR. SCI. (3), vol. 9, pp. 239–250, March. Abstract: JOUR. ZOOL., Paris, vol. 4, pp. 98–99; N. JAHRB., pp. 332–333, 1876.

E. A Statement of Affairs at Red Cloud Agency, made to the President of the United States. REPT. SPECIAL COMMISSION TO INVESTIGATE AFFAIRS RED CLOUD INDIAN AGENCY, pp. 1–113, Washington, July. Author's ed., pp. 1–38, New Haven.

F. Note on Reindeer Bones from a Clay Pit near North Haven. AMER. JOUR. SCI. (3), vol. 10, pp. 354–355, November.

G. On the *Odontornithes*, or Birds with Teeth. *Ibid.*, vol. 10, pp. 403–408, pls. ix–x, November; AMER. NAT., vol. 9, pp. 625–631, pls. ii, iii; JOUR. ZOOL., Paris, vol. 4, pp. 494–502, pl. xv; GEOL. MAG. (2), vol. 3, pp. 49–53, pl. ii, 1876. Abstract: N. JAHRB., pp. 333–334, 1876.

1876

A. Principal Characters of the *Dinocerata*. Pt. I. AMER. JOUR. SCI. (3), vol. 11, pp. 163–168, pls. ii–vi, February; JOUR. ZOOL., Paris, vol. 5, pp. 136–145, pl. iv. Abstract: ZEITS. GESAMMT. NATURW., vol. 14, pp. 31–32; N. JAHRB., pp. 780–781; POP. SCI. REV., London, pp. 326–327; NATURE, vol. 13, p. 374, March 9, 1876.

B. Principal Characters of the *Tillodontia*. Pt. I. AMER. JOUR. SCI. (3), vol. 11, pp. 249–252, pls. vii–ix, 1 fig., March; JOUR. ZOOL., Paris, vol. 5, pp. 244–248, pl. xi. Abstract: N. JAHRB., p. 781; NATURE, vol. 13, p. 374, March 9, 1876; ZEITS. GESAMMT. NATURW., vol. 14, pp. 32–33.

C. Principal Characters of the *Brontotheridae*. AMER. JOUR. SCI. (3), vol. 11, pp. 335–340, pls. x–xiii, 2 figs., April; JOUR. ZOOL., Paris, vol. 5, pp. 248–255, pl. xii. Abstract: NATURE, vol. 14, p. 36, May 11, 1876; ZEITS. GESAMMT. NATURW., vol. 14, pp. 33–34; N. JAHRB., p. 781.

D. On some Characters of the Genus *Coryphodon*, Owen. AMER. JOUR. SCI. (3), vol. 11, pp. 425–428, 1 pl., May. Abstract: POP. SCI. REV., London, p. 327; N. JAHRB., p. 781; ARCHIV. SCI. PHYS. NAT., Geneva, vol. 56, pp. 373–374.

E. Notice of a new Sub-order of *Pterosauria*. AMER. JOUR. SCI. (3), vol. 11, pp. 507–509, June. Abstract: ANN. MAG. NAT. HIST. (4), vol. 18, pp. 195–196; JOUR. ZOOL., Paris, vol. 5, pp. 457–458; N. JAHRB., pp. 781–782; ARCHIV. SCI. PHYS. NAT., Geneva, vol. 56, pp. 374–375.

F. Notice of new *Odontornithes*. AMER. JOUR. SCI. (3), vol. 11, pp. 509–511, June; JOUR. ZOOL., Paris, vol. 5, pp. 304–306. Abstract: POP. SCI. REV., London, p. 327; N. JAHRB., p. 782; ARCHIV. SCI. PHYS. NAT., Geneva, vol. 56, p. 373.

G. Recent Discoveries of Extinct Animals. AMER. JOUR. SCI. (3), vol. 12, pp. 59–61, July; AMER. NAT., vol. 10, pp. 436–439. Abstract: N. JAHRB., p. 782.

H. Notice of new Tertiary Mammals. Pt. V. AMER. JOUR. SCI. (3), vol. 12, pp. 401–404, November. Abstract: N. JAHRB., p. 557; POP. SCI. REV., London, pp. 97–98, 1877; ARCHIV. SCI. PHYS. NAT., Geneva, vol. 59, pp. 127–128, 1877.

I. Principal Characters of American Ptcrodactyls. AMER. JOUR. SCI. (3), vol. 12, pp. 479–480, December. Abstract: POP. SCI. REV., London, p. 97, 1877; N. JAHRB., pp. 557–558, 1877; ARCHIV. SCI. PHYS. NAT., Geneva, vol. 59, pp. 126–127, 1877.

J. Articles on *Hadrosaurus, Hesperornis*, Horse, *Hyaena, Hyaenodon, Hylaeosaurus, Hyopsodus, Hyrax, Ichthyosaurus, Iguana*, and *Iguanodon*. Johnson's Cyclopaedia, vol. 2.

1877

A. Brain of *Coryphodon*. AMER. NAT., vol. 11, p. 375, June. Abstract: NATURE, vol. 17, p. 340, Feb. 28, 1878.

B. Principal Characters of the *Coryphodontidae*. AMER. JOUR. SCI. (3), vol. 14, pp. 81–85, pl. iv, July; JOUR. ZOOL., Paris, vol. 6, pp. 380–385. Abstract: AMER. NAT., vol. 11, p. 500; N. JAHRB., p. 707.

C. Characters of the *Odontornithes*, with Notice of a new allied Genus. AMER. JOUR. SCI. (3), vol. 14, pp. 85–87, pl. v, July; JOUR. ZOOL., Paris, vol. 6, pp. 385–389. Abstract: N. JAHRB., p. 767.

D. Notice of a new and gigantic Dinosaur. AMER. JOUR. SCI. (3), vol. 14, pp. 87–88, July; JOUR. ZOOL., Paris, vol. 6, pp. 248–250. Abstract: N. JAHRB., pp. 767–768; POP. SCI. REV., London, p. 424.

E. Notice of some new Vertebrate Fossils. AMER. JOUR. SCI. (3), vol. 14, pp. 249–256, 1 fig., September. Abstract: AMER. NAT., vol. 11, pp. 629–631.

F. Introduction and Succession of Vertebrate Life in America. Vice-
    President's Address, American Association for the Advance-
    ment of Science, Nashville meeting, August, 1877. Author's ed.,
    57 pp., New Haven, August, 1877; NATURE, vol. 16, pp. 448–
    450, 470–472, 489–491, September 20, 27, October 4, 1877;
    AMER. JOUR. SCI. (3), vol. 14, pp. 337–378, November, 1877;
    POP. SCI. MO., vol. 12, pp. 513–527, 672–697, 1 pl., 1878; REV.
    SCIENTIF., Paris (2), vol. 7, pp. 1039–1046, 1064–1074, May 4,
    11, 1878. Abstract: N. JAHRB., pp. 442–444, 1878.

G. A new Order of Extinct *Reptilia* (*Stegosauria*), from the Jurassic
    of the Rocky Mountains. AMER. JOUR. SCI. (3), vol. 14, pp.
    513–514, December. Abstract: POP. SCI. REV., London, p. 103,
    1878.

H. Notice of new Dinosaurian Reptiles from the Jurassic Formation.
    AMER. JOUR. SCI. (3), vol. 14, pp. 514–516, December. Ab-
    stract: POP. SCI. REV., London, pp. 103–104, 1878.

I. Articles on *Lophiodon, Loxodon, Machaerodus*, Macrauchenidae,
    Mammoth, Mastodon, *Megaceros, Megalosaurus, Megatherium*,
    Mosasauridae, Odontornithes, Pterodactyl, and Quadrumana.
    Johnson's Cyclopaedia, vol. 3.

J. Speech at 72d Anniversary Celebration, New England Society in
    New York, Dec. 22, 1877. Abstract: [Ann. Rept.], p. 59.

1878

A. New Species of *Ceratodus*, from the Jurassic. AMER. JOUR. SCI.
    (3), vol. 15, p. 76, 1 fig., January; ANN. MAG. NAT. HIST. (5),
    vol. 1, p. 184. Abstract: POP. SCI. REV., London, p. 210; SCI.
    GOSSIP, vol. 14, p. 117.

B. Scientific Museums. Address at opening of American Museum of
    Natural History, Dec. 22, 1877. 9th ANN. REPT. AMER. MUS.
    NAT. HIST., pp. 52–54, January; POP. SCI. MO., vol. 12, pp.
    475–476.

C. Notice of new Dinosaurian Reptiles. AMER. JOUR. SCI. (3), vol.
    15, pp. 241–244, figs. 1, 2, March. Abstract: POP. SCI. REV.,
    London, pp. 210–211.

D. Notice of new Fossil Reptiles. AMER. JOUR. SCI. (3), vol. 15, pp.
    409–411, May. Abstract: N. JAHRB., p. 777; POP. SCI. REV.,
    London, p. 322.

E. Fossil Mammal from the Jurassic of the Rocky Mountains. AMER.
    JOUR. SCI. (3), vol. 15, p. 459, June; POP. SCI. REV., London,
    pp. 322–323; ANN. MAG. NAT. HIST. (5), vol. 2, p. 108. Ab-
    stract: N. JAHRB., p. 779.

F. New Pterodactyl from the Jurassic of the Rocky Mountains.

Amer. Jour. Sci. (3), vol. 16, pp. 233–234, September. Abstract: N. Jahrb., p. 895; Pop. Sci. Rev., London, p. 436.

G. Principal Characters of American Jurassic Dinosaurs. Pt. I. Amer. Jour. Sci. (3), vol. 16, pp. 411–416, pls. iv–x, November. Abstract: N. Jahrb., pp. 256–257, 1880; Kosmos, vol. 5, pp. 137–139, 1879.

H. Articles on *Coryphodon, Eohippus, Pteranodon, Sivatherium*, Tillodontia, *Tinoceras*, and *Titanotherium*. Johnson's Cyclopaedia, vol. 4 and Appendix.

1879

A. A new Order of Extinct Reptiles (*Sauranodonta*), from the Jurassic Formation of the Rocky Mountains. Amer. Jour. Sci. (3), vol. 17, pp. 85–86, January. Abstract: Ann. Mag. Nat. Hist. (5), vol. 3, pp. 175–176; Pop. Sci. Rev., London, p. 205; N. Jahrb., p. 256, 1880; Kosmos, vol. 5, pp. 139–140.

B. Principal Characters of American Jurassic Dinosaurs. Pt. II. Amer. Jour. Sci. (3), vol. 17, pp. 86–92, pls. iii–x, January. Abstract: N. Jahrb., pp. 257–258, 1880.

C. Additional Characters of the *Sauropoda*. Amer. Jour. Sci. (3), vol. 17, pp. 181–182, February.

D. The Vertebrae of recent Birds. *Ibid.*, vol. 17, pp. 266–269, figs. 1–5, April.

E. Polydactyl Horses, recent and extinct. *Ibid.*, vol. 17, pp. 499–505, 1 pl., figs. 1–4, June. Abstract: Pop. Sci. Rev., London, pp. 318–319; N. Jahrb., pp. 103–104, 1881; Kosmos, vol. 5, pp. 432–438.

F. Notice of a new Jurassic Mammal. Amer. Jour. Sci. (3), vol. 18, pp. 60–61, July. Ann. Mag. Nat. Hist. (5), vol. 4, pp. 167–168; Geol. Mag. (2), vol. 6, pp. 371–372. Abstract: Pop. Sci. Rev., London, p. 428; N. Jahrb., p. 217, 1880.

G. History and Methods of Palaeontological Discovery. President's Address, American Association for the Advancement of Science, Saratoga meeting, August, 1879. Author's ed., 51 pp., New Haven, August, 1879; Nature, vol. 20, pp. 494–499, 515–521, Sept. 18, 25, 1879; Amer. Jour. Sci. (3), vol. 18, pp. 323–359, Nov., 1879; Pop. Sci. Mo., vol. 16, pp. 219–236, 363–380, 1879–1880; Kosmos, vol. 6, pp. 339–352, 425–445; Proc. Amer. Assoc. Adv. Sci., 1879, vol. 28, pp. 1–42, 1880.

H. Additional Remains of Jurassic Mammals. Amer. Jour. Sci. (3), vol. 18, pp. 215–216, 1 fig., September. Abstract: Pop. Sci. Rev., London, p. 428; N. Jahrb., p. 216, 1880.

I. Notice of new Jurassic Mammals. Amer. Jour. Sci. (3), vol. 18,

pp. 396–398, 1 fig., November. Abstract: ANN. MAG. NAT. HIST.
(5), vol. 5, p. 84, 1880; N. JAHRB., pp. 217–218, 1880.

J. Notice of new Jurassic Reptiles. AMER. JOUR. SCI. (3), vol. 18,
pp. 501–505, pl. iii, 1 fig., December. Abstract: N. JAHRB., p.
108, 1880.

K. Address in Reply to Mayor of St. Louis, American Association for
the Advancement of Science, St. Louis meeting. PROC. AMER.
ASSOC. ADV. SCI., 1878, vol. 27, pp. 350–351.

L. Peabody Museum. YALE BOOK, vol. 2, pp. 178–186.

M. Report of National Academy of Sciences for 1878. FORTY-SIXTH
CONGRESS, 1ST SESS., House of Representatives, Misc. Doc.
No. 7, 25 pp., Washington.

1880

A. New Characters of Mosasauroid Reptiles. AMER. JOUR. SCI. (3),
vol. 19, pp. 83–87, pl. i, figs. 1–4, January. Abstract: N. JAHRB.,
pp. 104–105.

B. The Limbs of *Sauranodon*, with Notice of a new Species. AMER.
JOUR. SCI. (3), vol. 19, pp. 169–171, 1 fig., February. Abstract:
N. JAHRB., pp. 105–106; KOSMOS, vol. 7, pp. 74–77.

C. Principal Characters of American Jurassic Dinosaurs. Pt. III.
AMER. JOUR. SCI. (3), vol. 19, pp. 253–259, pls. vi–xi, 1 fig.,
March. Abstract: N. JAHRB., pp. 106–107; KOSMOS, vol. 7, pp.
213–215.

D. The Sternum in Dinosaurian Reptiles. AMER. JOUR. SCI. (3), vol.
19, pp. 395–396, pl. xviii, May. Abstract: N. JAHRB., pp. 104–
105, 1881; KOSMOS, vol. 7, pp. 317–318.

E. Note on *Sauranodon*. AMER. JOUR. SCI. (3), vol. 19, p. 491, June.

F. Odontornithes: a Monograph on the Extinct Toothed Birds of
North America. With 34 plates and 40 woodcuts. 4°, xv + 201
pp. U. S. GEOL. EXPLORATION 40TH PARALLEL, vol. 7, Washington; MEM. PEABODY MUS., YALE COLL., vol. 1, July. Abstract: NATURE, vol. 22, pp. 457–458, Sept. 16, 1880; GEOL.
MAG. (2), vol. 7, pp. 522–526; AMER. JOUR. SCI. (3), vol. 21,
pp. 255–276, 1881; SCIENCE, vol. 2, pp. 98–99, 147–151, March
5, April 2, 1881; ARCHIV. SCI. PHYS. NAT., Geneva, pp. 409–
430, 1881; KOSMOS, vol. 9, pp. 157–164, 1881; N. JAHRB., pp.
270–273, 1881.

G. Notice of Jurassic Mammals representing two new Orders. AMER.
JOUR. SCI. (3), vol. 20, pp. 235–239, figs. 1, 2, September. Abstract: ARCHIV. SCI. PHYS. NAT., Geneva, vol. 4, pp. 420–422.

H. List of Genera established by Prof. O. C. Marsh, 1862–1879.
Pp. 12, New Haven.

1881

A. Principal Characters of American Jurassic Dinosaurs. Pt. IV. Spinal Cord, Pelvis, and Limbs of *Stegosaurus*. AMER. JOUR. SCI. (3), vol. 21, pp. 167–170, pls. vi–viii, February. Abstract: N. JAHRB., pp. 109–110, 270–271; KOSMOS, vol. 9, pp. 319–321, 5 figs.

B. A new Order of Extinct Jurassic Reptiles (*Coeluria*). AMER. JOUR. SCI. (3), vol. 21, pp. 339–340, pl. x, April; KOSMOS, vol. 9, pp. 464–465. Abstract: N. JAHRB., pp. 414–415.

C. Discovery of a Fossil Bird in the Jurassic of Wyoming. AMER. JOUR. SCI. (3), vol. 21, pp. 341–342, April. ANN. MAG. NAT. HIST. (5), vol. 7, pp. 488–489. Abstract: N. JAHRB., p. 414.

D. Note on American Pterodactyls. AMER. JOUR. SCI. (3), vol. 21, pp. 342–343, April. Abstract: N. JAHRB., p. 415.

E. Principal Characters of American Jurassic Dinosaurs. Pt. V. AMER. JOUR. SCI. (3), vol. 21, pp. 417–423, pls. xii–xviii, May. Abstract: N. JAHRB., pp. 415–416; KOSMOS, vol. 9, pp. 465–466.

F. Notice of new Jurassic Mammals. AMER. JOUR. SCI. (3), vol. 21, pp. 511–513, June.

G. Restoration of *Dinoceras mirabile. Ibid.*, vol. 22, pp. 31–32, pl. ii, July. Abstract: ARCHIV. SCI. PHYS. NAT., Geneva, vol. 6, pp. 323–324.

H. Jurassic Birds and their Allies. SCIENCE, vol. 2, pp. 512–513; AMER. JOUR. SCI. (3), vol. 22, pp. 337–340, October; GEOL. MAG. (2), vol. 8, pp. 485–487; NATURE, vol. 25, pp. 22–23, Nov. 3, 1881; ARCHIV. SCI. PHYS. NAT., Geneva, vol. 7, pp. 312–318, 1882; ANN. MAG. NAT. HIST. (5), vol. 8, pp. 452–455; KOSMOS, vol. 10, pp. 231–234; POP. SCI. MO., vol. 20, pp. 312–315, 1882; REPT. BRIT. ASSOC. ADV. SCI., 51ST MEETING, YORK, pp. 661–662. Abstract: NATURE, vol. 24, p. 501, Sept. 22, 1881; REV. ZOOL. ET PAL., p. 409, 1882.

1882

A. Classification of the *Dinosauria*. AMER. JOUR. SCI. (3), vol. 23, pp. 81–86, January; KOSMOS, vol. 10, pp. 382–387; NATURE, vol. 25, pp. 244–246, Jan. 12, 1882; GEOL. MAG. (2), vol. 9, pp. 80–85, 1882; ANN. MAG. NAT. HIST. (5), vol. 9, pp. 79–84, 1882. Abstract: POP. SCI. REV., London, pp. 272–273, 1881.

B. List of Scientific Publications of O. C. Marsh, 1861–1881. Pp. 29, New Haven, March.

C. The wings of Pterodactyles. AMER. JOUR. SCI. (3), vol. 23, pp. 251–256, pl. iii, figs. 1, 2, April; NATURE, vol. 25, pp. 531–533, April 6, 1882; GEOL. MAG. (2), vol. 9, pp. 205–210; KOSMOS, vol. 11, pp. 103–108. Abstract: N. JAHRB., vol. 2, p. 267, 1883.

D. Evolution. Address delivered at the farewell dinner to Herbert Spencer, in New York, Nov. 9, 1882, pp. 4, New York; also in "Herbert Spencer and the Americans, and the Americans and Herbert Spencer," pp. 45–50, New York, 1883.

1883

A. Principal Characters of American Jurassic Dinosaurs. Pt. VI. Restoration of *Brontosaurus*. AMER. JOUR. SCI. (3), vol. 26, pp. 81–85, pl. i, August; GEOL. MAG. (2), vol. 10, pp. 386–388, pl. ix. Abstract: N. JAHRB., vol. 2, pp. 104–105, 1884; KOSMOS, vol. 13, pp. 549–552.

B. On the supposed Human Footprints recently found in Nevada. AMER. JOUR. SCI. (3), vol. 26, pp. 139–140, figs. 1, 2, August. Abstract: NATURE, vol. 28, pp. 370–371, Aug. 16, 1883; N. JAHRB., vol. 1, pp. 262–263, 1884.

C. Birds with Teeth. THIRD ANN. REPT. U. S. GEOL. SURV., pp. 45–88, 33 figs.

D. Report of National Academy of Sciences for 1882. Pp. 16, Washington.

1884

A. Principal Characters of American Jurassic Dinosaurs. Pt. VII. On the *Diplodocidae*, a new Family of the *Sauropoda*. AMER. JOUR. SCI. (3), vol. 27, pp. 160–167, pls. iii–iv, February; GEOL. MAG. (3), vol. 1, pp. 99–107, 10 figs. Abstract: N. JAHRB., vol. 1, p. 88, 1885; SCIENCE, vol. 3, p. 199, 3 figs.; KOSMOS, vol. 14, pp. 350–357.

B. Principal Characters of American Jurassic Dinosaurs. Pt. VIII. The Order *Theropoda*. AMER. JOUR. SCI. (3), vol. 27, pp. 329–340, pls. viii–xiv, April; GEOL. MAG. (3), vol. 1, pp. 252–262. Abstract: SCIENCE, vol. 3, pp. 542–544, figs., May 2, 1884; NATURE, vol. 30, pp. 201–202, June 26, 1884; KOSMOS, vol. 14, pp. 357–365; N. JAHRB., vol. 1, pp. 89–90, 1885.

C. A new Order of Extinct Jurassic Reptiles (*Macelognatha*). AMER. JOUR. SCI. (3), vol. 27, p. 341, 1 fig., April. Abstract: N. JAHRB., vol. 1, p. 473, 1885.

D. Principal Characters of American Cretaceous Pterodactyls. Pt. I. The Skull of *Pteranodon*. AMER. JOUR. SCI. (3), vol. 27, pp. 423–426, pl. xv, May; GEOL. MAG. (3), vol. 1, pp. 345–348. Abstract: N. JAHRB., vol. 1, p. 472, 1885.

E. On the united Metatarsal Bones of *Ceratosaurus*. AMER. JOUR. SCI. (3), vol. 28, pp. 161–162, figs. 1, 2, August. Abstract: KOSMOS, vol. 16, pp. 372–373, 1885; N. JAHRB., vol. 1, p. 90, 1885.

F. On the Classification and Affinities of Dinosaurian Reptiles. NA-
TURE, vol. 31, pp. 68–69, November 20, 1884; REPT. BRIT.
ASSOC. ADV. SCI., Montreal meeting, pp. 763–766, 1885. Ab-
stract: SCIENCE, vol. 4, p. 261, September 12, 1884.

G. Administrative Report to the Director of the U. S. Geological
Survey. FOURTH ANN. REPT. U. S. GEOL. SURV., pp. 41–42.

H. Report of the National Academy of Sciences for 1883. Pp. 143,
Washington.

I. Acting President's Address, National Academy of Sciences, Washington, April 15, 1879. PROC. NAT. ACAD. SCI., vol. 1, pp. 148–
153.

1885

A. *Dinocerata:* a Monograph of an Extinct Order of Gigantic Mammals. With 56 plates and 200 woodcuts. 4°, xviii + 237 pp.
MONOGRAPHS U. S. GEOL. SURV., vol. 10, Washington, 1886.
(Author's edition, title page dated 1884; published, February,
1885.) Abstract: AMER. JOUR. SCI. (3), vol. 29, pp. 173–204;
GEOL. MAG. (3), vol. 2, pp. 212–228; NATURE, vol. 32, pp. 97–
99, June 4, 1885; POP. SCI. MO., vol. 28, pp. 133–134; N.
JAHRB., vol. 1, pp. 339–341, 1886; ANN. SCI. GEOL., Paris, vol.
17, pp. 1–11, 1884.

B. Names of Extinct Reptiles. AMER. JOUR. SCI. (3), vol. 29, p. 169,
February.

C. On the Size of the Brain in Extinct Animals. Abstract: NATURE,
vol. 32, p. 562, October 8, 1885; SCIENCE, vol. 6, p. 360, October 23, 1885; REPT. BRIT. ASSOC. ADV. SCI., ABERDEEN
MEETING, 1885, p. 1065, 1886.

D. Administrative Report to the Director of the U. S. Geological
Survey. FIFTH ANN. REPT. U. S. GEOL. SURV., pp. 49–50.

E. The gigantic Mammals of the Order *Dinocerata.* FIFTH ANN.
REPT. U. S. GEOL. SURV., pp. 243–302, figs. 36–137.

F. On American Jurassic Mammals. REPT. BRIT. ASSOC. ADV. SCI.,
MONTREAL MEETING, 1884, pp. 734–736.

G. Report of National Academy of Sciences for 1884. Pp. 67, Washington.

H. Administrative Report to the Director of the U. S. Geological
Survey. SIXTH ANN. REPT. U. S. GEOL. SURV., pp. 71–72.

1886

A. Report of the National Academy of Sciences for 1885. Pp. 101,
Washington.

1887

A. American Jurassic Mammals. AMER. JOUR. SCI. (3), vol. 33, pp. 327–348, pls. vii–x, April; GEOL. MAG. (3), vol. 4, pp. 241–247, 289–299, pls. vi–ix. Abstract: NATURWISS. RUNDSCHAU, Braunschweig, vol. 2, p. 362; N. JAHRB., vol. 1, pp. 106–108, 1888.

B. Notice of new Fossil Mammals. AMER. JOUR. SCI. (3), vol. 34, pp. 323–331, figs. 1–12, October.

C. Principal Characters of American Jurassic Dinosaurs. Part IX. The Skull and Dermal Armor of *Stegosaurus. Ibid.*, vol. 34, pp. 413–417, pls. vi–ix, November; GEOL. MAG. (3), vol. 5, pp. 11–15, pls. i–iii, 3 figs., 1888.

D. Report of the National Academy of Sciences for 1886. Pp. 40, Washington.

E. Additional Genera established by Professor O. C. Marsh, 1880–1887. Pp. 13–15, New Haven.

1888

A. Notice of a new Genus of *Sauropoda* and other new Dinosaurs from the Potomac Formation. AMER. JOUR. SCI. (3), vol. 35, pp. 89–94, figs. 1–9, January.

B. Notice of a new Fossil Sirenian, from California. *Ibid.*, vol. 35, pp. 94–96, figs. 1–3, January.

C. List of Scientific Publications of Othniel Charles Marsh. Part II. 1882–1887. Pp. 5, New Haven, March.

D. A new Family of Horned *Dinosauria*, from the Cretaceous. AMER. JOUR. SCI. (3), vol. 36, pp. 477–478, pl. xi, December.

E. Report of the National Academy of Sciences for 1887. Pp. 55, Washington.

F. Administrative Report to the Director of the U. S. Geological Survey. SEVENTH ANN. REPT. U. S. GEOL. SURV., pp. 111–113.

1889

A. Restoration of *Brontops robustus*, from the Miocene of America. Abstract: AMER. JOUR. SCI. (3), vol. 37, pp. 163–165, pl. vi, February; REPT. BRIT. ASSOC. ADV. SCI., BATH MEETING, 1888, pp. 706–707; GEOL. MAG. (3), vol. 6, pp. 99–101, pl. iv.

B. Comparison of the principal Forms of the *Dinosauria* of Europe and America. Abstract: AMER. JOUR. SCI. (3), vol. 37, pp. 323–331, April; GEOL. MAG. (3), vol. 6, pp. 204–210.

C. Notice of new American *Dinosauria*. AMER. JOUR. SCI. (3), vol. 37, pp. 331–336, figs. 1–5, April. Abstract: N. JAHRB., vol. 2, p. 434, 1890.

D. Discovery of Cretaceous *Mammalia*. AMER. JOUR. SCI. (3), vol. 38, pp. 81–92, pls. ii–v, July.

E. Notice of gigantic Horned *Dinosauria* from the Cretaceous. *Ibid.*, vol. 38, pp. 173–175, 1 fig., August. Abstract: N. JAHRB., vol. 2, p. 435, 1890.

F. Discovery of Cretaceous *Mammalia*. Pt. II. AMER. JOUR. SCI. (3), vol. 38, pp. 177–180, pls. vii–viii, August.

G. The Skull of the gigantic *Ceratopsidae*. Abstract: *Ibid.*, vol. 38, pp. 501–506, pl. xii, December; GEOL. MAG. (3), vol. 7, pp. 1–5, pl. i, 1890.

H. Administrative Report to the Director of the U. S. Geological Survey. EIGHTH ANN. REPT. U. S. GEOL. SURV., pp. 173–174.

I. Administrative Report to the Director of the U. S. Geological Survey. NINTH ANN. REPT. U. S. GEOL. SURV., pp. 114–115.

1890

A. Description of new Dinosaurian Reptiles. AMER. JOUR. SCI. (3), vol. 39, pp. 81–86, pl. i, figs. 1, 2, January.

B. Reply to Professor Cope. NEW YORK HERALD, January 19, 1890; privately printed, 23 pp., New Haven, 1894.

C. Distinctive Characters of the Order *Hallopoda*. AMER. JOUR. SCI. (3), vol. 39, pp. 415–417, 1 fig., May.

D. Additional Characters of the *Ceratopsidae*, with notice of new Cretaceous Dinosaurs. *Ibid.*, vol. 39, pp. 418–426, pls. v–vii, figs. 1–3, May.

E. Additional Genera established by Professor O. C. Marsh, 1880–1889. Pp. 5, New Haven, May.

F. Notice of new Tertiary Mammals. AMER. JOUR. SCI. (3), vol. 39, pp. 523–525, June.

G. Notice of some Extinct *Testudinata*. *Ibid.*, vol. 40, pp. 177–179, pls. vii–viii, August.

H. Report of the National Academy of Sciences for 1888. Pp. 41, Washington.

I. Administrative Report to the Director of the U. S. Geological Survey. TENTH ANN. REPT. U. S. GEOL. SURV., pp. 158–159.

1891

A. A Horned Artiodactyle (*Protoceras celer*) from the Miocene. AMER. JOUR. SCI. (3), vol. 41, pp. 81–82, January.

B. On the gigantic *Ceratopsidae*, or Horned Dinosaurs, of North America. *Ibid.*, vol. 41, pp. 167–178, pls. i–x, February; GEOL. MAG. (3), vol. 8, pp. 193–199, figs. 1–19, pls. iv, v, pp. 241–248, figs. 1–34. Abstract: REPT. BRIT. ASSOC. ADV. SCI., LEEDS MEETING, 1890, pp. 793–795.

C. Restoration of *Triceratops* [and *Brontosaurus*]. AMER. JOUR. SCI. (3), vol. 41, pp. 339–342, pls. xv–xvi, April. Abstract: GEOL. MAG. (3), vol. 8, pp. 248–250, pl. vii.

D. Note on Mesozoic Mammalia. AMER. NAT., vol. 25, pp. 611–616, July; privately printed, 5 pp., New Haven, April. Abstract: PROC. ACAD. NAT. SCI. PHILADELPHIA, vol. 43, part II, pp. 237–241.

E. Restoration of *Stegosaurus*. AMER. JOUR. SCI. (3), vol. 42, pp. 179–181, pl. ix; GEOL. MAG. (3), vol. 8, pp. 385–387, pl. xi, August.

F. Geological Horizons as determined by Vertebrate Fossils. Abstract: AMER. JOUR. SCI. (3), vol. 42, pp. 336–338, pl. xii, October; privately printed, 3 pp., New Haven, August; COMPT. REND. CONG. GÉOL. INTERNAT., 5TH SESS., WASHINGTON, pp. 156–159, pl. (p. 157), 1893.

G. Notice of new Vertebrate Fossils. AMER. JOUR. SCI. (3), vol. 42, pp. 265–269, September.

H. Statement relating to the Founding of the Peabody Museum at Harvard. TWENTY-FIFTH ANN. REPT. PEABODY MUS. AMER. ARCHAEOL. ETHNOL., p. 1, December.

I. On the Cretaceous Mammals of North America. Abstract: REPT. BRIT. ASSOC. ADV. SCI., LEEDS MEETING, 1890, pp. 853–854.

J. Report of the National Academy of Sciences for 1889. Pp. 69, Washington.

K. Report of the National Academy of Sciences for 1890. Pp. 36, Washington.

L. Administrative Report to the Director of the U. S. Geological Survey. ELEVENTH ANN. REPT. U. S. GEOL. SURV., Part I, pp. 101–102.

M. Administrative Report to the Director of the U. S. Geological Survey. TWELFTH ANN. REPT. U. S. GEOL. SURV., Part I, pp. 118–119.

1892

A. The Skull of *Torosaurus*. AMER. JOUR. SCI. (3), vol. 43, pp. 81–84, pls. ii–iii, January.

B. Discovery of Cretaceous *Mammalia*. Pt. III. *Ibid.*, vol. 43, pp. 249–262, pls. v–xi, March.

C. Recent [and extinct] polydactyle Horses. *Ibid.*, vol. 43, pp. 339–355, figs. 1–21 and diagram, April.

D. A new Order of Extinct Eocene Mammals (*Mesodactyla*). *Ibid.*, vol. 43, pp. 445–449, figs. 1, 2, May.

E. Notice of new Reptiles from the Laramie Formation. *Ibid.*, vol. 43, pp. 449–453, figs. 1–4, May.

F. Notes on Triassic *Dinosauria*. *Ibid.*, vol. 43, pp. 543–546, pls. xv–xvii, June.

G. Notes on Mesozoic Vertebrate Fossils. *Ibid.*, vol. 44, pp. 171–176, pls. ii–v, August.

H. Restorations of *Claosaurus* and *Ceratosaurus. Ibid.*, vol. 44, pp. 343–349, pls. vi–vii, October.

I. Restoration of *Mastodon americanus*, Cuvier. *Ibid.*, vol. 44, p. 350, pl. viii, October; GEOL. MAG. (3), vol. 10, p. 164, pl. viii, 1893.

J. Report of the National Academy of Sciences for 1891. Pp. 39, Washington.

K. Administrative Report to the Director of the U. S. Geol. Surv. THIRTEENTH ANN. REPT. U. S. GEOL. SURV., Part I, pp. 155–157.

1893

A. A new Cretaceous Bird allied to *Hesperonis*. AMER. JOUR. SCI. (3), vol. 45, pp. 81–82, figs. 1–3, January.

B. The Skull and Brain of *Claosaurus. Ibid.*, vol. 45, pp. 83–86, pls. iv–v, January.

C. Restoration of *Anchisaurus. Ibid.*, vol. 45, pp. 169–170, pl. vi, February.

D. Restorations of *Anchisaurus*, *Ceratosaurus*, and *Claosaurus*. GEOL. MAG. (3), vol. 10, pp. 150–157, pls. vi, vii, fig. 1, April.

E. Some recent Restorations of Dinosaurs. NATURE, vol. 48, pp. 437–438, September 7, 1893; privately printed, 3 pp., New Haven, March, 1894.

F. Restoration of *Coryphodon*. AMER. JOUR. SCI. (3), vol. 46, pp. 321–326, pls. v–vi, October; GEOL. MAG. (3), vol. 10, pp. 481–487, figs. 1–6, pl. xviii.

G. Description of Miocene *Mammalia*. AMER. JOUR. SCI. (3), vol. 46, pp. 407–412, pls. vii–x, November.

H. Scientific Publications of Othniel Charles Marsh, 1861–1892. BIBLIOGRAPHIES OF THE PRESENT OFFICERS OF YALE UNIVERSITY, pp. 88–102.

I. Report of the National Academy of Sciences for 1892. Pp. 39, Washington.

J. Administrative Report to the Director of the U. S. Geologica, Survey. FOURTEENTH ANN. REPT. U. S. GEOL. SURV., Part II pp. 265 267.

1894

A. Restoration of *Camptosaurus*. AMER. JOUR. SCI. (3), vol. 47, pp. 245–246, pl. vi; GEOL. MAG. (4), vol. 1, pp. 193–195, pl. vi, March.

B. Restoration of *Elotherium*. AMER. JOUR. SCI. (3), vol. 47, pp. 407–408, pl. ix; GEOL. MAG. (4), vol. 1, pp. 294–295, pl. x, May.

C. A new Miocene Mammal. AMER. JOUR. SCI. (3), vol. 47, p. 409, 3 figs., May.

D. Footprints of Vertebrates in the Coal Measures of Kansas. *Ibid.*,
vol. 48, pp. 81–84, pls. ii–iii, July; SCI. AMER. SUPPL., No. 969,
pp. 15491–15492, figs., July 28, 1894. Abstract: GEOL. MAG.
(4), vol. 1, pp. 337–339, 432, pl. xi.

E. The Typical *Ornithopoda* of the American Jurassic. AMER. JOUR.
SCI., vol. 48, pp. 85–90, pls. iv–vii, July.

F. Eastern Division of the Miohippus Beds, with Notes on some of
the Characteristic Fossils. *Ibid.*, vol. 48, pp. 91–94, figs. 1, 2,
July.

G. Miocene Artiodactyles from the eastern Miohippus Beds. *Ibid.*,
vol. 48, pp. 175–178, figs. 1–7, August.

H. Description of Tertiary Artiodactyles. *Ibid.*, vol. 48, pp. 259–274,
figs. 1–34, September.

I. A gigantic Bird from the Eocene of New Jersey. *Ibid.*, vol. 48, p.
344, 5 figs., October.

J. A new Miocene Tapir. *Ibid.*, vol. 48, p. 348, October.

1895

A. On the *Pithecanthropus erectus*, Dubois, from Java. *Ibid.*, vol. 49,
pp. 144–147, pl. ii, fig. 2, February.

B. National Academy of Sciences on Electrical Measurement. *Ibid.*,
vol. 49, pp. 236–237, March.

C. Thomas Henry Huxley. *Ibid.*, vol. 50, pp. 177–183, August.

D. Address as Retiring President, delivered before the National
Academy of Sciences, Washington, April 19, 1895. Privately
printed, 6 pp., New Haven, August. Printed by the Academy,
6 pp., Washington.

E. The *Reptilia* of the Baptanodon Beds. *Ibid.*, vol. 50, pp. 405–406,
figs. 1–3, November.

F. Restorations of some European Dinosaurs, with Suggestions as
to their place among the *Reptilia*. Abstract: *Ibid.*, pp. 407–412,
pls. v–viii, 1 fig., November; REPT. BRIT. ASSOC. ADV. SCI.,
IPSWICH MEETING, 1895, pp. 685–688; GEOL. MAG. (4), vol. 3,
pp. 1–9, pls. i–iv, figs. 1, 2, 1896.

G. Restorations of extinct Animals. Plate I. Privately printed. New
Haven, November.

H. Restorations of Dinosaurian Reptiles. Plate II. Privately printed,
New Haven, November.

I. Note on Globular Lightning. NATURE, vol. 53, p. 152, December
19, 1895; AMER. JOUR. SCI. (4), vol. 1, pp. 13–14, January, 1896.

J. On the Affinities and Classification of the Dinosaurian Reptiles.
Abstract: AMER. JOUR. SCI. (3), vol. 50, pp. 483–498, pl. x, figs.
1–11, December; reprinted with alterations under the title
"Classification of Dinosaurs," GEOL. MAG. (4), vol. 3, pp. 388–

400, figs. 1–12, 1896; COMPT. REND. CONG. INTERNAT. ZOOL., 31ST SESS., LEYDEN, 1895, pp. 196–211, pl. i, figs. 1–11, 1896.

K. Report of the National Academy of Sciences for 1893. Pp. 47, Washington.

L. Report of the National Academy of Sciences for 1894. Pp. 43, Washington.

M. Address delivered before the National Academy of Sciences, Washington, April 19, 1889. PROC. NAT. ACAD. SCI., vol. 1, pp. 325–330.

N. Fossil Vertebrates. JOHNSON'S UNIVERSAL CYCLOPAEDIA, new ed., vol. 8, pp. 491–498, 1 pl.

O. Letter to the President of the Senate, transmitting the Report of the National Academy of Sciences on Electrical Units. FIFTY-THIRD CONGR., 3D SESSION, Senate Misc. Doc. No. 115, p. 1.

1896

A. The Age of the Wealden. AMER. JOUR. SCI. (4), vol. 1, p. 234, March; NATURE, vol. 53, p. 436, March 12, 1896.

B. On the *Pithecanthropus erectus*, from the Tertiary of Java. Abstract: AMER. JOUR. SCI. (4), vol. 1, pp. 475–482, pl. xiii, 4 figs., May; reprinted under the title "The Apeman from the Tertiary of Java," SCIENCE, vol. 3, pp. 789–793, figs. 1–4; ALBUM DER NATUR, Haarlem, pp. 270–274, 276–280.

C. A new Belodont Reptile (*Stegomus*) from the Connecticut River Sandstone. AMER. JOUR. SCI. (4), vol. 2, pp. 59–62, pl. i, figs. 1–3, July.

D. The Geology of Block Island. *Ibid.*, vol. 2, pp. 295–298, 375–377, October–November.

E. Amphibian Footprints from the Devonian. *Ibid.*, vol. 2, pp. 374–375, 1 fig.

F. The Jurassic Formation on the Atlantic Coast. Abstract: AMER. JOUR. SCI. (4), vol. 2, pp. 433–447, figs. 1, 2, December; SCIENCE, n. s., vol. 4, pp. 805 816, figs. 1, 2, Dec. 4, 1896.

G. List of Scientific Publications of Othniel Charles Marsh. Part III. 1888–1896. Pp. 13, New Haven, December.

H. The Dinosaurs of North America. 16th ANN. REPT. U. S. GEOL. SURV., Part I, pp. 133–244[414], pls. ii–lxxxv, figs. 1–66. Abstract: GEOL. MAG. (4), vol. 4, pp. 38–44.

I. Vertebrate Fossils [of the Denver Basin]. MONOGRAPHS U. S. GEOL. SURV., vol. 27, pp. 473–527[550], pls. xxi–xxxi, figs. 23–102.

1897

A. The *Stylinodontia*, a Suborder of Eocene Edentates. AMER. JOUR. SCI. (4), vol. 3, pp. 137–146, figs. 1–9, February.

B. The Affinities of *Hesperornis*. *Ibid.*, vol. 3, pp. 347–348, April; NATURE, vol. 55, p. 534, April 8, 1897; GEOL. MAG. (4), vol. 5, pp. 38–39, 1898.

C. Principal Characters of the *Protoceratidae*. AMER. JOUR. SCI. (4), vol. 4, pp. 165–176, pls. ii–vii, figs. 1–7, September.

D. The Skull of *Protoceras*. GEOL. MAG. (4), vol. 4, pp. 433–439, pl. xix, figs. 1, 2, October.

E. Recent Observations on European Dinosaurs. AMER. JOUR. SCI. (4), vol. 4, pp. 413–416, December; GEOL. MAG. (4), vol. 5, pp. 6–9, 1898.

F. List of Scientific Publications of Othniel Charles Marsh. Supplement. P. 1, New Haven.

1898

A. Presentation of Scientific Collections to Yale University. YALE ALUMNI WEEKLY, vol. 7, pp. 1, 4, January 20, 1898; SCIENCE, n. s., vol. 7, pp. 77–79, January 21, 1898. Abstract: REPT. PRESIDENT OF YALE UNIV. FOR 1897, pp. 74–79; AMER. JOUR. SCI. (4), vol. 5, pp. 156–157, February.

B. Informal Remarks at the Yale Alumni Dinner in New York, February 14, 1898. NEW HAVEN REGISTER, p. 11, February 20, 1898; YALE ALUMNI WEEKLY, vol. 7, p. 7, February 24, 1898.

C. The Vertebrate Paleontology of the United States Geological Survey and National Museum. Privately printed, 12 pp., New Haven (1st and 2d ed.), February, March.

D. New Species of *Ceratopsia*. AMER. JOUR. SCI. (4), vol. 6, p. 92, July.

E. Important Vertebrate Fossils for the National Museum. AMER. JOUR. SCI. (4), vol. 6, p. 101, July; SCIENCE, n. s., vol. 8, p. 43, July 8, 1898; AMER. GEOL., vol. 22, pp. 63–64. Abstract: NAT. SCI., vol. 13, p. 144.

F. The Proposed New Museum Building for Yale. YALE ALUMNI WEEKLY, vol. 7, pp. 1, 3, 16, July 12, 1898.

G. The Jurassic Formation on the Atlantic Coast—Supplement. AMER. JOUR. SCI. (4), vol. 6, pp. 105–115, 1 fig., August; (with additions) SCIENCE, n. s., vol. 8, pp. 145–154, 1 fig., Aug. 5, 1898.

H. Cycad Horizons in the Rocky Mountain Region. AMER. JOUR. SCI. (4), vol. 6, p. 197, August; SCIENCE, n. s., vol. 8, pp. 153–154, Aug. 5, 1898.

I. The Value of Type Specimens and Importance of their Preservation. AMER. JOUR. SCI. (4), vol. 6, pp. 401–405, November; PROC. 4TH INTERNAT. CONG. ZOOL., CAMBRIDGE, 1898, pp. 158–162, 1899.

J. The Origin of Mammals. AMER. JOUR. SCI. (4), vol. 6, pp. 406–409, November; SCIENCE, n. s., vol. 8, pp. 953–955, Dec. 30, 1898; GEOL. MAG. (4), vol. 6, pp. 13–16, 1899; PROC. 4TH INTERNAT. CONG. ZOOL., CAMBRIDGE, 1898, pp. 71–74, 1899.

K. The comparative Value of different Kinds of Fossils in determining geological Age. Abstract: AMER. JOUR. SCI. (4), vol. 6, pp. 483–486, December; GEOL. MAG. (4), vol. 5, pp. 565–568; REPT. BRIT. ASSOC. ADV. SCI., BRISTOL MEETING, 1898, pp. 869–872, 1899.

L. On the Families of Sauropodous *Dinosauria*. Abstract: AMER. JOUR. SCI. (4), vol. 6, pp. 487–488, December; REPT. BRIT. ASSOC. ADV. SCI., BRISTOL MEETING, 1898, pp. 909–910, 1899; GEOL. MAG. (4), vol. 6, pp. 157–158, 1899.

M. Vertebrate Fossils collected for the U. S. Geological Survey, 1882–1892. Pp. 4, New Haven.

1899

A. Footprints of Jurassic Dinosaurs. AMER. JOUR. SCI. (4), vol. 7, pp. 227–232, pl. v, 3 figs., March.

B. Note on a Bridger Eocene Carnivore. *Ibid.*, vol. 7, p. 397, May.

C. Reply for American Delegation at Opening of International Congress of Zoology, Cambridge, England, 1898. PROC. 4TH INTERNAT. CONG. ZOOL., pp. 49–50, 1899.

BIOGRAPHICAL SKETCHES OF O. C. MARSH

Sketch of Professor O. C. Marsh, by G. B. Grinnell. POP. SC. MO., Sept., 1878, pp. 612–617.

Professor Marsh, by W. H. Bidwell. ECLECTIC MAG., April, 1878, pp. 501–502.

Prof. O. C. Marsh, M. A. THE PHILO MIRROR, Phillips Academy, Andover, June, 1884, pp. 28–30.

Othniel Charles Marsh, by a Classmate [W. H. H.] SCIENTIF. AMER., May 1, 1886, p. 279.

Death of Professor Marsh, YALE ALUM. WKLY., March 22, 1899.

[Tribute] by Prof. George P. Fisher. *Ibid.*, March 29, 1899.

Othniel Charles Marsh, by J. L. Wortman. SCIENCE, April 21, 1899, pp. 561–565.

Othniel Charles Marsh, LL.D., Ph.D., by H. W[oodward]. GEOL. MAG., May, 1899, pp. 237–240.

Othniel Charles Marsh, by C. E. Beecher. AMER. JOUR. SCI., June, 1899, pp. 403–428. In abridged form, AMER. GEOL., Sept., 1899, pp. 135–157; BULL. GEOL. SOC. AMERICA, vol. 11, 1899, pp. 521–537.

Othniel Charles Marsh, by H. S. Williams. JOUR. GEOL., May–June, 1899, pp. 401–404.

Professor Othniel Charles Marsh, by R. L[ydekker]. NATURE, March 30, 1899, pp. 513–514.

Othniel Charles Marsh. NAT. SCI., vol. 14, 1899, pp. 409–410.

Othniel Charles Marsh. MINES AND MINERALS, vol. 19, 1899, pp. 225–257.

Othniele Carlo Marsh, by G. Capellini. RIV. ITAL. PAL., Bologne, vol. 5, 1899, pp. 41–43.

Othniel Charles Marsh, by C. von Voit. Sitz. k. bay. Akad., 1900, pp. 284–288.

Othniel Charles Marsh, Paleontologist, 1831–1899, by G. B. Grinnell. In LEADING AMERICAN MEN OF SCIENCE, ed. by David Starr Jordan, 1910, pp. 283–312.

The Yale Collection of Fossil Horses, by Richard S. Lull. COLLS. YALE UNIV., No. 1, 1913, 12 pp.

Some eminent Andover Alumni. 18, Othniel Charles Marsh, 1831–1899, by Scott H. Paradise. PHILLIPS BULL., vol. 24, Jan., 1930, pp. 16 25.

Centenary of the Birth of Othniel Charles Marsh, by Charles Schuchert and Richard S. Lull. SCIENCE, Dec. 25, 1931, pp. 647–648.

Biographical Memoir of Othniel Charles Marsh, 1831–1899, by Charles Schuchert. Nat. Acad. Sci., Biog. Mem., vol. 20, first mem., 1939, pp. 1–78.

Of the contemporary newspaper accounts, the following have special interest:

NEW HAVEN REGISTER, March 20, 1899.

NEW HAVEN EVENING TELEGRAM, March 23, 1899.

NEW YORK EVENING POST, March 21, 1899 (by D. Cady Eaton).

NEW YORK TRIBUNE, April 3, 1899 (by W. E. Park).

SAVANNAH NEWS, April 9, 1899, and many other papers (a syndicated article by Ray Stannard Baker, originally intended for Mc-Clure's Magazine).

INDEX

Asterisks denote illustrations.

C